Applied Probability and Statistics (*Continued*)

Tracts on Probability and Statistics

Introduction to
Mathematical Statistics

A WILEY PUBLICATION IN MATHEMATICAL
STATISTICS

Introduction to Mathematical Statistics

PAUL G. HOEL

Professor of Mathematics
University of California
Los Angeles

THIRD EDITION

John Wiley & Sons, Inc.

New York · London · Sydney

LIBRARY OF CONGRESS CATALOG CARD NUMBER: 62-18992

PRINTED IN THE UNITED STATES OF AMERICA

Preface

This edition is a rather modest modification of the second edition. The principal changes have been in organization and coverage of material. The organizational changes have resulted in an expansion of the chapter on probability, an earlier introduction of expected value techniques, and a smoother development of the theory. The coverage of topics has been modified somewhat to permit the inclusion of a few of the newer and more useful statistical techniques. In particular, a chapter on the elementary parts of general decision methods has been added.

For the benefit of those who are unacquainted with the earlier editions of this book, I should explain what my objectives were in the writing of it. I hoped to produce a text that would give students with only an elementary calculus background an introduction to the mathematical theory of statistics and at the same time provide them some experience with applications. Students in the physical sciences or engineering usually acquire the necessary background by the time they are juniors; however, students of the social and life sciences often do not do so until they are farther along in their studies.

The number of topics covered is large for a book of this size. I have purposely tried to give elementary treatments of a number of statistical techniques so that the student will get a taste of the wide range of such methods. I feel that it is more important at this level to give a survey-type course than it is to concentrate on a few topics at greater depth.

Although I believe a first course in statistical methods should strive for breadth rather than depth, I am also of the opinion that students will not really understand or appreciate the methods unless they apply them immediately to concrete problems. I have therefore attempted to illustrate and apply the theory as soon as it has been presented, and I have included a large number of exercises of varying degrees of difficulty. Many of the exercises are direct applications of formulas to empirical data, others are theoretical problems that can be solved by the methods that have been presented, and a few are of the type that require considerable ingenuity. The instructor is expected to select those exercises that will suit his objectives in the course. Answers to the even-numbered exercises may be obtained in pamphlet form from the publisher.

From time to time I have received letters from some of the readers of the earlier editions of this book with suggestions for its improvement. I have always appreciated such letters even though I may not have included the suggestions in a revision. I wish to take this opportunity to thank all who have used my book in the past and particularly those who were kind enough to write me concerning it. I am especially grateful to my colleague Thomas Ferguson for his numerous helpful suggestions, many of which have been incorporated in the present revision.

PAUL G. HOEL

Los Angeles, California
September 1962

Contents

CONTENTS

CHAPTER 1

Introduction

Statistical methods are essentially methods for dealing with data that have been obtained by a repetitive operation. For some sets of data, the operation that gave rise to the data is clearly of this repetitive type. This would be true, for example, of a set of diameters of a certain part in a mass-production manufacturing process or a set of percentages obtained from routine chemical analyses. For other sets of data, the actual operation may not seem to be repetitive, but it may be possible to conceive of it as being so. This would be true for the ages at death of certain insurance-policy holders or for the total number of mistakes an experimental set of animals made the first time they ran a maze.

Experience indicates that many repetitive operations or experiments behave as though they occurred under essentially stable circumstances. Games of chance, such as coin tossing or dice rolling, usually exhibit this property. Many experiments and operations in the various branches of science and industry do likewise. Under such circumstances, it is often possible to construct a satisfactory mathematical model of the repetitive operation. This model can then be employed to study properties of the operation and to draw conclusions concerning it. Although mathematical models are especially useful devices for studying real-life problems when the model is realistic of the actual operation involved, it often happens that such models prove useful even though the operation is not highly stable.

The mathematical model that a statistician selects for a repetitive operation is usually one that enables him to make predictions about the frequency with which certain results can be expected to occur when the operation is repeated a number of times. For example, the model for studying the inheritance of color in the propagation of certain flowers might be one that predicted three times as many flowers of one color as of another color. In the investigation of the quality of manufactured parts the model might be one that predicts the percentage of defective parts that can be expected in the manufacturing process.

1

Because of the nature of statistical data and models, it is only natural that probability should be the fundamental tool in statistical theory. The statistician looks on probability as an idealization of the proportion of times that a certain result will occur in repeated trials of an experiment; consequently, a probability model is the type of mathematical model selected by him. Because probability is so important in the theory and applications of statistical methods, a brief introduction to probability is given before the study of statistical methods as such is taken up.

The idea of a mathematical model for assisting in the solution of real-life problems is a familiar one in the various sciences. For example, a physicist studying projectile motion often assumes that the simple laws of mechanics yield a satisfactory model, in spite of the complexity of the actual problem. For more refined work, he introduces a more complicated model. Since a model is only an idealization of the actual situation, the conclusions derived from it can be relied on only to the extent that the model chosen is a sufficiently good approximation to the actual situation being studied. In any given problem, therefore, it is essential to be well acquainted with the field of application in order to know what models are likely to be realistic. This is just as true for statistical models as for models in the various branches of science.

The science student will soon discover the similarity between certain of the statistical methods and certain scientific methods in which the scientist sets up a hypothesis, conducts an experiment, and then tests the hypothesis by means of his experimental data. Although statistical methods are applicable to all branches of science, they have been applied most actively in the biological and social sciences because the laboratory methods of the physical sciences have not been sufficiently broad to treat many of the problems of those other sciences. Problems in the biological and social sciences often involve undesired variables that cannot be controlled, as contrasted to the physical sciences in which such variables can often be controlled satisfactorily in the laboratory. Statistical theory is concerned not only with how to solve certain problems of the various sciences but also with how experiments in those sciences should be designed. Thus the science student should expect to learn statistical techniques to assist him in treating his experimental data and in designing his experiments in a more efficient manner.

The theory of statistics can be treated as a branch of mathematics in which probability is the basic tool; however, since the theory developed from an attempt to solve real-life problems, much of it would not be fully appreciated if it were removed from such applications. Therefore the theory and the applications are considered simultaneously throughout this book, although the emphasis is on the theory.

In the process of solving a real-life problem in statistics three steps may be recognized. First, a mathematical model is selected. Second, a check is made of the reasonableness of the model. Third, the proper conclusions are drawn from this model to solve the proposed problem. In this book the emphasis is on the first and third steps. In order to do justice to the second step, it would be necessary to be well acquainted with the field of application. It would also be necessary to know how the conclusions are affected by changes in the assumptions necessary for the model.

Students who have not had experience with applied science are sometimes disturbed by the readiness with which a statistician will accept certain of his model assumptions as being sufficiently well satisfied in a given problem to justify confidence in the validity of the conclusions. One of the striking features of much of statistical theory is that its field of application is much broader than the assumptions involved would seem to justify. The rapid development of, and interest in, statistical methods during the last few decades can be attributed in part to the highly successful application of statistical techniques to so many different branches of science and industry.

REFERENCES

A fuller discussion of some of the preceding ideas may be found in the following books:

Cramér, H., *The Elements of Probability Theory and Some of Its Applications*, John Wiley and Sons, Chapters 1 and 2.

Fisher, R. A., *Statistical Methods for Research Workers*, Oliver and Boyd, Chapter 1.

Kendall, M. G., *The Advanced Theory of Statistics*, Griffin and Co., pp. 164–166.

Neyman, J., *First Course in Probability and Statistics*, Henry Holt and Co., pp. 1–6.

Wilks, S. S., *Mathematical Statistics*, Princeton University Press, pp. 1–4.

CHAPTER 2

Probability

2.1 Introduction

An individual's approach to probability depends on the nature of his interest in the subject. The pure mathematician usually prefers to treat probability from an axiomatic point of view, just as he does, say, the study of geometry. The applied statistician usually prefers to think of probability as the proportion of times that a certain event will occur if the experiment related to the event is repeated indefinitely. The approach to probability here is based on a blending of these two points of view.

The statistician is usually interested in probability only as it pertains to the possible outcomes of experiments. Furthermore, he is interested in only those experiments that are repetitive in nature or that can be conceived of as being so. Experiments such as tossing a coin, counting the number of defective parts in a box of parts, or reading the daily temperature on a thermometer are examples of simple repetitive experiments. An experiment in which several experimental animals are fed different rations in an attempt to determine the relative growth properties of the rations may be performed only once with those same animals; nevertheless, the experiment may be thought of as the first in an unlimited number of similar experiments and therefore may be conceived of as being repetitive.

2.2 Sample Space

Consider a simple experiment such as tossing a coin. In this experiment there are but two possible outcomes, a head and a tail. It is convenient to represent the possible outcomes of such an experiment, and experiments in general, by points on a line or by points in higher dimensions. Here it would be convenient to represent a head by the point 1 on the x axis and a tail by the point 0. This choice is convenient because the number corresponds to the number of heads obtained in the toss. If the

4

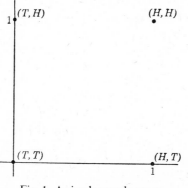

Fig. 1. A simple sample space.

experiment had consisted of tossing the coin twice, there would have been four possible outcomes, namely *HH, HT, TH, TT*. For reasons of symmetry, it would be desirable to represent these outcomes by the points (1, 1), (1, 0), (0, 1), and (0, 0) in the x,y plane. Figure 1 illustrates this choice of points to represent the possible outcomes of the experiment.

If the coin were tossed three times, it would be convenient to use three dimensions to represent the possible experimental outcomes. This representation, of course, is merely a convenience, and if desired one could just as well mark off any eight points on the x axis to represent the eight possible outcomes.

DEFINITION: *The set of points representing the possible outcomes of an experiment is called the sample space, or the event space, of the experiment.*

The idea of a sample space is introduced because it is a convenient mathematical device for developing the theory of probability as it pertains to the outcomes of experiments.

2.3   Sample Space Probabilities

Experience shows that for some experiments one possible outcome is much more likely to occur than another possible outcome. For example, in counting the number of defective screws in a box of screws purchased from a reputable firm, one is much more likely to find all good screws than all defective screws. In many simple games of chance, however, it often happens that all the possible outcomes will occur about equally often in a large number of repetitions of the experiment. Thus, in tossing a die repeatedly, each of the six sides will usually occur with about the same frequency.

Before it is possible to discuss the probability of some combination of possible experimental outcomes, it is necessary that probabilities be assigned to each of the sample points in the sample space. Since the interpretation of probability is going to be in terms of frequency, the probability that is assigned to a given sample point should be approximately equal to the proportion of times that the sample point will be obtained, or is expected to be obtained, in a large number of repetitions of the experiment. This frequency interpretation of probability requires that probabilities be non-negative and that the sum of the probabilities assigned to the sample points be equal to one; hence probabilities must be assigned with this restriction in mind. In the preceding illustration of tossing a coin twice, it would be natural to assign the probability of $\frac{1}{4}$ to each of the four sample points, unless experience has indicated that the coin is biased, that is, that one side comes up more frequently than the other. The assignment of probabilities to each of the possible outcomes in sampling a box of screws for defectives would need to be based on experience with the manufacturer's product. From a mathematical point of view, any set of non-negative numbers totaling one may be assigned to the sample points as probabilities; however, the conclusions derived from the theory are not likely to prove very realistic unless the sample point probabilities are chosen in a realistic manner. The assignment of probabilities to the sample points constitutes the first step in the process of choosing a mathematical model for the real-life experiment under consideration.

Since the development of the theory of probability is especially simple when there is only a finite number of sample points, it is assumed in the next few sections that the sample space is of this kind. Let the total number of sample points be denoted by n and let $p_1, p_2, \cdots, p_n$ be the probabilities assigned to the respective sample points. In most simple games of chance the p's are chosen to be equal from symmetry considerations. Thus in rolling a die one would naturally assign equal probabilities $(\frac{1}{6})$ to the six sample points that constitute the sample space. If experience with a particular die has shown that the six possible outcomes do not occur with approximately the same relative frequency, then a set of p's that is based on this experience should be assigned instead, provided this same die is to be used in future experiments. After the sample point probabilities have been assigned, one can begin to discuss the probability of events.

2.4   Events

Consider an experiment such that whatever the outcome of the experiment it can be decided whether an event A has occurred. This means that each sample point can be classified as one for which A will occur or as one for which A will not occur. Since the sample point probabilities give the expected relative frequency of occurrence of the corresponding outcomes, the sum of the sample point probabilities associated with A will give the expected relative frequency of occurrence of A, and therefore it should be called the probability of the occurrence of A. These considerations yield the following basic definition of probability for finite sample spaces:

(1) DEFINITION: *The probability that an event A will occur is the sum of the probabilities of the sample points that are associated with the occurrence of A.*

In symbols, if $P\{A\}$ denotes the probability that A will occur when the experiment is performed, then

(2)
$$P\{A\} = \sum_A p_i$$

where the sum is over the values of the p's for the sample points corresponding to the occurrence of A.

As an illustration, suppose a coin is tossed twice and suppose that all four sample points, as shown in Fig. 1, are assigned the same probability. Then the probability of getting a total of one head and one tail is $\frac{2}{4}$ because the two sample points (H, T) and (T, H), with associated probabilities of $\frac{1}{4}$, correspond to the occurrence of the desired event.

As a second illustration, consider the experiment of rolling two dice. The sample space here consists of 36 points corresponding to the 36 possible outcomes that are listed in Table 1.

TABLE 1

11	21	31	41	51	61
12	22	32	42	52	62
13	23	33	43	53	63
14	24	34	44	54	64
15	25	35	45	55	65
16	26	36	46	56	66

The first number of each pair denotes the number that came up on one of the dice and the second number denotes the number that came up on the other. It is assumed that the two dice are distinguishable or are rolled in order. The symmetric nature of dice, together with experience in rolling them, suggests that it is reasonable to assign the same probability $(\frac{1}{36})$ to all 36 sample points. Then the probability of getting a total of, say, seven points on the two dice is $\frac{6}{36}$ because the six sample points 16, 25, 34, 43, 52, 61 correspond to the occurrence of the desired event.

As an illustration in which all sample points are not assigned the same probability, consider a pair of modified dice in which each one-spot has been changed to a two-spot. As a result, each die will possess two 2's but no 1. In order to compensate for this alteration in Table 1, it is necessary merely to replace each 1 by a 2 in that table. The first two rows, and also the first two columns, will then become identical. If similar expressions are combined, the possible outcomes for this experiment are those listed in Table 2.

TABLE 2

22(4)	32(2)	42(2)	52(2)	62(2)
23(2)	33(1)	43(1)	53(1)	63(1)
24(2)	34(1)	44(1)	54(1)	64(1)
25(2)	35(1)	45(1)	55(1)	65(1)
26(2)	36(1)	46(1)	56(1)	66(1)

The numbers in parentheses following the outcomes give the number of outcomes in Table 1 yielding corresponding outcomes in Table 2. Thus a (4) follows the outcome 22 because the events 11, 12, 21, and 22 of Table 1 all reduce to 22 when each 1 is replaced by a 2. In view of the earlier assumption that each of the 36 possible outcomes of Table 1 will occur with the same relative frequency, the natural probabilities to assign the possible outcomes listed in Table 2 are those obtained by multiplying $\frac{1}{36}$ by the numbers in parentheses.

Now if A is the event of getting a total of seven points in the experiment of rolling the two altered dice, it will follow from Table 2 that

$$P\{A\} = \tfrac{2}{36} + \tfrac{1}{36} + \tfrac{1}{36} + \tfrac{2}{36} = \tfrac{1}{6}$$

because these numbers are the probabilities assigned to the four favorable outcomes, namely, 25, 34, 43, and 52. This result is the same as that of the earlier experiment of rolling two normal dice. If B is the event of getting a total of four points for the experiment of rolling the altered dice, then from Table 2 it is clear that 22 is the only favorable outcome, hence that

$$P\{B\} = \tfrac{4}{36}$$

This result is not the same as that obtained when two normal dice are rolled. From Table 1, the latter result is $\tfrac{3}{36}$.

2.5   Addition Theorem

Applications of probability are often concerned with a number of related events rather than with just one event. For simplicity, consider two such events, A_1 and A_2, associated with an experiment. One may be interested in knowing whether both A_1 and A_2 will occur when the experiment is performed. This joint event will be denoted by the product A_1A_2 and its probability by $P\{A_1A_2\}$. On the other hand, one may be interested in knowing whether at least one of the events A_1 and A_2 will occur when the experiment is performed. This event will be denoted by the sum $A_1 + A_2$ and its probability by $P\{A_1 + A_2\}$. At least one of the two events will occur if A_1 occurs but A_2 does not, or if A_2 occurs but A_1 does not, or if both A_1 and A_2 occur. The purpose of this section is to derive a formula for $P\{A_1 + A_2\}$.

Let the sample space for an experiment be represented by the points in Fig. 2 and let the sample points corresponding to the occurrence of A_1 and A_2 be the points interior to the regions labeled A_1 and A_2, respectively. The points common to these two regions determine a region that has been labeled A_1A_2. This notation makes it clear that the region A_1A_2 is part of the region A_1 and also part of the region A_2.

From definition (1), it follows that $P\{A_1 + A_2\}$ is the sum of the probabilities for the sample points lying inside the two regions A_1 and A_2 combined. Now $P\{A_1\}$ gives the sum of the probabilities for the points in A_1 and $P\{A_2\}$ for the points in A_2. The quantity $P\{A_1\} + P\{A_2\}$ would therefore give the sum of the probabilities for points lying inside the two regions combined, except for the fact that the probabilities for points inside the common region A_1A_2 would be summed twice. Since the latter sum is $P\{A_1A_2\}$, it is necessary to subtract this amount from the preceding sum before the correct answer can be obtained. These computations yield a fundamental theorem of probability known as the addition theorem.

(3) ADDITION THEOREM:

$$P\{A_1 + A_2\} = P\{A_1\} + P\{A_2\} - P\{A_1A_2\}$$

Two events A_1 and A_2 often have no sample points in common. When this occurs, the events A_1 and A_2 are said to be mutually exclusive because

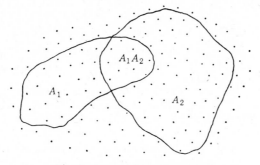

Fig. 2. A general sample space.

if one of the events occurs the other cannot occur. Formula (3) then reduces to the following formula:

$$(4) \qquad P\{A_1 + A_2\} = P\{A_1\} + P\{A_2\} \text{ when } A_1 \text{ and } A_2$$
$$\text{are mutually exclusive}$$

Formulas (3) and (4) can be generalized to more than two events. The generalization of (4) is obvious and is used in later work. The generalization of (3) is more complicated; however since the generalization is not needed in later work, it is not considered here.

2.6   Multiplication Theorem

The purpose of this section is to derive a formula for $P\{A_1 A_2\}$ in terms of probabilities of single events. In order to do so, it is necesary to introduce the notion of conditional probability. Suppose that one is interested in knowing whether A_2 will occur, subject to the condition that A_1 is certain to occur. Since A_1 is certain to occur only when the sample space is restricted to those points lying inside the region labeled A_1 in Fig. 2, it is necessary to consider how probabilities should be assigned to the points of this new smaller sample space. If, originally, a sample point in A_1 had been assigned, say, twice as large a probability as another point in A_1, then it should be assigned twice as large a probability in the new sample space also, because ignoring experimental outcomes that do not yield the event A_1 should not affect the two-to-one ratio of expected frequencies for those two sample points. It is merely necessary therefore to multiply the original probabilities assigned to points in A_1 by a constant factor c such that the sum of the new probabilities will be one. Thus, if π_i denotes the new probability corresponding to p_i in the original assignment, one should choose $\pi_i = cp_i$ where

$$1 = \sum_{A_1} \pi_i = c \sum_{A_1} p_i = cP\{A_1\}$$

As a result, $c = 1/P\{A_1\}$, and therefore

$$(5) \qquad \pi_i = \frac{p_i}{P\{A_1\}}$$

Now that the new sample space has been determined, one can calculate probabilities in the usual manner by merely applying definition (1). All such probabilities will be conditional probabilities, subject to the occurrence of A_1. If the probability that A_2 will occur, subject to the restriction that A_1 is certain to occur, is denoted by $P\{A_2 \mid A_1\}$, then it follows from definition (1) and formula (5) that

$$P\{A_2 \mid A_1\} = \sum_{A_1 A_2} \pi_i = \frac{\sum_{A_1 A_2} p_i}{P\{A_1\}}$$

The first sum is over those π_i corresponding to sample points lying inside $A_1 A_2$ because they are the only sample points inside A_1 associated with the occurrence of A_2. Since the numerator sum in the last expression is the one that defines $P\{A_1 A_2\}$, it follows that the formula for conditional probability reduces to

(6) $$P\{A_2 \mid A_1\} = \frac{P\{A_1 A_2\}}{P\{A_1\}}$$

It is assumed here that A_1 is an event for which $P\{A_1\} \neq 0$. This formula, when written in product form, yields the fundamental multiplication theorem for probabilities.

(7)   MULTIPLICATION THEOREM: $P\{A_1 A_2\} = P\{A_1\} P\{A_2 \mid A_1\}$.

Although formula (6) holds only when $P\{A_1\} \neq 0$, formula (7) may be treated as holding in general if it is agreed to give the right side the value 0 when the factor $P\{A_1\}$ is equal to 0. If the order of the two events is interchanged, formula (7) becomes

(8) $$P\{A_1 A_2\} = P\{A_2\} P\{A_1 \mid A_2\}$$

Now, suppose that A_1 and A_2 are two events such that $P\{A_2 \mid A_1\} = P\{A_2\}$ and such that $P\{A_1\} P\{A_2\} > 0$. Then the event A_2 is said to be independent in a probability sense, or more briefly, independent, of the event A_1. This name follows from the property that the probability of A_2 occurring is not affected by adding the condition that A_1 must occur. When A_2 is independent of A_1, (7) reduces to

(9) $$P\{A_1 A_2\} = P\{A_1\} P\{A_2\}$$

Conversely, when (9) is true, it follows from comparing (9) and (7) that A_2 is independent of A_1. If the right members of (8) and (9) are equated, it will be seen that $P\{A_1 \mid A_2\} = P\{A_1\}$. But this states that the event A_1 is independent of the event A_2. Thus, if A_2 is independent of A_1, it follows that A_1 must be independent of A_2. Because of this mutual independence and because (9) implies this independence, it is customary to define independence in the following manner:

(10)   DEFINITION: *Two events, A_1 and A_2, are said to be independent if* $P\{A_1 A_2\} = P\{A_1\} P\{A_2\}$.

Formulas (7) and (10) can be generalized in an obvious manner for more than two events by always combining events into two groups.

2.6.1 Illustrations

As illustrations of the application of the preceding rules of probability, consider a few simple problems related to games of chance. From symmetry considerations, it is usually assumed in such games that all possible outcomes should be assigned the same probability. This was done, for example, in discussing the probability of events in connection with Table 1. It was not done in connection with Table 2 because symmetry was missing in the experiment that gave rise to Table 2. When all sample points are assigned the same probability, the computation of $P\{A\}$ becomes especially simple because then it reduces to calculating the ratio of the number of sample points in A to the total number of sample points in the sample space. This follows directly from formula (2) because then $p_i = 1/n$ when the total number of sample points is n, and therefore the sum in (2) is equal to $1/n$ times the number of sample points in A. In the following illustrations it is assumed that symmetry is present and therefore that probabilities may be calculated in this simple manner.

(a) If two dice are rolled, what is the probability of getting either a total of 7 or a total of 11 points? Let A_1 and A_2 denote the events of getting a total of 7 and 11 points, respectively. Since these events are mutually exclusive, formula (4) may be applied. From Table 1 there are six sample points giving rise to event A_1 and two giving rise to A_2; consequently, under the symmetry assumption $P\{A_1\} = \frac{6}{36}$ and $P\{A_2\} = \frac{2}{36}$. Formula (4) then yields

$$P\{A_1 + A_2\} = \frac{6}{36} + \frac{2}{36} = \frac{8}{36}$$

This result is, of course, the same as that obtained by counting favorable and total outcomes in Table 1 and applying definition (1) directly.

(b) If two dice are rolled, what is the probability that each of them will show at least five points? Let A_1 denote the event of getting a 5 or 6 on the first die and A_2 the event of getting a 5 or 6 on the second die. If the dice are rolled properly, events A_1 and A_2 may be assumed to be independent; therefore formula (10) may be applied. Now one can treat the experiment of rolling two dice as composed of two consecutive independent experiments in which one die is rolled first and then the second die is rolled. From this point of view, the event A_1 is concerned with the first experiment only for which there are six sample points, two of which correspond to the occurrence of A_1. Under the symmetry assumption, it therefore follows that $P\{A_1\} = \frac{2}{6}$. The event A_2 plays the same role with respect to the second experiment as A_1 does in the first; hence $P\{A_2\} = \frac{2}{6}$. Formula (10) now yields the desired result, namely,

$$P\{A_1A_2\} = \frac{2}{6} \cdot \frac{2}{6} = \frac{4}{36}$$

This result could also have been obtained directly by counting sample points in the sample space of Table 1 for the complete experiment. Since there are 36 sample points and the four sample points given by the outcomes 55, 56, 65, 66 correspond to the occurrence of A_1A_2, it follows from definition (1) that $P\{A_1A_2\} = \frac{4}{36}$. The advantage of using formula (10) here is that it enables one to work with simpler sample spaces than the original sample space. The real purpose of these illustrations, however, is to develop familiarity with the formulas and not to simplify calculations, because in many problems the experimental sample space is not available for a direct application of definition (1).

(c) Two cards are drawn from an ordinary deck of 52 cards but the first card drawn is replaced before the second card is drawn. What is the probability that at least one of the cards will be a spade? Let A_1 denote the event of drawing a spade on the first draw and A_2 the event of drawing a spade on the second draw. The problem then is to calculate $P\{A_1 + A_2\}$ by means of formula (3). As in the preceding illustration, the complete experiment can be broken down into two consecutive independent experiments. Here $P\{A_1\} = \frac{13}{52} = \frac{1}{4}$ because A_1 is concerned with the first drawing only and there are 52 sample points, 13 of which are favorable (spades), in that experiment. Similarly, $P\{A_2\} = \frac{1}{4}$. Because of the independence of A_1 and A_2, it follows from formula (10) that $P\{A_1A_2\} = \frac{1}{4} \cdot \frac{1}{4} = \frac{1}{16}$. Application of formula (3) now gives

$$P\{A_1 + A_2\} = \frac{1}{4} + \frac{1}{4} - \frac{1}{16} = \frac{7}{16}$$

This problem can also be solved indirectly by first calculating the probability that neither card drawn will be a spade, which is $\frac{39}{52} \cdot \frac{39}{52}$, and then subtracting this result from 1. The reasoning here is that the opposite of "neither card will be a spade" is "at least one card will be a spade." Of course, one could also solve this problem by counting sample points and applying definition (1). The total number of sample points is $52 \cdot 52$, whereas the favorable number is $52 \cdot 52 - 39 \cdot 39$ because only those sample points corresponding to a pair of nonspades are unfavorable.

(d) Two cards are drawn from a deck of cards. What is the probability that both cards will be spades? As in the preceding illustration, let A_1 and A_2 denote the events of getting a spade on the first and second drawings, respectively. Since the first card drawn is not replaced before the second drawing, these events are certainly not independent; therefore formula (7) must be used. As before, the complete experiment may be treated as composed of two consecutive experiments; however, here they are not independent experiments. In the first experiment there are 52 sample points, of which 13 correspond to the occurrence of A_1; therefore $P\{A_1\} = \frac{13}{52}$. In calculating $P\{A_2 \mid A_1\}$ it is necessary to consider only that part of the original sample space for which A_1 is certain to occur. It will contain $13 \cdot 51$ sample points because to each of the 13 possible spades that may be obtained on the first drawing there are always 51 remaining cards that may be obtained on the second drawing. There are $13 \cdot 12$ points in this sample space that correspond to the occurrence of A_2, because to each of the 13 possible spades that may be obtained on the first drawing there are always 12 remaining spades that may be obtained on the second drawing to give $13 \cdot 12$ spade pairs. As a result, $P\{A_2 \mid A_1\} = 13 \cdot 12/13 \cdot 51 = \frac{12}{51}$. By using symmetry this computation could have been simplified considerably. Since the conditional probability of getting a spade on the second drawing, given that a space was obtained on the first drawing, should be equal to the corresponding probability when a particular spade is known to have been obtained on the first drawing, one could just as well have worked with the sample space in which a particular spade is obtained on the first drawing. This reduced sample space contains only 51 points, 12 of which are favorable. The calculation of $P\{A_2 \mid A_1\}$ now becomes $\frac{12}{51}$. The application of formula (7) can now be made and yields the result

$$P\{A_1 A_2\} = \tfrac{13}{52} \cdot \tfrac{12}{51} = \tfrac{1}{17}$$

Hereafter, formulas (4) and (7) will be applied without discussing the nature of the various sample spaces involved in the computations. Furthermore, symmetry considerations such as those used to simplify the preceding computations will be used whenever they are advantageous. If one is not certain in a given problem that his intuition is correct in choosing simple sample spaces, he should go back to the original sample space.

(e) This last illustration is a somewhat more complicated exercise in the manipulation of formulas (4) and (7). One box contains two red balls. A second box of identical appearance contains one red and one white ball. If a box is selected by chance and one ball is drawn from it, what is the probability that the first box was the selected one, if the drawn ball turns out to be red? Let A_1 denote the event of selecting the first box and $\bar{A}_1$ that of selecting the second box. Let A_2 denote the event of drawing a red ball and $\bar{A}_2$ that of drawing a white ball. Then the problem is to calculate the conditional probability $P\{A_1 \mid A_2\}$. Interchanging A_1 and A_2 in (6) will give

$$P\{A_1 \mid A_2\} = \frac{P\{A_1 A_2\}}{P\{A_2\}}$$

The numerator probability may be calculated by using formula (7) directly, with the understanding that to select a box by chance means that the probability of selecting, say, the first box is $\frac{1}{2}$. Thus

$$P\{A_1 A_2\} = P\{A_1\} P\{A_2 \mid A_1\} = \frac{1}{2} \cdot 1 = \frac{1}{2}$$

The denominator probability may be calculated by considering the event A_2 in conjunction with the selection of a box. Now A_2 will occur if, and only if, one of the two mutually exclusive events $A_1 A_2$ and $\bar{A}_1 A_2$ occurs. Thus, by formula (4),

(11) $$P\{A_2\} = P\{A_1 A_2\} + P\{\bar{A}_1 A_2\}$$

But

$$P\{\bar{A}_1 A_2\} = P\{\bar{A}_1\} P\{A_2 \mid \bar{A}_1\} = \frac{1}{2} \cdot \frac{1}{2} = \frac{1}{4}$$

Since $P\{A_1 A_2\}$ was found to be equal to $\frac{1}{2}$, it follows from (11) and this last result that $P\{A_2\} = \frac{3}{4}$, and hence that

$$P\{A_1 \mid A_2\} = \frac{\frac{1}{2}}{\frac{3}{4}} = \frac{2}{3}$$

This problem was designed to give practice in the use of the two basic probability formulas; however, it could have been solved more simply by looking at the sample space and applying definition (1). A sample space consisting of the four points I1, I2, II1, II2, would be quite natural here. The Roman numeral denotes the box number, and the Arabic numeral the ball number. One would assign equal probabilities to these four points. The condition A_2 restricts the sample space to the first three sample points if ball number 2 in the second box is understood to be the white one. Thus each of these three sample points must be assigned the probability $\frac{1}{3}$. Now, the first two sample points correspond to the occurrence of A_1; hence $P\{A_1 \mid A_2\} = \frac{2}{3}$.

2.7 Bayes' Formula

Illustration (e) of the preceding section is typical of problems in which one looks at the outcome of an experiment and then asks for the probability that the outcome was due to a particular one of the possible "causes" of the outcome. Thus in illustration (e) there are two possible causes, or ways, for a red ball to be obtained, and the problem is to calculate the probability that it was due to the first one. Although the solution to the problem was obtained by merely applying the two rules of probability in the proper sequence, the computations are sufficiently extensive to make it worthwhile to derive a formula for treating such problems systematically.

For the purpose of obtaining a formula, let the sample space of the experiment be divided into k mutually exclusive regions $H_1, H_2, \cdots, H_k$. These regions represent the k possible causes of an experimental outcome which are of interest. Thus in Fig. 2 there are four such regions displayed— the three closed regions bounded by curves and the rest of the sample space. Next, let A be the event that occurred when the experiment was performed and consider the problem of calculating the probability that H_i was the cause of the occurrence of A. This means that the sample point was one of the points inside H_i associated with the occurrence of A. From formula (6) this probability is given by

$$(12) \qquad P\{H_i \mid A\} = \frac{P\{H_i A\}}{P\{A\}}$$

But,

$$(13) \qquad P\{H_i A\} = P\{H_i\}P\{A \mid H_i\}$$

Now the event A can occur only in conjunction with one of the k possible events $H_1, H_2, \cdots, H_k$. Thus A will occur if, and only if, one of the mutually exclusive events $H_1 A, H_2 A, \cdots, H_k A$ occurs. The addition rule for mutually exclusive events therefore gives

$$P\{A\} = P\{H_1 A\} + P\{H_2 A\} + \cdots + P\{H_k A\}$$

If formula (13) is applied to each term on the right, one will obtain

$$P\{A\} = \sum_{i=1}^{k} P\{H_i\}P\{A \mid H_i\}$$

The substitution of this formula and formula (13) in (12) yields the desired formula for calculating probabilities of causes. The result may be summarized as follows:

BAYES' FORMULA: $$P\{H_i \mid A\} = \frac{P\{H_i\}P\{A \mid H_i\}}{\sum\limits_{i=1}^{k} P\{H_i\}P\{A \mid H_i\}}$$

Illustration (e) of the preceding section, which was solved by the expeditious use of the two rules of probability, is solved here to illustrate the direct use of Bayes' formula. Let H_1 and H_2 correspond to the events of getting box number 1 and box number 2, respectively, and let A be the event of getting a red ball. Since a box is selected by chance, $P\{H_1\} = P\{H_2\} = \frac{1}{2}$. Further, it is clear from the contents of the two boxes that $P\{A \mid H_1\} = 1$ and $P\{A \mid H_2\} = \frac{1}{2}$. Bayes' formula then yields

$$P\{H_1 \mid A\} = \frac{\frac{1}{2} \cdot 1}{\frac{1}{2} \cdot 1 + \frac{1}{2} \cdot \frac{1}{2}} = \frac{2}{3}$$

2.8 Combinatorial Formulas

The simplest problems on which to develop facility in applying the addition and multiplication rules of probability are some of those related to games of chance. For many such problems, however, the counting of sample points corresponding to various events becomes tedious unless compact counting methods are developed. A few of the formulas that yield such methods are derived in this section.

2.8.1 Permutations

Consider a set of n different objects, such as n blocks having different numbers or colors. Let r of the n objects be selected and arranged in a line. Such an arrangement is called a *permutation* of the r objects. If two of the r objects are interchanged in their respective positions, a different permutation results. In order to count the total number of permutations, it suffices to consider the r positions on the line as fixed and then count the number of ways in which blocks can be selected to be placed in the r positions. Starting from the position farthest to the left, any one of the n blocks may be chosen to fill this position. After the first position has been filled, there will be only $n - 1$ blocks left to choose from to fill the second position. For each choice for the first position, there are therefore $n - 1$ choices for the second position; hence $n(n - 1)$ total choices for the two positions. If this selection procedure is continued, there will be $n - r + 1$ blocks left to choose from for the rth position. If the total number of such permutations is denoted by $_nP_r$, it therefore follows that

(14) $$_nP_r = n(n - 1) \cdots (n - r + 1)$$

The symbol $_nP_r$ is usually called the number of permutations of n things taken r at a time.

As an illustration, suppose one is given the four letters a, b, c, d. The number of permutations of these four letters taken two at a time is given by $_4P_2 = 4 \cdot 3 = 12$. These permutations are easily enumerated as follows: *ab, ba, ac, ca, ad, da, bc, cb, bd, db, cd, dc*.

If *r* is chosen equal to *n*, (14) reduces to

$$(15) \qquad\qquad _nP_n = n(n-1) \cdots (1) = n!$$

In order to permit formulas that involve factorials to be correct even when $n = 0$, it is necessary to define $0! = 1$. This is consistent for $n = 1$ with the factorial property that $(n-1)! = n!/n$.

2.8.2   Combinations

If one is interested only in what particular objects are selected when *r* objects are chosen from *n* objects, without regard to their arrangement in a line, then the unordered selection is called a *combination*. Thus, if two letters are chosen from the four letters *a, b, c, d*, the combination *ab* is the same combination as *ba*, but of course it differs from the combination *ac*. The total number of combinations possible in selecting *r* objects from *n* different objects is denoted by the symbol $\binom{n}{r}$. This symbol is usually called the number of combinations of *n* things taken *r* at a time.

In order to derive a formula for $\binom{n}{r}$, it suffices to compare the total number of permutations and total number of combinations possible. Since a permutation is obtained by first selecting *r* objects and then arranging them in some order, whereas a combination is obtained by performing only the first step, it follows that the total number of permutations is obtained by taking every possible combination, the total number of which is $\binom{n}{r}$, and arranging them in all possible ways. But from (15) the total number of arrangements of *r* objects in *r* places is *r*!; hence the total number of permutations is given by multiplying the number of combinations, $\binom{n}{r}$, by *r*!. Thus $_nP_r = \binom{n}{r} \cdot r!$. Using formula (14), it therefore follows that

$$(16) \qquad\qquad \binom{n}{r} = \frac{n(n-1) \cdots (n-r+1)}{r!}$$

Since $n(n-1) \cdots (n-r+1) = n!/(n-r)!$, formula (16) may be written in the following more compact form:

$$(17) \qquad\qquad \binom{n}{r} = \frac{n!}{r!\,(n-r)!}$$

As an illustration, the number of combinations of two letters selected from the four letters a, b, c, d is given by $\binom{4}{2} = 4!/2!\,2! = 6$. The actual combinations are ab, ac, ad, bc, bd, cd.

2.8.3   Permutations When Some Elements Are Alike

In the preceding derivations it has been assumed that all the n objects are different. It sometimes happens, however, that the n objects contain a number of similar objects. Thus one might have five colored balls of which three are white and two black, instead of five distinct colors. Now suppose that there are only k distinct kinds of objects and that there are n_1 of the first kind, n_2 of the second kind, $\cdots$, and n_k of the kth kind, where $n_1 + n_2 + \cdots + n_k = n$. The total number of different permutations of these n objects arranged in a line is obviously less than $n!$. In order to find the total number of distinct permutations, it suffices to compare the number of permutations now, which is denoted by P, with the number that would be obtained if the like objects were given marks to distinguish them. The comparison is similar to that made between $\binom{n}{r}$ and $_nP_r$ in deriving formula (16). Each permutation in the problem under consideration gives rise to additional permutations when the like objects are made different by markings. For example, if the n_1 similar objects in a permutation are made different, they can be rearranged in their positions in $n_1!$ ways. Since this is true for each of the P permutations, there will be $n_1!$ times as many permutations when the n_1 similar objects are made different as before. In the same manner, the n_2 similar objects may be made different to give $n_2!$ times as many permutations as before. Continuing this procedure, the total number of permutations after all similar objects have been made different will be $n_1!\,n_2!\cdots n_k!$ times as large as the number of permutations before the similar objects were made different; hence the total number after these changes will be $Pn_1!\,n_2!\cdots n_k!$. But after all similar objects have been made different, the total number of permutations will be the number of permutations of n different things taken n at a time, which is $n!$. Equating these two results and solving for P, one obtains

$$(18) \qquad\qquad \frac{n!}{n_1!\,n_2!\cdots n_k!}$$

for the total number of permutations of n things in which there are n_1 alike, n_2 alike, $\cdots$, n_k alike. As an illustration, consider the number of permutations of the five letters a, a, a, b, b. Formula (18) yields $5!/3!\,2! =$ 10. These permutations are easily written down: *aaabb, aabab, abaab, baaab, aabba, ababa, baaba, abbaa, babaa, bbaaa.*

2.8.4 Illustrations of the Use of Combinatorial Formulas

(*a*) Consider a bridge hand consisting of 13 cards chosen from an ordinary deck. What is the probability that such a hand will contain exactly seven spades? Since a bridge hand is not concerned with the order in which the various cards are obtained, the total number of possible bridge hands is equal to the number of ways of choosing 13 objects from 52 objects, or $\binom{52}{13}$. This is therefore the total number of sample points in the sample space. The number of hands containing exactly seven spades is equal to the number of ways of choosing 7 spades from 13 spades, or $\binom{13}{7}$, multiplied by the number of ways of choosing 6 nonspades from 39 nonspades, or $\binom{39}{6}$. Hence the desired probability is given by

$$\frac{\binom{13}{7}\binom{39}{6}}{\binom{52}{13}} = \frac{13!\,39!\,13!\,39!}{7!\,6!\,6!\,33!\,52!}$$

(*b*) What is the probability that a bridge hand will contain at most one ace? The total number of bridge hands containing at most one ace consists of those with one ace and those with no ace. The number of hands with one ace is given by $\binom{4}{1}\binom{48}{12}$, whereas the number with no ace is given by $\binom{48}{13}$; consequently, the total number of favorable hands is

$$\binom{4}{1}\binom{48}{12} + \binom{48}{13}$$

Since the total number of possible bridge hands was found earlier to be $\binom{52}{13}$, the desired probability is given by the ratio

$$\frac{\binom{4}{1}\binom{48}{12} + \binom{48}{13}}{\binom{52}{13}}$$

(*c*) If you know that a bridge hand contains at most one ace, what is the probability that it contains no ace? The number of sample points in this sample space is given by the numerator of the preceding result. The number of those corresponding to the desired event, namely bridge hands with no ace, is given by $\binom{48}{13}$; consequently, the desired probability is given by the ratio

$$\frac{\binom{48}{13}}{\binom{4}{1}\binom{48}{12} + \binom{48}{13}}$$

(*d*) If a coin is tossed five times, what is the probability that three heads and two tails will be obtained? First, consider a fixed order in which the desired result can occur, say *HHHTT*. From (10) the probability of obtaining this particular order of events is $(\frac{1}{2})^5$. Any other ordering of these three *H*'s and two *T*'s will have the same probability of being obtained. Next, consider the number of possible orderings. This number is equal to the number of permutations of five letters, of which three are alike and two are alike, which by formula (18) is equal to $5!/3!\,2! = 10$. Since the 10 orderings constitute the mutually exclusive ways in which the desired event can occur, formula (4) yields the desired answer, namely, $10(\frac{1}{2})^5 = \frac{5}{16}$.

(*e*) A pair of coins is tossed 200 times. What is the probability that exactly *x* of the 200 tosses will show double heads? As in the preceding illustration, consider a fixed order in which the desired result can occur, say,

$$\overbrace{SS\cdots S}^{x} \quad \overbrace{FF\cdots F}^{200-x}$$

where *S* denotes a success, that is, a double head, and *F* a failure, and where there are *x* successes and $200 - x$ failures. Because of the independence of the trials, the probability that this particular ordering will be obtained is $(\frac{1}{4})^x(\frac{3}{4})^{200-x}$. The number of such orderings is equal to the number of permutations of the *S*'s and *F*'s, which in turn is equal to the number of permutations of 200 things, of which *x* are alike and $200 - x$ are alike. By formula (18), this number is $200!/x!\,(200 - x)!$. Since these orderings constitute the mutually exclusive ways in which the desired event can occur, it follows that the desired probability is given by

(19) $$\frac{200!}{x!\,(200 - x)!}\left(\frac{1}{4}\right)^x\left(\frac{3}{4}\right)^{200-x}$$

2.9 Random Variables

Consider a sample space corresponding to the tossing of two coins and suppose that interest is centered on the total number of heads that will be obtained. In order to study probabilities of such events, it is convenient to introduce a variable x to represent the total number of heads obtained. If the sample space suggested in 2.2 and displayed in Fig. 1 is used, the variable x will assume the value 0 at the sample point (0, 0), the value 1 at the sample points (1, 0) and (0, 1), and the value 2 at the sample point (1, 1). A numerical-valued variable x such as this is an example of a random, or chance, variable.

(20) DEFINITION: *A random variable is a numerical-valued variable defined on a sample space.*

As an illustration, if x denotes the sum of the points obtained in rolling two dice, then x is a random variable that can assume integral values from 2 to 12. The sample space here consists of 36 sample points. As another illustration, if four cards are drawn from a deck and if x denotes the number of black cards obtained, then x is a random variable that can assume integral values from 0 to 4. The sample space here consists of $\binom{52}{4}$ sample points.

The name random, or chance, is given to the variables in these illustrations because they are defined on sample spaces associated with physical experiments in which the outcome of any one experiment is uncertain and is therefore said to depend on chance.

2.10 Frequency Functions

After a random variable x has been defined on a sample space, interest usually centers on determining the probability that x will assume specified values in its range of possible values. From (1), the probability that x will assume a particular value, say x_0, is equal to the sum of the probabilities for the sample points for which $x = x_0$. The relationship between the value of x and its probability is expressed by means of a function called the frequency function, which is defined as follows:

(21) DEFINITION: *A function $f(x)$ that yields the probability that the random variable x will assume any particular value in its range is called the frequency function of the random variable x.*

A frequency function often consists of merely a table of values. Thus, if two coins are tossed and if x denotes the total number of heads obtained, it suffices to define $f(x)$ by means of the following set of values: $f(0) = \frac{1}{4}$, $f(1) = \frac{1}{2}, f(2) = \frac{1}{4}$.

In the following chapters, when explicit mathematical models are selected for experiments, several important frequency functions are given by means of formulas rather than by tables of values. The function defined by (19) is an example of a frequency function defined by a formula.

In order to judge quickly how a variable is distributed, that is, how its probability changes as the variable changes, it is convenient to graph the frequency function $f(x)$ by means of a line graph. As an illustration of such a graph, let x denote the sum of the points obtained in rolling a pair of dice. Enumeration of cases and the use of Table 1 will show that $f(2) = f(12) = \frac{1}{36}, f(3) = f(11) = \frac{2}{36}, f(4) = f(10) = \frac{3}{36}, f(5) = f(9) = \frac{4}{36}, f(6) = f(8) = \frac{5}{36}$, and $f(7) = \frac{6}{36}$. A line graph of $f(x)$ is given in Fig. 3.

A function closely related to the frequency function $f(x)$ is the *distribution function $F(x)$*. It is defined by the relation

(22)
$$F(x) = \sum_{t \leq x} f(t)$$

where the summation occurs over all those values of the random variable that are less than or equal to the specified value of x. Thus $F(x_0)$ gives the probability that the random variable x will assume a value less than or equal to x_0, as contrasted to $f(x_0)$, which gives the probability that x will assume the particular value x_0. The function $F(x)$ is called the distribution function by pure mathematicians, but it is sometimes called the cumulative distribution function by statisticians. The graph of $F(x)$ for the dice

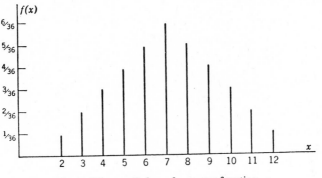

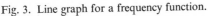
Fig. 3. Line graph for a frequency function.

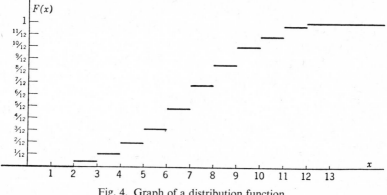

Fig. 4. Graph of a distribution function.

illustration of the preceding paragraph is given in Fig. 4. It should be noted that the value of $F(x)$ for x an integer is the upper value rather than the lower.

2.11 Joint Frequency Functions

Many experiments involve several random variables rather than just one. For simplicity, consider two random variables x and y. A mathematical model for these two variables is a function that gives the probability that x will assume a particular value while at the same time y will assume a particular value. A function $f(x, y)$ that gives such probabilities is called a *joint frequency function* of the two random variables x and y. The adjective joint is usually omitted, since there is little possibility of confusing a function of two variables with a function of one variable.

As an illustration, let x denote the number of spades obtained in drawing one card from an ordinary deck and let y denote the number of spades obtained in drawing a second card from the deck, without the first card being replaced. Then $f(x, y)$ is defined by the following table of values: $f(0, 0) = \frac{39}{52} \cdot \frac{38}{51}$; $f(1, 0) = \frac{13}{52} \cdot \frac{39}{51}$; $f(0, 1) = \frac{39}{52} \cdot \frac{13}{51}$; and $f(1, 1) = \frac{13}{52} \cdot \frac{12}{51}$. The graph of $f(x, y)$ as a line graph is given in Fig. 5.

As a second illustration, let x and y denote the number of red and white balls, respectively, obtained in drawing two balls from a bag containing two red, two white, and two black balls. Here the joint frequency function is given by

$$(23) \qquad f(x, y) = \frac{\binom{2}{x}\binom{2}{y}\binom{2}{2 - x - y}}{\binom{6}{2}}$$

This frequency function is defined by a formula; however, it could have been defined by means of a table of values, as in the first illustration. The numerator in (23) is obtained by realizing that the x red balls must come from the two red balls, the y white balls must come from the two white balls, and the remaining $2 - (x + y)$ balls must come from the two black balls.

In much of the statistical theory that is developed in the following chapters, the variables are unrelated in a probability sense. In the first illustration the variables x and y would have been such variables if the first card drawn had been replaced before the second card was drawn. To say that variables are unrelated in a probability sense means that the probability of one of the variables assuming a particular value is independent of the values the other variables assume. Random variables possessing this property are said to be independently distributed and are called independent random variables. In order to define independence more precisely, let $f(x_1, x_2, \cdots, x_n)$ be the joint frequency function of the indicated variables and let $f_i(x_i)$ denote the frequency function of the variable x_i. The function $f_i(x_i)$ merely gives the probability distribution of the variable x_i when the remaining variables are ignored.

The essential property of such variables follows from the definition of independent events given by (10) and may be formalized in the following manner:

(24)   DEFINITION: *If the joint frequency function $f(x_1, x_2, \cdots, x_n)$ can be factored in the form $f(x_1, x_2, \cdots, x_n) = f_1(x_1)f_2(x_2) \cdots f_n(x_n)$, where $f_i(x_i)$ is*

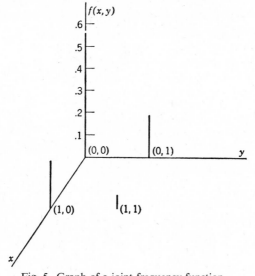

Fig. 5. Graph of a joint frequency function.

the frequency function of x_i, then the random variables $x_1, x_2, \cdots, x_n$ are said to be independently distributed.

As an illustration, consider the first of the two preceding illustrations, modified to the extent that the first card drawn is replaced before the second card is drawn. The frequency function of x, which is denoted by $f_1(x)$, is given by the formula

$$f_1(x) = \frac{\binom{13}{x}\binom{39}{1-x}}{\binom{52}{1}}$$

Since the first card is returned to the deck before the second drawing, the second drawing does not differ from the first drawing in properties; consequently, the frequency function of y, which is denoted by $f_2(y)$, is given by the same formula with x replaced by y. Since x and y are obviously independent here,

$$f(x, y) = \frac{\binom{13}{x}\binom{39}{1-x}}{\binom{52}{1}} \frac{\binom{13}{y}\binom{39}{1-y}}{\binom{52}{1}} = f_1(x)\,f_2(y)$$

As an example in which (24) does not hold, consider the second of the two preceding illustrations for which the joint frequency function is given by (23). If $f_1(x)$ denotes the frequency function of x alone, then

$$f_1(x) = \frac{\binom{2}{x}\binom{4}{2-x}}{\binom{6}{2}}$$

Similarly, if $f_2(y)$ denotes the frequency function of y alone, then

$$f_2(y) = \frac{\binom{2}{y}\binom{4}{2-y}}{\binom{6}{2}}$$

If (24) were to hold here, which means that $f(x, y)$ as given by (23) would have to be equal to $f_1(x)f_2(y)$, then it would be necessary that

$$\binom{4}{2-x}\binom{4}{2-y} = \binom{6}{2}\binom{2}{2-x-y}$$

Furthermore, this relationship would be required to hold for all experimentally possible values of x and y. It obviously does not hold for $x = 1$ and $y = 1$. As a matter of fact, it does not hold for a single pair of possible values.

Even though a joint frequency function of two variables may appear to be the product of a function of x alone and a function of y alone, it does not necessarily follow that the variables are independently distributed. A simple illustration of this fact can be obtained by modifying the problem that was just considered. As before, let x and y denote the number of red and white balls, respectively, obtained in drawing two balls from the bag, but now let the bag contain two red and two white balls only. Then the joint frequency function of x and y is given by

$$(25) \qquad f(x, y) = \frac{\binom{2}{x}\binom{2}{y}}{\binom{4}{2}}$$

This frequency function appears to factor properly for independence, but these variables are obviously not independent. As a matter of fact, y is completely determined by x and could be replaced by $2 - x$ in this formula. For independence it is necessary that the joint frequency function can be factored into the product of the individual frequency functions of the two variables. In this illustration (25) is the frequency function of x alone if y is replaced by $2 - x$. Since, by symmetry, the frequency function of y alone is the same as that for x alone, it is clear that $f(x, y)$ is not equal to the product of the individual frequency functions here and that it cannot be made so.

2.12 Marginal and Conditional Distributions

In the preceding section it was necessary to obtain the frequency functions of the individual variables before one could decide whether the variables in a joint frequency function were independent. Since it is important to know whether a set of variables is independent, it would be desirable to have a systematic way of finding the frequency functions of the individual variables. Such a method is readily obtained by means of formula (7) for the case of two variables. Although one can easily extend the method so that it will apply to more than two variables, there is no need for the extension in later work; therefore the discussion is limited to two variables.

Consider an experiment for which A_1 is the event that a random variable will assume the value x and A_2 is the event that a second random variable will assume the value y. The multiplication formula

$$(26) \qquad P\{A_1A_2\} = P\{A_1\}P\{A_2 \mid A_1\}$$

can then be expressed in terms of frequency functions. Since $P\{A_1A_2\}$ now gives the probability that the two random variables will assume the values x and y, respectively, it is equivalent to $f(x, y)$, the value of the joint frequency function at the point (x, y). Similarly, $P\{A_1\}$ is the probability that the first variable will assume the value x; therefore it is equivalent to $f(x)$, the value of the frequency function of the first variable at the point x. Since $P\{A_2 \mid A_1\}$ gives the probability that the second variable will assume the value y, given that the first variable is known to have the value x, it is equivalent to the value of a conditional frequency function, which is denoted by $f(y \mid x)$. Formula (26) now becomes

$$(27) \qquad f(x, y) = f(x)f(y \mid x)$$

Since $f(y \mid x)$ gives the conditional probability that the second random variable will assume the value y when the first random variable has the fixed value x, the sum of $f(y \mid x)$ over all possible values of y for this fixed value of x must equal 1. Hence, if both sides of (27) are summed over all possible values of y, the formula for $f(x)$ given below in (28) will be obtained. In connection with the joint frequency function $f(x, y)$, the function $f(x)$ is called the x *marginal frequency function*; however, it is merely the frequency function of the first random variable. This result may be expressed as

$$(28) \quad \text{MARGINAL DISTRIBUTION:} \quad f(x) = \sum_y f(x, y)$$

In a similar manner, the y marginal frequency function can be obtained, say $g(y)$, by summing $f(x, y)$ over all values of x with y held fixed. Thus $g(y) = \sum_x f(x, y)$. These results show that if one has the joint frequency function of two random variables and if one desires the frequency function of one of them, it is merely necessary to sum the joint frequency function over all values of the other variable.

The conditional frequency function $f(y \mid x)$ gives the distribution of the second random variable when the first variable is held fixed. This distribution is sometimes called the x array distribution of the joint distribution. Because of (27), if $f(x) \neq 0$, one may therefore write

$$(29) \quad \text{CONDITIONAL DISTRIBUTION:} \quad f(y \mid x) = \frac{f(x, y)}{f(x)}$$

The conditional distribution for x with y held fixed is given by an analogous formula. This shows that if one has the joint frequency function of two variables and desires the conditional frequency function for one of them when the other is held fixed, it is merely necessary to divide the joint frequency function by the frequency function of the fixed variable.

For the purpose of illustrating the preceding ideas, suppose that a bag contains two white and four black balls and that two balls are drawn from the bag. Let x and y represent the results of the two drawings, 0 corresponding to a black ball and 1 corresponding to a white ball. Then, every possible result will be represented by one of the four points in the x,y plane shown in Fig. 6. From the contents of the bag and the order in which the drawings are made, it follows directly from formula (27) that

$$f(0, 0) = f(0)f(0 \mid 0) = \tfrac{4}{6} \cdot \tfrac{3}{5} = \tfrac{6}{15}$$

$$f(0, 1) = f(0)f(1 \mid 0) = \tfrac{4}{6} \cdot \tfrac{2}{5} = \tfrac{4}{15}$$

$$f(1, 0) = f(1)f(0 \mid 1) = \tfrac{2}{6} \cdot \tfrac{4}{5} = \tfrac{4}{15}$$

$$f(1, 1) = f(1)f(1 \mid 1) = \tfrac{2}{6} \cdot \tfrac{1}{5} = \tfrac{1}{15}$$

The values of $f(x, y)$ have been graphed in Fig. 6 by means of a simple line chart.

In order to illustrate the method of obtaining a marginal distribution and a conditional distribution from the joint distribution, assume now that only the final values of $f(x, y)$ just calculated are known. Thus the only information available is that given in Fig. 6. One should erase from his mind how these numbers were obtained.

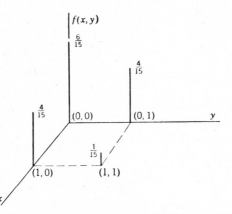

Fig. 6. Theoretical distribution for two discrete variables.

The x marginal frequency function can be obtained by applying formula (28). Thus

$$f(0) = f(0, 0) + f(0, 1) = \tfrac{6}{15} + \tfrac{4}{15} = \tfrac{2}{3}$$
$$f(1) = f(1, 0) + f(1, 1) = \tfrac{4}{15} + \tfrac{1}{15} = \tfrac{1}{3}$$

If the four points in the x,y plane are thought of as mass points whose total mass is 1, then the x marginal distribution represents the distribution of mass along the x axis after the points in the x,y plane have been projected on the x axis.

The conditional frequency function of y for x fixed can be obtained by applying formula (29) and using the results just obtained. Thus, if x is assigned the value $x = 1$,

$$f(0 \mid 1) = \frac{f(1, 0)}{f(1)} = \frac{\tfrac{4}{15}}{\tfrac{1}{3}} = \frac{4}{5}$$

$$f(1 \mid 1) = \frac{f(1, 1)}{f(1)} = \frac{\tfrac{1}{15}}{\tfrac{1}{3}} = \frac{1}{5}$$

Geometrically, $f(y \mid 1)$ represents the distribution of probability mass along the line $x = 1$ when the two points on this line have had their probability masses multiplied by a number, $1/f(1)$, to make the sum of their masses equal 1.

As a second illustration, in which the joint frequency function is given directly, consider the frequency function defined by the formula

$$f(x, y) = \tfrac{1}{27}(x + y + 1)$$

where x and y can assume only the integer values 0, 1, or 2. The sample space with its probabilities calculated by means of this formula is shown in Fig. 7.

From formula (28), the marginal frequency function of x is given by

$$f(x) = \sum_{y} \tfrac{1}{27}(x + y + 1)$$

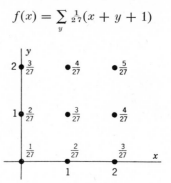

Fig. 7. Sample space for $f(x, y) = (x + y + 1)/27$.

In carrying out the summation it is clear from Fig. 7 that y may range over all its possible values regardless of the value of x that was fixed; hence

$$(30) \qquad f(x) = \sum_{y=0}^{2} \tfrac{1}{27}(x + y + 1) = \tfrac{1}{9}(x + 2)$$

By symmetry, the marginal frequency function of y will be the same as that for x; hence

$$g(y) = \tfrac{1}{9}(y + 2)$$

It is clear that $f(x, y)$ is not equal to the product of its marginal frequency functions here and therefore that x and y are not independent random variables.

From formula (29) and the result given in (30), it follows that the conditional frequency function of y for x fixed is given by

$$f(y \mid x) = \frac{\tfrac{1}{27}(x + y + 1)}{\tfrac{1}{9}(x + 2)} = \frac{x + y + 1}{3(x + 2)}$$

If x is assigned the value 2, for example,

$$f(y \mid 2) = \tfrac{1}{12}(y + 3)$$

This function would be useful if one wished to calculate probabilities for various values of y when it is known that x has the value 2. It can easily be checked that this is a probability function by summing the three probabilities obtained from this formula by letting $y = 0$, 1, and 2 and verifying that the sum is 1.

It was a simple matter to find the marginal frequency function in the preceding problem because the sum over y in formula (28) was over all possible values of y regardless of the fixed value of x. The problem would have been somewhat more difficult if the frequency function had been given by the formula

$$f(x, y) = \tfrac{1}{18}(x + y + 1)$$

and the sample space had been the one shown in Fig. 8. This sample space differs from the one in Fig. 7 in that y is not permitted to exceed x

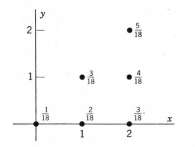

Fig. 8. Sample space for $f(x, y) = (x + y + 1)/18$.

in value. Now if one wanted the marginal value $f(1)$, the sum in (28) would become

$$f(1) = \sum_{y=0}^{1} \tfrac{1}{18}(y + 2) = \tfrac{5}{18}$$

However, if one wanted the marginal value $f(2)$, the sum would become

$$f(2) = \sum_{y=0}^{2} \tfrac{1}{18}(y + 3) = \tfrac{12}{18}$$

Thus the values of y over which the sum is to be taken depend upon what marginal value of x is desired. Although the simplest procedure here is to perform the summation separately for each value of x, one can sum for a general x. Calculations for a general x will show that the marginal function can be expressed by means of the formula

$$f(x) = \tfrac{1}{36}(x + 1)(3x + 2)$$

2.13   Continuous Frequency Functions

Thus far the discussion of probability has been confined to finite sample spaces. This simplification made it possible to derive the fundamental rules of probability in an elementary manner. It is assumed hereafter that these rules may also be applied to sample spaces in which there may be an infinite number of sample points. As an illustration of a problem for which this extension of the applicability of the rules of probability is needed, calculate the probability that the first head obtained in tossing a coin repeatedly will occur on or before the fourth toss. Here the sample space might conveniently consist of the infinite number of sample points represented by the infinite sequence of outcomes $H, TH, TTH, TTTH,$ $\cdots$. If it is assumed that the coin is not biased, the probabilities that would be assigned to these sample points are $\tfrac{1}{2}, (\tfrac{1}{2})^2, (\tfrac{1}{2})^3, (\tfrac{1}{2})^4, \cdots$. It will be observed that the sum of these sample point probabilities is 1, as it should be. The random variable x here is a variable that can assume any one of the values $1, 2, 3, \cdots$, and the problem is to calculate the value of $F(4)$.

The random variable of the preceding illustration is an example of a discrete variable. A *discrete random variable* is a random variable that can assume only a finite number, or an infinite sequence, of distinct values. This means that the values can be arranged in a definite order.

Although the extension of the applicability of the rules of probability as indicated above enables one to consider a much larger class of problems than before, there are many important classes of problems that are still not covered. These problems involve sample spaces that contain all the points in an interval or intervals rather than just a discrete set of points. For example, suppose an experiment consists in the weighing of an adult male from the population of a given city. Although there is only a finite number of individuals in the city, hence only a finite number of possible outcomes of the experiment, the mathematical model for such an experiment is much simpler if one conceives of an infinite number of individuals and of all possible weights in some interval as being possible outcomes of the experiment. If the random variable x denoting the weight of an individual is introduced, then this assumes that x could take on any value in the interval, say, 150 to 160 pounds. A random variable that may assume any value in some interval or intervals is called a *continuous random variable*. Such variables as weights, lengths, temperatures, and velocities, which involve measurement, are considered to be continuous. Although there are variables that are a mixture of the discrete and continuous types, the important problems in statistics usually involve either one or the other; hence only these two distinct types are considered.

For the purpose of discussing properties of continuous variables, consider a particular continuous random variable x that represents the thickness of a metal washer obtained from a certain machine turning out washers. If the machine were permitted to turn out, say, 100 washers, and if the thicknesses of these 100 washers were measured to the nearest .001 inch, there would be available 100 values of x with which to study the behavior of the machine. If these 100 values were collected and represented in table form, one might find a table of values such as that displayed in Table 3 that gives the absolute frequency f with which various values of

TABLE 3

x	.231	.232	.233	.234	.235	.236	.237	.238	.239
f	1	2	8	18	28	24	13	4	2

x occurred. The word "frequency" usually implies the ratio of the observed number of values of x to the total number of observational values; however, it is also used to denote the numerator of this ratio. If throughout the subsequent chapters there is any question which meaning is being used, the words "relative frequency" and "absolute frequency" will be employed. Absolute frequencies are recorded in Table 3.

For the purpose of displaying these results graphically, a graph called a *histogram* is used. A histogram is a graph of the type shown in Fig. 9, in which areas are used to represent observed frequencies, particularly relative frequencies. Thus the area of the rectangle that is centered at $x = .234$ should equal the relative frequency .18; however, in practice it is customary

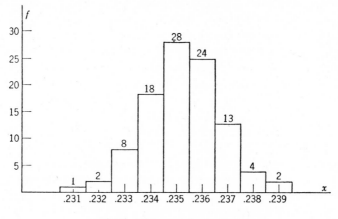

Fig. 9. Histogram for Table 3.

to choose any convenient unit on the y axis, with the result that the areas of the rectangles may be only proportional to the corresponding frequencies rather than equal to them. The histogram shown in Fig. 9 for the data of Table 3 has been constructed with such a convenient choice of units; hence areas there are only proportional to frequencies.

If the histogram is to be constructed so that areas will be equal to relative frequencies, then the total area of the histogram must equal 1 because the sum of the relative frequencies must equal 1. If h denotes the distance between consecutive x values, the height of the rectangle centered at, say, x_i will be f_i/Nh, where f_i denotes the absolute frequency of x_i. This result is obvious when it is realized that this ordinate when multiplied by the base h must equal the relative frequency f_i/N.

The histogram of Fig. 9 indicates the frequency with which various values of x were obtained for 100 runs of the experiment. If 200 runs had been made, the resulting histogram would have been twice as large as that based on 100 runs. In order to compare histograms based on different numbers of experiments, it is necessary to choose units on the y axis, as discussed in the preceding paragraph, in such a manner that the area of the histogram will always be equal to one. With this choice of units, the histogram would be expected to approach a fixed histogram as the number of runs of the experiment is increased indefinitely. Furthermore, if it is assumed that x can be measured as accurately as desired so that the unit on the x axis, h, can be made as small as desired, then the histogram would be expected to smooth out and approximate a continuous curve as the number of runs of the experiment is increased indefinitely and h is chosen very small. Such a curve is thought of as an idealization for the relative frequency with which different values of x would be expected to be obtained for runs of the actual experiment.

When the area of the histogram is made equal to 1, it follows from the preceding discussion that the sum of the areas of several neighboring rectangles is equal to the relative frequency with which the value of x was observed to lie in the interval that forms the base of those rectangles. Since this property will continue to hold as the number of runs of the experiment increases indefinitely, the area under the expected limiting, or idealized, curve between any two given values of x should be equal to the relative frequency with which x would be expected to lie in the interval determined by those values of x. The function $f(x)$ whose graph is conceived as being the limiting form of the histogram is treated as the mathematical model for the continuous random variable x and is called the frequency function of the variable. Since relative frequency in the case of a histogram is replaced by probability in the case of a mathematical model, the definition of a frequency function for a continuous variable may be stated in the following form:

(31)   DEFINITION: *A frequency function for a continuous random variable x is a function $f(x)$ that possesses the following properties:*

(i) $$f(x) \geq 0$$

(ii) $$\int_{-\infty}^{\infty} f(x)\,dx = 1$$

(iii) $$\int_{a}^{b} f(x)\,dx = P\{a < x < b\}$$

where a and b are any two values of x, with $a < b$.

Property (i) is obviously necessary since negative probability has no meaning. Property (ii) corresponds to the requirement that the probability of an event that is certain to occur should be equal to one. Here x is certain to assume some real value when an observation of it is made. Although it is certain to assume some value, the probability that it will assume a stated value is 0 for a continuous random variable. At first this may seem somewhat paradoxical, but if one wants the probability that x will assume some value in the interval from x_0 to $x_0 + \Delta x$, it is given by the integral

$$\int_{x_0}^{x_0 + \Delta x} f(x)\,dx$$

The mean value theorem of integral calculus may be applied here under the assumption that $f(x)$ is a continuous function to give the value

$$\Delta x f(x_0 + \theta \, \Delta x), \qquad 0 < \theta < 1$$

But when Δx is allowed to approach 0, this probability will approach 0, and therefore the probability that x will assume the particular value x_0 must certainly be 0. Thus, in dealing with continuous random variables, one asks only for the probability that the variable will lie in some interval or intervals. As a result, probabilities for continuous variables are always given by integrals, whereas those for discrete variables are given by sums. If the range of x is not the entire real line, it is assumed that $f(x)$ is defined to be equal to 0 for those values outside the specified range of the variable.

As an illustration, consider the possibility of using $f(x) = ke^{-x}$ as a frequency function for x where k is some constant. From (i) it is clear that k must be positive. Since the integral of e^{-x} from $-\infty$ to $+\infty$ is infinite, it follows that the range of x must be restricted; hence assume, for example, that x can take on only non-negative values. Then $f(x)$ will be defined to be 0 for negative values and to be given by the formula for non-negative values. From (ii) it then follows that k must be equal to 1 because the integral of e^{-x} from 0 to ∞ is equal to 1. The calculation of, say, $P\{1 < x < 2\}$ would then become

$$\int_1^2 e^{-x}\, dx = e^{-1} - e^{-2} = .23$$

The graph of this frequency function and the representation of $P\{1 < x < 2\}$ as an area is given in Fig. 10.

Although $f(x)$ may be chosen at will in any given problem, a choice for which the resulting probabilities are not approximated well by observed relative frequencies is not likely to be a useful choice. As in the case of discrete variables, there are particular frequency functions that have proved very useful in statistical work and whose explicit formulas are considered later.

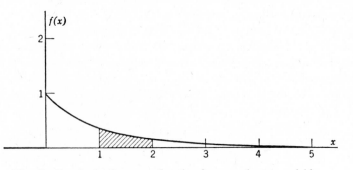

Fig. 10. Graph of a frequency function for a continuous variable.

The frequency function for a continuous variable is often called the probability density function, or density function, of the variable; however, it is very convenient, and becoming increasingly common, to use only the single name "frequency function" for both discrete and continuous variables.

The *distribution function*, $F(x)$, for the continuous variable x is defined by

$$(32) \qquad F(x) = \int_{-\infty}^{x} f(t)\, dt$$

The graph of $F(x)$ for the preceding illustration is given in Fig. 11. It should be noted that $P\{1 < x < 2\}$ is now given by $F(2) - F(1)$, that is, by the difference of the ordinates on the graph of $F(x)$. Here the graph was constructed by first determining $F(x)$ from definition (32). Thus

$$F(x) = \int_{0}^{x} e^{-t}\, dt = 1 - e^{-x}, \quad x \geq 0$$
$$= 0, \quad x < 0$$

The frequency function is the one commonly used in the applications of statistical theory; however, the distribution function is also very useful in deriving some of that theory. For example, it is often easier to find the distribution function of a random variable than it is to find the frequency function. But after the distribution function has been found, the frequency function can be obtained by differentiating the distribution function, since, by employing a familiar calculus formula for differentiating an integral with respect to its variable upper limit, it follows from (32) that

$$\frac{dF(x)}{dx} = f(x)$$

This technique, of course, cannot be used on discrete variable distributions. For such distributions it is necessary to take differences of $F(x)$ values to obtain $f(x)$ values.

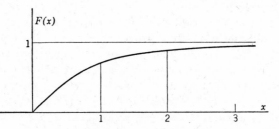

Fig. 11. Graph of the distribution function for a continuous variable.

2.14   Joint Continuous Frequency Functions

A frequency function for several continuous variables is the natural generalization of a frequency function for one variable. Thus a frequency function for two variables x and y would be denoted by $f(x, y)$ and would be represented geometrically by a surface in three dimensions, just as a frequency function of one variable, $f(x)$, was represented by a curve in two dimensions. The volume under the surface lying above the rectangle determined by $a < x < b$ and $c < y < d$ would give the probability that the random variables x and y will assume values corresponding to points lying inside this rectangle. The essential properties for a frequency function of several variables may be formalized as follows:

(33)   DEFINITION: *A frequency function for n continuous random variables* $x_1, x_2, \cdots, x_n$ *is a function* $f(x_1, x_2, \cdots, x_n)$ *that possesses the following properties:*

(i) $$f(x_1, x_2, \cdots, x_n) \geq 0$$

(ii) $$\int_{-\infty}^{\infty} \cdots \int_{-\infty}^{\infty} f(x_1, x_2, \cdots, x_n) \, dx_1 \, dx_2 \cdots dx_n = 1$$

(iii) $$\int_{a_n}^{b_n} \cdots \int_{a_1}^{b_1} f(x_1, x_2, \cdots, x_n) \, dx_1 \, dx_2 \cdots dx_n$$
$$= P\{a_1 < x_1 < b_1, \cdots, a_n < x_n < b_n\}$$

As an illustration, consider the function $f(x, y) = e^{-(x+y)}$, which is a two-dimensional generalization of the example used in the preceding section. If $f(x, y)$ is defined to be zero for negative values of x and y, it will be observed that (i) and (ii) are satisfied. From (iii), the calculation of, say, $P\{1 < x < 2, 0 < y < 2\}$ will then be given by

$$\int_0^2 \int_1^2 e^{-x} e^{-y} \, dx \, dy = (e^{-1} - e^{-2})(e^0 - e^{-2}) = .20$$

The graph of $f(x, y)$ and the representation of $P\{1 < x < 2, 0 < y < 2\}$ as a volume is given in Fig. 12.

Continuous random variables that are unrelated in a probability sense are said to be independently distributed, just as in the case of discrete random variables. To say that continuous random variables are unrelated in a probability sense means that the probability that one of the variables will assume a value in a given interval is independent of the values the other variables assume. In order that this property shall hold it suffices to define independence here exactly as it was done for discrete variables; hence definition (24) applies to continuous variables also.

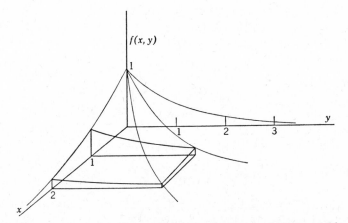

Fig. 12. Graph of a joint frequency function for two continuous variables.

For the purpose of showing that the desired property holds, let $f(x_1, x_2, \cdots, x_n)$ be a frequency function satisfying (24). Then property (iii) of (33) implies that

$$P\{a_1 < x_1 < b_1, \cdots, a_n < x_n < b_n\}$$

$$= \int_{a_n}^{b_n} \cdots \int_{a_1}^{b_1} f_1(x_1) f_2(x_2) \cdots f_n(x_n) \, dx_1 \, dx_2 \cdots dx_n$$

$$= \int_{a_1}^{b_1} f_1(x_1) \, dx_1 \int_{a_2}^{b_2} f_2(x_2) \, dx_2 \cdots \int_{a_n}^{b_n} f_n(x_n) \, dx_n$$

$$= P\{a_1 < x_1 < b_1\} P\{a_2 < x_2 < b_2\} \cdots P\{a_n < x_n < b_n\}$$

This result states that the probability that the variables $x_1, \cdots, x_n$ will simultaneously satisfy the indicated inequalities is equal to the product of the probabilities of the individual variables satisfying these inequalities. This property is the analogue for continuous variables of property (10) for events.

The frequency function whose graph is given in Fig. 12 is an illustration of a joint frequency function of two independent random variables. In the present notation $f_1(x_1) = e^{-x_1}$ and $f_2(x_2) = e^{-x_2}$.

It should be noted that in writing probability statements for continuous variables, such as in (33) (iii), it is irrelevant whether $a_i < x_i < b_i$ or $a_i \leq x_i \leq b_i$ is used to determine the desired region because the integral is the same for the two cases. This property does not hold, however, for discrete variables.

By using integrals in place of sums, formulas can be derived for marginal and conditional distributions just as in the case of discrete variables.

Since the derivations are somewhat sophisticated at this stage of the theory and are not needed for some time, they are postponed to a later chapter.

REFERENCES

A more extensive treatment of the various ideas and definitions of this chapter may be found in the following two books:

Feller, W., *An Introduction to Probability Theory and Its Applications*, Vol. 1, Second Edition, John Wiley and Sons.

Parzen, E., *Modern Probability Theory and Its Applications*, John Wiley and Sons.

EXERCISES

1. A die has 2 of its sides painted red, 2 black, and 2 yellow. If the die is rolled twice, describe a 2-dimensional sample space for the experiment. What probabilities would you assign to the various sample points?

2. A coin is tossed 3 times. Describe a 1-dimensional sample space for the experiment. What probabilities would you assign to the various sample points?

3. If the die in problem 1 is rolled until a red side comes up, describe a sample space for the experiment. What probabilities would you assign to the various sample points?

4. A box contains 3 white and 2 black balls. One ball is to be drawn from it. Describe a sample space and assign probabilities to the sample points when (*a*) the balls are also numbered, (*b*) like colored balls cannot be distinguished.

5. A box contains 2 white and 2 black balls. Two balls are to be drawn from the box. Describe a 2-dimensional sample space and assign probabilities to the sample points when (*a*) the balls are also numbered, (*b*) like colored balls cannot be distinguished.

6. A bag contains 3 white and 1 black ball. Two balls are to be drawn from it. Describe a 2-dimensional sample space consisting of 4 points based on color and draw and assign probabilities to the sample points. Would 3 points have sufficed?

7. Two balls are drawn from an urn containing 2 white, 3 black, and 4 green balls. (*a*) What is the probability that the first is white and the second is black? (*b*) What is this probability if the first ball is replaced before the second drawing?

8. One urn contains 2 white and 2 black balls; a second urn contains 2 white and 4 black balls. (*a*) If 1 ball is chosen from each urn, what is the probability that they will be the same color? (*b*) If an urn is selected by chance and 1 ball is drawn from it, what is the probability that it will be a white ball? (*c*) If an urn is selected by chance and 2 balls are drawn from it, what is the probability that they will be the same color?

9. Compare the chances of rolling a 4 with 1 die and rolling a total of 8 with 2 dice.

10. If 6 dice are rolled, what is the probability that each of the numbers 1 through 6 will occur?

11. Assuming that the ratio of male children is $\frac{1}{2}$, find the probability that in a family of 6 children (a) all children will be of the same sex; (b) the 4 oldest children will be boys and the 2 youngest will be girls; (c) exactly half the children will be boys.

12. Successive drawings of a card from an ordinary deck are made with replacement each time. How many drawings are necessary before the probability is at least $\frac{1}{2}$ that an ace will be obtained at least once?

13. Two boxes contain 1 black and 2 white balls and 2 black and 1 white ball, respectively. One ball is transferred from the first to the second box, after which a ball is drawn from the second box. What is the probability that it is white?

14. A coin is tossed. If it comes up heads, a die is thrown and you are paid the number showing in dollars. If it comes up tails, two dice are thrown and you are paid in dollars the sum of the numbers showing. What is the probability that you will be paid at most four dollars?

15. A card is drawn from an ordinary deck. What is the probability that it is a king, given that it is a face card?

16. Two dice are rolled. What is the probability that the sum of the faces exceeds 8, given that one (or more) of the faces is a 6?

17. A box contains 2 red tickets numbered 1 and 2 and 2 green tickets numbered 1 and 2. If two tickets are drawn from the box, what is the probability that both will be red, given that one of them is known to be (a) red, (b) red ticket numbered 1?

18. A group of businessmen consists of 30 per cent Democrats and 70 per cent Republicans. If 20 per cent of the Democrats and 40 per cent of the Republicans smoke cigars, what is the probability that a cigar-smoking businessman is a Republican?

19. A test for detecting cancer which appears promising has been developed. It was found that 98 per cent of the cancer patients in a large hospital reacted positively to the test, whereas only 4 per cent of those not having cancer did so. If 3 per cent of the patients in the hospital have cancer, what is the probability that a patient selected by chance who reacts positively to the test will actually have cancer?

20. Each of 3 boxes has 2 drawers. One box contains a gold coin in each drawer, another contains a silver coin in each drawer, and the third contains a gold coin in one drawer and a silver coin in the other. A box is chosen, a drawer is opened and found to contain a gold coin. What is the probability that the coin in the other drawer is silver?

21. A, B, and C in order toss a coin. The first one to throw a head wins. What are their respective chances of winning? Note that the game may continue indefinitely.

22. Fourteen quarters and 1 five-dollar gold piece are in one purse and 15 quarters are in another purse. Ten coins are taken from the first purse and placed in the second, and then 10 coins are taken from the second and placed in the first. How much money could you expect to get if you chose the first purse? How much if you chose the second purse?

23. If a poker hand of 5 cards is drawn from a deck, what is the probability that it will contain 2 aces?

24. What is the probability that a bridge hand will contain 13 cards of the same suit?

25. If a box contains 40 good and 10 defective fuses and 10 fuses are selected, what is the probability that all will be good?

26. From a group of 50 people, 3 are to be chosen. Find the probability that none of 10 certain people in the group will be chosen.

27. If the numbers $1, 2, \cdots, n$ are arranged in order by chance, what is the probability that the numbers 1 and 2 will appear next to each other?

28. What is the probability that the bridge hands of north and south together contain exactly 3 aces?

29. If a bridge player and his partner have 9 spades between them, what is the probability that the 4 spades held by their opponents will be split two and two?

30. What is the probability that of 4 cards drawn from a deck 2 will be black and 2 red?

31. If you hold 3 tickets to a lottery for which n tickets were sold and 5 prizes are to be given, what is the probability that you will win at least 1 prize?

32. Let x and y denote the respective number of heads obtained in tossing 2 coins twice. Calculate the probability that $y - x$ will be less than 1.

33. A tosses 3 coins and B tosses 2 coins, simultaneously. The one with the greater number of heads wins. (a) What is the probability that A will win? (b) What is this probability if the experiment is repeated whenever a tie occurs?

34. A bag contains 1 black ball and 2 white balls. A ball is drawn and replaced by a ball of the opposite color. Then another ball is drawn from the bag. Find the conditional probability that the first ball drawn was white, given that the second ball drawn was white.

35. Find the probability that a poker hand of 5 cards will contain only black cards, (a) given that it contains at least 3 black cards, (b) given that it contains at least 3 spades.

36. Find the probability that a poker hand (5 cards) contains no card smaller than 7, given that it contains at least 1 card over 10, where aces are considered as high cards.

37. Three cards are drawn from an ordinary deck. (a) If it is known that the hand contains at least 2 aces, what is the probability that it contains 3 aces? (b) If it is known that the hand contains the 2 red aces, what is the probability that it contains 3 aces?

38. Show that $\dbinom{n}{r-1} + \dbinom{n}{r} = \dbinom{n+1}{r}$.

39. Given the discrete frequency function $f(x) = e^{-1}/x!$, $x = 0, 1, 2, \cdots$, (a) calculate $P\{x = 2\}$; (b) calculate $P\{x < 2\}$; and (c) show that e^{-1} is the proper constant for this frequency function.

40. A coin is tossed until a head appears. (a) What is the probability that a head will first appear on the third toss? (b) What is the probability $f(x)$ that x tosses will be required to produce a head? (c) Graph the frequency function $f(x)$.

41. If the probability is $\frac{1}{2}$ that a finesse in bridge will be successful, (a) what is the probability that 3 out of 5 such finesses will be successful? (b) What is the probability, $f(x)$, that x out of 5 such finesses will be successful? (c) Graph the frequency function $f(x)$.

42. Graph the distribution function $F(x)$ for the frequency function obtained in problem 40.

43. Graph the distribution function $F(x)$ for the frequency function obtained in problem 41.

44. Two dice are rolled. Let x be the difference of the face numbers showing, the higher minus the lower. Find the frequency function of x.

45. A box contains 3 red and 2 black balls. Two balls are drawn from the box. Let x equal the number of red balls obtained. Find the frequency function of x and also its distribution function.

46. A die is tossed once. If a 4, 5, or 6 comes up, let x equal the number showing. If a 1, 2, or 3 comes up, toss the die again and let x equal the sum of the two numbers that came up. Find the frequency function of x.

47. In the game of odd man wins, 3 people toss a coin. The game continues until someone has an outcome different from the other 2. The individual with the different outcome wins. Let x equal the number of games needed before a decision is reached. Find the frequency function of x.

48. There are N tickets numbered $1, 2, \cdots, N$, from which n are chosen. Let x equal the smallest number appearing on the tickets drawn. Find the frequency function of x.

49. Let x and y denote the number of heads obtained in tossing a coin twice. Find an expression for the frequency function $f(x, y)$.

50. Let x and y denote the number of heads obtained in tossing a pair of coins twice. Find an expression for the frequency function $f(x, y)$.

51. Six dice are rolled. Let x denote the number of 1's and y the number of 2's that show. Find an expression for $f(x, y)$, the probability of obtaining x 1's and y 2's.

52. Five cards are drawn from a deck. Let x denote the number of aces and y denote the number of kings that show. Find an expression for $f(x, y)$, the probability of obtaining x aces and y kings.

53. For the first illustration in section 2.11, calculate the values of (a) $f(1)$, (b) $g(0)$, (c) $f(y \mid 1)$, (d) $g(x \mid 0)$.

54. For the distribution given by (23) in section 2.11, find expressions for the marginal and conditional distributions $f(1)$ and $f(y \mid 1)$.

55. For the distribution of problem 49, find the marginal distribution $f(x)$ and the conditional distribution $f(y \mid x)$. Comment.

56. For the distribution of problem 50, find an expression for the conditional distribution $g(x \mid y)$.

57. Calculate the marginal values $f(1)$ and $g(3)$ for problem 51.

58. Use a result from problem 57 to obtain an expression for the conditional distribution $f(y \mid 1)$ for the distribution of problem 51.

59. Consider a deck of cards consisting of the ace, king, queen, and jack of each of the 4 suits. If 2 cards are drawn from this deck, and x and y denote the

number of spades and hearts obtained, find (*a*) the marginal distribution of x and (*b*) an expression for the conditional distribution of y for $x = 1$.

60. Given $f(x, y) = cxy$ at the points (1, 1), (2, 1), (2, 2), (3, 1), and zero elsewhere, (*a*) evaluate c; (*b*) find $f(x)$; (*c*) find $f(y \mid x)$.

61. Explain why 2 variables x and y cannot be independently distributed, regardless of the nature of $f(x, y)$, if the region in the xy plane where $f(x, y)$ is positive is the triangular region of Fig. 8.

62. Explain why 2 variables x and y cannot be independently distributed if the region in the xy plane where $f(x, y)$ is positive is not a rectangle (possibly infinite) with sides parallel to the coordinate axes.

63. Given the continuous frequency function $f(x) = cxe^{-x}, x \geq 0$, (*a*) determine the proper value for c; (*b*) calculate $P\{x < 1\}$; and (*c*) calculate $P\{1 < x < 3\}$.

64. Given the continuous frequency function $f(x) = c, 0 \leq x \leq 2$, (*a*) determine the proper value for c; (*b*) calculate $P\{x < 1\}$; and (*c*) calculate $P\{x > 1.5\}$.

65. Find the distribution function $F(x)$ and graph it if the frequency function of x is (*a*) $f(x) = 1, 0 \leq x \leq 1$; (*b*) $f(x) = x$ for $0 \leq x \leq 1$ and $f(x) = -x + 2$ for $1 < x \leq 2$; and (*c*) $f(x) = [\pi(1 + x^2)]^{-1}$.

66. If $f(x) = e^{-x}$, $x > 0$, find a number x_0 such that the probability is $\frac{1}{2}$ that x will exceed x_0.

67. Suppose the life in hours, x, of a type of radio tube has the frequency function $f(x) = c/x^2$, $x > 500$. (*a*) Evaluate c. (*b*) Find the distribution function of x. (*c*) Calculate the probability that a tube will last at least 1000 hours.

68. Suppose the probability that an atom of a radioactive material will disintegrate in time t is given by $1 - e^{-at}$, where a is a constant depending on the material. Find the frequency function of x, the length of life for such an atom.

69. If half the radioactive material of problem 68 will disintegrate in 1000 units of time, calculate the probability that the life of an atom of this material will exceed 2000 units of time.

70. Given the joint frequency function $f(x, y) = xye^{-(x+y)}$, $x \geq 0$, $y \geq 0$, calculate $P\{x < 1, y < 1\}$.

71. Given the joint frequency function $f(x, y) = 8xy, 0 \leq x \leq 1, 0 \leq y \leq x$, calculate (*a*) $P\{x < .5, y < .25\}$; (*b*) $P\{x < .5\}$; and (*c*) $P\{y < .25\}$. (*d*) From the preceding calculations, what conclusions can be made concerning the independence of the variables x and y?

72. If x and y are independent random variables with the same continuous distribution function F, find an expression for $P\{x \leq t, y \leq t\}$. Use this to find the distribution function $G(z)$ of the variable $z = \max \{x, y\}$.

73. If $f(x) = \mu^x e^{-\mu}/x!$, $x = 0, 1, 2, \cdots$, and $f(y \mid x) = \binom{x}{y} p^y (1 - p)^{x-y}, y = 0, 1, 2, \cdots, x$, show that the marginal frequency function of y is given by $g(y) = (\mu p)^y e^{-\mu p}/y!$.

74. Show that for the events A, B, C, the probability that at least one of the events will occur is given by $P\{A\} + P\{B\} + P\{C\} - P\{AB\} - P\{AC\} - P\{BC\} + P\{ABC\}$.

75. Give an example of two random variables x and y that are not independent but such that x^2 and y^2 are independent.

CHAPTER 3

Nature of Statistical Methods

3.1 Mathematical Models

The preceding two chapters have indicated to some extent the nature of statistical methods. The emphasis there was on experiments of the repetitive type, whether real or conceptual. Statisticians are mainly interested in constructing and applying mathematical models for experiments of this type. The advantage of such a model is that it enables the statistician to study properties of the experiment and to make predictions about the outcomes of future trials of the experiment, both of which would be difficult or impossible to do without such a model.

The process of constructing a model on the basis of experimental data and drawing conclusions from it is an example of *inductive inference*. When it is applied to statistical problems, it is usually called *statistical inference*. Thus statisticians are principally engaged in making statistical inferences.

Most often the statistician is interested in constructing a mathematical model for a random variable associated with an experiment rather than for the experiment itself. For example, if x represents the number of defective parts that will be found in a lot of 100 parts submitted for inspection, he would prefer to have a model that predicts the frequency with which the various values of x will be obtained rather than one that predicts the frequency with which the various possible experimental outcomes will occur when 100 parts are selected from the production process. As a consequence, most of the models chosen by statisticians are frequency functions of random variables. Statistical inferences are therefore usually inferences about frequency functions.

As an illustration of the preceding ideas, suppose a biologist has observed that 44 out of 200 insects of a given type possess markings that are different from those of the rest. Suppose, further, that the biologist suspects that the markings are inherited according to a law which implies that 25 per cent of such insects would be expected to possess the less

45

common markings. If he assumes that the inheritance law is operating here and lets x represent the number of insects out of 200 that will possess the less common markings, then the model that he would naturally select is the frequency function

(1)
$$f(x) = \frac{200!}{x!\,(200 - x)!} \left(\frac{1}{4}\right)^x \left(\frac{3}{4}\right)^{200-x}$$

This particular frequency function is the same as the frequency function given by (19), Chapter 2, because the two problems are equivalent from a probability point of view if the observations made on insects are considered as independent trials of an experiment.

If there had been no theory to suggest that $\frac{1}{4}$ of such insects should possess the unusual markings, the biologist might have chosen this same frequency function with the probability $\frac{1}{4}$ replaced by the observed relative frequency .22.

By means of (1) it would be possible for the biologist to make predictions about future sets of 200 observations and thus detect disagreements with his theory.

In its most general formulation, statistical inference is a type of decision making based on probability. The statistician is largely engaged in constructing methods for making decisions. In a more limited sense, however, a large share of the inferences, or decisions, made by statisticians fall into one of two categories. Either they involve the testing of some hypothesis about the frequency function selected as the model, or they involve the estimation of parameters or other characteristics of this frequency function. These two types of statistical inference will be studied briefly in the next two sections from a general point of view but are applied throughout the book and studied further in Chapter 9.

3.2 Testing Hypotheses

Since the variety of statistical hypotheses that occur in applications is very large, a fairly general definition of what constitutes a statistical hypothesis is needed. Such a definition is the following:

(2) DEFINITION: *A statistical hypothesis is an assumption about the frequency function of a random variable.*

As an illustration for a discrete variable, consider the problem of the preceding section. If p denotes the proportion of all insects possessing the less common markings, then the assumption that $p = \frac{1}{4}$ is a statistical hypothesis. As an illustration for a continuous variable, suppose the random variable x represents the time that elapses between two successive trippings of a Geiger counter in studying cosmic radiation and suppose it is assumed that the frequency function for x is a function of the form

(3) $$f(x; \theta) = \theta e^{-\theta x}$$

where θ is a parameter whose value depends on the experimental conditions. The assumption that the frequency function is a function of this particular form is obviously a statistical hypothesis. If it is assumed that the parameter θ is equal to 2, then this assumption is also a statistical hypothesis.

Now consider what is meant by testing a statistical hypothesis. A general definition can be expressed in the following form:

(4) DEFINITION: *A test of a statistical hypothesis is a procedure for deciding whether to accept or reject the hypothesis.*

This definition permits the statistician unlimited freedom in designing a test; however, he will obviously be guided by its desirable properties. Thus a simple but ordinarily useless test is one in which a coin is tossed and it is agreed to accept the hypothesis in question if, and only if, the coin turns up a head.

In order to illustrate how the statistician proceeds in attempting to design a test that possesses desirable properties, consider a problem related to the frequency function (3). Suppose a physicist is certain, from theoretical or experimental considerations, that the time that elapses between two successive trippings on a counter possesses the frequency function (3). Suppose further that he is quite certain that for the material with which he is working the value of the parameter is either 2 or 1, with his intuition favoring the value 2. To assist him in making a choice, the statistician might proceed in the following manner.

Assume that the frequency function (3) applies. Although this assumption constitutes a statistical hypothesis, it will not be tested here because the physicist is quite certain of the validity of this assumption. Assume that the parameter θ has the value 2. This assumption is the statistical hypothesis to be tested. Denote this hypothesis by H_0. Let H_1 denote the alternative hypothesis that $\theta = 1$. Thus the problem is one of testing the hypothesis H_0 against the single alternative H_1.

To test H_0, a single observation is made on the random variable x; that is, a single time interval between two successive trippings of the counter is measured. In real-life problems one usually takes several observations, but to avoid complicating the discussion at this stage only one observation is taken here. On the basis of the value of x obtained, a decision will be made either to accept H_0 or to reject it. The latter decision, of course, is equivalent to accepting H_1. The problem then is to determine what values of x should be selected for accepting H_0 and what values for rejecting H_0. If a choice has been made of the values of x that will correspond to rejection, then the remaining values of x will necessarily correspond to acceptance. It is customary to call the rejection values the critical region of the test. For this problem, the sample space may be considered as the positive half of the x axis. Every possible outcome can be represented by a point on this line with its x coordinate giving the value of the associated random variable x. Since only one observation is being made here, the sample space is one dimensional. If n observations were to be taken, the corresponding sample space would be n dimensional, with one coordinate axis for each observation. In order to have a definition of the critical region that is applicable to more general sample spaces, it is formulated as follows:

(5) DEFINITION: *The critical region of a test of a statistical hypothesis is that part of the sample space that corresponds to the rejection of the hypothesis being tested.*

In terms of the foregoing language, the problem of constructing a test of H_0 for the problem under discussion is therefore the problem of choosing a critical region for the test.

3.2.1 Two Types of Error

Now suppose that the statistician arbitrarily selects the part of the x axis to the right of $x = 1$ as the critical region. To decide whether this was a wise choice, consider its consequences. If H_0 is actually true and the observed value of x exceeds 1, H_0 will be rejected because it has been agreed to reject H_0 whenever the sample point falls in the critical region. This, of course, is an incorrect decision. This kind of error is called the type I error. On the other hand, if H_1 is actually true and the observed value of x does not exceed 1, H_0 will be accepted. This also is an incorrect

TABLE 1

	H_0 True	H_1 True
$x > 1$ (reject H_0)	Type I error	Correct decision
$x \leq 1$ (accept H_0)	Correct decision	Type II error

decision. This kind of error is called the type II error. These two incorrect decisions, as well as the two correct decisions that are possible here, are displayed in Table 1.

It is necessary to measure in some way the seriousness of making either one of these errors before one can judge whether the choice of a critical region was wise. This can be accomplished by using what is known as the size of an error as the measure of its seriousness.

(6) DEFINITION: *The size of the type I error is the probability that the sample point will fall in the critical region when H_0 is true; the size of the type II error is the probability that the sample point will fall in the non-critical region when H_1 is true.*

Now, in terms of the sizes of the two types of error, it is possible to introduce a simple principle to follow in determining good tests of hypotheses. It may be expressed as follows.

(7) PRINCIPLE: *Among all tests possessing the same size type I error, choose one for which the size of the type II error is as small as possible.*

Other principles can easily be suggested: for example, minimizing the sum of the sizes of the two types of error. However, principle (7) has proved to be very useful in constructing tests. A statistician often determines in advance what size type I error he will tolerate. Then if the number of runs of his experiment is fixed, he will attempt to construct his test to minimize the size of the type II error. For a fixed number of runs of an experiment, the size of the type II error will usually increase if the size of the type I error is decreased; hence one cannot make the type I error as small as desired without paying for an increasingly large type II error. In real-life experiments it is often necessary to adjust the type I error until a satisfactory balance has been reached between the sizes of the two errors. The type I and type II error sizes are usually denoted by the letters α and β, respectively. For the sake of avoiding lengthy discussions regarding the practical consequences of possible choices for the sizes of these two errors, a convention of almost always choosing the size of the type I error as .05 is adopted. This means that approximately 5 per cent of the time true hypotheses being tested will be rejected. The value of $\alpha = .05$ is quite arbitrary here and some other value could have been agreed on; however, it is the value of α most commonly used by applied statisticians. In any applied problem one can calculate the value of β and then adjust the value of α if the value of β is unsatisfactory when $\alpha = .05$. This works both ways, of course. For a very large experiment, with α fixed at .05, it might turn out that β would be considerably smaller than .05. If the type I error were considered more serious than a type II error, one would need to adjust the test to make α smaller than β, which would then make α smaller than .05.

Now consider the problem under discussion from the point of view of this principle. If the sizes of the two types of error for the selected critical region, namely $x \geq 1$, are denoted by α and β, respectively, then, because the two competing hypotheses here are $H_0 : \theta = 2$ and $H_1 : \theta = 1$, it follows from (3) and (6) that

$$\alpha = \int_1^\infty 2e^{-2x}\, dx = .135$$

and

$$\beta = \int_0^1 e^{-x}\, dx = .632$$

Since probabilities correspond to areas under graphs of frequency functions, these values may be represented geometrically as indicated in Fig. 1.

In order to decide whether the preceding test, that is, the choice of a critical region, was a good one, it follows from (7) that it is necessary to compare this test with other tests for which $\alpha = .135$. Here only one other test is considered as a competitor, namely, the test that uses the left "tail" rather than the right "tail" of the graph of the frequency function under H_0 as the critical region. Thus the critical region for the competing test consists of the part of the axis to the left of the point x_0 where x_0 is such that

$$\int_0^{x_0} 2e^{-2x}\, dx = .135$$

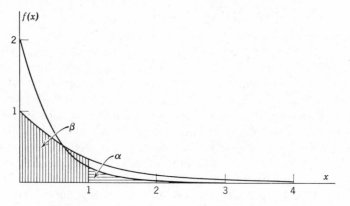

Fig. 1. Graphs showing sizes of two types of error.

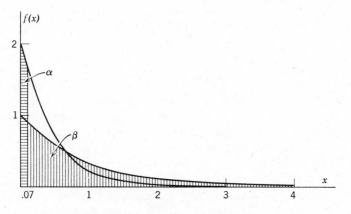

Fig. 2. Graphs for a competing test.

If the integration is performed and tables of exponentials are consulted, it will readily be found that $x_0 = .07$. From (6), it then follows that

$$\beta = \int_{.07}^{\infty} e^{-x}\, dx = .932$$

Graphs showing the sizes of the two types of error for the competing test are given in Fig. 2.

It is clear from comparing the two values of β that the first test is superior to the second. The second test would incorrectly reject H_1 93 per cent of the time, whereas the first test would do so only 63 per cent of the time. Both tests have very large type II errors, but this is to be expected when only one observation is taken. By using methods that are developed in Chapter 9, it can be shown that the first test selected is the best test that can be constructed for this problem according to principle (7).

These principles of test construction apply to discrete variable problems also. As a simple illustration of how to make discrete variable computations, consider the following academic problem. A coin is known to be either an honest coin or one that yields twice as many heads as tails. A decision is to be made as to which type of coin it is by tossing it three times and observing the number of heads, x, that result.

The problem may be formalized by choosing

$$H_0 : p = \tfrac{1}{2} \qquad \text{and} \qquad H_1 : p = \tfrac{2}{3}$$

Here p denotes the probability that a head will be obtained when the coin is tossed once. Since the coin is to be tossed three times, the random variable x can assume only the values 0, 1, 2, or 3. The four points on the

Fig. 3. H_0 probabilities.

x axis corresponding to these values may be chosen as the sample space here, even though the natural sample space for the experiment of tossing three coins would be one consisting of eight points in three dimensions. If one is interested only in the number of heads that turn up, then the four-point sample space is more convenient to work with than the original sample space. When H_0 is true, the probabilities that should be assigned to the four sample points in this space are those displayed in Fig. 3. These values were calculated in the manner illustrated in exercise (d) of 2.8.4.

Now consider two different choices for the critical region of this test, namely, the point $x = 0$ and the point $x = 3$. Except for convenience, these two parts of the sample space were chosen quite arbitrarily. They should serve to illustrate techniques and principles in test construction for discrete variables. From Fig. 3 it will be seen that both of these critical regions yield a type I error of size $\alpha = \frac{1}{8}$; hence they are equally good as far as making type I errors is concerned.

When H_1 is true, calculations similar to those employed in illustrations (d) and (e) of 2.8.4 with $p = \frac{2}{3}$ will show that the probabilities that should be assigned to the four sample points are those listed in Fig. 4. Now when $x = 0$ is chosen as the critical region for the test, the size of the type II error is equal to $\beta = \frac{26}{27}$ because that is the probability that x will not assume the value 0. On the other hand, when $x = 3$ is chosen as the critical region, the value of β is $\frac{19}{27}$ because that is the probability that x will not assume the value 3. Thus it is clear that $x = 3$ is a better critical region than $x = 0$ for testing H_0 against H_1.

In discussing critical regions, it is customary to call them *critical regions of size* α if the magnitude of the type I error is α. Thus in the preceding illustration the two competing critical regions there were of size $\frac{1}{8}$.

One difficulty in applying these methods to discrete variable problems is that critical regions of specified sizes cannot always be chosen without resorting to other devices. In the preceding illustration, for example, one cannot directly choose a critical region of size $\alpha = \frac{1}{10}$. This difficulty is seldom much of a problem in real-life applications because then experiments are usually sufficiently large to permit a wide choice of sizes for

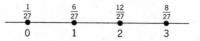

Fig. 4. H_1 probabilities.

the type I error. Moreover, there are techniques available, which are discussed in a later chapter, that enable one to construct critical regions of any desired size, even for problems such as the preceding one.

In the following chapters tests of hypotheses are made without being concerned whether the critical region selected is the best possible; however, after Chapter 9 has been studied it will be found that the tests in the earlier chapters were well chosen from this point of view. For the simpler problems, the critical region that the experimenter carefully selects on an intuitive basis is likely to be a good one from the point of view of principle (7).

3.2.2 Power Function

The problem considered in the preceding sections to illustrate the general methods for selecting a good test was easy to discuss largely because there was only a single alternative H_1 to the hypothesis H_0 being tested. Most problems, however, involve more than a single alternative. For example, if one were interested in knowing whether the proportion of defective parts in a manufacturing process is increasing, he might wish to test the hypothesis $H_0 : p = p_0$, in which p_0 is the proportion of defectives found in the past, against the hypothesis $H_1 : p > p_0$. For the first problem discussed in 3.2.1, it might well be that the physicist would have preferred to test the hypothesis $H_0 : \theta = 2$ against the alternative $H_1 : \theta < 2$ rather than against the alternative $H_1 : \theta = 1$. The experimenter often has theoretical or empirical reasons for knowing what value of the parameter to test, but he seldom knows what particular alternative value will hold if H_0 is false.

For such more general classes of alternatives, the size of the type II error β will depend on the particular alternative value of θ being considered. In order to determine how good the chosen test may be, compared to a competing test, it is therefore necessary to compare the type II errors for all possible alternative values of θ rather than for just one alternative value as before. For this purpose, it is necessary to consider the calculation of the size of the type II error as a function of θ. The size of this error is denoted by $\beta(\theta)$. Now, from (6), $\beta(\theta)$ is the probability that the sample point will fall in the noncritical region when θ is the true value of the parameter. It is usually more convenient to work exclusively with the critical region; therefore it is customary to calculate $1 - \beta(\theta)$, which is the probability that the sample point will fall in the critical region when θ is the true value of the parameter. The function $1 - \beta(\theta)$ is called the power function and may be defined formally as follows.

(8) DEFINITION: *The power function $P(\theta)$ of a test is the function of the parameter that gives the probability that the sample point will fall in the critical region of the test when θ is the true value of the parameter.*

Since $P(\theta) = 1 - \beta(\theta)$, seeking for a test that minimizes the type II error $\beta(\theta)$ is equivalent to seeking for one that maximizes the power $P(\theta)$.

The problems that were considered in the preceding section are used to illustrate how the power function can assist one in selecting good tests when there is more than a single alternative value of the parameter. For the first illustration, let the hypothesis to be tested be $H_0 : \theta = 2$, as before, but let the alternative hypothesis now be $H_1 : \theta < 2$ rather than $H_1 : \theta = 1$. As before, let $x > 1$ and $x < .07$ be the respective critical regions of size $\alpha = .135$ for the two competing tests, and let $P_1(\theta)$ and $P_2(\theta)$ denote the power functions for the two tests. From (8), the power functions of these tests are given by integrating the frequency function (3) over the respective critical regions; hence

(9) $$P_1(\theta) = \int_1^\infty \theta e^{-\theta x} \, dx = e^{-\theta}$$

and

$$P_2(\theta) = \int_0^{.07} \theta e^{-\theta x} \, dx = 1 - e^{-.07\theta}$$

The graphs of $P_1(\theta)$ and $P_2(\theta)$, which are called the power curves for the two tests, are shown in Fig. 5. These curves must intersect at the point $(2, .135)$ because the power function gives the probability that the sample point will fall in the critical region and this probability has been chosen equal to $\alpha = .135$ when $H_0 : \theta = 2$ is true. Since the power curve for the first test lies above the power curve for the second test for all values of $\theta < 2$ and the only alternative values permitted in the problem are those given by $H_1 : \theta < 2$, it follows that the first test is superior to the second for the problem under discussion.

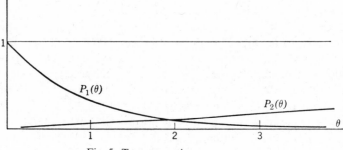

Fig. 5. Two competing power curves.

By means of a theorem that will be studied in Chapter 9, it can be shown that any test whose critical region is of size $\alpha = .135$ will yield a power curve that nowhere lies above the power curve for this first test; consequently, this test is the best possible for the problem under discussion. It was stated in an earlier section that this is the best possible test for the alternative $H_1 : \theta = 1$, but now a stronger statement is being made, namely, that this test is the best possible for every alternative value of θ satisfying the inequality $\theta < 2$.

Not only is the power function useful for assisting one in comparing tests and finding best tests when more than one alternative value of the parameter exists, but it is also useful for determining the effectiveness of a given test for making the correct decision as a function of the parameter value. For example, the power function $P_1(\theta)$ given by (9) shows that the probability is .37 of making the correct decision, namely, rejecting H_0 when $\theta = 1$, and that this probability rises to .61 when $\theta = \frac{1}{2}$. By studying the power function, or power curve, of a test the experimenter can determine his chances of detecting various possible alternative values of the parameter that may occur and thus determine whether his experiment is large enough to give him the confidence that he would like in whatever decision will be made by the test.

For the second illustration of the preceding section, consider the construction of the power function for the better of the two tests discussed there. The construction for the other test would be similar. Since the critical region consists of the point $x = 3$, it is necessary to calculate the probability that x will assume the value 3, given that the probability of a head in a single toss of the coin is p. But this is merely the probability of getting three heads in three tosses of the coin. Since the tosses are independent, this probability is p^3; consequently, the power function here is given by

$$P(p) = p^3$$

The graph of this power function is shown in Fig. 6. It is clear from Fig. 6 that the critical region $x = 3$ is a poor one if the coin is biased in favor of tails. For example, if p were equal to $\frac{1}{3}$, the probability of rejecting the incorrect hypothesis H_0 that the coin is honest is only $\frac{1}{27}$. The test is really not much good unless the alternative value of p is close to 1. Thus, if p were equal to $\frac{4}{5}$, the probability of rejecting H_0 would rise to $\frac{64}{125}$. In order to obtain a good test here, it would be necessary to toss the coin considerably more than three times.

The preceding material on how statistical hypotheses are set up and tested may appear somewhat artificial to someone experienced with real-life problems in testing hypotheses. Very often one has no precise value

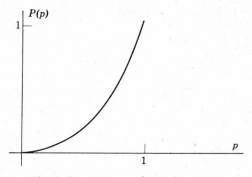

Fig. 6. A power curve for testing a coin.

θ_0 of a parameter θ to test but only an approximate value based on experience. If this approximate value is treated as the precise value θ_0 to be tested and the test accepts the hypothesis H_0, this does not mean that one believes θ_0 is the true value of θ. Rather, it means that the true value of θ is probably in the neighborhood of θ_0 and that from a practical point of view it is safe to treat θ_0 as the true value. The practical conclusions to be drawn from the test of a statistical hypothesis are by no means the same as the statistical conclusions obtained by following the procedure outlined above for testing a precise hypothesis. Further information on the practical interpretation of statistical methods is given in the following chapters in the applications of the theory. The next section takes up the problem of determining how close a θ_0 based on experience is likely to be to the true value of θ.

Although this book is concerned principally with methods for testing hypotheses and estimating parameters of frequency functions, there are many problems that cannot be treated adequately by means of such methods. For example, a decision-making problem may involve choosing one of three possible decisions rather than one of two. One would therefore like to know how best to proceed in making the choice. Some of these methods are discussed in a later chapter.

3.3   Estimation

Most of the problems of estimation in statistics are those of estimating parameters of frequency functions. For example, the physicist interested in studying cosmic radiation would be interested in estimating the parameter θ in the frequency function (3) because this parameter determines the rate of the radiation. By taking a number of observations on his variable x, he could use the resulting data to estimate the value of θ.

Two kinds of estimates of parameters are in common use. One is called a point estimate and the other is called an interval estimate. A point estimate is the familiar kind of estimate; that is, it is a number obtained from computations on the observed values of the random variable which serves as an approximation to the parameter. For example, the observed proportion of defective parts in 50 consecutive parts turned out by a machine is a point estimate of the true proportion p for that machine. An interval estimate is an interval determined by two numbers obtained from computations on the observed values of the random variable that is expected to contain the true value of the parameter in its interior. Interval estimates are considered briefly in Chapter 6 and more fully in Chapter 9; therefore, only point estimates are discussed here.

In order to know how to use several observations of a random variable in an intelligent manner for constructing a point estimate of a parameter of the frequency function of the random variable, it is desirable to have some general principle to follow, just as it was in testing hypotheses. The principle, or method, should be such that the estimates obtained by using the method will possess desirable properties. For example, if two different methods are applied to the same sets of observations and if one method produces estimates that are consistently closer to the value of the parameter being estimated than those of the other method, then the first method would obviously be preferred. Properties of good point estimates are considered in some detail in Chapter 9; here it suffices to describe a method that is usually preferred by most statisticians and to state that the method possesses many desirable properties. This method of estimation, known as the maximum likelihood method, is used in the following chapters whenever the problem arises of finding a point estimate of a parameter of a frequency function. It is defined after some necessary notation has been introduced.

Let $f(x; \theta)$ be the frequency function of the random variable x, where θ is the parameter to be estimated. Suppose that n observations are to be made of the variable x. Let $x_1, x_2, \cdots, x_n$ denote the n random variables corresponding to these n observations. Then the function given by

(10) $$L(x_1, \cdots, x_n; \theta) = f(x_1; \theta)f(x_2; \theta) \cdots f(x_n; \theta)$$

defines a function of the random variables $x_1, x_2, \cdots, x_n$ and the parameter θ which is known as the *likelihood function*.

For the purpose of interpreting this function, suppose that the observational values are obtained from n independent trials of an experiment for which $f(x; \theta)$ is the frequency function of a discrete random variable x. Then, for any particular set of observational values, because of (24), Chapter 2, the likelihood function gives the probability of obtaining that set of values, including their order of occurrence. If, however, x is a continuous variable, the likelihood function gives the probability density at the sample point $(x_1, x_2, \cdots, x_n)$, where the sample space is thought of as being n dimensional.

Now, for a given set of observational values, an estimate of θ is merely a number obtained from calculations made on the observational values; however, from the point of view of procedure, an estimate is a function of the observational values. For example, the function

$$(x_1 + x_2 + \cdots + x_n)/n$$

is a typical estimate. It is customary for some statisticians to use the word *estimator* for the function and the word *estimate* for the value of the function after the observational values have been inserted. Thus

$$(x_1 + x_2 + \cdots + x_n)/n$$

would be called an estimator of θ, whereas its numerical value in any given problem would be called an estimate of θ. Other statisticians, however, use the word estimate both for the function and its numerical value.

Using the notation and terminology of the preceding paragraphs, the method of maximum likelihood estimation may be defined in the following manner:

(11) DEFINITION: *A maximum likelihood estimator $\hat{\theta}$ of the parameter θ in the frequency function $f(x; \theta)$ is an estimator that maximizes the likelihood function $L(x_1, \cdots, x_n; \theta)$ as a function of θ.*

If the x_i are treated as fixed, the likelihood function becomes a function of θ only, say $L(\theta)$; consequently, the problem of finding a maximum likelihood estimator is the problem of finding the value of θ that maximizes $L(\theta)$. This maximizing value of θ is, of course, a function of the x_i that have been treated as fixed; hence, if one is discussing a maximum likelihood estimator it is necessary to write $\hat{\theta} = \hat{\theta}(x_1, x_2, \cdots, x_n)$ to show that the estimator is a function of the observational values rather than just a number.

Maximum likelihood estimators can usually be obtained by calculus methods because the relative maximum of the likelihood function obtained by differentiating $L(x_1, \cdots, x_n; \theta)$ with respect to θ and setting the derivative equal to zero is usually an absolute maximum.

As an illustration of the calculus technique for finding maximum likelihood estimates, consider the problem of estimating the parameter θ in the frequency function (3) if five observations on x yielded the values $x_1 = .9$, $x_2 = 1.7$, $x_3 = .4$, $x_4 = .3$, and $x_5 = 2.4$.

The maximum likelihood estimator is first obtained as follows. By means of (3) and (10), the likelihood function is

$$L = \theta e^{-\theta x_1} \cdot \theta e^{-\theta x_2} \cdots \theta e^{-\theta x_n}$$

$$= \theta^n e^{-\theta \sum\limits_{i=1}^{n} x_i}$$

Then, differentiating with respect to θ, and collecting terms,

$$\frac{\partial L}{\partial \theta} = \theta^{n-1} e^{-\theta \sum x_i} (-\theta \sum x_i + n)$$

Setting $\partial L/\partial \theta = 0$ and solving for θ, it will be observed that either $\theta = 0$ or the quantity in brackets is 0. Since there is no frequency function when $\theta = 0$, the only nontrivial solution of this equation is

(12) $$\hat{\theta} = \frac{n}{\sum x_i}$$

This is the desired maximum likelihood estimator of θ. It will be observed that this estimator is merely the reciprocal of the arithmetic mean of the x_i.

In order to find the maximum likelihood estimate for the given observations, it is merely necessary to choose $n = 5$ and insert the five given observational values in (12). Computations yield the estimate $\hat{\theta} = .88$.

As a second illustration, let p be the probability that an event A will occur when an experiment is performed and let the experiment be repeated until A does occur. Further, let x denote the number of experiments that are required before A occurs. Here the frequency function of x is

(13) $$f(x) = (1 - p)^{x-1} p$$

because $x - 1$ successive failures, followed by a success, for the event A must occur if the event A is to occur the first time on experiment number x. The problem is to find the maximum likelihood estimator of p. Now the function given by (13) is also the likelihood function; therefore its maximum with respect to the parameter p must be found. It is convenient here to take logarithms and then maximize the log $f(x)$ by calculus methods. The value of p that maximizes $\log f(x)$ will be the same as the value that maximizes $f(x)$. Thus

$$\log f(x) = (x - 1) \log (1 - p) + \log p$$

Hence

$$\frac{\partial \log f(x)}{\partial p} = -\frac{x - 1}{1 - p} + \frac{1}{p}$$

If this derivative is set equal to 0, it will be found that the value of p which satisfies the resulting equation is given by

$$\hat{p} = \frac{1}{x}$$

Thus, if A were the event of getting a 1 to turn up in rolling a die, the estimate of p, whose value is $\frac{1}{6}$ here, would be the reciprocal of the number of rolls needed before a 1 appeared.

As a slight generalization of this problem, suppose a set of n such experiments is carried out. Let $x_1, x_2, \cdots, x_n$ denote the number of trials of the experiment required before A occurs in each group of experiments. Each of the x_i possesses the frequency function given in (13); therefore the likelihood function now is

$$L = \prod_{i=1}^{n} f(x_i)$$
$$= (1 - p)^{x_1 - 1} p \cdot (1 - p)^{x_2 - 1} p \cdots (1 - p)^{x_n - 1} p$$
$$= (1 - p)^{\Sigma x_i - n} p^n$$

As before, the maximum is easier to find if one first takes logarithms. Thus

$$\log L = (\textstyle\sum x_i - n) \log (1 - p) + n \log p$$

Hence

$$\frac{\partial \log L}{\partial p} = -\frac{\sum x_i - n}{1 - p} + \frac{n}{p}$$

The solution of the equation obtained by setting this derivative equal to zero is given by

$$\hat{p} = \frac{n}{\sum x_i}$$

The similarity of this result with that given in (12) should not tempt one to generalize about the nature of maximum likelihood estimates.

Although the discussion of estimation has been limited to that of estimating a parameter of a frequency function, there are methods available for estimating various properties of a frequency function, such as its maximum value. In addition, there are methods for estimating the frequency function itself. In doing so it is customary to estimate the distribution function either by a broken line curve, which corresponds to a point estimate, or by a pair of such curves that are expected to contain the true distribution function curve between them, which corresponds to an interval estimate.

Problems of estimation are often more delicate than those of testing hypotheses because there is usually more danger of being misled when estimating a parameter of an incorrect model than when testing a hypothesis about it. For example, an experiment may be designed to compare two groups of animals, one treated and the other untreated. If the two groups do differ and one tests the hypothesis that they do not, then in a well-designed experiment one is likely to reject that hypothesis even though an incorrect model may have been chosen to represent the behavior of the animals. Estimates of a parameter for the two groups, however, might be very misleading in describing the behavior of the animals if the model chosen to do so were unrealistic.

REFERENCES

More extensive discussions of the ideas presented in this chapter may be found in several of the books listed in the references for Chapter 1.

EXERCISES

1. Given the frequency function $f(x; \theta) = 1/\theta$, $0 \leq x \leq \theta$, and 0 elsewhere, if you are testing the hypothesis $H_0: \theta = 1$ against $H_1: \theta = 2$ by means of a single observed value of x, (a) what would the sizes of the type I and type II errors be if you chose the interval $.5 \leq x$ as the critical region? (b) What would the sizes of these errors be if you chose the interval $1 \leq x \leq 1.5$ as the critical region?

2. Suppose you wish to test a hypothesis H_0 against an alternative H_1 by tossing a coin once and agreeing to accept H_0 if a head shows and to accept H_1 otherwise. (a) What are the values of α and β for this test? (b) What would the values of α and β be if you tossed the coin twice and agreed to accept H_0 if 2 heads showed and to accept H_1 otherwise?

3. Given that x has the frequency function $f(x; \theta) = \frac{1}{2}$, $\theta - 1 \leq x \leq \theta + 1$, and 0 elsewhere, if $H_0: \theta = 4$ and $H_1: \theta = 5$ and the critical region is to be of size $\alpha = .25$ and to consist of a single interval, show by a sketch which critical region you would choose and determine what the value of β would be for that choice, assuming that the test is to be based on a single observed value of x.

4. What critical region with $\alpha = .5$ would you choose in problem 1 if you wanted a critical region of this size that minimizes β?

5. Given $f(x; \theta) = (1 + \theta)x^\theta$, $\theta > 0$, $0 \leq x \leq 1$, and 0 elsewhere, if the hypothesis $H_0: \theta = 1$ is to be tested by taking a single observation on x and using the interval $x < .5$ as the critical region, (a) calculate the value of α and (b) calculate the probability of determining that H_0 is false if the true value of θ is 2.

6. Let x be a random variable whose frequency function values under H_0 and H_1 are as follows.

x	1	2	3	4	5	6	7
$f(x \mid H_0)$	.01	.02	.03	.05	.05	.07	.77
$f(x \mid H_1)$	.03	.09	.10	.10	.20	.18	.30

(a) List all critical regions whose size is equal to .10
(b) List all critical regions whose size does not exceed .10
(c) Among the critical regions in (a), which has the smallest value of β?
(d) Are there any in (b) which have a still smaller value of β?

7. A box is known to contain either 3 red and 7 black balls or 7 red and 3 black balls. Three balls are to be drawn from the box, and on the basis of their colors a decision relating to the contents of the box will be made. If H_0 denotes the hypothesis that there are 3 red and 7 black balls and if H_0 will be accepted unless 3 red balls are obtained, what are the values of α and β here?

8. A bag is known to contain 9 black balls and either 1 or 2 white balls. To test the hypothesis that there is only 1 white ball, balls are drawn until a white one appears. Let x equal the number of balls drawn and find $f(x)$ under both hypotheses. Choose a good critical region for the test and find its value of α and β.

9. Find the power function for problem 5 and graph it.

10. If the region $x > 4.5$ is used as the critical region in problem 3, find the power function for $\theta \geq 4$ and sketch it. Using your result, determine what alternative values of $\theta \geq 4$ are such that $\beta \leq .25$.

11. If p denotes the probability that an event A will occur in a single trial of an experiment, then $f(x; p) = (1 - p)^{x-1}p$ is the frequency function for x, the number of trials needed before A occurs. Find the power function for testing $H_0\!:\!p = \frac{1}{5}$ if the critical region consists of the points $x = 1, 2, 3$. Criticize this choice of critical region.

12. Given the frequency function $f(x; \theta) = e^{-\frac{1}{2}(x-\theta)^2}/\sqrt{2\pi}$, find the maximum likelihood estimator of θ based on a sample of size n.

13. Given the frequency function $f(x; \theta) = e^{-\theta}\theta^x/x!$, where x can assume only non-negative integer values, and given the six observed values 6, 11, 4, 8, 7, and 6, find the maximum likelihood estimate for θ.

14. Find the maximum likelihood estimator for θ based on n observations for the frequency function $f(x; \theta) = (1 + \theta)x^\theta$, $\theta > -1$, $0 \leq x \leq 1$.

15. Given the frequency function $f(x; \theta) = e^{-\frac{x^2}{2\theta^2}}/\theta\sqrt{2\pi}$, find the maximum likelihood estimator for θ.

16. In problem 15 treat θ^2 as the parameter to be estimated and write the frequency function as $f(x; \lambda) = e^{-\frac{x^2}{2\lambda}}/\sqrt{2\pi\lambda}$, where $\lambda = \theta^2$. Now find the maximum likelihood estimator for λ and compare with the result for problem 15.

17. A box contains 10 balls, of which the proportion p are white. Let x equal the number of white balls obtained in drawing 2 balls from the box. Find the frequency function $f(x; p)$ and then find the value of p that will maximize $f(x; p)$. Here the only values that p can assume are $p = i/10$, $i = 0, 1, \cdots, 10$.

18. For the frequency function $f(x; \theta) = 1/\theta$, $0 \le x \le \theta$, and 0 elsewhere, show that for n observations on this variable, the estimate $\hat{\theta}$ that maximizes the likelihood $(1/\theta)^n$ must be $\hat{\theta} = \max \{x_1, x_2, \cdots, x_n\}$, that is, the largest of the n observations.

19. Show that the likelihood function $L(\theta)$ will be maximized when $\log L(\theta)$ is maximized if standard calculus methods may be used to obtain the maximum.

CHAPTER 4

Empirical Frequency Distributions of One Variable

4.1 Introduction

In this chapter and the next, statistical methods that involve only one random variable will be studied. This chapter is concerned with methods for extracting information from data that will be useful in helping to determine a model for the random variable giving rise to the data. For example, if x represents the range error in a radar tracking experiment and if 200 trackings have been made, it is important to know how to use the experimental data to help determine what frequency function should be selected for x. The emphasis in this chapter is on the practical mechanics of handling data, whereas the next chapter is concerned with the actual selection of the model. After the material of this chapter and the next have been completed, the problems of statistical inference discussed in the preceding chapter can begin to be solved.

It is convenient in discussing statistical methods to call the totality of possible experimental outcomes the *population* of such outcomes. Then a set of data obtained from performing the experiment a number of times is called a *sample* from the population. In this language statistical inference consists in drawing conclusions about a population by means of a sample extracted from the population. This chapter, therefore, is concerned with methods for extracting information from samples for use in studying the populations from which the samples were drawn.

The type of information that should be extracted from a set of data depends upon the nature of the data and upon the model that is likely to be selected. In some problems one knows from theoretical considerations or from experience with similar problems what model should be used. For example, the frequency function that was introduced in (1), Chapter 3, is such a model. The frequency function given in (3), Chapter 3, is another. All that is really needed from experimental data for such

64

models is information that will give one good estimates of the parameters involved. In other problems neither theory nor experience is available to assist one in selecting a model. Then it is necessary to use experimental data to decide on a reasonable type of model before one can test hypotheses about it or estimate its parameters. Fortunately, in testing certain hypotheses about frequency functions it is not necessary to know the frequency function too precisely, and therefore the information concerning it that can be obtained from moderate amounts of data may suffice to describe it adequately for testing purposes.

In considering the nature of the data it is particularly important to distinguish between those sets of data for which the order in which the observations were obtained yields useful information and those sets for which it does not. For example, if one were interested in studying weather phenomena or the stock market from day to day, the order would be very important. Industrial experience indicates that the information obtained from considering the order in which articles are manufactured is indispensable for efficient production. However, if one were interested in studying certain characteristics of college students and had selected a set of students by choosing every twentieth name in a college directory, he would hardly expect the order in which the names were obtained to be of any value in the study. Methods for dealing with data for which order is important are considered in later chapters. In this chapter the emphasis is on techniques that do not use order information. The material in these later chapters will enable the investigator to decide whether he is justified in assuming that he may ignore the order information present in his data.

4.2 Classification of Data

Suppose one is given the weights of 200 college men and he wishes to use them to study the weight distribution of such men. Now it is very difficult to look at 200 measurements and obtain any reasonably accurate idea of how those measurements are distributed. For the purpose of obtaining a better idea of the distribution of weights it is therefore convenient to condense the data somewhat by classifying the measurements into groups. It will then be possible to graph the modified distribution and learn more about how weights are distributed. This condensation will also be useful for simplifying the computations of various averages that need to be evaluated, particularly if fast computing facilities are not available. These averages will supply additional information about the distribution. Thus the purpose of classifying data is to assist in the extraction of certain kinds of useful information concerning the underlying distribution.

If the data are for a discrete variable, there is usually no need for classifi-cation. Thus data on the number of petals on flowers of a given species or the number of yeast cells on a square of a hemacytometer are naturally classified. There is usually little difficulty in performing the classification when there appears to be a need for it.

If the data are for a continuous type of variable such as length, weight, or time, they are recorded to a certain digit or decimal accuracy. For example, if the diameter of a steel rod is measured to the nearest thousandth of an inch, a diameter of .431 inch assumes that the measurement, if taken to more decimal places, would lie between .4305 and .4315 inch.

In classifying data for a continuous variable experience indicates that for most data it is desirable to use 10 to 20 classes. With less than 10 classes too much accuracy is lost, whereas with more than 20 classes the computations become unnecessarily tedious. In order to determine boundaries for the various class intervals, it is merely necessary to know the smallest and largest observations of the set. As an illustration, sup-pose that 200 steel rods were measured and it was found that the smallest and largest diameters were .431 and .503 inch, respectively. Since the range of values, which is .072 inch here, is to be divided into 10 to 20 equal intervals, the class interval should be chosen as some convenient number between .0036 and .0072. A class interval of .005 inch will evidently be convenient. Since the first class interval should contain the smallest measurement of the set, it must begin at least as low as .4305. Further-more, in order to avoid having measurements fall on the boundary of two adjacent class intervals, it is convenient to choose class boundaries to $\frac{1}{2}$ a unit beyond the accuracy of the measurements. Thus in this problem it would be convenient to choose the first class interval as .4305–.4355. The remaining class boundaries are then determined by merely adding the class interval .005 repeatedly until the largest measurement is enclosed in the final interval. If .4305–.4355 is chosen as the first class interval, there will be 15 class intervals and the last class interval will be .5005–.5055. When the class boundaries have been determined, it is a simple matter to list each measurement of the set in its proper class interval by merely recording a short vertical bar to represent it. When the number of bars corresponding to each class interval has been recorded, the data are said to have been classified into a frequency table. It is assumed in such a classification that all measurements in a given class interval, say the ith interval, have the value at the midpoint of the interval. This value is called the *class mark* and is denoted by x_i. Thus $x_1 = .433$ and $x_{15} = .503$ in the example just considered. The number of measurements found in the ith class interval is denoted by f_i, and the total number of measure-ments is denoted by n. Table 1 illustrates the tabulation and resulting frequency table for the set of steel rods mentioned previously.

It is a common practice for many applied statisticians to indicate class intervals in a slightly different form from that suggested above. They record not actual class interval boundaries but rather noncontiguous boundaries. Thus they would indicate the first three class intervals by .431–.435, .436–.440, and .441–.445. When interval boundaries are so indicated, the true boundaries are ordinarily halfway between the upper

TABLE 1

Class boundaries	Frequencies	Class marks: x	Frequencies: f
0.4305–0.4355	//	0.433	2
.4355– .4405	/////	.438	5
.4405– .4455	///// //	.443	7
.4455– .4505	///// ///// ///	.448	13
.4505– .4555	///// ///// ///// ////	.453	19
.4555– .4605	///// ///// ///// ///// ///// //	.458	27
.4605– .4655	///// ///// ///// ///// ///// ////	.463	29
.4655– .4705	///// ///// ///// ///// /////	.468	25
.4705– .4755	///// ///// ///// ///// ///	.473	23
.4755– .4805	///// ///// ////	.478	14
.4805– .4855	///// ///// /////	.483	15
.4855– .4905	///// ////	.488	9
.4905– .4955	///// /	.493	6
.4955– .5005	////	.498	4
.5005– .5055	//	.503	2

and lower recorded boundaries of adjacent intervals. Another common method of recording class intervals is to employ common boundaries but to agree that an interval includes measurements up to but not including the upper boundary. Then the first three class intervals above would be indicated by .431–.436, .436–.441, and .441–.446. A measurement that falls on a boundary is placed in the higher of the two intervals. If one knows the accuracy of measurement of the variable, there is little difficulty in determining the true class boundaries and class marks for these two methods of classification. It is important to use the exact class marks; otherwise a systematic error will be introduced in many of the computations to follow.

4.3 Graphical Representation of Empirical Distributions

A rough idea of how the values of a random variable are distributed can be obtained from inspecting its histogram. The histogram for the data of Table 1 for absolute frequencies is given in Fig. 1. It should be

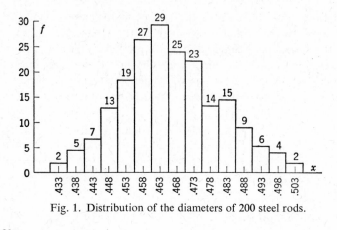

Fig. 1. Distribution of the diameters of 200 steel rods.

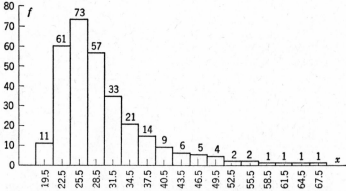

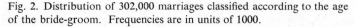

Fig. 2. Distribution of 302,000 marriages classified according to the age of the bride-groom. Frequencies are in units of 1000.

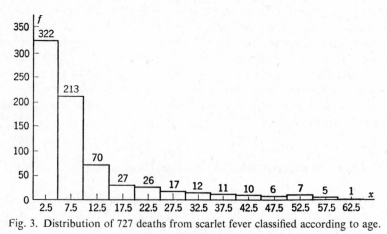

Fig. 3. Distribution of 727 deaths from scarlet fever classified according to age.

noted that the class marks are at the midpoints of the bases of the rectangles making up the histogram. If preferred, the histogram may be drawn to show the class boundaries rather than the class marks.

Fortunately, many important frequency distributions to be found in nature and industry are of a relatively simple form. They usually range from a bell-shaped distribution, like that in Fig. 1, to something resembling the right half of a bell-shaped distribution. A distribution of the latter type is said to be skewed, *skewness* meaning lack of symmetry with respect to a vertical axis. It will be found, for example, that the following variables have frequency distributions that possess such forms in approximately increasing degrees of skewness: stature; various industrial measurements; weight; age at marriage; mortality age for certain diseases; and wealth. Figures 1, 2, and 3 represent three typical distributions with increasing degrees of skewness.

4.4   Arithmetical Representation of Empirical Distributions

As explained earlier, the principal reason for classifying data and drawing the histogram of the resulting frequency table is to determine the nature of the distribution. Some of the theory that is developed in later chapters requires that the distribution be one that possesses a graph similar to that displayed in Fig. 1; consequently, it is necessary to know whether one has this type of distribution before attempting to apply such theories to it.

Although a histogram yields a considerable amount of general information concerning the distribution of a set of sample measurements, more precise and useful information for studying a distribution can be obtained from an arithmetical description of the distribution. For example, if the histogram of weights for a sample of 200 men from one college were available for comparison with the histogram of a similar sample from another college, it might be difficult to state, except in very general terms, how the two distributions differ. Rather than compare the two weight distributions in their entirety, it might suffice to compare the average weights and the variation in weights of the two groups.

The nature of a statistical problem largely determines whether a few simple arithmetical properties of the distribution will be enough to describe it satisfactorily. Most of the problems that are encountered in this book are the type that requires only a few simple properties of the distribution for its solution. For simple frequency distributions, such as those whose graphs are given in Figs. 1, 2, and 3, this description is accomplished satisfactorily by means of the low-order *moments* of the distribution, which are defined in (1). In many problems the statistician is concerned only with the first and second moments. In a few problems he uses the first four moments, but seldom does he use more than four. One reason for this is that the higher moments are so unstable in repeated sampling experiments that little additional reliable information can be obtained from them.

For data that have been classified let x_i be the class mark for the ith class interval, f_i the observed absolute frequency for the ith interval, h the number of intervals, and n the sum of the absolute frequencies. With this notation, empirical moments are defined as follows:

(1) DEFINITION: *The kth moment about the origin of an empirical frequency distribution is given by*

$$m_k' = \frac{1}{n} \sum_{i=1}^{h} x_i^k f_i$$

If the data have not been classified, x_i will represent the value of the ith observation, the f_i will all be equal to 1, and h will be equal to n. The prime placed on m_k is to distinguish this kth moment from another moment to be defined later.

Physics and calculus students are usually familiar with moments as they pertain to masses f_i located on the x axis at distances x_i from the origin. For example, the moment of inertia is essentially the second moment. Statistical interpretations of the low-order moments are given in the next two sections.

4.4.1   The First Moment as a Measure of Location

The first moment about the origin, m_1', is called the *mean* and is usually denoted by $\bar{x}$; hence

(2)
$$\bar{x} = \frac{1}{n} \sum_{i=1}^{h} x_i f_i$$

For unclassified data $\bar{x}$ reduces to the familiar formula for the average of a set of numbers. Formula (2) is sometimes spoken of as the formula for the *weighted mean*; however, it is merely a variation of the familiar form adapted to classified data. Geometrically, the mean represents the point on the x axis where a sheet of metal in the shape of the histogram would balance on a knife edge. For a histogram like that of Fig. 1 it is clear that $\bar{x}$ defines a measure of location, that is, a value at which the data tend to center. The mean is ordinarily meant when the word average is used. For example, the statement that the average weight of a group of people is 140 pounds implies that this is their mean weight.

If the x_i and f_i are not large, the value of $\bar{x}$ is easily computed from its definition, particularly if a calculating machine is available. Otherwise considerable time is saved for frequency tables having equal class intervals by using a short method based on introducing a new variable u, which takes on only small integral values and which is defined by

$$(3) \qquad\qquad x_i = cu_i + x_0$$

Here c is the class interval and x_0 is a conveniently chosen class mark. The computations are somewhat easier if x_0 is chosen as a class mark near the middle of the distribution. When this expression is substituted for x_i in (2),

$$\bar{x} = \frac{1}{n} \sum_{i=1}^{h} (cu_i + x_0)f_i$$

$$= \frac{1}{n} \sum_{i=1}^{h} (cu_i f_i + x_0 f_i)$$

$$= \frac{1}{n} \sum_{i=1}^{h} cu_i f_i + \frac{1}{n} \sum_{i=1}^{h} x_0 f_i$$

Since c and x_0 are constants with respect to these summations, they may be factored out and placed in front of the summation signs; hence

$$\bar{x} = c \frac{1}{n} \sum_{i=1}^{h} u_i f_i + x_0 \frac{1}{n} \sum_{i=1}^{h} f_i$$

From (2) it is clear that the coefficient of c is $\bar{u}$, and from the definition of n the coefficient of x_0 is 1; therefore

$$(4) \qquad\qquad \bar{x} = c\bar{u} + x_0$$

Since the computations needed to find $\bar{u}$ are relatively easy, the value of $\bar{x}$ can be obtained quite easily without the aid of a calculating machine. This short method is illustrated in Table 2. The data for this frequency distribution are taken from 1000 telephone conversations in seconds, recorded to the nearest second. Here x_0 was chosen as 449.5 because this choice gives rise to smaller products in the uf column than other choices, although 549.5 is nearly as good. When (4) is applied to Table 2,

$$\bar{x} = 100 \left(\frac{257}{1000} \right) + 449.5 = 475.2$$

For certain common types of distributions, the mean is superior to other ordinary measures of location, some of which are considered briefly later. This superiority rests largely on the fact that in repeated sampling experiments from such distributions the mean usually tends to be more stable than these other measures of location. For example, suppose one took a sample of five trees from a forest and calculated their mean height. Instead of the mean, one could have chosen, say, the middle height of the five as the measure of location. Now, if one repeated this experiment a large number of times, he would usually find that the set of means would tend to be more closely clustered than the set of middle measurements.

TABLE 2

x	f	u	uf
49.5	6	−4	−24
149.5	28	−3	−84
249.5	88	−2	−176
349.5	180	−1	−180
449.5	247	0	
549.5	260	1	260
649.5	133	2	266
749.5	42	3	126
849.5	11	4	44
949.5	5	5	25
Totals	1000		257

This property of greater stability is particularly important in later work when a precise estimate of a population mean is desired. It should be clearly understood that the mean possesses these advantages only for certain types of distributions of particular importance which are considered in later chapters. There are other well-known distributions for which the mean is a very poor measure of location.

4.4.2 The Second Moment as a Measure of Variation

The concept of variation is of paramount importance in statistics. Statistical methods have often been called methods for studying variation. The problem of measuring variation occurs repeatedly in the various sciences and in certain branches of industry. For example, in order to detect any lack of uniformity in the quality of a manufactured product, it is first necessary to know the variability of the product. This may be illustrated in the following manner. Suppose a purchaser of wire will not tolerate wire that does not possess a tensile strength of at least 50 pounds and that he is considering buying it from one or the other of two firms. If equal samples taken from the products of these two firms gave empirical

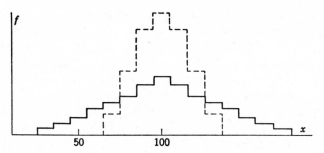

Fig. 4. Hypothetical distribution of tensile strength.

frequency distributions like those shown in Fig. 4, it is clear that the product of only one of the firms would satisfy the purchaser's requirement. Since the mean tensile strength was 100 pounds in each sample, the purchaser would have had no basis for making a decision if the variation in tensile strength had been ignored.

It is customary to assume that variation means variation of the data about a measure of location. Since the mean is being used as the measure of location here, it is necessary to introduce moments about the mean in order to obtain a measure of variation from moments. Empirical moments about the mean are defined as follows:

(5)   DEFINITION: *The kth moment about the mean of an empirical frequency distribution is given by*

$$m_k = \frac{1}{n} \sum_{i=1}^{h} (x_i - \bar{x})^k f_i$$

Now it will be shown that the second moment about the mean, m_2, can be considered as a measure of variation. Since it is often convenient to have a measure of variation in the same units of measurement as for the data, $\sqrt{m_2}$ is usually selected instead. This quantity is called the *standard deviation* and is denoted by s; hence

(6) $$s = \sqrt{\frac{1}{n} \sum_{i=1}^{h} (x_i - \bar{x})^2 f_i}$$

The second moment about the mean, s^2, which is more convenient than the standard deviation as a measure of variation in certain situations, is called the *variance*. Some authors define these two quantities with n replaced by $n - 1$. Their definitions have certain advantages for later work but seem quite unnatural here. This matter is considered in Chapter 9.

If one considers the computation of s for two distributions of differing spread, such as those whose histograms are given in Fig. 4, it should be clear that s does measure relative variation or spread for these distributions. The distribution with the large tails will have a relatively larger value of s because the large deviations $x_i - \bar{x}$, when squared and multiplied by their relatively large frequencies f_i, will contribute heavily to the value of the sum and will more than compensate for the larger frequencies for small deviations in the concentrated distribution. The interpretation of the standard deviation as a measure of absolute variation is presented a few paragraphs later. At present it is merely a number in the same units as x which seems to measure the relative extent to which data are concentrated about the mean and which becomes larger as the data become more dispersed.

The calculation of the standard deviation from its definition (6) becomes inaccurate unless an accurate value of $\bar{x}$ is used, and then the computations usually become tedious. The change of variable introduced for computing the mean is also useful for obtaining a short method of computing the standard deviation for frequency tables having equal class intervals. From (3) and (4) it follows that

$$x_i - \bar{x} = c(u_i - \bar{u})$$

Consequently,

$$\frac{1}{n}\sum(x_i - \bar{x})^2 f_i = \frac{1}{n}\sum c^2(u_i - \bar{u})^2 f_i$$

$$= \frac{c^2}{n}\sum(u_i^2 - 2u_i\bar{u} + \bar{u}^2)f_i$$

$$= c^2\left(\frac{\sum u_i^2 f_i}{n} - 2\bar{u}\frac{\sum u_i f_i}{n} + \bar{u}^2\frac{\sum f_i}{n}\right)$$

$$= c^2\left(\frac{\sum u_i^2 f_i}{n} - \bar{u}^2\right)$$

The short method for computing the standard deviation is therefore given by

(7)
$$s = c\sqrt{\frac{\sum u_i^2 f_i}{n} - \bar{u}^2}$$

Hereafter, as in this derivation, the indicated range of summation will be omitted from the summation sign whenever the range is obvious.

For data that have not been classified, it is assumed in (5) that x_i represents the ith observation, that all the f_i are equal to 1, and that h equals n. The application to this case of the algebraic manipulations used to obtain (7) from (6) will yield the formula

$$s = \sqrt{\frac{\sum x_i^2}{n} - \bar{x}^2}$$

This form is often more convenient than (6) for unclassified data, particularly when the x_i contain at most two digits each.

Table 3 illustrates the technique for computing s for the data of Table 2.

TABLE 3

x	f	u	uf	u^2f
49.5	6	-4	-24	96
149.5	28	-3	-84	252
249.5	88	-2	-176	352
349.5	180	-1	-180	180
449.5	247	0		
549.5	260	1	260	260
649.5	133	2	266	532
749.5	42	3	126	378
849.5	11	4	44	176
949.5	5	5	25	125
Totals	1000		257	2351

When (7) is applied to Table 3,

$$s = 100 \sqrt{\frac{2351}{1000} - (.257)^2} = 151$$

correct to the nearest integer.

In order to interpret the standard deviation as a measure of variation, it is necessary to anticipate certain results of later work. For a set of data that has been obtained by sampling a particular type of population called a normal population it will be shown that the interval $(\bar{x} - s, \bar{x} + s)$ will usually include about 68 per cent of the observations and that the interval $(\bar{x} - 2s, \bar{x} + 2s)$ will usually include about 95 per cent of the observations, provided that n is large. A sketch of a particular normal distribution is shown in Fig. 5, Chapter 5.

As an illustrative example of this property, consider the data for which the standard deviation was just computed. Previous calculations gave $\bar{x} = 475$ and $s = 151$, correct to the nearest integer; consequently, the foregoing two intervals are $(324, 626)$ and $(173, 777)$, respectively. The number of observations lying within these intervals may be found approximately by interpolating as though the observations in a given interval were dispersed uniformly throughout the interval. This assumption implies that on the histogram any fractional part of a class interval will include the same fractional part of the frequencies in that interval. For ease of interpolation, the histogram for this frequency distribution is shown in Fig. 5. If interpolation is carried to the nearest unit, it will be found that the interval $(324, 626)$ will include $136 + 247 + 260 + 35$

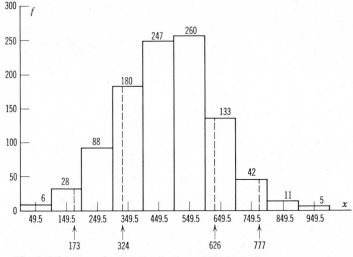

Fig. 5. Histogram for the distribution of 1000 telephone conversations.

measurements, which is 67.8 per cent of them. The interval (173, 777) excludes $6 + 21 + 9 + 11 + 5$ measurements, which is 5.2 per cent. For a histogram as irregular as this, these results are unusually close to the theoretical percentages. However, even for histograms possessing a considerable lack of symmetry, the actual percentages are often surprisingly close to the theoretical percentages, primarily because the large percentage of measurements in the short tail included by such an interval is compensated to a considerable extent by the small percentage of measurements in the long tail which are included.

For certain common types of data the standard deviation is superior to other common measures of variation, some of which are considered briefly later. The superiority rests partly on its greater stability in repeated sampling experiments and partly on its convenience for developing statistical theory. The situation with respect to other measures of variation is very much like that of the mean with respect to other measures of location.

4.4.3 Higher Moments

The two preceding sections were designed to give a statistical interpretation or meaning to the first two moments. It is more difficult to give satisfactory statistical meanings to the moments of higher order. Any general interpretation is likely to fail for even fairly reasonable kinds of distributions.

The principal use of empirical moments beyond the second has been in fitting theoretical frequency distributions to empirical distributions, and this use has been restricted largely to the third and fourth moments about the mean. In such fitting problems it is customary to calculate the quantities

(8)
$$a_3 = \frac{m_3}{s^3} \quad \text{and} \quad a_4 = \frac{m_4}{s^4}$$

and then use the four quantities $\bar{x}$, s, a_3, and a_4 to describe the empirical distribution. The reason for using a_3 and a_4 rather than m_3 and m_4 is that the former are independent of the units of measurement and the latter are not. The quantity a_3 is often called a measure of skewness because its value is 0 for a symmetrical distribution and is likely to be a large positive number for a distribution with a large right tail such as that in Fig. 3. The value of a_3 may be zero, however, for a nonsymmetrical distribution so that care must be used in interpreting a_3 as a measure of skewness. The quantity a_4 is occasionally given an interpretation as a measure of the peakedness of the distribution, but this interpretation is rather vague and of questionable value. It should suffice to use the first four moments as quantities which usually describe empirical distributions fairly well without necessarily giving these moments geometrical interpretations.

In the next chapter, when theoretical frequency distributions are considered, it will be found that the higher moments play an essential role in the theory. The reason for this is that it is often necessary to know the values of all the theoretical moments before a theoretical frequency function is completely determined. Thus moments beyond the second may be very important theoretically in determining frequency distributions even though empirical moments are not used a great deal to describe empirical frequency distributions.

4.4.4   Other Descriptive Measures

Among the other common measures of location are the median, mode, and geometric mean.

For a set of measurements arranged in order of magnitude the median is defined as the middle measurement, if there is one, otherwise as the interpolated middle value. Thus for the set of measurements 2, 3, 3, 4, 5, 5, 6, 6, 7, 7, 7, 9 the median is 5.5. For classified data the median is defined as the abscissa which divides the area of the histogram into two equal parts. Some workers prefer the median to the mean when the distribution is heavily skewed because they feel that it is more representative of what a measure of location should be than the mean is under such circumstances. They might, for example, prefer the median when discussing the notion of average wage of a community because a few very large incomes would produce a mean wage higher than the notion of average wage implies, whereas the median wage would not be so affected.

The mode of a set of measurements is defined as the measurement with the maximum frequency, if there is one. For the set of measurements in the preceding paragraph, the mode is 7. If there is more than one measurement with the maximum frequency, no completely satisfactory definition exists. The mode is used occasionally in situations similar to those for which the median might be selected. Since the mode is of questionable value in descriptive statistics, it will not be considered further here.

The geometric mean of a set of measurements, assuming that they are positive, is defined as $\sqrt[n]{x_1^{f_1} x_2^{f_2} \cdots x_h^{f_h}}$. If the data are classified, x_i represents the ith class mark; otherwise it represents the ith measurement, in which event all the f_i equal 1. It will be observed that the logarithm of the geometric mean is equal to the arithmetic mean of the logarithms. This measure is used principally in working with business index numbers, for which it possesses certain advantages.

Among the more common measures of variation are the range and mean deviation. The range, which is the difference between the largest and smallest measurement in the set, is used as a measure of variation largely because of its ease of computation. It is often applied in certain industrial engineering work. It has two important disadvantages. First, its value usually increases with n because there is a better chance of obtaining extreme measurements if a large sample of data is taken than if a small sample is taken. It is possible, however, to make allowance for this growth and thus eliminate this disadvantage of the range. Second, the range is usually quite unstable in repeated sampling experiments of the same size when n is large; consequently, its use is ordinarily restricted to sets of data containing less than 10 observations each. Because of its importance in various fields, the range will be studied more fully in a later chapter.

The mean deviation is defined as $\Sigma \mid x_i - \bar{x} \mid f_i/n$, where the absolute values, that is, the positive values of deviations, are employed. This measure of variation is often used because it appears to be easier to calculate and understand than the standard deviation. It will be found, however, that the short method of calculating the standard deviation is about as fast as calculating the mean deviation, when n is large.

Consideration was given to these other measures of location and variation only because they appear quite often in certain fields of application and the student of statistical methods should be acquainted with them. However, for the present, moments will be selected as the preferred set of descriptive measures unless there are valid reasons for doing otherwise.

An interesting example of a theoretical distribution for which moments are a poor choice of descriptive measures is the distribution whose frequency function is

$$(9) \qquad\qquad f(x) = \frac{1}{\pi[1 + (x - \theta)^2]}$$

For this distribution, which is known as the Cauchy distribution, it turns out that the theoretical moments, which are defined in the next chapter, are all infinite. It also turns out that the mean of a sample of n observations is no better than a single observation for estimating the parameter θ. The median here is a much better measure of location than the mean. This example illustrates the fact that there are no universal methods for solving all statistical problems.

REFERENCES

Lengthy treatments of moments and other descriptive measures for empirical distributions may be obtained in either of the following two books.

Kendall, M. G., *The Advanced Theory of Statistics*, Vol. 1, Griffin and Co.

Yule and Kendall, *Introduction to the Theory of Statistics*, Griffin and Co.

EXERCISES

1. Weights of 300 entering freshmen ranged from 98 to 226 pounds, correct to the nearest pound. Determine class boundaries and class marks for the first and last class intervals.

2. The thickness of 400 washers ranged from .421 to .563 inch. Determine class boundaries and class marks for the first and last class intervals.

3. Given the following frequency table of the heights in centimeters of 1000 students, draw its histogram, indicating the class marks.

x	155–157	158–160	etc.											
f	4	8	26	53	89	146	188	181	125	92	60	22	4	1	1

4. Given the following frequency table of the diameters in feet of 56 shrubs from a common species, (a) draw its histogram and (b) guess by merely inspecting the histogram the values of $\bar{x}$ and s.

x	1	2	3	4	5	6	7	8	9	10	11	12
f	1	7	11	16	8	4	5	2	1	0	0	1

5. For the data of problem 4 calculate $\bar{x}$ by (a) definition and (b) the short method.

6. For the data of problem 4 calculate s by (a) definition and (b) the short method.

7. Given the frequency function
$$f(x) = [5!/x!\,(5-x)!](\tfrac{1}{3})^x(\tfrac{2}{3})^{5-x}, \quad x = 0, 1, \cdots, 5,$$
multiply $f(x)$ by 243 and treat the resulting numbers as observed frequencies for the corresponding x values. (a) Calculate $\bar{x}$ by definition. (b) Calculate s by the short method.

8. Given the frequency function $f(x) = (\tfrac{4}{5})^{x-1}\tfrac{1}{5}$, $x = 1, 2, 3, \cdots$, multiply $f(x)$ by 1000 and treat the resulting numbers, after rounding off to the nearest integer, as observed frequencies. (a) Calculate $\bar{x}$. (b) Calculate s.

9. For the histogram of problem 4, using the results in problems 5 and 6, calculate the approximate percentages of the data that lie within the intervals $\bar{x} \pm s$ and $\bar{x} \pm 2s$. Explain why these percentages are fairly close to normal distribution percentages in spite of the obvious non-normality of this distribution.

10. Show that $\sum\limits_{i=1}^{h} (x_i - \bar{x})f_i = 0$.

11. If stature of adult males may be assumed to possess a normal distribution, what would you guess the standard deviation of stature to be if you estimate a 2-standard deviation interval about the mean through your knowledge of male stature?

12. If the scores on a set of examination papers are changed by (a) adding 10 points to all scores and (b) increasing all scores by 10 per cent, what effects will these changes have on the mean and standard deviation?

13. What would you judge a distribution to be like if the variable can assume only positive values and the mean and standard deviation are equal?

14. Show that formula (6) in the text is equivalent to the formula $m_2 = m_2' - m_1'^2$.

15. By expanding the binomial in formula (5) in the text and summing term by term, derive a formula for calculating the kth moment about the mean in terms of the kth and lower-order moments about the origin.

16. Suppose only the 2 means $\bar{x}_1$ and $\bar{x}_2$ are available from 2 sets of observations of sizes n_1 and n_2 made on the variable x. Show that the mean of the combined set $\bar{x}$ is given by $\bar{x} = (n_1\bar{x}_1 + n_2\bar{x}_2)/(n_1 + n_2)$.

17. If the 2 standard deviations s_1 and s_2 are also available in problem 16, show that the standard deviation of the combined set s can be obtained from $s^2 = (n_1 s_1^2 + n_2 s_2^2)/(n_1 + n_2) + n_1 n_2 (\bar{x}_1 - \bar{x}_2)^2/(n_1 + n_2)^2$.

18. For the data of problem 3, (*a*) calculate $\bar{x}$ and s by the short method, (*b*) calculate the approximate percentages of the data that lie in the intervals $\bar{x} \pm s$ and $\bar{x} \pm 2s$ and compare with normal distribution percentages, (*c*) calculate the crude median and mode, and (*d*) estimate the range for the data.

19. Given the following 4 mass points, calculate the mean and third moment about the mean and explain what this example shows concerning the third moment about the mean as a measure of symmetry. A mass of 5 at $x = -4$; a mass of 10 at $x = -1$; a mass of 10 at $x = 2$; and a mass of 2 at $x = 5$.

20. Sketch a histogram for which you believe the value of s will be large, yet for which most of the distribution will be concentrated near the mean, so that the interval $\bar{x} \pm 2s$ will include at least 99 per cent of the data.

CHAPTER 5

Theoretical Frequency Distributions of
One Variable

5.1 Introduction

The purpose of this chapter is to introduce a few of the commonly
used theoretical frequency distributions as models for empirical distributions. As pointed out and illustrated in 4.1, in some problems one
knows from theoretical considerations what model should be used. In
other problems one must rely on samples and experience to determine
a satisfactory model. Ordinarily the sample is not large enough to determine the population distribution with much precision; however, there
is often enough information in the sample, together with information
obtained from other sources, to suggest the general type of population
distribution involved.

In many problems it suffices to consider certain properties of a distribution rather than to study the entire distribution. In particular, it often
suffices to know the low-order moments of a distribution. This chapter,
therefore, is concerned with theoretical moments as well as with theoretical
frequency distributions.

5.2 Discrete Variables

Most of the discrete variables that occur in statistical experiments
are the counting type. For example, the variable might be the number of
accidents a car owner has per year or the number of insects surviving a
spraying. Variables such as these assume only non-negative integral
values. The discrete random variables that are considered here are
variables of this type, that is, those that assume non-negative integral
values only.

5.2.1 Moments

Before considering particular theoretical frequency distributions for discrete variables, a brief discussion of theoretical moments is given because of the importance of theoretical moments in determining models and in deriving statistical theory.

Theoretical moments for a discrete variable of the type being considered are defined as follows:

(1) DEFINITION: *The kth moment about the origin of a theoretical frequency distribution with frequency function f(x) is given by*

$$\mu_k' = \sum_{x=0}^{\infty} x^k f(x)$$

If this definition is compared with that of an empirical frequency distribution as given by (1), Chapter 4, it will be noted that the probability $f(x)$ takes the place of the observed frequency ratio f_i/n in that definition.

The kth moment of a distribution is also commonly called the kth moment of the random variable whose distribution is being studied. Thus one may speak of μ_k' as being the kth moment of x or as the kth moment of the distribution of x.

Since theoretical moments about the mean are used extensively, they also need to be defined. As before, it is assumed that the random variable x can assume only non-negative integral values.

(2) DEFINITION: *The kth moment about the mean of a theoretical frequency distribution with frequency function f(x) is given by*

$$\mu_k = \sum_{x=0}^{\infty} (x - \mu_1')^k f(x)$$

This definition is the theoretical analogue of the corresponding definition for empirical distributions as given by (5), Chapter 4.

Since the first moment about the origin, which is the theoretical mean, and the square root of the second moment about the mean, which is the theoretical standard deviation, are both used so often, they are given special symbols, namely μ and σ. Thus $\mu = \mu_1'$ and $\sigma = \sqrt{\mu_2}$.

In evaluating μ_2 it is usually more convenient to evaluate the first two moments about the origin and then calculate μ_2 from them rather than evaluate μ_2 directly from definition (2). This is accomplished by expanding the binomial in (2) for $k = 2$ in the following manner.

$$\mu_2 = \sum_{x=0}^{\infty} (x - \mu)^2 f(x)$$

$$= \sum_{x=0}^{\infty} x^2 f(x) - 2\mu \sum_{x=0}^{\infty} x f(x) + \mu^2 \sum_{x=0}^{\infty} f(x)$$

But from (1) this may be written

$$\mu_2 = \mu_2' - 2\mu\mu + \mu^2$$

Combining terms, the desired formula is obtained, namely

(3) $$\mu_2 = \mu_2' - \mu^2$$

5.2.2 Moment Generating Function

Even though the direct computation of theoretical moments from definition (1) may be easy, it is convenient for later theory to be able to calculate such moments indirectly by another method. This method is introduced here and used throughout several chapters for proving theorems. It involves what is known as the moment generating function. As the name implies, the moment generating function is a function that generates moments. It is defined as follows:

(4) DEFINITION: *The moment generating function of a random variable x with frequency function f(x) is given by*

$$M_x(\theta) = \sum_{x=0}^{\infty} e^{\theta x} f(x)$$

This series is a function of the parameter θ only, but the subscript is placed on $M(\theta)$ to show what variable is being considered. The parameter θ has no real meaning here; it is merely a mathematical device introduced to assist in the determination of moments.

In order to see how $M_x(\theta)$ does produce moments, assume that $f(x)$ is a frequency function for which the series in (4) converges. Now expand $e^{\theta x}$ in a power series and sum term by term. Since the power series for e^z is

$$e^z = 1 + z + \frac{z^2}{2!} + \frac{z^3}{3!} + \cdots$$

it follows from (4) and (1) that

(5) $$M_x(\theta) = \sum_{x=0}^{\infty} \left[1 + \theta x + \frac{\theta^2 x^2}{2!} + \frac{\theta^3 x^3}{3!} + \cdots \right] f(x)$$

$$= \sum_{x=0}^{\infty} f(x) + \theta \sum_{x=0}^{\infty} x f(x) + \frac{\theta^2}{2!} \sum_{x=0}^{\infty} x^2 f(x) + \cdots$$

$$= 1 + \theta \mu_1' + \frac{\theta^2}{2!} \mu_2' + \frac{\theta^3}{3!} \mu_3' + \cdots$$

It will be observed that the coefficient of $\theta^k/k!$ in this expansion is the kth moment about the origin; consequently, if the moment generating function can be found for a variable x and can be expanded into a power series in θ, the moments of the variable can be obtained by merely inspecting the expansion. If a particular moment is desired, it may be more convenient to evaluate it by computing the proper derivative of $M_x(\theta)$ at $\theta = 0$, since repeated differentiation of (5) will show that

$$(6) \qquad \mu_k' = \frac{d^k M}{d\theta^k}\bigg|_{\theta=0}$$

Applications of the preceding definitions are begun in the next section.

5.2.3 Binomial Distribution

Consider an experiment of the repetitive type in which only the occurrence or nonoccurrence of an event is recorded. Suppose the probability that the event will occur when the experiment is performed is p. Let $q = 1 - p$ denote the probability that it will fail to occur. If the event occurs at a given trial of the experiment, it will be called a success, otherwise a failure. Let n independent trials be made and denote by x the number of successes obtained in the n trials. Then consider the problem of determining the probability of obtaining precisely x successes in n trials of the experiment. A formula for this probability would be needed, for example, if one knew that the probability of a marksman hitting a target is $\frac{1}{10}$ and if one wished to calculate the probability of getting at least two hits in taking 20 shots at the target.

For the purpose of deriving the desired formula, first determine the probability of obtaining x consecutive successes followed by $n - x$ consecutive failures. These n events are independent; therefore, by (10), Chapter 2, this probability is

$$\overbrace{p \cdot p \cdots p}^{x} \cdot \overbrace{q \cdot q \cdots q}^{n-x} = p^x q^{n-x}$$

The probability of obtaining precisely x successes and $n - x$ failures in some other order of occurrence is the same as in this particular order because the p's and q's are merely rearranged to correspond to the other order. In order to solve the problem, it is therefore necessary to count the number of orders.

The number of orders is the number of permutations possible with n letters of which x are alike (p's) and the remaining $n - x$ are alike (q's). But by formula (18), Chapter 2, the number of such permutations is equal to

$$(7) \qquad \frac{n!}{x!\,(n - x)!}$$

Now, by (4), Chapter 2, the probability that one or the other of a set of mutually exclusive events will occur is the sum of their separate probabilities; consequently it is necessary to add $p^x q^{n-x}$ as many times as there are different orders in which the desired result can occur. Since (7) gives the number of such orders, the probability of obtaining x successes in some order is therefore given by multiplying $p^x q^{n-x}$ by the quantity in (7). The resulting probability, which is that of obtaining x successes in n independent trials of an experiment for which p is the probability of success in a single trial, defines what is known as the binomial or Bernoulli frequency function. Consequently,

(8)   BINOMIAL DISTRIBUTION: $f(x) = \dfrac{n!}{x!\,(n-x)!}\, p^x q^{n-x}$

Bernoulli was one of the first mathematicians to develop probability theory for discrete variables; hence this distribution has been named after him. The more commonly used name of binomial distribution comes from the relationship of (8) to the following binomial expansion.

(9) $(q+p)^n = q^n + nq^{n-1}p + \dfrac{n(n-1)}{2} q^{n-2}p^2 + \cdots + p^n$

$\qquad = \displaystyle\sum_{x=0}^{n} \frac{n!}{x!\,(n-x)!}\, p^x q^{n-x}$

From (8) it is clear that (9) may be written

$$(q+p)^n = \sum_{x=0}^{n} f(x)$$

Thus the various terms in the binomial expansion of $(q+p)^n$ give the probabilities of the various possible results in their natural order.

The binomial frequency function is an example of a mathematical model that can be applied to many real-life problems involving a discrete variable. In any given application it is necessary to know or to estimate the values of the two parameters p and n before (8) can be used.

5.2.3.1 Illustrations. As illustrations of the direct application of formula (8), first consider two impractical problems related to the rolling of a die. If a true die is rolled five times, what is the probability that precisely two of the rolls will show 1's? Here success consists in obtaining a 1; hence $p = \frac{1}{6}, q = \frac{5}{6}$, and $n = 5$. When (8) is applied, the solution is

$$f(2) = \frac{5!}{2!\,3!}\left(\frac{1}{6}\right)^2\left(\frac{5}{6}\right)^3 = .16$$

If the die is rolled five times, what is the probability of obtaining at most two 1's? To answer this question it is necessary to compute the

probabilities of obtaining precisely no 1's, one 1, and two 1's. Applying (8),

$$f(0) = \frac{5!}{0!\,5!}\left(\frac{1}{6}\right)^0\left(\frac{5}{6}\right)^5 = .40$$

$$f(1) = \frac{5!}{1!\,4!}\left(\frac{1}{6}\right)^1\left(\frac{5}{6}\right)^4 = .40$$

Since these three possibilities are mutually exclusive events, it follows that

$$P\{x \leq 2\} = f(0) + f(1) + f(2) = .96$$

As a somewhat more earthy problem, consider the one mentioned just
before the derivation of (8), namely, that of calculating the probability
of getting at least two hits on a target in taking 20 shots at it if the probability of a hit for a single shot is $\frac{1}{10}$. Here $p = \frac{1}{10}$ and $n = 20$; hence

$$P\{x \geq 2\} = 1 - f(0) - f(1)$$

$$= 1 - \left(\frac{9}{10}\right)^{20} - 20\left(\frac{1}{10}\right)^1\left(\frac{9}{10}\right)^{19}$$

$$= 1 - .122 - .270$$

$$= .608$$

The validity of using the binomial model in the last illustration is not
so obvious as it is in the first two illustrations. The derivation of the
binomial formula was based on independent trials with p constant from
trial to trial. If the same man takes repeated shots at the same target, it
might be expected that his chances of making a hit would increase somewhat with practice. If a different man were used each time, p would
undoubtedly change from trial to trial. Possible deviations in the basic
assumptions should be taken into account when interpreting a resulting
probability such as .608.

5.2.3.2 Binomial Moments. The first two moments of the binomial
distribution will be needed shortly; therefore consider their computation.
In order to illustrate the two methods for computing moments, these
moments are calculated directly from definition and indirectly by means
of the moment generating function.

If (1) is applied to (8) and if a few algebraic manipulations are made,
it will be seen that

(10)
$$\mu = \sum_{x=0}^{n} x\,\frac{n!}{x!\,(n-x)!}\,p^x q^{n-x}$$

$$= \sum_{x=1}^{n} x\,\frac{n!}{x!\,(n-x)!}\,p^x q^{n-x}$$

$$= \sum_{x=1}^{n} \frac{n!}{(x-1)!\,(n-x)!}\,p^x q^{n-x}$$

If n and p are factored out, this becomes

$$\mu = np \sum_{x=1}^{n} \frac{(n-1)!}{(x-1)!\,(n-x)!}\, p^{x-1} q^{n-x}$$

Letting $y = x - 1$, the right side can be written

$$\mu = np \sum_{y=0}^{n-1} \frac{(n-1)!}{y!\,(n-1-y)!}\, p^{y} q^{n-1-y}$$

But by (8) the quantity being summed is the probability of y successes in $n - 1$ trials. Since the sum is over all possible values of y, the sum must equal one; hence $\mu = np$.

The second moment is calculated in a similar manner by using the identity $x^2 = x(x - 1) + x$. From (1) and (10), it follows that

$$\mu_2' = \sum_{x=0}^{n} x^2 \frac{n!}{x!\,(n-x)!}\, p^{x} q^{n-x}$$

$$= \sum_{x=0}^{n} [x(x-1) + x] \frac{n!}{x!\,(n-x)!}\, p^{x} q^{n-x}$$

$$= \sum_{x=0}^{n} x(x-1) \frac{n!}{x!\,(n-x)!}\, p^{x} q^{n-x} + \mu$$

Since the terms for $x = 0$ and $x = 1$ are equal to 0 because of the factor $x(x - 1)$, the summation can begin with $x = 2$; hence

$$\mu_2' = \sum_{x=2}^{n} x(x-1) \frac{n!}{x!\,(n-x)!}\, p^{x} q^{n-x} + \mu$$

$$= \sum_{x=2}^{n} \frac{n!}{(x-2)!\,(n-x)!}\, p^{x} q^{n-x} + \mu$$

If $n(n - 1)p^2$ is factored out, this becomes

$$\mu_2' = n(n-1)p^2 \sum_{x=2}^{n} \frac{(n-2)!}{(x-2)!\,(n-x)!}\, p^{x-2} q^{n-x} + \mu$$

Letting $z = x - 2$, the right side can be written as

$$\mu_2' = n(n-1)p^2 \sum_{z=0}^{n-2} \frac{(n-2)!}{z!\,(n-2-z)!}\, p^{z} q^{n-2-z} + \mu$$

The quantity being summed is the probability of z successes in $n - 2$ trials. Since the sum is over all possible values of z, its value must be one. Using this result and the earlier result that $\mu = np$, μ_2' reduces to

$$(11) \qquad\qquad \mu_2' = n(n-1)p^2 + np$$

If formula (3) is applied to the results just obtained for the binomial distribution,

$$\mu_2 = n(n - 1)p^2 + np - n^2p^2$$
$$= -np^2 + np$$
$$= npq$$

These calculations show that the mean and the standard deviation of a binomial distribution are given by the formulas

(12)
$$\mu = np$$
$$\sigma = \sqrt{npq}$$

Now consider the computation of these moments by means of the moment generating function. If (4) is applied to (8),

$$M_x(\theta) = \sum_{x=0}^{n} e^{\theta x} \frac{n!}{x!\,(n - x)!}\, p^x q^{n - x}$$

$$= \sum_{x=0}^{n} \frac{n!}{x!\,(n - x)!}\, (pe^\theta)^x q^{n - x}$$

But from (9) this sum can be written as a binomial raised to the nth power because the expansion is purely algebraic and need not be interpreted in terms of probabilities. Hence

(13)
$$M_x(\theta) = (q + pe^\theta)^n$$

The desired moments may be obtained by applying (6). If (13) is differentiated twice with respect to θ and terms are combined,

$$M'(\theta) = npe^\theta(q + pe^\theta)^{n-1}$$

and

$$M''(\theta) = npe^\theta(q + pe^\theta)^{n-2}(q + npe^\theta)$$

The values of these derivatives at $\theta = 0$ are np and $np(q + np)$, respectively; hence they are the values of μ and μ_2' respectively. If q is replaced by $1 - p$, it will be observed that μ_2' here agrees with the value obtained in (11). For this problem the moments are easier to obtain indirectly by means of the moment generating function than directly from definition.

5.2.4 Poisson Distribution

If the number of trials n is large, the computations involved in using formula (8) become quite lengthy; therefore, a convenient approximation to the binomial distribution would be very useful. It turns out that for large n there are two well-known frequency functions that give good approximations to the binomial frequency function: one when p is very small and the other when this is not the case. The approximation that applies when p is very small is known as the Poisson frequency function and is defined by

(14)   POISSON DISTRIBUTION: $f(x) = \dfrac{e^{-\mu}\mu^x}{x!}$

It will presently be seen that the parameter μ is the mean of the distribution; hence, it is proper to label it μ. Although the Poisson distribution is being introduced here as an approximation to the binomial distribution, it is a well-known and useful distribution in its own right and therefore should not be regarded as merely an approximation for the binomial distribution. It has been named after another pioneer in the theory of probability.

5.2.4.1 Poisson Approximation to the Binomial. In order to verify the fact that (14) does serve as a good approximation to the binomial distribution for very large n and very small p, consider what happens to the binomial frequency function when n becomes infinite and p approaches zero in such a manner that the mean $\mu = np$ remains fixed.

First, rewrite (8) as follows:

$$f(x) = \frac{n(n-1)\cdots(n-x+1)}{x!}\,p^x(1-p)^{n-x}$$

If numerator and denominator are multiplied by n^x and the indicated algebraic manipulations are performed,

(15) $f(x) = \dfrac{n(n-1)\cdots(n-x+1)}{n^x x!}\,(np)^x(1-p)^{n-x}$

$\qquad = \dfrac{n(n-1)\cdots(n-x+1)}{n\cdot n\cdots n}\,\dfrac{\mu^x}{x!}(1-p)^{n-x}$

$\qquad = \left(1-\dfrac{1}{n}\right)\left(1-\dfrac{2}{n}\right)\cdots\left(1-\dfrac{x-1}{n}\right)\dfrac{\mu^x}{x!}(1-p)^{n-x}$

$\qquad = \dfrac{\left(1-\dfrac{1}{n}\right)\left(1-\dfrac{2}{n}\right)\cdots\left(1-\dfrac{x-1}{n}\right)}{(1-p)^x}\,\dfrac{\mu^x}{x!}(1-p)^{n}$

Next, express $(1-p)^n$ in the form

$$(1-p)^n = [(1-p)^{-\frac{1}{p}}]^{-np} = [(1-p)^{-\frac{1}{p}}]^{-\mu}$$

Now, from the definition of e,

$$\lim_{z \to 0} (1 + z)^{\frac{1}{z}} = e$$

hence, letting $z = -p$,

$$\lim_{p \to 0} [(1 - p)^{-\frac{1}{p}}]^{-\mu} = e^{-\mu}$$

Furthermore,

$$\lim_{n \to \infty} \frac{\left(1 - \frac{1}{n}\right)\left(1 - \frac{2}{n}\right) \cdots \left(1 - \frac{x-1}{n}\right)}{(1 - p)^x} = 1$$

because $p \to 0$ as $n \to \infty$ when $np = \mu$ is fixed. By applying these two results to the right side of (15), it will be seen that

$$\lim_{n \to \infty} f(x) = \frac{e^{-\mu}\mu^x}{x!}$$

This result may be expressed as a theorem.

THEOREM 1: *If the probability of success in a single trial p approaches 0 while the number of trials n becomes infinite in such a manner that the mean $\mu = np$ remains fixed, then the binomial distribution will approach the Poisson distribution with mean μ.*

Figures 1 and 2 were constructed to indicate how rapidly the binomial distribution approaches the Poisson distribution. The broken lines represent the fixed Poisson distribution for μ chosen equal to 4 and the solid lines the binomial distribution for $p = \frac{1}{3}$ and $p = \frac{1}{24}$, respectively. It appears from inspecting these graphs that the Poisson approximation

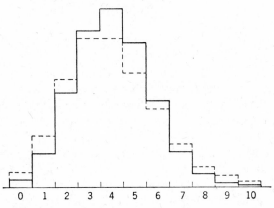

Fig. 1. Binomial (———) and Poisson (– – –) distributions for $\mu = 4$ and $p = \frac{1}{3}$.

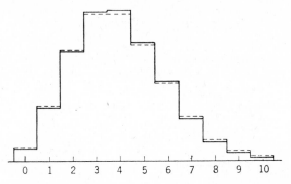

Fig. 2. Binomial (———) and Poisson (- - -) distributions for $\mu = 4$ and $p = \frac{1}{24}$.

should be sufficiently accurate for most applications if $n \geq 100$ and $p \leq .05$.

5.2.4.2 Applications. As an illustration of the use of the Poisson distribution as an approximation to the binomial distribution, consider the problem of calculating the probability that at most five defective fuses will be found in a box of 200 fuses if experience shows that 2 per cent of these fuses are defective. Here $\mu = np = 200(.02) = 4$; hence, using (14), the approximate answer is given by

$$P\{x \leq 5\} = \sum_{x=0}^{5} \frac{e^{-4}4^{x}}{x!}$$

$$= e^{-4}\left(1 + 4 + \frac{4^2}{2} + \frac{4^3}{6} + \frac{4^4}{24} + \frac{4^5}{120}\right)$$

$$= .785$$

Lengthy calculations using (8) yield the answer .788; hence the approximation is very good here.

As an illustration of an empirical distribution that may be thought of as possessing Poisson characteristics, consider the data of Table 1 on the distribution of yeast cells in the 400 squares of a hemacytometer.

The procedure for obtaining the observed frequencies consists in diluting the yeast cells in a liquid, thoroughly mixing the dilution, filling a counting chamber that has been ruled into 400 squares with the mixture, and then counting the number of yeast cells on each square under a microscope. It is possible to conceive of these data as having come from a binomial population by reasoning in the following manner. If the mixture is thought of as consisting of yeast cells and groups of molecules of the liquid about equal in size to the yeast cells, the yeast cells will constitute only a very small percentage of such units of volume; nevertheless, the total number of such units on one square of the hemacytometer is so large that several yeast cells may be found among them. The number of trials here corresponds to the total number of units on a square, and the number of successes corresponds to the number of yeast cells on the square. If the mixing has been thorough, one would expect the yeast cells to be distributed uniformly throughout the mixture and the units on a square to constitute a set of independent trials.

TABLE 1

No. cells (x) per square	0	1	2	3	4	5	6	7	8	9	10
Observed frequency	103	143	98	42	8	4	2	0	0	0	0
Expected frequency	107	141	93	41	14	4	1	0	0	0	0

The mean of x for the empirical distribution given in Table 1 will be found to be $\bar{x} = 1.32$. If it is assumed on the basis of the preceding discussion that x possesses a Poisson distribution and if the value of μ is approximated well by $\bar{x}$, the frequencies that would be expected here may be obtained to a good approximation from (14) by computing the successive values of

(16)
$$400 \frac{e^{-1.32}(1.32)^x}{x!}$$

The results of such computations correct to the nearest unit are given in the third row of Table 1. There appears to be excellent agreement here. By the expected frequency for a given value of x is meant the mean number of successes for that value of x when the problem is treated as a binomial problem in which $n = 400$ and $p = e^{-\mu}\mu^x/x!$, hence in which (16) gives np for the binomial problem when $\mu = 1.32$.

If there had been poor agreement between the observed and expected frequencies here, the Poisson model would have been considered unacceptable. Since any errors introduced by replacing the unknown μ by its sample estimate $\bar{x}$ would be very small because $\bar{x}$ is based on 400 observations and the Poisson approximation to the binomial model as described above is certainly excellent, any disagreement between observed and expected frequencies would have been attributed to the binomial assumptions not being satisfied. Thus, if the yeast cells had not been mixed thoroughly, or if there had been a tendency for the yeast cells to cluster, the binomial assumptions would have been questioned. Since experience has shown that the Poisson model is a valid model for many techniques of this kind, the Poisson distribution can be used to check on the soundness of these techniques.

The preceding illustration is an example of a spatial type distribution. Variables distributed over time or space can often be assumed to possess Poisson distributions. For example, the Poisson distribution has been found to be a satisfactory model for the number of disintegrating atoms from a radioactive substance, or for the number of telephone calls on a line, in a fixed time interval. The number of meteorites found on an acre of desert land is another spatial variable to which the Poisson distribution is applicable.

If one assumes that the number of events occurring in a time interval is independent of the number that occurred in earlier time intervals and one makes a few other plausible assumptions, then it can be shown that the number of occurrences will possess a Poisson distribution. The same type of derivation can be applied to the number of events occurring in a region in space. Thus the Poisson distribution is a useful distribution independent of its use as an approximation for the binomial distribution.

In Chapter 3 it was stated that point estimates of parameters would usually be obtained by applying the maximum likelihood principle given by (11), Chapter 3. In the preceding illustration of how yeast cells are distributed, $\bar{x}$ was used to estimate the parameter μ of a Poisson distribution. To verify that $\bar{x}$ is the maximum likelihood estimator of μ, calculate the likelihood function using (10), Chapter 3, and (14). Thus

$$L \doteq \frac{e^{-\mu}\mu^{x_1}}{x_1!} \frac{e^{-\mu}\mu^{x_2}}{x_2!} \cdots \frac{e^{-\mu}\mu^{x_n}}{x_n!}$$

$$= \frac{e^{-n\mu}\mu^{\sum_1^n x_i}}{\prod_1^n x_i!}$$

Taking logarithms and differentiating,

$$\frac{\partial \log L}{\partial \mu} = -n + \sum_1^n x_i \cdot \frac{1}{\mu}$$

The maximum likelihood estimator $\hat{\mu}$ is given by setting $\dfrac{\partial \log L}{\partial \mu}$ equal to 0 and solving for μ, which gives

$$\hat{\mu} = \frac{\sum_1^n x_i}{n} = \bar{x}$$

5.3   Continuous Variables

In the preceding sections two particular discrete frequency functions were studied. In the next few sections two particular continuous frequency functions will be studied. Since it will be necessary to calculate the moments of these distributions, the definition of the kth moment for continuous distributions is considered first.

5.3.1   Moments

Let $f(x)$ be a continuous frequency function which is zero outside some finite interval (a, b). Figure 3 gives the graph of such a function. Let the interval (a, b) be divided into n equal subintervals and let x_i be the midpoint of the ith subinterval. Form the sum

$$(17) \qquad \sum_{i=1}^{n} x_i^k f(x_i) \Delta x$$

where Δx is the width of a subinterval. The quantity $f(x_i) \Delta x$ is the area of the shaded rectangle; hence $x_i^k f(x_i) \Delta x$ represents the approximate kth moment of this rectangular area about the origin and (17) represents the sum of such approximate kth moments of area. Since the rectangles approximate the area under the curve, the natural procedure is to define the kth moment of $f(x)$ as the limit of this sum as the width of the subinterval approaches 0. Thus the kth moment of a continuous distribution with frequency function $f(x)$ is defined by

$$(18) \qquad \mu_k' = \int_a^b x^k f(x)\, dx$$

It is often desirable to calculate moments of a function of x, say $g(x)$, rather than of x itself. For example, if $g(x) = x - \mu$, then the kth moment of $g(x)$ would be the kth moment of x about its mean. A general definition in terms of an arbitrary function $g(x)$ will enable one to shift

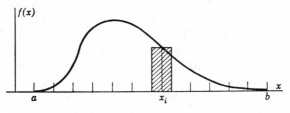

Fig. 3. A continuous frequency function.

from moments about the origin to moments about the mean and also to consider various other useful changes of variable. Such a definition is the following:

(19) DEFINITION: *If f(x) is the frequency function of the random variable x, the kth moment of the function g(x) is given by*

$$\mu'_{k:g(x)} = \int_{-\infty}^{\infty} g^k(x) f(x)\, dx$$

If $f(x)$ is positive for all values of x, the limits $-\infty$ and ∞ are required; however, if $f(x)$ is zero over part of the x axis, there is still no harm done in using these limits.

5.3.2 Moment Generating Function

The moment generating function for a continuous variable is defined by analogy with (4) to be

$$(20) \qquad M_x(\theta) = \int_{-\infty}^{\infty} e^{\theta x} f(x)\, dx$$

If $e^{\theta x}$ is expanded in a power series and if the integration is performed term by term, it will be found that $M_x(\theta)$ will assume the same expanded form as that in (5); hence (20) generates moments in the same manner as (4) does.

In order to be able to generate moments of the type given by (19), it is necessary to generalize the definition of the moment generating function. From the manner in which $M_x(\theta)$ generates moments, it is clear that moments of $g(x)$ will be generated if $e^{\theta x}$ is replaced by $e^{\theta g(x)}$ in (20). The desired definition is the following:

(21) DEFINITION: *If f(x) is the frequency function of the random variable x, the moment generating function of g(x) is given by*

$$M_{g(x)}(\theta) = \int_{-\infty}^{\infty} e^{\theta g(x)} f(x)\, dx$$

This generalized form of the moment generating function is used to derive a number of theorems, but in such derivations two properties of moment generating functions are needed; therefore, consider those properties now.

Let c be any constant and let $h(x)$ be a function of x for which the moment generating function exists. Then, since $g(x)$ in (21) represents an arbitrary function, $g(x)$ may be chosen as $g(x) = ch(x)$; consequently,

$$M_{ch}(\theta) = \int_{-\infty}^{\infty} e^{\theta ch(x)} f(x)\, dx = M_h(\theta c)$$

The second property is obtained by choosing $g(x) = h(x) + c$. Then

$$M_{h+c}(\theta) = \int_{-\infty}^{\infty} e^{\theta[h(x)+c]} f(x) \, dx$$

$$= e^{\theta c} \int_{-\infty}^{\infty} e^{\theta h(x)} f(x) \, dx$$

$$= e^{\theta c} M_h(\theta)$$

If $h(x)$ is replaced by $g(x)$, these results may be summarized in two important formulas.

(22)   PROPERTIES: *If c is any constant and g(x) is any function for which the moment generating function exists,*

(i) $M_{cg(x)}(\theta) = M_{g(x)}(c\theta)$

(ii) $M_{g(x)+c}(\theta) = e^{c\theta} M_{g(x)}(\theta)$

These two properties enable one to dispose of a bothersome constant c which multiplies, or is added to, a function $g(x)$. By replacing integrals by sums it is easily shown that these formulas apply to discrete variables also. It is assumed that $g(x)$ and $f(x)$ are such that the integral in (21), or the corresponding sum, is finite. This implies that all the moments of $g(x)$ are finite. Applications of the preceding formulas are made in the following sections.

5.3.3   Rectangular Distribution

Perhaps the simplest continuous frequency function is the one that is constant over some interval (a, b) and is 0 elsewhere. This frequency function defines what is known as the rectangular or uniform distribution; hence

(23)   RECTANGULAR DISTRIBUTION: $f(x) = \begin{cases} 1/(b-a), & a \leq x \leq b \\ 0, & elsewhere \end{cases}$

The graph of a typical rectangular distribution is given in Fig. 4.

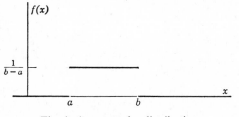

Fig. 4. A rectangular distribution.

The rectangular distribution arises, for example, in the study of rounding errors when measurements are recorded to a certain accuracy. Thus, if measurements of daily temperatures are recorded to the nearest degree, it would be assumed that the difference in degrees between the true temperature and the recorded temperature is some number between $-.5$ and $.5$ and that the error is uniformly distributed throughout this interval.

The kth moment of the rectangular distribution is easy to compute. For example, if $a = 0$ and $b = 1$, application of (18) to (23) gives

$$\mu_k{}' = \int_0^1 x^k \, dx = \frac{1}{k+1}$$

The moment generating function is also easy to compute. Application of (20) to (23) gives

$$M_x(\theta) = \int_0^1 e^{\theta x} \, dx = \frac{e^\theta - 1}{\theta}$$

If one wished to obtain the kth moment from $M_x(\theta)$, it would be necessary to expand e^θ and simplify as follows:

$$M_x(\theta) = \frac{1}{\theta}\left(1 + \theta + \frac{\theta^2}{2!} + \frac{\theta^3}{3!} + \cdots - 1\right)$$

$$= 1 + \frac{\theta}{2!} + \frac{\theta^2}{3!} + \cdots + \frac{\theta^k}{(k+1)!} + \cdots$$

Since $\mu_k{}'$ is the coefficient of $\theta^k/k!$, it will be seen from this expansion that $\mu_k{}' = k!/(k+1)! = 1/(k+1)$, which agrees with the preceding result. This computation was made for the purpose of becoming familiar with the moment generating function and not as a suggested method for computing the moments. The direct computation is obviously much simpler here.

The rectangular frequency function is of somewhat limited use as a model for real-life distributions; however, it is of considerable theoretical value and is the simplest continuous frequency function on which to illustrate general formulas.

5.3.4 Normal Distribution

The histogram shown in Fig. 1 and Fig. 5 of Chapter 4 are examples of distributions whose general characteristics are encountered rather often. These two distributions are quite symmetrical, die out rather quickly at the tails, and possess a shape much like that of a bell. A mathematical model that has proved very useful for distributions such as these, and which presently will be seen to be very important theoretically, is a distribution called the *normal* or *Gaussian* distribution. It is defined as

(24)   NORMAL DISTRIBUTION: $f(x) = ce^{-\frac{1}{2}\left(\frac{x-a}{b}\right)^2}$

Here a, b, and c are parameters that make $f(x)$ a frequency function. For example, c must be such that the area under the graph of $f(x)$ is equal to one.

5.3.4.1 Moments. The graph of a typical normal curve is given in Fig. 5. From (24) it is clear that the curve is symmetrical about the line $x = a$; hence by symmetry the mean must be given by $\mu = a$.

Instead of finding the moments directly, they may be found indirectly by means of the moment generating function. Furthermore, since it is easier here to find moments about the mean than about the origin, consider the evaluation of $M_{x-\mu}(\theta)$. From definition (21), with $g(x)$ chosen equal to $x - \mu$,

$$M_{x-\mu}(\theta) = c \int_{-\infty}^{\infty} e^{\theta(x-\mu)} \cdot e^{-\frac{1}{2}\left(\frac{x-\mu}{b}\right)^2} dx$$

Let $z = (x - \mu)/b$; then $dx = b\,dz$ and

$$M_{x-\mu}(\theta) = bc \int_{-\infty}^{\infty} e^{\theta bz - \frac{z^2}{2}} dz$$

Complete the square in the exponent as follows:

$$\theta bz - \frac{z^2}{2} = -\frac{1}{2}(z - \theta b)^2 + \frac{1}{2}\theta^2 b^2$$

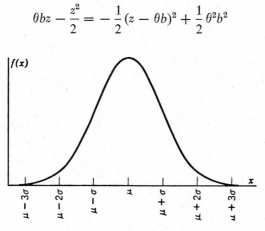

Fig. 5. Typical normal distribution.

Then,

$$M_{x-\mu}(\theta) = bce^{\frac{1}{2}\theta^2 b^2} \int_{-\infty}^{\infty} e^{-\frac{1}{2}(z-\theta b)^2} dz$$

If $t = z - \theta b$, then $dz = dt$ and

$$M_{x-\mu}(\theta) = bce^{\frac{1}{2}\theta^2 b^2} \int_{-\infty}^{\infty} e^{-\frac{t^2}{2}} dt$$

The value of this integral can be found in any standard table of integrals. Or it may be evaluated directly by the following device. Let

$$I = \int_0^{\infty} e^{-\frac{t^2}{2}} dt$$

Then

$$I^2 = \int_0^{\infty} e^{-\frac{x^2}{2}} dx \int_0^{\infty} e^{-\frac{y^2}{2}} dy$$

$$= \int_0^{\infty} \int_0^{\infty} e^{-\frac{x^2+y^2}{2}} dx\, dy$$

In polar coordinates this double integral assumes the form

$$I^2 = \int_0^{\pi/2} \int_0^{\infty} e^{-\frac{r^2}{2}} r\, dr\, d\theta$$

$$= \int_0^{\frac{\pi}{2}} -e^{-\frac{r^2}{2}} \Big|_0^{\infty} d\theta$$

$$= \int_0^{\frac{\pi}{2}} d\theta = \frac{\pi}{2}$$

Hence

$$\int_{-\infty}^{\infty} e^{-\frac{t^2}{2}} dt = \sqrt{2\pi}$$

and

(25) $$M_{x-\mu}(\theta) = \sqrt{2\pi}\, bce^{\frac{1}{2}\theta^2 b^2}$$

From (5) it follows that for any moment generating function $M(0) = 1$; hence from (25) it follows that $\sqrt{2\pi}\, bc = 1$ and that

(26) $$M_{x-\mu}(\theta) = e^{\frac{1}{2}\theta^2 b^2}$$

If this exponential is expanded in a power series,

$$M_{x-\mu}(\theta) = 1 + b^2 \frac{\theta^2}{2} + b^4 \frac{\theta^4}{8} + \cdots$$

Since the odd powers of θ are missing, the odd moments of x about its mean μ must be 0, which of course is true for any symmetrical distribution possessing such moments. The coefficient of $\theta^2/2!$ is the second moment of x about its mean; therefore, $b^{2\cdot} = \mu_2 = \sigma^2$, or $b = \sigma$. Since $\sqrt{2\pi}\,bc = 1$, $c = 1/\sigma\sqrt{2\pi}$; consequently, (24) can be written in the form

$$(27) \qquad f(x) = \frac{1}{\sigma\sqrt{2\pi}}\, e^{-\frac{1}{2}\left(\frac{x-\mu}{\sigma}\right)^2}$$

This result shows that a normal distribution is completely determined by specifying its mean and standard deviation. It should be noted that the only difference between (24) and (27) is that the parameters in (24) have now been reduced to two independent parameters which have been given statistical meaning.

A formula for $M_x(\theta)$, expressed in terms of statistical parameters, will be needed in subsequent sections. It can be obtained from (26) by replacing b^2 with σ^2 and using the second of the two properties in (22) with $g(x) = x$ and $c = -\mu$. These substitutions yield the result

$$(28) \qquad M_x(\theta) = e^{\mu\theta + \frac{1}{2}\sigma^2\theta^2}$$

For the purpose of interpreting the standard deviation geometrically, consider the points of inflection of a normal curve. When (27) is differentiated twice,

$$f' = -\frac{1}{\sigma^2}(x-\mu)f$$

$$f'' = -\frac{1}{\sigma^2}\left[1 - \left(\frac{x-\mu}{\sigma}\right)^2\right]f$$

From the first derivative it is clear that there is but one maximum point, which occurs at $x = \mu$. From the second derivative it follows that points of inflection occur at $x = \mu \pm \sigma$. Geometrically, then, the standard deviation is the distance from the axis of symmetry to a point of inflection.

In Chapter 4 meaning was given to the standard deviation as a measure of variation by stating that for histograms approximating a normal curve the interval $\bar{x} \pm s$ included about 68 per cent of the data; $\bar{x} \pm 2s$ included about 95 per cent of the data. This property will now be verified. For (27) the probability that x will fall in the interval $\mu \pm \sigma$ is given by

$$\int_{\mu-\sigma}^{\mu+\sigma} \frac{1}{\sigma\sqrt{2\pi}}\, e^{-\frac{1}{2}\left(\frac{x-\mu}{\sigma}\right)^2}\, dx$$

When $t = (x - \mu)/\sigma$, then $dx = \sigma \, dt$ and

$$\int_{\mu-\sigma}^{\mu+\sigma} \frac{1}{\sigma\sqrt{2\pi}} e^{-\frac{1}{2}\left(\frac{x-\mu}{\sigma}\right)^2} dx = \frac{1}{\sqrt{2\pi}} \int_{-1}^{1} e^{-\frac{t^2}{2}} dt = 2 \frac{1}{\sqrt{2\pi}} \int_{0}^{1} e^{-\frac{t^2}{2}} dt$$

The value of the last integral multiplied by the factor $1/\sqrt{2\pi}$, found in Table II in the back of the book, is .3413. Hence the value of the desired integral is .68, correct to two digits. For the limits $\mu \pm 2\sigma$ one may verify that $t = \pm 2$ and that the area between is .95. The unit of measurement given by $t = (x - \mu)/\sigma$ is called a *standard unit*. Table II is therefore a table for the normal distribution with 0 mean and unit standard deviation, that is, for standard units.

5.3.4.2 Fitting to Histograms. Consider the problem of fitting a normal curve to a histogram. If one has reasons for believing that a set of data represents a random sample from some normal population, then the fitted normal curve would serve as an approximation to the population curve. Since a normal distribution is completely determined by its mean and standard deviation and these quantities can be rather accurately estimated for n fairly large, one would have considerably more confidence in the fitted normal curve as representing the population distribution than in the histogram of the data as doing so. There is not much occasion to fit normal curves to histograms. Frequency curve fitting is important in some statistical fields; however, for most statistical purposes it is principally an exercise to acquaint the student with the normal curve and with the extent to which normal data are found in statistical practice.

As an illustration of the technique of fitting a normal curve to a histogram, consider once more the data of Table 2, Chapter 4, for which the histogram is shown in Fig. 5, Chapter 4. These data are also given in

TABLE 2

Class boundaries x	$\dfrac{x - 475}{151}$ t	Area to left of t A	Area for interval to left of t ΔA	Theoretical frequency $n\,\Delta A$	Observed frequency
99.5	−2.49	.0064	.0064	6.4	6
199.5	−1.82	.0344	.0280	28.0	28
299.5	−1.16	.1230	.0886	88.6	88
399.5	−0.50	.3085	.1855	185.5	180
499.5	0.16	.5636	.2551	255.1	247
599.5	0.82	.7939	.2303	230.3	260
699.5	1.49	.9319	.1380	138.0	133
799.5	2.15	.9842	.0523	52.3	42
899.5	2.81	.9975	.0133	13.3	11
999.5	3.47	.9997	.0022	2.2	5

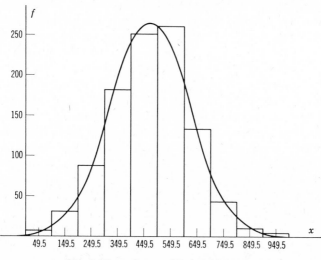

Fig. 6. Normal curve fitted to histogram.

Table 2 of this chapter, and the histogram is shown in Fig. 6. Since μ and σ are unknown, they must be estimated from the data. The methods explained in Chapter 3 show that the maximum likelihood estimators of μ and σ are given by $\hat{\mu} = \bar{x}$ and $\hat{\sigma} = s$; therefore, the estimates $\bar{x} = 475$ and $s = 151$ are used. Then, by (27), the desired fitted normal frequency function is

$$(29) \qquad f(x) = \frac{e^{-\frac{1}{2}\left(\frac{x-475}{151}\right)^2}}{151\sqrt{2\pi}}$$

The graph of this function, of course, has unit area, hence $f(x)$ must be multiplied by the total area of the histogram if it is to fit the histogram. However, except for the purpose of seeing how well the curve fits, it is not necessary to calculate ordinates, since the agreement between the fitted curve and the histogram is determined by comparing the corresponding areas under the curve and the histogram for the various class intervals. In the fitting technique it is therefore convenient to work with percentage areas under the normal curve. These percentage areas for the various class intervals of the histogram are calculated systematically by starting with the first class interval. Now, to any value of x, say x_0, for the curve (29) there corresponds a value $t_0 = (x_0 - 475)/151$ for the *standard normal curve*

$$(30) \qquad f(t) = \frac{e^{-\frac{t^2}{2}}}{\sqrt{2\pi}}$$

such that the percentage of area to the left of x_0 in (29) is the same as the percentage of area to the left of t_0 in (30). For, since $t = (x - 475)/151$, $dx = 151\, dt$ and

$$\int_{-\infty}^{x_0} \frac{e^{-\frac{1}{2}\left(\frac{x-475}{151}\right)^2}}{151\sqrt{2\pi}}\, dx = \int_{-\infty}^{t_0} \frac{e^{-\frac{t^2}{2}}}{\sqrt{2\pi}}\, dt$$

The value of this integral can be obtained from Table II. The procedure for finding these normal curve frequencies is illustrated in Table 2.

The agreement seems to be excellent except for the rather large difference between 230.3 and 260. The extent of such discrepancies is more readily realized by comparing the graphs of the histogram and the fitted normal curve as shown in Fig. 6. The question whether the fit may be considered satisfactory is considered in a later chapter.

5.3.4.3 Applications. The interesting and important applications of normal distributions are considered in later chapters after further essential theory has been developed. Here, only one simple illustration of its direct applicability is given.

Many college instructors of large classes assign letter grades on examinations by means of the normal distribution. The procedure followed is to ignore that part of the distribution lying outside the interval $\mu \pm 2.5\sigma$, or $\mu \pm 3\sigma$, and then divide this interval into five equal parts corresponding to the letter grades F, D, C, B, and A. If $\mu \pm 2.5\sigma$ is used, each interval will be σ units in length; consequently, the six values of x determining these five intervals will be $\mu - 2.5\sigma$, $\mu - 1.5\sigma$, $\mu - 0.5\sigma$, $\mu + 0.5\sigma$, $\mu + 1.5\sigma$, and $\mu + 2.5\sigma$. The corresponding values of $t = (x - \mu)/\sigma$ will be -2.5, -1.5, -0.5, 0.5, 1.5, and 2.5. From Table II it will be found that the areas within these five intervals are .06, .24, .38, .24, and .06, respectively. Since these percentages do not total 100 per cent, it is customary to allow the two end intervals to extend to infinity. Then the percentages of students who will be assigned the corresponding letter grades are 7 per cent F, 24 per cent D, 38 per cent C, 24 per cent B, and 7 per cent A.

5.3.4.4 Normal Approximation to Binomial. In 5.2.4.1 the Poisson distribution was introduced as an approximation to the binomial distribution when n is large and p is small. It was stated there that another distribution gives a good approximation for large n when p is not small. The normal distribution is the distribution with this property. Before investigating the nature of this approximation in general, consider a numerical example.

Let $n = 12$ and $p = \frac{1}{3}$ and construct the graph of the corresponding binomial distribution. This is hardly a large value of n, so that a good normal approximation is not to be expected here. Since $f(x)$ is to be computed for all values of x from 0 to 12, it is easier to compute each value, after the first, from the preceding one rather than to compute each value by itself. Here, by (8),

$$f(x) = \frac{12!}{x!\,(12-x)!}\left(\frac{1}{3}\right)^x\left(\frac{2}{3}\right)^{12-x}$$

It is easily verified that for this frequency function

$$f(x+1) = \frac{12-x}{x+1}\frac{1}{2}f(x)$$

After $f(0)$ was computed, this relationship was used to obtain the following values.

$$\begin{array}{ll}
f(0) = & .007707 \\
f(1) = \; 6f(0) = .046242 \\
f(2) = \tfrac{11}{4}f(1) = .127166 \\
f(3) = \tfrac{5}{3}f(2) = .211943 \\
f(4) = \tfrac{9}{8}f(3) = .238436 \\
f(5) = \tfrac{4}{5}f(4) = .190749 \\
f(6) = \tfrac{7}{12}f(5) = .111270
\end{array}$$

(31)

$$\begin{array}{ll}
f(7) = \tfrac{3}{7}f\,(6) = .047687 \\
f(8) = \tfrac{5}{16}f\,(7) = .014902 \\
f(9) = \tfrac{2}{9}f\,(8) = .003312 \\
f(10) = \tfrac{3}{20}f\,(9) = .000497 \\
f(11) = \tfrac{1}{11}f(10) = .000045 \\
f(12) = \tfrac{1}{24}f(11) = .000002
\end{array}$$

Since $f(0)$ was computed correct to four digits only, the remaining values would not be expected to be correct to more than four digits, even though they have been recorded to six decimals for the sake of appearances. The graph of this binomial distribution is shown in Fig. 7. It appears that this histogram could be fitted fairly well by the proper normal curve.

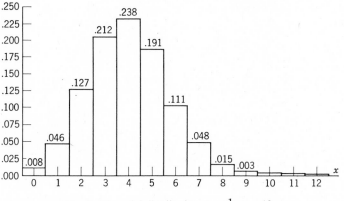

Fig. 7. Binomial distribution, $p = \tfrac{1}{3}$, $n = 12$.

Since a normal curve is completely determined by its mean and standard deviation, the natural normal curve to use here is the one with the same mean and standard deviation as the binomial distribution. Hence, because of (12), choose

$$\mu = 12 \cdot \tfrac{1}{3} = 4$$

and

$$\sigma = \sqrt{12 \cdot \tfrac{1}{3} \cdot \tfrac{2}{3}} = 1.63$$

As a test of the accuracy of the normal curve approximation here and as an illustration of the use of normal curve methods for approximating binomial probabilities, consider a few problems related to Fig. 7.

If the probability that a marksman will hit a target is $\tfrac{1}{3}$ and if he takes 12 shots, what is the probability that he will score at least six hits? The exact answer is obtained by adding the values of $f(x)$ from $x = 6$ to $x = 12$, which, by using (31), is .178, correct to three decimal places. Geometrically, this answer is the area of that part of the histogram in Fig. 7 lying to the right of $x = 5.5$. Therefore, to approximate this probability by normal curve methods, it is merely necessary to find the area under that part of the fitted normal curve which lies to the right of 5.5. Since the fitted curve has $\mu = 4$ and $\sigma = 1.63$, it follows that

$$t = \frac{x - \mu}{\sigma} = \frac{5.5 - 4}{1.63} = 0.92$$

But, from Table II, the area to the right of $t = 0.92$ is .179, which, compared to the correct value of .178, is in error by only about $\tfrac{1}{2}$ per cent.

To test the accuracy of normal curve methods over a shorter interval, calculate the probability that a marksman will score precisely six hits in the 12 shots. From (31) the answer correct to three decimals is $f(6) = .111$. To approximate this answer, it is merely necessary to find the area under the fitted normal curve between $x = 5.5$ and $x = 6.5$. Thus

$$t_2 = \frac{6.5 - 4}{1.63} = 1.53, \quad A_2 = .4370$$

$$t_1 = \frac{5.5 - 4}{1.63} = 0.92, \quad A_1 = .3212$$

Therefore the required area is .116, which is in error by about 5 per cent. From these two examples it appears that normal curve methods are quite accurate, even for some situations such as that considered here in which n is not very large.

Thus far the fact that the binomial distribution can be approximated well for large n by the normal distribution with $\mu = np$ and $\sigma = \sqrt{npq}$

has been made plausible by numerical examples. Now consider the verification of this fact by means of the moment generating function. Here it is convenient to use the variable

$$t = \frac{x - \mu}{\sigma} = \frac{x - np}{\sqrt{npq}}$$

From properties (22) and (13), it follows that

$$M_t(\theta) = M_{x-\mu}\left(\frac{\theta}{\sigma}\right)$$

$$= e^{-\frac{\mu\theta}{\sigma}} M_x\left(\frac{\theta}{\sigma}\right)$$

$$= e^{-\frac{\mu\theta}{\sigma}} (q + pe^{\frac{\theta}{\sigma}})^n$$

Taking the logarithm of both sides to the base e gives

$$\log M_t(\theta) = -\frac{\mu\theta}{\sigma} + n \log (q + pe^{\frac{\theta}{\sigma}})$$

Expanding $e^{\frac{\theta}{\sigma}}$ and replacing $q + p$ by 1 yields

$$\log M_t(\theta) = -\frac{\mu\theta}{\sigma} + n \log \left\{1 + p\left[\left(\frac{\theta}{\sigma}\right) + \frac{1}{2!}\left(\frac{\theta}{\sigma}\right)^2 + \frac{1}{3!}\left(\frac{\theta}{\sigma}\right)^3 + \cdots\right]\right\}$$

If n is chosen sufficiently large, $\sigma = \sqrt{npq}$ can be made so large that for any fixed value of θ the sum of the series in brackets will be less than 1 in absolute value. If p times this sum is denoted by z, then for sufficiently large n it follows that $|z| < 1$. Since the logarithm on the right may be treated as of the form $\log \{1 + z\}$, where $|z| < 1$, the expansion

$$\log \{1 + z\} = z - \frac{z^2}{2} + \frac{z^3}{3} - \frac{z^4}{4} + \cdots$$

may be applied to give

$$(32) \quad \log M_t(\theta) = -\frac{\mu\theta}{\sigma}$$

$$+ n\left\{p\left[\left(\frac{\theta}{\sigma}\right) + \frac{1}{2!}\left(\frac{\theta}{\sigma}\right)^2 + \cdots\right] - \frac{p^2}{2}\left[\left(\frac{\theta}{\sigma}\right) + \frac{1}{2!}\left(\frac{\theta}{\sigma}\right)^2 + \cdots\right]^2 + \cdots\right\}$$

Collecting terms in powers of θ gives

$$\log M_t(\theta) = \left(-\frac{\mu}{\sigma} + \frac{np}{\sigma}\right)\theta + n\left(\frac{p}{\sigma^2} - \frac{p^2}{\sigma^2}\right)\frac{\theta^2}{2!} + \cdots$$

But, since $np = \mu$ and $\sigma^2 = npq$, the coefficient of θ vanishes and the coefficient of $\theta^2/2!$ reduces to 1; consequently,

$$\log M_t(\theta) = \frac{\theta^2}{2} + \text{terms in } \theta^k, \quad k = 3, 4, \cdots$$

From an inspection of (32), which shows how terms in θ^k arise, it is clear that all terms in θ^k contain n/σ^k as a common factor. The other factor for each such term is a constant times a power of p. Since this other factor does not involve n and since

$$\frac{n}{\sigma^k} = \frac{n}{(npq)^{\frac{k}{2}}}$$

with $k \geq 3$ here, all such terms will approach zero as n becomes infinite. This implies that

$$\lim_{n \to \infty} \log M_t(\theta) = \frac{\theta^2}{2}$$

which in turn implies that

(33) $$\lim_{n \to \infty} M_t(\theta) = e^{\frac{\theta^2}{2}}$$

A justification of these expansions and limits would require a knowledge of advanced calculus methods and therefore is not considered here.

Now consider the moment generating function of a normal variable as given by (26) with $b = \sigma$. Using property (22) once more, it follows that for a normal variable

$$M_{\frac{x-\mu}{\sigma}}(\theta) = M_{x-\mu}\left(\frac{\theta}{\sigma}\right) = e^{\frac{\theta^2}{2}}$$

A comparison of this result and (33) shows that the modified binomial variable $t = (x - np)/\sqrt{npq}$ has a moment generating function that approaches the moment generating function of the normal variable whose mean is 0 and whose standard deviation is 1. This implies that all the moments of this variable approach those of the standard normal variable.

In order to complete this discussion, it is necessary to introduce two very important theorems of advanced theoretical statistics.

The first theorem states that a distribution function is uniquely determined by its moment generating function when it exists. For example, if the moment generating function of some variable z is found to be $e^{\frac{1}{2}\theta^2}$, then z must be a standard normal variable.

The second theorem states that if a variable, which depends upon n, has a moment generating function that approaches the moment generating function of a second variable, then the distribution function of the first variable must approach the distribution function of the second variable as $n \to \infty$.

The preceding theorems insure that the distribution of the modified binomial variable $(x - np)/\sqrt{npq}$ will approach that of a standard normal variable because by (33) its moment generating function approaches the moment generating function of a standard normal variable. A precise statement of these two theorems, including conditions under which they hold, is not made here; however, these theorems are used on several occasions. A direct application of these theorems to (33) yields the following important result.

THEOREM 2: *If x represents the number of successes in n independent trials of an event for which p is the probability of success in a single trial, then the variable* $(x - np)/\sqrt{npq}$ *has a distribution that approaches the normal distribution with mean* 0 *and standard deviation* 1 *as the number of trials becomes increasingly large.*

This theorem justifies the use of normal curve methods for approximating probabilities related to successive trials of an event when n is large. Experience indicates that the approximation is fairly good as long as $np > 5$ when $p \leq \frac{1}{2}$, and $nq > 5$ when $p > \frac{1}{2}$. A very small value of p, together with a moderately large value of n, would yield a small mean and thus produce a skewed distribution. Similarly, if p is very close to one and n is only moderately large, most of the distribution will be piled up close to $x = n$, thus preventing a normal curve from fitting well. If the mean is at least five units away from either extremity, the distribution has sufficient room to become fairly symmetrical. Figures 8 and 9 indicate how rapidly the distribution of the variable $(x - np)/\sqrt{npq}$ approaches

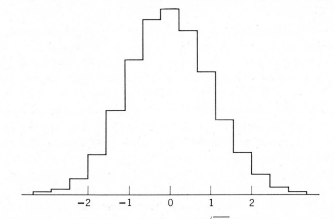

Fig. 8. Binomial distribution of $(x - np)/\sqrt{npq}$ for $p = \frac{1}{3}$ and $n = 24$.

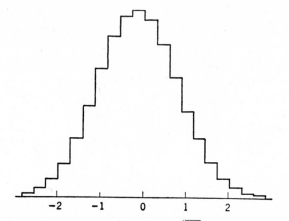

Fig. 9. Binomial distribution of $(x - np)/\sqrt{npq}$ for $p = \frac{1}{3}$ and $n = 48$.

normality when $p = \frac{1}{3}$, and $n = 24$ and 48, respectively. The common y scale for these two graphs is approximately 17 times that for the x axis.

There are numerous occasions when it is more convenient to work with the proportion of successes in n trials than with the actual number of successes. Since

$$\frac{x - np}{\sqrt{npq}} = \frac{\dfrac{x}{n} - p}{\sqrt{pq/n}}$$

the following useful corollary to Theorem 2 may be obtained.

(34) COROLLARY: *The proportion of successes* x/n *will be approximately normally distributed with mean* p *and standard deviation* $\sqrt{pq/n}$ *if* n *is sufficiently large.*

The two approximations that have been considered for the binomial distribution, namely the Poisson and normal distributions, are sufficient to permit one to solve all the simpler problems that require the computation of binomial probabilities. If n is small, one uses formula (8) directly because the computations are then quite easy. Tables of factorials and logarithms are helpful here. If n is large and p is small or large, the Poisson approximation may be used. If n is large and p is not small or large, the normal approximation may be used. Thus all possibilities have been covered.

5.3.4.5 Applications. Certain types of practical problems dealing with percentages can be solved by means of the normal approximation to the binomial distribution. As a first illustration, consider the following genetics problem. According to Mendelian inheritance theory, certain crosses of peas should give yellow and green peas in a ratio of $3:1$. In an experiment 176 yellow and 48 green peas were obtained. Do these conform to theory?

This problem may be considered as a problem of testing a statistical hypothesis. The 224 peas may be treated as 224 trials of an experiment for which the probability of obtaining a success, that is a yellow pea, in a single trial is $\frac{3}{4}$. Thus the number of yellow peas x is treated as a binomial variable and the hypothesis to be tested is

$$H_0 : p = \tfrac{3}{4}$$

Under H_0,

$$\mu = np = 168 \text{ and } \sigma = \sqrt{npq} = 6.5$$

From the experimenter's point of view an experiment corroborates theory if its results are sufficiently close to expectation. In this problem it is therefore a question of deciding whether 176 is sufficiently close to 168. Since poor experimental results correspond to large deviations from the mean, whether positive or negative, the experimenter would naturally choose the two tails of the binomial distribution for his critical region. If a critical region of size .05 is selected, which is the size that is almost always selected in this book, it is necessary to determine how far out on the tails of the binomial histogram to go so that the areas of the two extremities will total .05. Since n is sufficiently large to yield an excellent normal curve approximation to the binomial histogram, it will suffice to determine how far out on the tails of the fitted normal curve to go so that the areas of the two extremities will total .05. Because $|t| = 2$, where $t = (x - \mu)/\sigma$, corresponds to an interval of two standard deviations on both sides of the mean and this interval includes 95 per cent, to the nearest per cent, of the normal curve area, it is customary to go out a distance of two standard deviations to determine the desired critical region rather than the more accurate Table II value of $|t| = 1.96$. For this problem, therefore, the critical region will consist of the two tail intervals

$$x < \mu - 2\sigma = 168 - 13 = 155$$

and

$$x > \mu + 2\sigma = 168 + 13 = 181$$

If an experimental value should fall in this critical region, the hypothesis H_0 would be rejected, which means that the experimental value would not be considered as compatible with Mendelian theory. Such an experimental value would be said to be *significant* because it signifies that some other theory is needed to explain the experimental outcome. On the other hand, if the experimental value should fall in the acceptance region, then the experimental value would be considered as corroborating the theory. Since the experimental value of 176 falls within the acceptance interval of 155–181, there is no reason on this basis for doubting that Mendelian inheritance is operating here.

In solving this problem, the mathematical model selected was the binomial frequency function with $n = 224$ and $p = \frac{3}{4}$. The normal frequency function was used only as an approximation to determine the critical region for testing the hypothesis H_0.

Because of the nature of his problem, the experimenter would undoubtedly choose as his alternative hypothesis

$$H_1 : p \neq \tfrac{3}{4}$$

This type of alternative is similar to that considered in 3.2.2, which gave rise to the power function. The approximate power function could be obtained here by using the normal approximation to the binomial. By means of the power function one could tell how effective the choice of the two equal tails as the critical region is for detecting various possible alternative values of p. It can be shown by methods that are considered in Chapter 9, that there is no choice of critical region that is best for all possible alternative values of p. However, it can also be shown that the choice of the two equal tails is an excellent compromise, thereby justifying the selection made on intuitive grounds.

As a second illustration, consider the following problem. From past experience the manufacturer of parts finds that when a machine is functioning properly 5 per cent of the parts are defective on the average. During the course of a day's operation by a certain operator 400 parts are turned out, 30 of which are defective. Is the operator running the machine properly?

The answer to this question depends upon what is meant by the word properly. Here it will be assumed that properly means that the number of defective parts should not be greater than what could be reasonably attributed to chance for a normal operator. If the operator in question is considered normal, the 400 parts may be thought of as 400 trials of an experiment for which the probability of obtaining a defective part in a single trial is .05. The number of defective parts x is treated as a binomial variable and the problem then becomes a problem of testing the statistical hypothesis

$$H_0 : p = .05$$

Since the employer would be interested only in knowing whether this operator is normal, as contrasted to being worse than normal, he would be interested in knowing what the probability is that a normal operator will turn out 30 or more defective parts in a lot of 400. This probability could be obtained by using (8) with $n = 400$ and $p = .05$ to calculate the successive values of $f(30), f(31), \cdots, f(400)$ and then adding these probabilities. It is much easier, to put it mildly, to approximate the sum of these probabilities by finding the area to the right of 29.5 under the approximating normal curve. Since

$$\mu = np = 20 \text{ and } \sigma = \sqrt{npq} = 4.36$$

it is merely necessary to find the area in Table II to the right of the value

$$t = \frac{x - \mu}{\sigma} = \frac{29.5 - 20}{4.36} = 2.18$$

This area is .015; consequently, the probability is approximately .015 that a normal operator will turn out 30 or more defective parts in a lot of 400. Now this day's experience may be thought of as but one of an indefinite sequence of similar days' experiences for normal operators. The result may therefore be interpreted by stating that a normal operator would have a day as bad or worse than this only about 15 days in every 1000, on the average. From the employer's point of view this operator has undoubtedly turned out more defective parts than can be reasonably attributed to chance; consequently, he would be accused of not running the machine properly.

The critical region for testing H_0 here would be chosen to be the right tail of the binomial distribution, rather than both tails as in the preceding illustration, because the logical alternative hypothesis here from the employer's point of view is

$$H_1 : p > .05$$

If, as is customary, a critical region of size .05 had been selected, the value of $x = 30$ would have been judged significant, hence H_0 would have been rejected in favor of H_1. By computing the probability of .015, however, it was possible to determine how small a type I error could have been used and still have H_0 rejected.

If the normal approximation is used, it can be shown by the methods of Chapter 9 that the power curve for the foregoing choice of critical region is nowhere exceeded by the power curve of any other critical region of size .05 for $p > .05$; consequently, the foregoing test is the best possible, based on the normal approximation.

The practical reasonableness of the decision made in this problem depends upon the extent to which the mathematical model used here represents the actual situation. If the successive parts turned out by normal operators do not behave like independent trials of an experiment for which p is constant from trial to trial, then theoretically one is not

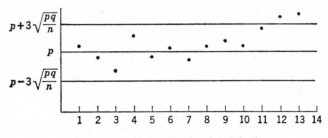

Fig. 10. Control chart for fraction defective.

justified in applying these methods, although practically they may give good results. It might happen, as it often does, that the variability of normal operators is much larger than that given by $\sigma = \sqrt{npq}$ or that the percentage of defective parts varies with the day of the week or the condition of the machine.

As a third illustration, consider the problem just alluded to of determining whether daily percentages of defectives may be treated as independent trials of an experiment for which p is constant from trial to trial. Industrial experience has shown that most production processes do not behave in this idealized manner and that much valuable information is obtained concerning the process if the order in which data are obtained is preserved. A simple graphical method, called a *quality-control chart*, has been found highly useful in the solution of this problem. Such a chart for the proportion of defectives is illustrated in Fig. 10. The middle line is thought of as corresponding to the process proportion defective, although it is usually merely the mean of past daily proportions. The other two lines serve as control limits for daily proportions of defectives. From (34) it will be observed that these two control lines are spaced three standard deviations from the mean line. The time units for successive samples are recorded along the x axis. If now the production process behaves in the idealized manner and if the normal approximation to the binomial distribution may be used, the probability that a daily proportion when plotted on this chart will fall outside the control band is approximately equal to the probability that a normal variable will assume a value more than three standard deviations away from its mean, which, from Table II, is .003. Because of this small probability, it is reasonable to assume that the production process is no longer behaving properly when a point falls outside the control band; consequently, the production engineer checks over the various steps in the process when this event occurs. From an inspection of Fig. 10 it will be observed that the process in question went out of control on the twelfth day.

Industrial experience shows that only rarely does a production process behave in this idealized manner when the control-chart technique is first applied. Nevertheless, the technique is highly useful because it enables one to discover causes of a lack of control and thus to improve on the production process until gradually statistical control has been obtained.

This illustration and discussion of a quality-control chart gives an incomplete picture of how quality-control methods operate. Such methods constitute an extensive field of applied statistics, and numerous articles and books concerning them are available.

As a final illustration, consider the problem of determining how large a sample of university students should be taken if it is desired to estimate the proportion of students who work part time to within .04 units of the true proportion. Since the accuracy of estimates cannot be guaranteed unless most of the population is sampled, it is customary to express the accuracy of an estimate by stating the probability that the error of estimate will not exceed a fixed amount. In this problem let the probability be .95 that the error of estimate will not exceed .04. From a geometrical point of view, this means that 95 per cent of the time the estimate x/n should fall within .04 units of the true proportion p. Since p is obviously not very small nor very large here and a fairly large sample is going to be needed, it may be assumed that x/n is approximately normally distributed. Now, for a normal variable, the variable will fall within .04 unit of the mean with a probability of .95 only if .04 unit is equal to two standard deviations of the variable; hence it is necessary that

$$2\sigma_{\frac{x}{n}} = .04$$

But, from (34), $\sigma_{\frac{x}{n}} = \sqrt{pq/n}$; hence it is necessary that

$$2\sqrt{pq/n} = .04$$

or, solving for n, that

(35) $$n = 2500\,pq$$

Since p is unknown, it is necessary to estimate p in some manner. It is easy to show by calculus methods that the function $pq = p(1 - p)$ assumes its maximum value for $p = \frac{1}{2}$; hence, if this value of p is used, the maximum possible sample size will be obtained. Thus, if $n = 625$, the sample will certainly be large enough. A more economical approach would be first to take a preliminary sample of, say, 100, estimate p from it, and then use this estimate in (35) to estimate total n. For still greater accuracy one would take only part, say $\frac{1}{2}$, of the sample indicated by the estimated value of n, combine the two preliminary samples to obtain a new estimate of p, and use this estimate in (35) to obtain a final estimate of total n.

5.4 Other Distributions

This section defines and discusses very briefly two other discrete distributions that are important in statistical work, and in addition it discusses the problem of transforming continuous non-normal distributions so that they become approximately normal. Thus the purpose of this section is to extend somewhat the methods of the preceding sections to a wider class of problems.

5.4.1 Hypergeometric Distribution

The binomial distribution was derived on the basis of n independent trials of an experiment; however, if the experiment consists of selecting individuals from a finite population of individuals, the trials will not be independent. For example, if a sample of 20 students is to be chosen from a group of 100 students for the purpose of studying the extent to which students work part time, it is clear that the probability of selecting a student who works part time need not remain fixed as successive individuals are selected for the sample. For large finite populations the error arising from assuming that p is constant and the trials are independent, when sampling the population, is very small and it may be ignored, in which case the binomial model is satisfactory. However, for problems in which the population is so small that a serious error will be introduced in using the binomial distribution it is necessary to apply a more appropriate distribution known as the *hypergeometric distribution*. It can be derived as follows.

Let N denote the size of the population from which a sample of n is to be drawn. Let the proportion of individuals in this finite population who possess, say, property A be denoted by p. If x is the random variable corresponding to the number of individuals in the sample of n who possess property A, then the problem is to find the frequency function of x. Since the x individuals must come from the Np individuals in the population with property A and the remaining $n - x$ individuals must come from the $N - Np$ who do not possess the property, it follows from the methods illustrated in 2.8.4 that the desired frequency function will be given by the following formula.

(36) HYPERGEOMETRIC DISTRIBUTION: $$f(x) = \frac{\binom{Np}{x}\binom{N - Np}{n - x}}{\binom{N}{n}}$$

Calculations with this formula will show that when n is only a small percentage of N the value of N must be quite small before there will be any appreciable difference between the values given by this formula and the binomial formula in (8). As an illustration, suppose a population consists of 100 individuals, of whom 10 per cent have high blood pressure. Then calculations will show, for example, that the probability of getting at most two individuals with high blood pressure in a sample of 10 is

$$P\{x \leq 2\} = \sum_{x=0}^{2} \frac{\binom{10}{x}\binom{90}{10-x}}{\binom{100}{10}} = .94$$

If the binomial formula (8) is used, additional calculations will show that one then obtains

$$P\{x \leq 2\} \doteq \sum_{x=0}^{2} \frac{10!}{x!\,(10-x)!}\left(\frac{1}{10}\right)^{x}\left(\frac{9}{10}\right)^{10-x} = .93$$

The hypergeometric distribution will not be needed until a later chapter; however, it is introduced here to show how one can employ a more refined model than the binomial distribution for binomial-type problems when the binomial assumptions are not strictly realized.

5.4.2 Multinomial Distribution

The binomial distribution is capable of solving only those successive trials problems in which each outcome can be classified as either a success or a failure. Problems frequently arise, however, in which it is desirable to have more than two categories of classification. For example, in studying blood types it is necessary to use four groupings in order to treat such problems adequately. One can always reduce more than two categories to only two by combining them, but this procedure is likely to throw away much valuable information; therefore it would be desirable to have a distribution that takes account of all such categories. Such a distribution exists in what is known as the *multinomial distribution*. It is obtained in the following manner.

Consider an experiment in which there are k mutually exclusive possible outcomes $A_1, A_2, \cdots, A_k$. Let p_i be the probability that event A_i will occur at a trial of the experiment and let n trials be made. Then the probability that event A_1 will occur x_1 times, event A_2 will occur x_2 times, etc., where $\sum_{1}^{k} x_i = n$, may be calculated by using the same reasoning as that used in deriving the binomial distribution. In this connection, consider the particular sequence of events given by

$$\overbrace{A_1, \cdots, A_1}^{x_1}, \overbrace{A_2, \cdots, A_2}^{x_2}, \cdots, \overbrace{A_k, \cdots, A_k}^{x_k}$$

Since the trials are independent, the probability of obtaining this particular sequence of events is

$$(37) \qquad p_1^{x_1} p_2^{x_2} \cdots p_k^{x_k}$$

Now every arrangement of the preceding set of A's has this same probability of occurring and satisfies the conditions of the problem; consequently, it is necessary to count the number of arrangements. But this is merely the number of permutations of n things of which x_1 are alike, x_2 are alike, etc., which by (18), Chapter 2, is equal to

$$(38) \qquad \frac{n!}{x_1!\, x_2! \cdots x_k!}$$

Since all these arrangements are the mutually exclusive ways in which the desired event can occur and since each of them has the probability given by (37), the desired probability is obtained by multiplying the quantities given in (37) and (38). This result may be summarized as follows.

(39) MULTINOMIAL DISTRIBUTION:

$$f(x_1, x_2, \cdots, x_k) = \frac{n!}{x_1!\, x_2! \cdots x_k!}\, p_1^{x_1} p_2^{x_2} \cdots p_k^{x_k}$$

This name is given to the distribution because (39) represents the general term in the expansion of the multinomial function

$$(p_1 + p_2 + \cdots + p_k)^n$$

just as the binomial frequency function represents the general term in the expansion of the binomial function $(q + p)^n$.

As it stands, the multinomial distribution is not very convenient for calculating probabilities unless n is small. The problem of finding an approximation here is considerably more difficult than in the case of the binomial distribution. As in the case of the hypergeometric distribution, this distribution will not be needed until a later chapter, but it is introduced here to show how the binomial distribution model can be generalized to treat more complicated problems of the repeated-trials-counting type.

5.4.3 Change of Variable

The normal distribution is a very useful model for continuous variables that possess empirical distributions resembling the one shown in Fig. 1, Chapter 4; however, something different is needed for empirical distributions like the one in Fig. 3, Chapter 4. There are numerous techniques that can be used to solve statistical problems when the basic distribution differs from that of a normal variable. Some of them are discussed in later chapters. One of them is discussed here to point out how methods based on the assumption of an underlying normal distribution actually have a wider range of applicability than might otherwise be assumed. The technique that is explained here is that of transforming the basic variable.

Suppose one has a random variable x whose frequency function $f(x)$ differs considerably from that of a normal variable. Is it possible to find a change of variable, say $y = h(x)$, such that the frequency function of y will be approximately normal? If one thinks of what this means geometrically, one would surmise that the answer is yes. In this connection, compare the graph of a particular frequency function, $f(x)$, given in Fig. 11, with that of a standard normal variable, $g(y)$, shown in the same sketch.

To any value of x, say x_0, one can find a corresponding value of y, denoted by y_0, such that the areas to the left of these values under the corresponding frequency curves will be equal. If one chooses a large number of values of x and obtains the corresponding values of y by means of Table II, then this set of x and y values will yield a functional relationship which may serve as a change of variable that transforms the non-normal $f(x)$ into the normal $g(y)$. This relationship is a numerical one and therefore is only an approximation of the complete relationship. If the complete relationship $y = h(x)$ were known, one could transform any x value over to its corresponding y value and treat it as an observation taken from a standard normal variable population.

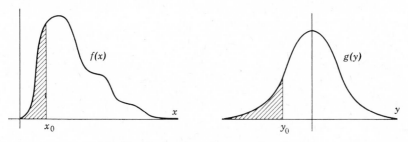

Fig. 11. Graphs of two frequency functions.

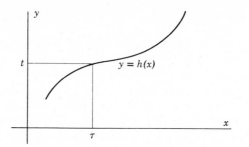

Fig. 12. The graph of an increasing function.

One can reverse the preceding process by starting with a given frequency function $f(x)$ and a given change of variable $y = h(x)$ and ask for the frequency function $g(y)$ of the new variable. If $g(y)$ should turn out to be a normal variable, or approximately so, then the transformation $y = h(x)$ would have accomplished the desired objective. Now it is relatively easy to find $g(y)$ if the function $h(x)$ in the transformation is an increasing function of x, or a decreasing function, throughout the range of x values. The technique for doing this, which is now demonstrated, is based upon finding the distribution function of y.

It follows from formula (32), Chapter 2, that the distribution function of y, which is denoted by $G(y)$, satisfies the relations

(40) $G(t) = P\{y \leq t\} = P\{h(x) \leq t\},$

where t is any desired value. Now the inequality $h(x) \leq t$ can be expressed as an inequality on x. The relationship between y and x where $h(x)$ is an increasing function is like that shown in Fig. 12. For such a relationship there is a unique value of x to each value of y. Here the value of x corresponding to the value t for y has been denoted by τ; consequently, since $h(x) \leq t$ if, and only if, $x \leq \tau$,

$$P\{h(x) \leq t\} = P\{x \leq \tau\} = \int_{-\infty}^{\tau} f(x)\, dx$$

Thus from (40)

$$G(t) = \int_{-\infty}^{\tau} f(x)\, dx$$

Now, as shown in Chapter 2, a continuous frequency function can be obtained by differentiating the corresponding distribution function. In view of the fact that τ is a function of t, it follows from the calculus formula for differentiating an integral with respect to its upper limit that

$$\frac{dG(t)}{dt} = \frac{dG(t)}{d\tau}\frac{d\tau}{dt} = f(\tau)\frac{d\tau}{dt}$$

Since t and τ were any pair of corresponding values of y and x, respectively, and were introduced to keep from confusing upper-limit variables with dummy variables of integration, this relationship may be rewritten

$$\frac{dG(y)}{dy} = f(x)\frac{dx}{dy}$$

But in view of the relationship between a distribution function and its frequency function, the left side is the frequency function of y; hence the desired formula is

$$g(y) = f(x)\frac{dx}{dy}$$

If one follows through this derivation for a change of variable $y = h(x)$ in which $h(x)$ is a decreasing function, he will obtain the negative of this result. Since dx/dy will be negative in this case, a formula that is valid for both cases will be given by

(41) $$g(y) = f(x)\left|\frac{dx}{dy}\right|$$

Before this formula can be applied, it is necessary to replace x in $f(x)$ by its value in terms of y, which means that it is necessary to solve the relation $y = h(x)$ for x in terms of y. One can calculate dx/dy from this inverse relationship, or else calculate dy/dx from the original relationship $y = h(x)$ and take its reciprocal.

Because of the importance and usefulness of this formula for later work, the result of this derivation is expressed formally.

(42) CHANGE OF VARIABLE TECHNIQUE: *If $y = h(x)$ is an increasing or decreasing function and $f(x)$ is the frequency function of x, then $g(y)$, the frequency function of y, is given by the formula*

$$g(y) = f(x)\left|\frac{dx}{dy}\right|$$

in which x is to be replaced by its value in terms of y by means of the relation $y = h(x)$.

Although formula (41) will not be valid unless $h(x)$ is either an increasing or a decreasing function, the procedure used to derive the formula can be applied to more complicated problems.

As an illustration of the use of formula (41), consider the problem of finding the frequency function of y if $y = \sqrt{x}$ and $f(x) = e^{-x}$, $x \geq 0$. Since $y = \sqrt{x}$ is an increasing function of x, formula (41) may be applied

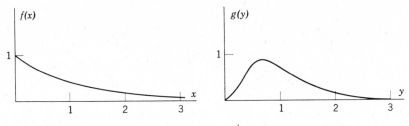

Fig. 13. Distribution of x and $y = x^{\frac{1}{2}}$ for $f(x) = e^{-x}$, $x \geq 0$.

without the absolute value signs. The inverse relationship is $x = y^2$; hence

$$g(y) = e^{-y^2} \frac{dx}{dy} = 2ye^{-y^2}$$

The relationship between these two frequency functions is shown geometrically in Fig. 13. Incidentally, it will be observed that $g(y)$ is considerably more like a normal curve in appearance than is $f(x)$.

As a second illustration, consider the problem of finding the frequency function of the kinetic energy $E = mv^2/2$, given the distribution of the velocity v. The frequency function of v, the velocity for a gas molecule with mass m, is given by

$$f(v) = av^2e^{-bv^2}$$

where $v > 0$, b is a constant depending on the gas, and a is determined to yield unit area. Since $E = mv^2/2$ is an increasing function of v for positive values of v, formula (41) may be applied by choosing $x = v$ and $y = E$. Here the inverse relationship is $v = \sqrt{2E/m}$; therefore

$$g(E) = a\frac{2E}{m} e^{-\frac{b2E}{m}} \frac{1}{\sqrt{2mE}}$$

or

$$g(E) = \alpha E^{\frac{1}{2}}e^{-\beta E}$$

where α and β are constants depending upon a, b, and m.

5.4.3.1 Chi-Square Distribution. As mentioned in the preceding section, the technique that was used to derive formula (41) can be used to obtain $g(y)$, even though the function $h(x)$ is not increasing or decreasing throughout its range of x values. This fact is illustrated by obtaining a frequency function, known as a chi-square function, which has many important uses in statistical theory and practice.

Toward this end, consider the problem of finding $g(y)$ when $y = x^2$ and $f(x) = e^{-\frac{x^2}{2}}/\sqrt{2\pi}$. Here one starts with a standard normal variable x and wishes to find the distribution of the variable x^2. The function $y = x^2$ is certainly not increasing or decreasing for all values of x; therefore formula (41) cannot be employed directly. Proceeding as in the derivation of (41),

$$G(t) = P\{y < t\} = P\{x^2 \leq t\} = P\{-\sqrt{t} \leq x \leq \sqrt{t}\}$$

But

$$P\{-\sqrt{t} \leq x \leq \sqrt{t}\} = \frac{1}{\sqrt{2\pi}} \int_{-\sqrt{t}}^{\sqrt{t}} e^{-\frac{x^2}{2}} dx = \frac{2}{\sqrt{2\pi}} \int_{0}^{\sqrt{t}} e^{-\frac{x^2}{2}} dx$$

Since this integration cannot be performed, it is necessary to differentiate at this stage. Thus, using the same calculus formulas as before,

$$\frac{dG(t)}{dt} = \frac{2}{\sqrt{2\pi}} e^{-\frac{t}{2}} \frac{d\sqrt{t}}{dt} = \frac{t^{-\frac{1}{2}} e^{-\frac{t}{2}}}{\sqrt{2\pi}}$$

The desired frequency function is now obtained by replacing t by y. Thus

$$(43) \qquad\qquad g(y) = \frac{y^{-\frac{1}{2}} e^{-\frac{y}{2}}}{\sqrt{2\pi}}, \quad y \geq 0$$

This function defines what is known as the chi-square distribution with one degree of freedom because it is a special case of a more general chi-square distribution. The more general frequency function depends on a parameter, called the number of degrees of freedom, and (43) is obtained by setting the parameter equal to 1. The preceding result can be stated by saying that the square of a standard normal variable possesses a chi-square distribution with one degree of freedom. This result is used on a number of occasions in later chapters.

REFERENCES

Additional material on the moment generating function may be found in A. E. Aitken, *Statistical Mathematics*, Oliver and Boyd.

The two theorems concerning the relationship between moment generating functions and frequency functions that were needed in deriving the normal approximation to the binomial distribution require additional mathematical training for their complete understanding; however, they are available in E. Parzen, *Modern Probability Theory and Its Applications*, John Wiley and Sons.

Discussions of other frequency functions often used as mathematical models may be found in the preceding reference.

A number of other interesting applications of the binomial and Poisson distributions may be found in W. Feller, *An Introduction to Probability Theory and Its Applications*, John Wiley and Sons.

For binomial problems in which n is sufficiently large to yield a good normal or Poisson approximation much computational labor may be saved by using tables giving sums of binomial probabilities. Such tabulated sums are available in the National Bureau of Standards, AMS 6, *Tables of the Binomial Probability Distribution*. Tables for sums of Poisson probabilities are available in E. C. Molina, *Poisson's Exponential Binomial Limit*, D. Van Nostrand Co.

EXERCISES

1. Calculate the mean and variance for x, the face number that comes up when rolling an honest die.

2. A die is loaded so that the probability of a given face turning up is proportional to the number on that face. Calculate the mean and variance for x, the face number showing.

3. Calculate the mean for x, the sum of the face numbers that come up when rolling 2 honest dice.

4. Calculate the mean for the distribution given in Table 2, Chapter 2, for the 2 altered dice.

5. A random variable can assume only the values 2 and 3. If its mean is $\frac{8}{3}$, find the probabilities for those 2 points.

6. A and B match pennies. Calculate the mean and variance of x, where x is the amount won by A after 2 matchings.

7. In problem 6 calculate the mean and variance if A quits after the first matching, provided he wins it, but B does not employ this strategy. What does this result say concerning A's strategy?

8. A coin is tossed until a head appears. If a head appears on the first toss, the player receives \$2 from the bank. If it appears for the first time on the second toss, he receives \$4. In general, if it appears first on toss number k, he receives 2^k dollars. If his payment exceeds \$1,000,000, he receives only \$1,000,000. Calculate the mean amount to be won by the player of this game. What effect would placing no limit on the amount to be won have on the mean?

9. If an urn contains 10 white and 5 black balls and 3 balls are drawn without replacement, what is the mean number of black balls that will be obtained? Calculate the mean by using definition (1) of the text, where x denotes the number of black balls obtained.

10. Given $f(x) = (\frac{1}{2})^x$, $x = 1, 2, 3, \cdots$, and zero elsewhere, find its moment generating function. Use it to calculate the mean and variance of x.

11. Eight dice are rolled. Calling a 5 or 6 a success, find the probability of getting (*a*) 3 successes, (*b*) at most 3 successes.

12. Suppose a sample of 10 is taken from a day's output of a machine that normally produces 5 per cent defective parts. If the day's production is inspected 100 per cent whenever the sample of 10 gives 2 or more defectives, what is the probability that a day's production will be inspected 100 per cent?

13. Suppose that weather records show that on the average 3 of the 30 days in November are rainy days. (*a*) Assuming a binomial distribution with each day of November as an independent trial, find the probability that next November will have at most 2 rainy days. (*b*) Give reasons why you may not be justified in using the binomial distribution in solving (*a*).

14. In calculating binomial probabilities, it is convenient to calculate $f(x + 1)$ from $f(x)$ by the formula $f(x + 1) = k(x)f(x)$, where $k(x) = \dfrac{n - x}{x + 1}\dfrac{p}{q}$. Show that this formula is correct.

15. If x has the frequency function $f(x) = x/2$, $0 \le x \le 2$, calculate the probability that (*a*) both of 2 sample values will exceed 1 and (*b*) exactly 2 of 4 sample values will exceed 1.

16. If x has the frequency function $f(x) = 1$, $0 \le x \le 1$, (*a*) what is the probability that at least 2 of 3 sample values will exceed .6? (*b*) What value of x is such that the probability is $\frac{1}{2}$ that at least 2 of 3 sample values will exceed it?

17. Given that a binomial variable has mean 12 and variance 8, find p and n.

18. Experience shows that 10 per cent of the individuals reserving tables at a night club will not appear. If the night club has 50 tables and takes 53 reservations, what is the probability that it will be able to accommodate everyone appearing?

19. In the world series for baseball, the series is concluded when 1 team has won 4 games. Let p be the probability of team A winning a single game and assume that this probability remains constant in the series. Show that the probabilities of the series ending in 4, 5, 6, or 7 games are .125, .25, .3125, and .3125, respectively, when $p = \frac{1}{2}$, and .21, .30, .27, and .22, respectively, when $p = \frac{2}{3}$.

20. Use the Poisson approximation to calculate the probability of getting 9 successes in 1000 trials of an experiment for which $p = .01$.

21. Use the Poisson approximation to calculate the probability that at most 1 person in 500 will have a birthday on Christmas. Assume 365 days in the year.

22. Assume that the number of particles emitted from a radioactive source follows a Poisson distribution with an average emission of 1 particle per second. (*a*) Find the probability that at most 1 particle will be emitted in 3 seconds. (*b*) How low an emission rate would be necessary before the probability of getting at most 1 emission in 3 seconds would be at least .80?

23. Assume that the number of items of a certain kind purchased in a store during a week's time follows a Poisson distribution with $\mu = 100$. How large a stock should the merchant have on hand to yield a probability of .99 that he will be able to supply the demand?

24. Suppose the number of telephone calls an operator receives from 9:00 to 9:05 follows a Poisson distribution with $\mu = 3$. (*a*) Find the probability that the operator will receive no calls in that time interval tomorrow. (*b*) Find the probability that in the next 3 days the operator will receive a total of 1 call in that time interval.

25. Solve problem 13, using the Poisson approximation to the binomial distribution and compare answers to see how good the approximation is.

26. Assume that customers enter a store at the rate of 120 persons per hour. (a) What is the probability that during a 2-minute interval no one will enter the store? (b) What time interval is such that the probability is $\frac{1}{2}$ that no one will enter the store during that interval?

27. (a) Given that x possesses a Poisson distribution with mean μ, show that the moment generating function of x is given by $M_x(\theta) = e^{\mu(e^\theta - 1)}$. (b) By differentiating $M_x(\theta)$, verify that the mean is μ and show that the variance is also equal to μ.

28. Show that the Poisson probabilities increase and then decrease unless $\mu \leq 1$. Determine what value of x (function of μ) has maximum probability. Consider the ratio of neighboring probabilities.

29. What is the probability that one will arrive at a red signal at an intersection if one's time of arrival is by chance and the signal alternates from 20 seconds of green to 40 seconds of red?

30. Two students agree to meet at a restaurant between 6 and 7 P.M. Find the probability that they will meet if each agrees to wait 10 minutes for the other and they arrive independently at random times between 6 and 7.

31. Three points are chosen by chance on the circumference of a circle. What is the probability that they will all lie on a semicircle?

32. Let t denote the life of a radio tube in hours with frequency function $f(t) = ae^{-at}$, $t \geq 0$. If $a = \frac{1}{100}$, for how many hours of life should the manufacturer guarantee his tubes if he wants the probability to be .90 that a tube will satisfy the guarantee?

33. A random variable has the frequency function $f(x) = a + bx^2, 0 \leq x \leq 1$. Determine a and b so that its mean will be $\frac{2}{3}$.

34. If $f(x) = 1$, $0 \leq x \leq 1$, find (a) the mean and variance of x and (b) the mean and variance of x^2.

35. Given that $f(x) = cx$, $0 \leq x \leq 1$, find (a) c, (b) μ_k' by integration, (c) $M_x(\theta)$, (d) μ_k' from $M_x(\theta)$.

36. Given that $f(x) = ce^{-x}$, $x \geq 0$, find (a) c, (b) $M_x(\theta)$, (c) μ_k' from $M_x(\theta)$.

37. Given that $f(x) = cx^\alpha e^{-x}$, $x \geq 0$, α a positive integer, find (a) c, using the fact that $\int_0^\infty x^\alpha e^{-x}\, dx = \alpha!$ for α a positive integer, (b) μ_k' from definition, (c) $M_x(\theta)$, (d) μ_k' from $M_x(\theta)$.

38. Assume that the length of telephone conversations x has the frequency function $f(x) = ae^{-ax}$. Show that the probability of a conversation lasting more than $t_1 + t_2$ minutes, given that it has already lasted at least t_1 minutes, is equal to the unconditional probability that it will last more than t_2 minutes.

39. Find the moment generating function for the triangular distribution whose frequency function is given by $f(x) = x$, $0 \leq x \leq 1$, $f(x) = 2 - x$, $1 < x \leq 2$.

40. If x is normally distributed with $\mu = 1$ and $\sigma = \frac{1}{2}$, find (a) $P\{x > 2\}$ and (b) $P\{0 < x < 1\}$.

41. If x is normally distributed with $\mu = 1$ and $\sigma = 2$, find a number x_0 such that (a) $P\{x > x_0\} = .10$ and (b) $P\{x > -x_0\} = .20$.

42. Assume that the life in hours of a radio tube is normally distributed with mean 200 hours. If a purchaser requires at least 90 per cent of them to have lives exceeding 150 hours, what is the largest value that σ can have and still have the purchaser satisfied?

43. Assume that height of adult males is normally distributed with $\mu = 69$ inches and $\sigma = 3$ inches. What is the conditional probability that an individual will be taller than 72 inches if it is known that he is taller than 70 inches?

44. Fit a normal curve to the histogram for the data of problem 3, Chapter 4.

45. Find μ_k for the normal distribution by using the integral definition and repeated integration by parts.

46. A coin is tossed 12 times. Find the probability, both exactly and by the normal curve approximation, of getting (a) 4 heads and (b) at most 4 heads.

47. A die is tossed 12 times. Counting a 5 or 6 as a success, what is the probability, using the normal curve approximation, of getting (a) 4 successes and (b) at most 4 successes?

48. Given $p = .4$ and $n = 1350$ for the binomial variable x, use the normal approximation to calculate (a) $P\{510 \leq x \leq 560\}$, (b) $P\{x < 580\}$.

49. A die is tossed 90 times. Find the probability of getting 15 aces (a) using the binomial formula and tables of factorials and (b) using the normal curve approximation.

50. Find a number x_0 such that the probability of getting a number of heads between $500 - x_0$ and $500 + x_0$, inclusive, in 1000 tosses of a coin is .90.

51. A coin is tossed 400 times. Would 215 heads be considered a reasonable result?

52. Experience shows that 20 per cent of a certain kind of seed germinates. If 50 of 400 seeds germinated, would you reject the hypothesis that $p = .20$?

53. About 9 per cent of the population of the country is between 20 and 24 years of age. A city of 12,000 has 1300 in this age group. Test to see if this city is typical with respect to this age group.

54. A manufacturer has found from experience that 3 per cent of his product is rejected because of flaws. A new lot of 800 units comes up for inspection. (a) How many units would reasonably be expected to be rejected? (b) What is the approximate probability that less than 30 units will be rejected?

55. A manufacturer of cotter pins knows that 5 per cent of his product is defective. If he sells cotter pins in boxes of 100 and guarantees that not more than 10 pins will be defective, what is the approximate probability that a box will fail to meet the guaranteed quality?

56. Suppose that you wish to construct a control chart for the proportion p' of words incorrectly typed by a stenographer per hour. If she typed 1200 words an hour, on the average, for 6 hours a day, for 10 days, and she mistyped 360 words in that total period of time, what 2 numbers would you use for boundaries for the control chart?

57. In the manufacturing of parts, the following data were obtained for the daily percentage defective for a production averaging 1000 parts a day. Construct a control chart and indicate times when production was out of control.

The data are to be read a row at a time.

2.2	2.3	2.1	1.7	3.8	2.5	2.0	1.6	1.4	2.6
1.5	2.8	2.9	2.6	2.5	2.6	3.2	4.6	3.3	3.0
3.1	4.3	1.8	2.6	2.1	2.2	1.8	2.4	2.4	1.6
1.7	1.6	2.8	3.2	1.8	2.6	3.6	4.2		

58. A sample is to be taken in a city to estimate the percentage of families willing to pay 200 dollars for a home freezer. It is desired to have, with a probability of .95, an estimate correct to within $2\frac{1}{2}$ per cent absolute. Tentatively, it is estimated that the true percentage is near 20 per cent. How large a sample will be required?

59. If you wished to estimate the proportion of Republicans in a certain district and wanted your estimate to be correct within .02 unit with a probability of .90, how large a sample should you take (a) if you know that the true proportion is near .4, (b) if you have no idea what the true proportion is?

60. (a) If you rolled a die 240 times and obtained 50 sixes, would you decide the die was biased in favor of sixes? (b) If you repeated the experiment and obtained 48 sixes, would you conclude that the second experiment justified your decision in (a) or would you conclude differently?

61. Assume that telephone calls coming into a switchboard follow a Poisson distribution at the rate of 15 calls per minute. If the switchboard can handle at most 25 calls per minute, what is the probability that in one minute the switchboard will be overloaded? Use a normal approximation in your calculations based on the results of problem 27.

62. Assuming that the number of white blood cells per unit of volume of diluted blood counted under a microscope follows a Poisson distribution with $\mu = 121$, what is the probability, using a normal approximation, that a count of 100 or less will be observed? Use the results of problem 27.

63. If the number of telephone calls coming in to a given switchboard during a period of a minute follows a Poisson distribution with $\mu = 10$ and the switchboard can handle at most 20 calls per minute, (a) what is the probability, using a normal approximation, that during the next minute the switchboard will be overtaxed? (b) What is the approximate probability that it will not be overtaxed during an hour's service if the numbers of calls in consecutive minutes are assumed to be independently distributed?

64. For $n = 12$ and $p = \frac{1}{4}$, plot on the same piece of graph paper (a) the binomial histogram, (b) the Poisson histogram, and (c) the fitted normal curve by ordinates. Note the extent to which (b) and (c) approximate the binomial.

65. A source of liquid is known to contain bacteria with the mean number of bacteria per cubic centimeter equal to 3. Ten 1-cubic centimeter test tubes are filled with the liquid. Assuming the Poisson distribution is applicable, calculate the probability (a) that all 10 test tubes will show growth, that is, contain at least 1 bacterium each and (b) that exactly 7 test tubes will show growth.

66. If $f(x) = cxe^{-\frac{x^2}{2}}$, $x \geq 0$, find (a) c, (b) the mean of x, and (c) the variance of x.

67. In firing at a target assume that the horizontal distance a shot hits from the center line is normally distributed with $\sigma = 2$ feet. (a) In 200 shots how many would be expected to miss the target if it is 10 feet wide and sufficiently high? (b) How many shots would you need to fire to be certain with a probability of .95 of getting 50 or more shots within 3 feet of the centerline?

68. Fit a Poisson function to the following "famous" data on the number of deaths from the kick of a horse per army corps per year, for 10 Prussian Army Corps for 20 years. The total number of units here, an army-corps year, is 200.

x	0	1	2	3	4
f	109	65	22	3	1

69. Fit a binomial function to the following data on the number of seeds germinating among 10 seeds on damp filter paper for 80 sets of seeds.

x	0	1	2	3	4	5	6	7	8	9	10
f	6	20	28	12	8	6	0	0	0	0	0

70. A sample of 2 is taken from a box of 10 articles. If 4 of the articles are defective, what is the probability of getting no defectives in the sample?

71. In considering a lot of 100 items, a purchaser agrees to buy if a sample of 10 shows at most 1 defective. If the lot actually contains 10 per cent defectives, what is the probability that the purchase will be made? Compare your result with that based on a binomial approximation.

72. A box contains 100 items of which 5 are defective. Let x denote the number of defectives found in a sample of 10. (a) Calculate the probability that $x = 2$. (b) Use the binomial approximation to make the calculation. (c) Use the Poisson approximation to make the calculation.

73. A bag contains 2 red, 3 green, and 4 black balls. If 4 balls are drawn in succession with replacement each time, what is the probability of getting 1 red, 1 green, and 2 black balls?

74. Work problem 73 if there are no replacements of the drawn balls.

75. Calculate the probability of getting a total of 6 if 3 dice are thrown simultaneously.

76. A game of chance consists in tossing a ball into boxes numbered 1, 2, 3, and 4. If the probabilities for landing in these boxes are $\frac{12}{25}$, $\frac{6}{25}$, $\frac{4}{25}$, and $\frac{3}{25}$, respectively, and one receives in dollars the number on the box, what is the probability of winning at least 5 dollars when taking 2 tosses?

77. What is the probability in 12 rolls of a die that each side will come up twice? Show that no other possible result has a higher probability of occurring.

78. Given $f(x) = e^{-x}$, $x \geq 0$, find, by the change of variable technique, the frequency function of the variable (a) $y = 1/x$ and (b) $y = \log_e x$.

79. Given $f(x) = xe^{-\frac{x^2}{2}}$, $x \geq 0$, find the frequency function of the variable (a) $y = x + 1$, (b) $y = x^2$, (c) $y = \log_e x$.

80. Given that θ is uniformly distributed over the interval $-\pi/2$ to $\pi/2$, find the frequency function of $z = A \sin \theta$, where A is a constant.

81. Let x be a standard normal variable. Find the frequency function of (a) $2x + 1$, (b) $2x^2 + 1$.

82. Given that x is uniformly distributed over the interval -1 to 1, find the frequency function of (a) x^2, (b) $-\log_e |x|$.

83. Given $f(x) = 2(1 - x)$, $0 \le x \le 1$, find the distribution of $z = x^2$.

84. Given that x has the continuous distribution function $F(x)$, find expressions for the distribution functions of the variables (a) $y = e^x$, (b) $y = \log x$, (c) $y = F(x)$.

85. A variable x is said to have a log-normal distribution if $y = \log_e x$ is normally distributed. Given that the mean and variance of y are 0 and 1, respectively, find the frequency function of x.

86. Show that the Cauchy distribution given by (9), Chapter 4, does not possess a mean.

87. Show that the mean of the hypergeometric distribution is $\mu = np$ by employing the relation $\binom{Np}{x} = \frac{Np}{x}\binom{Np - 1}{x - 1}$.

88. An experiment is to be conducted 100 times to determine whether a possible outcome has probability $p = .4$ or $p > .4$. If x denotes the number of outcomes and if $x \ge 48$ is chosen as the critical region for testing H_0: $p = .4$, find an expression for the power function of the test.

89. In problem 88 use the normal approximation to find an expression for the power function.

90. A box containing 100 items has an unknown but small proportion p of defectives. If x denotes the number of defectives in a sample of 10 and one is interested in testing the hypothesis H_0: $p = \frac{1}{20}$ against $p < \frac{1}{20}$ by using $x \le 2$ as a critical region, find an expression for the power function of the test.

91. Assume that the number of persons per minute buying ferry tickets is 10. Find an expression for the probability that at least t minutes will elapse before 50 tickets will be sold.

CHAPTER 6

Elementary Sampling Theory for One Variable

In Chapter 5 a beginning was made in testing hypotheses and estimating parameters; however, the problems considered there were mostly concerned with the binomial distribution. In the present chapter this beginning is extended to other distributions, particularly to continuous distributions. Only a few of the simpler problems are considered here; the more complicated problems will be studied in Chapter 11.

6.1 Random Sampling

In the applications of the binomial distribution in the preceding chapter it was pointed out that the binomial model is strictly valid only if the trials of the experiment are independent and p is constant from trial to trial. In the language of sampling, this means that samples must be obtained by a method that possesses these two properties.

The theory that is about to be developed for continuous variables is based on assumptions very similar to those used to derive the binomial distribution. The first assumption is that the successive trials of the experiment are independent and the second is that the frequency function of the random variable remains the same from trial to trial. If the theory is to be applicable to real experimental data, it is necessary that the data be obtained by a sampling method that possesses these two properties. In order to express these properties in a mathematical form, consider the following notation and procedure.

Let $f(x)$ be the frequency function of the continuous random variable x and let a sample of size n be drawn. The resulting sample values are denoted by $x_1', x_2', \cdots, x_n'$. If a second sample of size n were drawn, the resulting sample values would be denoted by $x_1'', x_2'', \cdots, x_n''$, and similarly for additional samples. These values are conveniently arranged as follows:

$$x_1', \quad x_2', \quad \cdots, \quad x_n'$$
$$x_1'', \quad x_2'', \quad \cdots, \quad x_n''$$
$$x_1''', \quad x_2''', \quad \cdots, \quad x_n'''$$
$$\cdot \quad \quad \cdot \quad \quad \quad \cdot$$
$$\cdot \quad \quad \cdot \quad \quad \quad \cdot$$
$$\cdot \quad \quad \cdot \quad \quad \quad \cdot$$

Now consider the values in the first column. These values may be treated as the values of a random variable x_1 with a frequency function $f_1(x_1)$. In the same manner the values in the second column may be treated as the values of a random variable x_2 with frequency function $f_2(x_2)$ and similarly for the remaining columns.

In this notation the requirement that the frequency function of the random variable x shall remain constant from trial to trial means that the random variables $x_1, x_2, \cdots, x_n$ must possess the original frequency function, that is, that

$$f_1(x) = f_2(x) = \cdots = f_n(x) = f(x)$$

In this same notation the requirement that the trials shall be independent means that the variables $x_1, x_2, \cdots, x_n$ must be independent. A method of sampling that possesses these two properties is called *random sampling*. In view of formula (24), Chapter 2, and the preceding discussion, random sampling may be defined mathematically in the following manner.

(1)   DEFINITION: *Random sampling is a method of sampling for which*

$$f(x_1, x_2, \cdots, x_n) = f(x_1)f(x_2) \cdots f(x_n)$$

where $f(x)$ is the frequency function of the population being sampled and where $x_1, x_2, \cdots, x_n$ are random variables corresponding to the n trials of the sample.

Although the variable x in the preceding discussion was treated as a continuous variable, definition (1) applies to both continuous and discrete variables.

As an illustration of a continuous random variable for which the sampling method approximates random sampling, let x be the distance the end of a spinning pointer is from the 0 point, as measured along the circumference, after it comes to rest. Figure 1 indicates the nature of this variable. If a sample of size 5 were desired, the pointer would be spun five times and the distances recorded. Now, if a pointer is spun repeatedly.

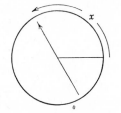

Fig. 1. A game of chance.

and the resulting values of x are marked off into consecutive sets of five, it will usually be found that the empirical distributions of the variables $x_1, \cdots, x_5$ will approach the rectangular distribution $f(x) = 1/c$, where c is the circumference. It will also be found that tests of independence, which will be studied later, usually substantiate independence of trials here.

It should be noted that definition (1) defines a method of sampling and says nothing about particular samples. It is legitimate to call a sample a random sample only if it has been obtained by a random sampling method.

It is frequently not feasible to check many real life sampling methods for randomness because of the expense or difficulty of obtaining enough data to test the properties in definition (1). Then one must rely on judgment and experience to determine whether the method is sufficiently random to permit the use of models derived on the basis of random sampling.

6.2   Moments of Multivariate Distributions

Since random sampling involves the frequency function $f(x_1, x_2, \cdots, x_n)$, it is necessary to study properties of this function. In particular, it is necessary to define moments and the moment generating function for multivariate functions. The moment notation that was introduced in Chapter 5 becomes quite cumbersome when it is applied to multivariate situations. Furthermore, it lacks flexibility in deriving formulas; consequently, a new type of notation involving an expected value symbol E is introduced here. This notation is presented first for a single random variable in order to show its relationship to earlier material, after which it is generalized to multivariate functions.

If the continuous random variable x has the frequency function $f(x)$, its *expected value* $E[x]$ is defined as

$$(2) \qquad E[x] = \int_{-\infty}^{\infty} x f(x) \, dx$$

Thus the expected value of a random variable is its mean value. More generally, if $h(x)$ is any function of x, the expected value of $h(x)$ is defined as

$$(3) \qquad E[h(x)] = \int_{-\infty}^{\infty} h(x) f(x) \, dx$$

Moments and moment generating functions, as defined in Chapter 5, can be expressed as expected values. For example, the kth moment of x is obtained from (3) by choosing $h(x) = x^k$ and therefore is given by

$$E[x^k] = \int_{-\infty}^{\infty} x^k f(x) \, dx$$

Similarly, the moment generating function of x is given by

$$E[e^{\theta x}] = \int_{-\infty}^{\infty} e^{\theta x} f(x) \, dx$$

Corresponding expressions that are valid for a discrete random variable can be obtained by merely replacing the preceding integrals by sums.

Since the expected value symbol E was designed to produce mean values, the question naturally arises whether the expected value of a function of x, say $h(x)$, as given by (3), is really the mean value of that function. To show that this is so, first let $y = h(x)$ in order to simplify the notation. Since y is a random variable with a frequency function, say $g(y)$, it follows from (2) that its mean value is certainly given by the integral

$$(4) \qquad E[y] = \int_{-\infty}^{\infty} y \, g(y) \, dy$$

Now if $h(x)$ is an increasing function of x, the change of variable technique given in (42), Chapter 5, may be employed to yield the relation

$$g(y) \, dy = f(x) \, dx$$

As a consequence, (4) may be written in the form

$$E[y] = \int_{-\infty}^{\infty} y \, f(x) \, dx$$

Since $y = h(x)$, this result is equivalent to (3). Although the equivalence of (3) and (4) was shown for $h(x)$ an increasing function, the equivalence holds quite generally. The advantage of evaluating the integral given in (3) rather than in (4) to find the mean value of $h(x)$ lies in the fact that (3) does not require one first to find the frequency function of $h(x)$. When $h(x)$ is not an increasing, or decreasing, function of x, this may require considerable effort.

Now consider the generalization of these definitions to multivariate functions. In this connection let $g(x_1, x_2, \cdots, x_n)$ be any function of the random variables $x_1, x_2, \cdots, x_n$ whose frequency function is $f(x_1, x_2, \cdots, x_n)$. Then the *expected value* of $g(x_1, x_2, \cdots, x_n)$ is defined by

$$(5) \quad E[g] = \int_{-\infty}^{\infty} \cdots \int_{-\infty}^{\infty} g(x_1, x_2, \cdots, x_n) f(x_1, x_2, \cdots, x_n) \, dx_1 \, dx_2 \cdots dx_n$$

The variables of which g is a function have been omitted on the left side for notational convenience. Just as for one variable, it is possible to demonstrate that the value given by (5) is the mean value of g and therefore is the same as that obtained by finding the frequency function of g and applying the elementary definition (2) to the random variable g.

The particular quantities that are needed in this chapter are the kth moment of $g(x_1, x_2, \cdots, x_n)$ and the moment generating function of $g(x_1, x_2, \cdots, x_n)$. In terms of expected values, the kth moment of $g(x_1, x_2, \cdots, x_n)$ is defined as

$$(6) \quad E[g^k] = \int_{-\infty}^{\infty} \cdots \int_{-\infty}^{\infty} g^k(x_1, x_2, \cdots, x_n) f(x_1, x_2, \cdots, x_n) \, dx_1 \, dx_2 \cdots dx_n$$

Corresponding to this definition, the moment generating function of $g(x_1, x_2, \cdots, x_n)$ is defined as

(7)

$$M_g(\theta) = E[e^{\theta g}] = \int_{-\infty}^{\infty} \cdots \int_{-\infty}^{\infty} e^{\theta g(x_1, x_2, \cdots, x_n)} f(x_1, x_2, \cdots, x_n) \, dx_1 \, dx_2 \cdots dx_n$$

That (7) generates moments in the same manner as (21), Chapter 5, is easily verified by expanding $e^{\theta g}$ and integrating term by term.

Since expected value methods are used to assist in the development of the theory in this chapter, three of the most useful properties of the expected value symbol E are derived next.

6.3   Properties of E

If c is any constant, it follows directly from (5), after factoring out c from the integral on the right side, that

$$(8) \qquad\qquad E[cg] = cE[g]$$

Next, since the integral of a sum is equal to the sum of the integrals, it follows from (5) that

$$(9) \qquad\qquad E[g_1 + g_2] = E[g_1] + E[g_2]$$

where g_1 and g_2 are any two functions of a set of random variables.

Finally, if g_1 and g_2 are independently distributed, which means that their joint frequency function can be factored into the product of the two individual frequency functions, one can write

$$(10) \qquad E[g_1 g_2] = \int_{-\infty}^{\infty} \int_{-\infty}^{\infty} g_1 g_2 f_1(g_1) f_2(g_2)\, dg_1\, dg_2$$

Here f_1 and f_2 are the frequency functions of the random variables g_1 and g_2, respectively. The formulation in (10) is in terms of the random variables g_1 and g_2 themselves and not in terms of the basic random variables $x_1, x_2, \cdots, x_n$ as in (5). But the double integral in (10) can be written in the product form

$$\int_{-\infty}^{\infty} g_1 f_1(g_1)\, dg_1 \int_{-\infty}^{\infty} g_2 f_2(g_2)\, dg_2$$

Since this is the product of the individual expected values, it follows that when g_1 and g_2 are independently distributed

$$(11) \qquad E[g_1 g_2] = E[g_1]\, E[g_2]$$

It should be noted that the expected value of a sum of random variables is equal to the sum of their expected values, whether or not the variables are independently distributed, whereas the expected value of a product need not be equal to the product of the expected values unless the variables are independently distributed.

As an illustration of expected value techniques, which at the same time will illustrate how useful such methods are, consider the problem of finding the mean and variance of a sum of independent variables.

Let $x_1, x_2, \cdots, x_n$ be a set of independent variables with means $\mu_1, \mu_2, \cdots, \mu_n$ and variances $\sigma_1^2, \sigma_2^2, \cdots, \sigma_n^2$ and let

$$z = x_1 + x_2 + \cdots + x_n$$

From formula (9) it follows that

$$(12) \qquad \mu_z = E[z] = \sum_{i=1}^{n} E[x_i] = \sum_{i=1}^{n} \mu_i$$

Next, write

$$z - \mu_z = (x_1 - \mu_1) + (x_2 - \mu_2) + \cdots + (x_n - \mu_n)$$

Then

$$(z - \mu_z)^2 = \sum_{i=1}^{n} \sum_{j=1}^{n} (x_i - \mu_i)(x_j - \mu_j)$$

Application of formula (9) will give

$$(13) \qquad E(z - \mu_z)^2 = \sum_{i=1}^{n} \sum_{j=1}^{n} E(x_i - \mu_i)(x_j - \mu_j)$$

The bracket notation for expected values is usually omitted, as it is here, when it becomes cumbersome and no confusion results from doing so. Now, since the variables x_i and x_j are independent random variables when $i \neq j$, formula (11) may be applied to give

$$E(x_i - \mu_i)(x_j - \mu_j) = E(x_i - \mu_i)E(x_j - \mu_j), \qquad i \neq j$$

But $E(x_i - \mu_i) = 0$; therefore (13) reduces to

$$E(z - \mu_z)^2 = \sum_{i=1}^{n} E(x_i - \mu_i)^2$$

Since $E(x_i - \mu_i)^2 = \sigma_i^2$, this result can be expressed as

$$(14) \qquad \sigma_z^2 = \sum_{i=1}^{n} \sigma_i^2$$

Formula (12) states that the mean of a sum of random variables is equal to the sum of the means of the variables. The derivation of that formula did not require the independence of the variables; therefore, as stated before, the formula holds regardless of this assumption. Formula (14) states that the variance of a sum of independent random variables is equal to the sum of the variances of the variables.

As a particular application of these two formulas, consider the problem of finding the mean and variance of a binomial variable. This problem was solved in 5.2.3.2 by a direct application of moment definitions.

Let $x_1, x_2, \cdots, x_n$ be binomial variables corresponding to n independent trials of an experiment for which p is the probability of success in a single trial. Thus $x_i = 1$ if a success occurs and $x_i = 0$ if a failure occurs on the ith trial. Next, let

$$z = x_1 + x_2 + \cdots + x_n$$

In view of the definition of x_i, it follows that z is equal to the total number of successes in the n trials of the experiment; consequently, the problem is to find the mean and variance of z.

For discrete variables definition (2) must be replaced by

$$E[x] = \sum_{x=0}^{\infty} x f(x)$$

Since the variable x_i can assume the values 0 and 1 only with probabilities q and p, respectively, it follows from this last formula that

$$E[x_i] = 0 \cdot q + 1 \cdot p = p$$

This result, when applied to (12) gives

$$\mu_z = np$$

The technique used to calculate $E[x_i]$ may be applied to obtain the value of $E(x_i - \mu_i)^2 = E(x_i - p)^2$. Thus

$$\sigma_i^2 = E(x_i - \mu_i)^2 = (0 - p)^2 \cdot q + (1 - p)^2 \cdot p = pq$$

As a result, formula (14) gives

$$\sigma_z^2 = npq$$

These two results, of course, agree with formulas (12), Chapter 5.

6.4   Sum of Independent Variables

A very useful formula for developing theory about sample means can be obtained when the variables $x_1, x_2, \cdots, x_n$ are independent and when $g(x_1, x_2, \cdots, x_n)$ is the special linear function

$$g(x_1, x_2, \cdots, x_n) = x_1 + x_2 + \cdots + x_n$$

The moment generating function of this sum is

$$M_{x_1 + \cdots + x_n}(\theta) = E[e^{\theta(x_1 + \cdots + x_n)}]$$
$$= E[e^{\theta x_1} \cdot e^{\theta x_2} \cdots e^{\theta x_n}]$$

But because of the independence of these exponential functions, it follows from (11) that

$$M_{x_1 + \cdots + x_n}(\theta) = E[e^{\theta x_1}] \cdot E[e^{\theta x_2}] \cdots E[e^{\theta x_n}]$$
$$= M_{x_1}(\theta) \, M_{x_2}(\theta) \cdots M_{x_n}(\theta)$$

Since this result is used so often, it is stated in the form of a theorem.

THEOREM 1: *The moment generating function of the sum of n independent variables is equal to the product of the moment generating functions of the individual variables, that is,*

$$M_{x_1 + \cdots + x_n}(\theta) = M_{x_1}(\theta) M_{x_2}(\theta) \cdots M_{x_n}(\theta)$$

6.5   Distribution of $\bar{x}$ from a Normal Distribution

In this section the distribution of a sample mean based on a random sample of size n from a normal population is derived.

Let x be normally distributed with mean μ and standard deviation σ. Consider a random sample of size n from this normal population. The mean of such a sample,

$$\bar{x} = \frac{1}{n}(x_1 + x_2 + \cdots + x_n)$$

will be a random variable because the variables $x_1, x_2, \cdots, x_n$ corresponding to the n trials of the sample are random variables. After a particular random sample has been taken, $\bar{x}$ will be a number, but before it has been drawn, it will be a random variable capable of assuming any value that the original variable x can assume. For the purpose of finding the frequency function of $\bar{x}$, consider its moment generating function.

If the first formula given in (22), Chapter 5, is used, it will follow that

$$M_{\bar{x}}(\theta) = M_{\frac{1}{n}(x_1 + \cdots + x_n)}(\theta) = M_{x_1 + \cdots + x_n}\left(\frac{\theta}{n}\right)$$

Since the sampling is random, the variables $x_1, x_2, \cdots, x_n$ are independent, and therefore Theorem 1 may be applied to give

$$M_{\bar{x}}(\theta) = M_{x_1}\left(\frac{\theta}{n}\right) M_{x_2}\left(\frac{\theta}{n}\right) \cdots M_{x_n}\left(\frac{\theta}{n}\right)$$

But random sampling as given by definition (1) also implies that all the variables $x_1, x_2, \cdots, x_n$ have the same frequency function, namely that of x, hence the same moment generating function. Consequently, all the M's on the right are the same function, namely, the moment generating function of the variable x. Thus

(15) $$M_{\bar{x}}(\theta) = M_x{}^n\left(\frac{\theta}{n}\right)$$

Now, from formula (28), Chapter 5, it is known that if x is normally distributed

(16) $$M_x(\theta) = e^{\mu\theta + \frac{1}{2}\theta^2\sigma^2}$$

If this result, with θ replaced by θ/n, is used in (15), that formula will reduce to

$$M_{\bar{x}}(\theta) = \left[e^{\mu\frac{\theta}{n} + \frac{1}{2}\left(\frac{\theta}{n}\right)^2\sigma^2}\right]^n = e^{\mu\theta + \frac{1}{2}\theta^2\frac{\sigma^2}{n}}$$

Since the function on the right, when compared with (16), is seen to be the moment generating function of a normal variable with mean μ and standard deviation $\sigma/\sqrt{n}$ and since a moment generating function uniquely determines a frequency function, this result proves the following theorem.

THEOREM 2: *If x is normally distributed with mean μ and standard deviation σ and a random sample of size n is drawn, then the sample mean $\bar{x}$ will be normally distributed with mean μ and standard deviation $\sigma/\sqrt{n}$.*

This theorem shows how the precision of a sample mean for estimating the population mean increases as the sample size is increased. Since

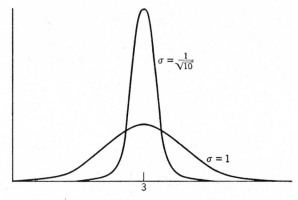

Fig. 2. Normal distributions of x and $\bar{x}$ for $n = 10$.

the standard deviation of $\bar{x}$ measures the variation of sample $\bar{x}$'s about μ and may be treated as a measure of the precision of estimating μ by means of $\bar{x}$, it is clear from the theorem that it is necessary to take four times as large a sample if one wishes to double the precision of an estimate at hand. Figure 2 shows the graph of a normal distribution with $\mu = 3$ and $\sigma = 1$, together with the graph of the distribution of $\bar{x}$ for samples of size 10 drawn from it.

6.5.1   Applications

As an illustration of the application of the theorem, consider the following problem. A manufacturer of string has found from past experience that samples of a certain type of string have a mean breaking strength of 15.6 pounds and a standard deviation of 2.2 pounds. A time-saving change in the manufacturing process of this string is tried. A sample of 50 pieces is then taken, for which the mean breaking strength turns out to be 14.5 pounds. On the basis of this sample can it be concluded that the new process has had a harmful effect on the strength of the string? Now, experience indicates that the breaking strength of string is approximately normally distributed. Hence it will be assumed that the breaking strength x is normally distributed with $\mu = 15.6$ and $\sigma = 2.2$. This problem can be treated as the problem of testing the hypothesis

$$H_0 : \mu = 15.6$$

against the alternative hypothesis

$$H_1 : \mu < 15.6$$

In this form one is testing the hypothesis that no change has occurred in the mean breaking strength against the possibility that the mean has been lowered. If the sample is treated as a random sample of size 50 from the original normal population, then, by Theorem 2, $\bar{x}$ will be normally distributed with

$$\mu_{\bar{x}} = 15.6 \quad \text{and} \quad \sigma_{\bar{x}} = \frac{2.2}{\sqrt{50}} = .31$$

The value of $\bar{x}$ for this one sample of 50 is 14.5; hence the corresponding value of t is

$$t = \frac{\bar{x} - \mu_{\bar{x}}}{\sigma_{\bar{x}}} = \frac{14.5 - 15.6}{.31} = -3.55$$

From Table II the probability of obtaining a value of $t \leq -3.55$, hence a value of $\bar{x} \leq 14.5$, is only about .0002. Since this probability is much smaller than the probability of .05 being used as the size of the critical region for testing hypotheses, the value 14.5 is certainly significant and accordingly the hypothesis is rejected.

By the methods of Chapter 9 it can be shown that the choice of the left tail of the $\bar{x}$ distribution for the critical region is the best possible choice from the point of view of Chapter 3.

In this problem, as with most applied problems, it is necessary to consider the reasonableness of the model being used. The normality assumption is usually difficult to verify, unless one has a large amount of data; however, it will be seen very shortly that little harm usually results from x not being normally distributed. The assumption that the sample of 50 is a random sample from the production process is a more serious assumption, partly because the effect of nonrandomness on the theory is unknown and partly because data obtained from an industrial production line are seldom random. Defective items tend to come in groups because of a poor batch of material or similar causes. If the randomness assumption in the preceding problem is reasonable, then the practical implications of this test are that the mean breaking strength has dropped. Whether the drop is sufficiently great to give concern is outside the scope of the present discussion.

For problems of the type just considered it is rather common in applied statistics to call $\sigma/\sqrt{n}$ the standard error of the mean. The name *standard error* is also used in connection with random variables other than the mean, being always the same as the standard deviation of that random variable. The expression probable error is also fairly common in some circles. It is related to the standard error by means of the approximate formula P.E. = .6745 S.E. For a normal variable x the probability is $\frac{1}{2}$ that x will fall in the interval $\mu \pm$ P.E. Since it is more convenient to work with standard deviations than with probable errors, the use of the probable error is being abandoned.

As another illustration, consider the following problem. Since the mean in the preceding problem was changed by the change in the production process, the question how accurate the sample mean is as an estimate of the new mean arises. As before, assume that x is normally distributed with standard deviation 2.2 but with unknown mean μ. Then $\bar{x}$ will be normally distributed with mean μ and standard deviation .31; consequently, the probability is .95 that $\bar{x}$ will not deviate from μ by more than .62 unit because this deviation corresponds to two standard deviations. Thus one can feel quite certain that the sample mean $\bar{x} = 14.5$ does not differ from the true mean by more than .62 pound.

As a final illustration, consider the problem of determining how large an additional sample will be needed if one wishes to estimate the true mean in the preceding problem to within $\frac{1}{2}$ pound. As in the preceding problem, it is assumed that x is normally distributed and that the standard deviation was not affected by the change in production methods. For a sample of size n, $\bar{x}$ will then be normally distributed with mean μ and standard deviation $2.2/\sqrt{n}$. If, as in the last illustration of 5.3.4.5, one wishes the maximum error to be exceeded only 5 per cent of the time, then it is necessary that the maximum error of $\frac{1}{2}$ correspond to two standard deviations of $\bar{x}$. Therefore n must be such that

$$\frac{1}{2} = 2\sigma_{\bar{x}}$$

This is equivalent to

$$\frac{1}{2} = \frac{2\sigma}{\sqrt{n}} = \frac{2(2.2)}{\sqrt{n}}$$

The solution of this equation to the nearest integer is $n = 77$. Since a sample of size 50 is already available, only 27 additional observations should be necessary.

It should be noted that the population standard deviation was assumed known in these problems. In most problems the population standard deviation is not known. Then the sample estimate of the standard deviation is often used in place of the unknown population value; however, this procedure introduces an error. The error is not serious for large samples, but for small samples a more refined procedure which does not require such approximations is necessary. Such methods will be studied in Chapter 11.

6.6 Distribution of $\bar{x}$ from Non-normal Distributions

Since many variables of interest possess distributions that are not even approximately normal, it is important to know to what extent the theory developed on the basis of assuming normality holds for other distributions. Here it is assumed that x is not normally distributed but does possess a distribution for which the moment generating function exists. Then it is shown that the distribution of $\bar{x}$ approaches a normal distribution as the size of the sample increases.

Just as in the proof that the distribution of a binomial variable approaches that of a normal variable as $n \to \infty$, it is necessary to work with standard variables, that is, variables with zero means and unit variances. It is therefore necessary to find the mean and variance of $\bar{x}$ for non-normal variables before proceeding with the proof. This is done by means of the expected value operator E.

From properties (8) and (9) it follows that

$$E[\bar{x}] = E\left[\frac{1}{n}(x_1 + x_2 + \cdots + x_n)\right] = \frac{1}{n}\sum_{i=1}^{n} E[x_i]$$

But since the sampling is random, $E[x_i] = E[x] = \mu$; consequently,

$$E[\bar{x}] = \frac{1}{n}\sum_{i=1}^{n} \mu = \mu$$

This shows that the mean of $\bar{x}$ is the same as the mean of x, whether x is a normal variable or not.

Since $n\bar{x} = x_1 + x_2 + \cdots + x_n$ is the sum of n independent variables, all of which have the same variance σ^2, it follows from formula (14) that

$$\sigma_{n\bar{x}}^2 = n\sigma^2$$

But the variance of a constant times a variable is equal to the square of the constant times the variance of the variable; therefore

$$\sigma_{n\bar{x}}^2 = n^2\sigma_{\bar{x}}^2$$

Equating these two results yields the formula

$$\sigma_{\bar{x}}^2 = \frac{\sigma^2}{n}$$

This demonstrates that the variance of $\bar{x}$ for x a non-normal variable is the same as for x a normal variable. It is assumed, of course, that the variable x possesses first and second moments.

In view of the preceding results, it follows that the variable $t = (\bar{x} - \mu)\sqrt{n}/\sigma$ is a standard variable. This is the variable whose distribution will be shown to approach that of a standard normal variable; therefore, consider next the moment generating function of this variable. If properties (22), Chapter 5, and formula (15) are applied, it follows that

$$M_t(\theta) = M_{\bar{x} - \mu}\left(\frac{\sqrt{n}\theta}{\sigma}\right)$$

$$= e^{-\frac{\mu\sqrt{n}\theta}{\sigma}} M_{\bar{x}}\left(\frac{\sqrt{n}\theta}{\sigma}\right)$$

$$= e^{-\frac{\mu\sqrt{n}\theta}{\sigma}} M_x^{\,n}\left(\frac{\theta}{\sigma\sqrt{n}}\right)$$

Taking logarithms of both sides to the base e gives

$$\log M_t(\theta) = -\frac{\mu\sqrt{n}\theta}{\sigma} + n \log M_x\left(\frac{\theta}{\sigma\sqrt{n}}\right)$$

After replacing $M_x(\theta/\sigma\sqrt{n})$ by its expanded form, as given by (5), Chapter 5, it follows that

$$\log M_t(\theta) = -\frac{\mu\sqrt{n}\theta}{\sigma} + n \log\left(1 + \mu_1'\frac{\theta}{\sigma\sqrt{n}} + \mu_2'\frac{\theta^2}{2\sigma^2 n} + \cdots\right)$$

If n is chosen sufficiently large, the logarithm on the right may be treated as of the form $\log[1 + z]$ with $|z| < 1$ and then expanded in the same manner as in (32), Chapter 5; hence

$$\log M_t(\theta) = -\frac{\mu\sqrt{n}\theta}{\sigma} + n\left[\left(\mu_1'\frac{\theta}{\sigma\sqrt{n}} + \mu_2'\frac{\theta^2}{2\sigma^2 n} + \cdots\right)\right.$$

$$\left. -\frac{1}{2}\left(\mu_1'\frac{\theta}{\sigma\sqrt{n}} + \mu_2'\frac{\theta^2}{2\sigma^2 n} + \cdots\right)^2 + \cdots\right]$$

$$= \left(-\frac{\mu\sqrt{n}}{\sigma} + \mu_1'\frac{\sqrt{n}}{\sigma}\right)\theta + \left(\frac{\mu_2' - \mu_1'^2}{\sigma^2}\right)\frac{\theta^2}{2}$$

$$+ \text{ terms in } \theta^k, \quad k \geq 3$$

Since $\mu_1' = \mu$ and $\sigma^2 = \mu_2' - \mu_1'^2$,

(17) $$\log M_t(\theta) = \frac{\theta^2}{2} + \text{ terms in } \theta^k, \quad k \geq 3$$

From an inspection of terms in θ^k, it will be seen that the only function of n they contain is the factor $n^{-\frac{k}{2}+1}$. Since $k \geq 3$, all such terms will approach 0 as n becomes infinite; consequently,

$$\lim_{n \to \infty} \log M_t(\theta) = \frac{\theta^2}{2}$$

which implies that

$$\lim_{n \to \infty} M_t(\theta) = e^{\frac{\theta^2}{2}}$$

The two theorems discussed in the paragraph immediately preceding Theorem 2, Chapter 5, can now be applied to give the desired result. Since the moment generating function of the variable $t = (\bar{x} - \mu)\sqrt{n}/\sigma$ approaches the function $e^{\theta^2/2}$, which is the moment generating function of a standard normal variable, these theorems insure that the variable t possesses a distribution that is approaching the distribution of a standard normal variable. This result may be stated as follows.

THEOREM 3: *If x has a distribution with mean μ and standard deviation σ for which the moment generating function exists, then the variable $t = (\bar{x} - \mu)\sqrt{n}/\sigma$ has a distribution that approaches the standard normal distribution as n becomes infinite.*

This theorem is known as a *central limit theorem.* Such theorems have been studied a great deal by mathematicians interested in probability. Although the preceding proof required the existence of the moment generating function of x, a proof very similar to the preceding proof can be constructed that requires only the existence of the first two moments; however it requires a knowledge of complex variables. From a practical point of view, this theorem is exceedingly important because it permits the use of normal curve methods on problems related to means of the type illustrated in the preceding section even when the basic variable x has a distribution that differs considerably from normality. Of course the more the distribution differs from normality, the larger n must become to

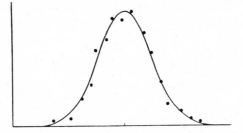

Fig. 3. Distribution of $\bar{x}$ from a rectangular distribution.

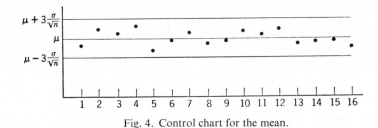

Fig. 4. Control chart for the mean.

guarantee approximate normality for $\bar{x}$. Sampling experiments have shown that for $n > 50$ the form of $f(x)$ has little influence on the form of $f(\bar{x})$ for ordinary types of $f(x)$. Figure 3 shows the empirical distribution of $\bar{x}$ for 100 samples of size 10 each from the rectangular distribution given by $f(x) = 1$, $0 \le x \le 1$, together with the fitted normal curve. The convergence toward normality appears to be quite rapid here.

6.6.1 Applications

The control-chart technique introduced in 5.3.4.5 was designed to check on successive sample proportions to determine whether they behaved like random samples from a binomial population. A similar chart may be constructed for sample means. Because of Theorem 3, it is not essential that the basic variable be exactly normally distributed for such charts; consequently, they are of wide applicability. Such a chart is shown in Fig. 4. It will be observed that the process appears to be under control. It should be noted that the control band is a three-standard deviation band about the mean, and therefore for a normal variable the probability should be only .003 that a point will fall outside this band. Since many industrial variables are not normally distributed, and since the sample means used in control charts are often based on only four or five measurements, one could hardly expect the probability of .003 to be very realistic. Three standard deviation control limits are chosen because industrial experience has found them to be especially useful rather than because they correspond to a desirable probability.

6.7 Distribution of the Difference of Two Means

A frequently occurring problem in science is that of determining whether real differences exist between two sets of similar data. One method of treating the problem is to test whether the means of the populations from which the data were obtained are essentially equal.

Let $\bar{x}$ and $\bar{y}$ be the sample means of two sets of data based on random samples of size n_x and n_y, respectively. Since the samples are random, $\bar{x}$ and $\bar{y}$ will be independently distributed. If x and y are normally distributed, or if n_x and n_y are sufficiently large to justify the practical implications of Theorem 3, $\bar{x}$ and $\bar{y}$ will be normally distributed or at least approximately so. It is assumed therefore that $\bar{x}$ and $\bar{y}$ are normally distributed.

Now consider the moment generating function of the variable $\bar{x} - \bar{y}$. If Theorem 1, property (22) of Chapter 5, formula (16), and Theorem 2 are applied in succession, it will be found that

$$M_{\bar{x}-\bar{y}}(\theta) = M_{\bar{x}}(\theta)M_{-\bar{y}}(\theta)$$
$$= M_{\bar{x}}(\theta)M_{\bar{y}}(-\theta)$$
$$= e^{\mu_{\bar{x}}\theta + \frac{\sigma_{\bar{x}}^2\theta^2}{2}} \cdot e^{-\mu_{\bar{y}}\theta + \frac{\sigma_{\bar{y}}^2\theta^2}{2}}$$
$$= e^{(\mu_x - \mu_y)\theta + \left(\frac{\sigma_x^2}{n_x} + \frac{\sigma_y^2}{n_y}\right)\frac{\theta^2}{2}}$$

Since this function is the moment generating function of a normal variable, this result proves the following theorem.

THEOREM 4: *If $\bar{x}$ and $\bar{y}$ are normally and independently distributed, then $\bar{x} - \bar{y}$ is normally distributed with mean $\mu_{\bar{x}-\bar{y}} = \mu_x - \mu_y$ and standard deviation $\sigma_{\bar{x}-\bar{y}} = \sqrt{\sigma_x^2/n_x + \sigma_y^2/n_y}$.*

6.7.1 Applications

Consider the following problem. A potential buyer of light bulbs bought 50 bulbs of each of two brands. On testing these bulbs, he found that brand A had a mean life of 1282 hours with a standard deviation of 80 hours, whereas brand B had a mean life of 1208 hours with a standard deviation of 94 hours. Can the buyer be quite certain that the two brands do differ in quality? To answer this question, it will suffice to test the hypothesis

$$H_0 : \mu_x = \mu_y$$

against the alternative

$$H_1 : \mu_x \neq \mu_y$$

Since $\bar{x}$ and $\bar{y}$ are based on samples of 50, it is safe to assume that $\bar{x}$ and $\bar{y}$ are normally distributed. The samples are obviously independent; hence Theorem 4 may be applied to yield the conclusion that $\bar{x} - \bar{y}$ is normally distributed with

$$\mu_{\bar{x}-\bar{y}} = 0 \quad \text{and} \quad \sigma_{\bar{x}-\bar{y}} = \sqrt{\frac{\sigma_x^2}{50} + \frac{\sigma_y^2}{50}}$$

Since σ_x and σ_y are unknown, it is necessary to estimate them by means of their sample values. Such approximations introduce an error, but for samples as large as 50 this error is not serious. It can be shown that the error in $\sigma_{\bar{x}-\bar{y}}$ very likely does not exceed 10 per cent here. With these approximations

$$\mu_{\bar{x}-\bar{y}} = 0 \quad \text{and} \quad \sigma_{\bar{x}-\bar{y}} \doteq \sqrt{\frac{(80)^2}{50} + \frac{(94)^2}{50}} = 17.5$$

Hence

$$t = \frac{\bar{x} - \bar{y} - \mu_{\bar{x}-\bar{y}}}{\sigma_{\bar{x}-\bar{y}}} \doteq \frac{74}{17.5} \doteq 4.23$$

Because of the choice of H_1, the critical region for this test is chosen to consist of the two equal tails of the distribution of $\bar{x} - \bar{y}$. This choice for H_1 is made because there is no external reason for believing that one brand should be better than the other. If, as usual, a critical region of size .05 is selected, then a value of $|t| > 2$ suffices to reject H_0. The value $t = 4.23$ is certainly significant, and therefore H_0 is rejected. It seems quite certain that the two brands differ in quality as far as mean burning time is concerned and that brand A is to be preferred.

After a test has indicated a significant difference, it is usually of interest to determine how large a difference in the population means may be reasonably assumed to exist. This problem is considered in Chapter 11. If only a point estimate of $\mu_x - \mu_y$ is desired, it suffices to choose $\bar{x} - \bar{y} = 74$ as the estimate. This estimate is easily shown to be the maximum likelihood estimate of $\mu_x - \mu_y$ under the assumption that $\bar{x}$ and $\bar{y}$ are independently normally distributed.

6.8   Distribution of the Difference of Two Proportions

If two sets of data drawn from two binomial populations are to be compared, it is necessary to work with the proportion of successes rather than with the number of successes, unless the number of trials in each set is the same. For example, 40 heads in 100 tosses of a coin would not be compared with 30 heads in 50 tosses unless they were both placed on a percentage basis. Now, from (34), Chapter 5, it follows that the proportion of successes $p' = x/n$ may be assumed to be normally distributed with mean p and standard deviation $\sqrt{pq/n}$, provided that n is large.

Let p_1' and p_2' be two independent sample proportions based on n_1 and n_2 trials, respectively, from two binomial populations with probabilities p_1 and p_2, respectively, and assume that n_1 and n_2 are large enough to treat p_1' and p_2' as normal variables. Then, if one proceeds with $p_1' - p_2'$, as was done in 6.7 for $\bar{x} - \bar{y}$, it follows that

$$M_{p_1'-p_2'}(\theta) = M_{p_1'}(\theta)M_{p_2'}(-\theta)$$

$$= e^{p_1\theta + \frac{p_1q_1\theta^2}{2n_1}} \cdot e^{-p_2\theta + \frac{p_2q_2\theta^2}{2n_2}}$$

$$= e^{(p_1-p_2)\theta + \left(\frac{p_1q_1}{n_1} + \frac{p_2q_2}{n_2}\right)\frac{\theta^2}{2}}$$

Since this is the moment generating function of a normal variable, these results yield the following theorem.

THEOREM 5: *When the number of trials n_1 and n_2 are sufficiently large, the difference of the sample proportions $p_1' - p_2'$ will be approximately normally distributed with $\mu_{p_1'-p_2'} = p_1 - p_2$ and $\sigma_{p_1'-p_2'} = \sqrt{p_1q_1/n_1 + p_2q_2/n_2}$.*

Just as for the simple binomial distribution, the normal approximation will usually be satisfactory in applications if each n_ip_i exceeds 5 when $p_i \leq \frac{1}{2}$ and n_iq_i exceeds 5 when $p_i > \frac{1}{2}$.

6.8.1 Applications

As a first illustration, consider the following problem. A railroad company installed two sets of 50 red oak ties each. The two sets were treated with creosote by two different processes. After a number of years of service, it was found that 22 ties of the first set and 18 ties of the second set were still in good condition. Is one justified in claiming that there is no real difference between the preserving properties of the two processes? To answer this question, let p_1 and p_2 denote the respective probabilities that a railroad tie treated by the corresponding process will be in good condition after this number of years of service. Then set up the hypothesis

$$H_0 : p_1 = p_2$$

against the alternative

$$H_1 : p_1 \neq p_2$$

If the common value of p_1 and p_2 under H_0 is denoted by p, then by Theorem 5 it follows that

$$\mu_{p_1'-p_2'} = 0 \quad \text{and} \quad \sigma_{p_1'-p_2'} = \sqrt{\frac{pq}{50} + \frac{pq}{50}} = \frac{\sqrt{pq}}{5}$$

The value of p is unknown, and so its value must be estimated from sample values. Since the hypothesis H_0 treats the two samples as though they

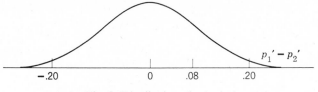

Fig. 5. Distribution of $p_1' - p_2'$.

were drawn from populations with the same p, the samples may be combined into one sample of 100 for which there were 40 successes. Hence a good estimate of p here is .40. With this estimate,

$$\mu_{p_1' - p_2'} = 0 \quad \text{and} \quad \sigma_{p_1' - p_2'} \doteq .10$$

The situation is described geometrically in Fig. 5.

Since $p_1' - p_2' = .44 - .36 = .08$ lies well within a two-standard deviation interval of the mean, the hypothesis H_0 will be accepted. The fact that the value of p must be estimated from the sample values and that $p_1' - p_2'$ is only approximately normally distributed makes this test somewhat inaccurate. Both samples are large enough in this illustration, however, to insure a fairly reliable test.

As a second illustration, consider a problem that arises frequently in the construction of tests. A civil-service examination is given to a group of 200 candidates. On the basis of their total scores, the 200 candidates are divided into two groups, the upper 30 per cent and the remaining 70 per cent. Consider the first question on this examination. In the first group, 40 had the correct answer; in the second group, 80 had the correct answer. On the basis of these results, can one conclude that the first question is no good at discriminating ability of the type being examined here? To solve this problem, set up the hypothesis

$$H_0 : p_1 = p_2$$

where p_1 and p_2 denote the respective probabilities of an individual from each of the two groups getting the correct answer on the first question. The natural alternative hypothesis here is

$$H_1 : p_1 > p_2$$

because the better candidates would be expected to do at least as well as the weaker candidates on all questions. As before, it follows that

$$\mu_{p_1' - p_2'} = 0 \quad \text{and} \quad \sigma_{p_1' - p_2'} = \sqrt{\frac{pq}{60} + \frac{pq}{140}}$$

where p is the common value of $p_1 = p_2$ under H_0. To estimate p, combine the two groups to give 120 successes in 200 trials, or an estimate of .60. Using this estimate for p,

$$\sigma_{p_1' - p_2'} \doteq .076$$

Now, $p_1' - p_2' = 40/60 - 80/140 = .10$; therefore,

$$t = \frac{p_1' - p_2'}{\sigma_{p_1' - p_2'}} \doteq 1.32$$

Since $t < 1.64$, the hypothesis H_0 will be accepted. This implies that the first question is not satisfactory for distinguishing between the stronger and the weaker candidates and therefore should be deleted from the examination. It might happen, however, that quite a few of the questions will fail to show discriminating ability as judged by individual significance tests such as this but when taken together will show such ability. Hence, from a practical point of view, one does not always reject a question merely because it does not reject the hypothesis H_0.

6.9   Chi-square Distribution

The techniques that have been developed in this chapter enable one to solve certain problems relating to radial distances. As an example, suppose a marksman is shooting at a circular target and suppose it may be assumed that the horizontal and vertical components of his errors are independently normally distributed with a common variance. If x and y denote those errors, as shown in Fig. 6, then the radial error is given by $r = \sqrt{x^2 + y^2}$. The frequency function of r can be obtained by the methods of this chapter.

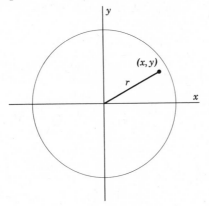

Fig. 6. A radial error problem.

A similar problem in three dimensions would involve the sum of squares of three random variables. Now, it is not much more difficult to treat n variables than three variables; therefore, in order to have a general result that will handle all such problems, the general situation is considered here. Furthermore, it will be discovered later that this general result is very useful in the development of certain branches of statistical theory.

It is a simple matter, by means of (42), Chapter 5, to find the distribution of the square root of a variable if one knows the distribution of the variable itself; therefore it will suffice to find the distribution of the variable

$$w = \sum_{i=1}^{n} x_i^2$$

where the variables $x_1, x_2, \cdots, x_n$ constitute a random sample from a normal population with mean 0 and standard deviation 1. From the formula of Theorem 1 in section 6.4, together with properties of random samples, it follows that

(18)
$$\begin{aligned} M_w(\theta) &= M_{x_1^2 + \cdots + x_n^2}(\theta) \\ &= M_{x_1^2}(\theta) M_{x_2^2}(\theta) \cdots M_{x_n^2}(\theta) \\ &= M_{x^2}^n(\theta) \end{aligned}$$

Now x is a standard normal variable; therefore

$$\begin{aligned} M_{x^2}(\theta) &= \frac{1}{\sqrt{2\pi}} \int_{-\infty}^{\infty} e^{\theta x^2} e^{-\frac{x^2}{2}} \, dx \\ &= \frac{1}{\sqrt{2\pi}} \int_{-\infty}^{\infty} e^{-\frac{x^2}{2}(1-2\theta)} \, dx \end{aligned}$$

Let $y = x\sqrt{1-2\theta}$; then this integral reduces to

$$\begin{aligned} M_{x^2}(\theta) &= (1-2\theta)^{-\frac{1}{2}} \frac{1}{\sqrt{2\pi}} \int_{-\infty}^{\infty} e^{-\frac{y^2}{2}} \, dy \\ &= (1-2\theta)^{-\frac{1}{2}} \end{aligned}$$

From this result and (18), it therefore follows that

(19)
$$M_w(\theta) = (1-2\theta)^{-\frac{n}{2}}$$

All that remains to be done is to find a frequency function corresponding to this moment generating function and then apply the uniqueness argument concerning frequency functions and moment generating functions. In the method employed here the answer is written down and its correctness is verified. That is, a particular frequency function is written down, and it is then shown that a variable having this frequency function possesses the moment generating function given by (19). The frequency function that corresponds to (19) defines what is known as the chi-square distribution. A special case of this distribution was obtained in (43), Chapter 5. Although it is a cumbersome variable to use, the basic variable here is usually denoted by the Greek letter χ^2. In terms of this notation, the chi-square distribution is defined as follows:

$$(20) \qquad \text{CHI-SQUARE DISTRIBUTION: } f(\chi^2) = \frac{(\chi^2)^{\frac{\nu}{2}-1} e^{-\frac{\chi^2}{2}}}{2^{\frac{\nu}{2}}\Gamma\left(\frac{\nu}{2}\right)}$$

The symbol $\Gamma(x)$ denotes the *gamma* or *factorial* function of x, which has the property that $\Gamma(x+1) = x\Gamma(x)$. Because of this property, a table of values of the gamma function for $1 \leq x \leq 2$ will suffice to evaluate the function for other positive values of x. If x is an integer, no tables are needed because $\Gamma(1) = 1$ and then $\Gamma(x + 1) = x!$ The necessary tables for x not an integer can be found in any handbook of mathematical tables. In particular, they show that $\Gamma(\frac{1}{2}) = \sqrt{\pi}$.

The parameter ν is called the number of degrees of freedom of the distribution. This name is given to it because it is equal to the number of independent variables occurring in w. If ν is set equal to 1, it will be observed that (20) reduces to the function obtained in (43), Chapter 5. For the more general problem being considered here, the value of ν is n. A graph of (20) for several values of ν is given in Fig. 7.

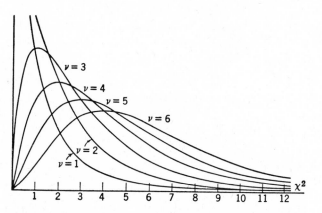

Fig. 7. Distribution of χ^2 for various degrees of freedom.

For convenience in finding the moment generating function of a χ^2 variable, let the variable be denoted by z. Then the generating function of χ^2 will be given by

$$M_z(\theta) = \int_0^\infty e^{\theta z} f(z)\, dz$$

$$= \frac{1}{2^{\frac{\nu}{2}} \Gamma\left(\frac{\nu}{2}\right)} \int_0^\infty e^{\theta z} z^{\frac{\nu}{2}-1} e^{-\frac{z}{2}}\, dz$$

$$= \frac{1}{2^{\frac{\nu}{2}} \Gamma\left(\frac{\nu}{2}\right)} \int_0^\infty e^{-\frac{z}{2}(1-2\theta)} z^{\frac{\nu}{2}-1}\, dz$$

Let $y = z(1 - 2\theta)/2$; then $dz = 2dy/(1 - 2\theta)$ and

$$M_z(\theta) = \frac{1}{2^{\frac{\nu}{2}} \Gamma\left(\frac{\nu}{2}\right)} \int_0^\infty e^{-y} \left(\frac{2y}{1 - 2\theta}\right)^{\frac{\nu}{2}-1} \frac{2}{1 - 2\theta}\, dy$$

$$= \frac{(1 - 2\theta)^{-\frac{\nu}{2}}}{\Gamma\left(\frac{\nu}{2}\right)} \int_0^\infty e^{-y} y^{\frac{\nu}{2}-1}\, dy$$

But, as shown in any standard set of mathematical tables, this integral is the integral that defines $\Gamma\left(\frac{\nu}{2}\right)$; hence the moment generating function of χ^2 for ν degrees of freedom is given by

$$(21) \qquad\qquad M_{\chi^2}(\theta) = (1 - 2\theta)^{-\frac{\nu}{2}}$$

A comparison of this result with formula (19) shows that w has the moment generating function of a χ^2 variable with n degrees of freedom. Since a distribution is uniquely determined by its moment generating function, the preceding derivation proves the following theorem.

THEOREM 6: *If x is normally distributed with zero mean and unit variance, the sum of the squares of n random sample values of x has a χ^2 distribution with n degrees of freedom.*

As an illustration of the use of this distribution in radial error problems, consider the problem of calculating the probability that an antiaircraft shell designed to burst at a specified point in space will have a radial error of at most 100 feet if it is assumed that the x, y, and z errors of a co-ordinate system with the origin at the specified point are independently normally distributed with a common standard deviation of 50 feet. For convenience of notation, let $x_1 = x/50$, $x_2 = y/50$, and $x_3 = z/50$. Then x_1, x_2, x_3 will be independent, normally distributed variables with zero means and unit variances; consequently, by Theorem 6, $x_1^2 + x_2^2 + x_3^2$ will possess a χ^2 distribution with three degrees of freedom. Using (20), one can therefore write

$$P\{\sqrt{x^2 + y^2 + z^2} < 100\} = P\{x^2 + y^2 + z^2 < 100^2\}$$
$$= P\{x_1^2 + x_2^2 + x_3^2 < 4\}$$
$$= \frac{1}{2^{\frac{3}{2}}\Gamma\left(\frac{3}{2}\right)} \int_0^4 w^{\frac{1}{2}} e^{-\frac{w}{2}} \, dw$$

Although such tables are not presented in this book, there are statistical tables that enable one to evaluate integrals of this type. Reference to the proper tables will show that the preceding answer reduces to $P = .72$.

The χ^2 distribution was introduced here in connection with radial distance problems; however, it is one of the most important theoretical distributions in statistics and appears repeatedly in later chapters in connection with various types of problems.

REFERENCES

An interesting discussion of random sampling may be found in M. G. Kendall, *The Advanced Theory of Statistics*, Vol. 1, Griffin and Co.

A proof of Theorem 3 that requires some additional mathematical background may be found in E. Parzen, *Modern Probability Theory and Its Applications*, John Wiley and Sons.

An elementary discussion of the control chart technique for the mean is available in L. H. C. Tippett, *Technological Applications of Statistics*, John Wiley and Sons.

Tables for evaluating the integral in connection with the χ^2 distribution are available in Fisher and Yates, *Statistical Tables*, Oliver and Boyd.

EXERCISES

1. Suggest how to sample randomly from (a) students at a university, (b) households in a city, (c) the adult public, (d) a carload of wheat.

2. Explain which features of random sampling are satisfied and which features are not satisfied if you wish to estimate the distribution of students' grade-point averages and do so by taking a sample of 100 students from the registration files by consulting a table of random numbers corresponding to the enrollment but always ignoring any grade-point average less than .8. Assume that the student enrollment is very large.

3. Show that $E(x - c)^2$ is a minimum when $c = E[x]$.

156   INTRODUCTION TO MATHEMATICAL STATISTICS

4. Give an example of two random variables for which $E[xy] \neq E[x] E[y]$.

5. Given an example of 2 dependent random variables for which the variance of their sum is (a) larger than the sum of their variances (b) smaller than the sum of their variances.

6. Given $f(x, y) = e^{-(x+y)}$, $x \geq 0$, $y \geq 0$, (a) calculate the value of $E[z]$ where $z = x + y$, (b) calculate the value of $E[z^2]$, (c) find $M_z(\theta)$.

7. By using moment generating function methods, show that the sum of 2 independent binomial variables with the same parameter p is also a binomial variable. How could you argue this result directly?

8. By using moment generating function methods and the result in problem 27, Chapter 5, show that the sum of 2 independent Poisson variables with means μ_1 and μ_2 is also a Poisson variable with mean $\mu_1 + \mu_2$.

9. Using the methods of problem 8, explain why the difference of 2 independent Poisson variables will not be a Poisson variable.

10. Let x have the distribution $f(x) = pq^x$, $x = 0, 1, 2, \cdots$ (a)Calculate$E[x]$ by using the formula $1/(1 - q) = 1 + q + q^2 + q^3 \cdots$ and its derivative. (b) Calculate the variance of x by first calculating $E[x(x - 1)]$ by means of similar techniques.

11. Cards numbered 1 through n are shuffled and laid out in a line. Let $x_k = 1$ if the number on the kth card is smaller than the number on the $(k + 1)$th card and let $x_k = 0$ otherwise. Let $z = \sum_{k=1}^{n-1} x_k$, which means that z represents the total number of increases in the sequence. Calculate the mean and variance of z.

12. If x is normally distributed with $\mu = 20$ and $\sigma = 5$, calculate the probability that (a) $x > 21$, (b) $\bar{x} > 21$, if $\bar{x}$ is based on a random sample of size 25.

13. Past experience indicates that wire rods purchased from a company have a mean breaking strength of 400 pounds and a standard deviation of 15 pounds. (a) If 16 rods are selected, between what 2 values could you reasonably expect their mean to be? (b) How many rods would you select so that you would be certain with a probability of .95 that your resulting mean would not be in error by more than 2 pounds?

14. If you wish to estimate the mean of a normal population whose variance is 10, how large a sample should you take so that the probability is .80 that your estimate will not be in error by more than .4 unit?

15. A research worker wishes to estimate the mean of a population by using a sample large enough that the probability will be .95 that the sample mean will not differ from the true mean by more than 25 per cent of the standard deviation. How large a sample should be taken?

16. The following data represent the initial velocities in meters per second of projectiles fired from the same gun. (a) Determine the accuracy of the sample mean $\bar{x}$ as an estimate of the true mean velocity. (b) Calculate the approximate probability, using the value of s for the data in place of σ, that a sample mean $\bar{x}$ based on a sample of this size will deviate more than $\frac{1}{2}$ unit from the true mean. (c) Why are the methods used in (a) and (b) not very satisfactory here?

| 455 | 454 | 450 | 453 | 452 | 451 | 450 | 454 |
| 451 | 451 | 452 | 454 | 450 | 454 | 454 | |

17. Suppose one mixes the ingredients for concrete to attain a mean breaking test of 2000 pounds. If the mean drops below 1800 pounds, the composition will be changed. How many tests will need to be made in order that $\alpha = .05$ and $\beta = .10$ in testing the hypothesis $H_0:\mu = 2000$ against $H_1:\mu = 1800$ if $\sigma = 200$ and one assumes normality?

18. Find an expression for the power function of the test when testing $H_0:\mu = 10$ against $H_1:\mu > 10$ for a normal variable with unit variance. Use the right tail of the $\bar{x}$ distribution as critical region with $n = 25$ and $\alpha = .10$.

19. Have each member of the class perform the following experiment 10 times. Select 10 one-digit random numbers from the table of random numbers in the back of the book. Calculate the mean for each set of 10. Bring these 10 experimental means to class, where the total set of such means may be classified, the histogram drawn, and the mean and standard deviation computed. These results should then be compared with those expected under Theorem 3. The population here has $\mu = 4.5$ and $\sigma = 2.87$.

20. The same test was given to 2 classes. The first class of 20 students averaged 123 points with a standard deviation of 32 points; the second class of 30 averaged 130 points with a standard deviation of 24 points. Is it safe to conclude that the second class is superior?

21. Two sets of 100 students each were taught to read by 2 different methods. After instruction was over, a reading test gave the following results: $\bar{x} = 73.4$, $\bar{y} = 70.3$, $s_x = 8$, $s_y = 10$. (a) Test the hypothesis that $\mu_x = \mu_y$. (b) Determine the accuracy of $\bar{x} - \bar{y}$ as an estimate of $\mu_x - \mu_y$. (c) Determine how large an equal-size sample from each group should have been used if it were desired to estimate $\mu_x - \mu_y$ to within 1 unit with a probability of .95.

22. Suppose that you wish to test whether there is a tendency for an individual's right foot to be longer than his left foot. (a) Explain why it would be incorrect to take a random sample of, say, 100 individuals and apply the usual technique for testing $\mu_x = \mu_y$, where x and y correspond to the right and left foot, respectively. (b) Explain how you could sample differently or handle the data differently to overcome the difficulty here.

23. Suppose that $\bar{x}$ and $\bar{y}$ are the means of 2 samples of size n each from a normal population with variance σ^2. Determine n so that the probability will be about .99 that the 2 sample means will differ by less than σ.

24. Two different samplers X and Y were sent into the same forest to select trees at random. Each sampler took a sample of 100 trees and measured their diameters with the following results: $\bar{x} = 19.2$, $\bar{y} = 20.3$, $s_x = 3.2$, $s_y = 2.6$. (a) Does the smaller standard deviation for Y imply that he is a more accurate sampler than X? (b) What conclusions can be drawn concerning the accuracy of X and Y? (c) If you knew that the true mean was 19.7, could you draw any further conclusions?

25. Suppose $\mu_x - \mu_y = \frac{1}{2}$ and $\sigma_x = \sigma_y = 1$ for 2 independent normal variables. How large an equal-size sample from each population should be taken so that the probability of rejecting the false hypothesis $H_0:\mu_x = \mu_y$ will be .90 if the critical region is two-sided and $\alpha = .05$.

26. In a large-scale experiment 2000 children were split into 2 groups of 1000 each. One group received a serum for the prevention of a disease; the other

group received no serum. The number of children in each group who contracted the disease was 30 and 50, respectively. Treating these 2 numbers as sample values of 2 Poisson variables which may be considered as approximately normally distributed, test the hypothesis that $\mu_1 = \mu_2$.

27. In a poll taken among college students, 46 of 200 fraternity men favored a certain proposition, whereas 51 of 300 nonfraternity men favored it. Is there a real difference of opinion on this proposition?

28. A manufacturer of housedresses sent out advertising by mail. He sent samples of material to each of 2 groups of 1000 women, but for 1 group he used a white envelope and for the other group he used a blue envelope. He received orders from 10 and 13 per cent, respectively. Is it quite certain that the blue envelope will help sales?

29. A civil service examination was given to 200 people. On the basis of their total scores, they were divided into the upper 30 per cent, the middle 40 per cent, and the lower 30 per cent. On a certain question, 39 of the upper group and 29 of the lower group answered correctly. Is this question likely to be useful for discriminating the ability of the type being tested?

30. If the percentage of defective parts turned out by the same machine on 2 consecutive days is 6 and 8 per cent and 500 parts were turned out on each of those days, would the inspector be justified in claiming that the quality had slipped?

31. A test of 100 youths and 200 adults showed that 50 of the youths and 60 of the adults were poor drivers. Use these data to test the claim that the youth percentage of poor drivers is larger than the adult percentage by 10 percentage points, against the possibility of a still larger difference.

32. Two players each play a game of chance 100 times. If 1 dollar is paid for every win and the probability of winning at a single trial is $\frac{1}{5}$, what is the approximate probability that the first player will finish with at least 5 dollars more than the second player?

33. (a) Construct a control chart for $\bar{x}$ for the following data on the blowing time of fuses, samples of 5 being taken every hour. Each set of 5 has been arranged in order of magnitude. Estimate $\sigma_{\bar{x}}$ by first estimating σ by means of s calculated for all 60 values. (b) Comment on whether production seems to be under control, assuming that these are the first data collected.

42	42	19	36	42	51	60	18	15	69	64	61
65	45	24	54	51	74	60	20	30	109	91	78
75	68	80	69	57	75	72	27	39	113	93	94
78	72	81	77	59	78	95	42	62	118	109	109
87	90	81	84	78	132	138	60	84	153	112	136

34. Using moment generating function methods and the results of problem 6 (c) and of problem 37 (c), Chapter 5, find the frequency function of $z = x + y$ given in problem 6.

35. Prove that if x and y are independent variables having the same rectangular distribution with range 1 and mean $\frac{1}{2}$ then $x + y$ will not have a rectangular distribution.

36. Calculate $P\{x_1^2 + x_2^2 < 1\}$ and $P\{x_1^2 + x_2^2 < 2\}$ for a random sample of size 2 from the frequency function (a) $f(x) = \frac{1}{2}$, $-1 \leq x \leq 1$, and (b) $f(x) = e^{-\frac{x^2}{2}}/\sqrt{2\pi}$.

37. Find the frequency function of $n\bar{x}$ for a random sample of size n from the population with frequency function $f(x) = e^{-x}$, $x \geq 0$.

38. Prove that a linear combination of independent normal variables is also a normal variable.

39. Use the moment generating function of a χ^2 variable with ν degrees of freedom to find its mean and variance.

40. Use expected value operator methods on $w = \sum_1^n x_i^2$ to find the mean and variance of a χ^2 variable with n degrees of freedom.

41. If $x_1, x_2, \cdots, x_n$ is a random sample from the distribution with frequency function $f(x)$, calculate $P\{x_1 < t, \cdots, x_n < t\}$ and use it to find the frequency function of the variable $z = \max\{x_1, \cdots, x_n\}$. Express the result in terms of $f(x)$ and its distribution function $F(x)$.

42. Use the result in problem 41 to find the distribution of the lifetime of a piece of electronic equipment that has n vital parts with lifetimes $x_1, \cdots, x_n$ which are independently and identically distributed with frequency function $f(x) = \alpha e^{-\alpha x}$, $x \geq 0$, if it is assumed that one functioning vital part is sufficient to operate the equipment.

CHAPTER 7

Correlation and Regression

The statistical methods presented thus far have been largely concerned with a single variable x and its frequency function. Many of the problems in statistical work, however, involve several variables. This chapter is devoted to explaining some of the simpler methods for dealing with data associated with two or more variables. The emphasis is on two variables. Chapter 8 is concerned with the construction of models and other theoretical aspects of the problems brought up in this chapter.

In some problems the several variables are studied simultaneously to see how they are interrelated; in others there is one particular variable of interest and the remaining variables are studied for their possible aid in throwing light on this particular variable. These two classes of problems are usually associated with the names of *correlation* and *regression* respectively. They are considered in that order.

7.1 Linear Correlation

A simple correlation problem arises when an individual asks himself whether there is any relationship between a pair of variables that interests him. For example, is there any relationship between smoking and heart ailments, between music appreciation and scientific aptitude, between radio reception and sunspot activity, between beauty and brains?

Consider two random variables x and y and the problem of determining the extent to which they are related. The investigation of the relationship between two such variables, based on a set of n pairs of measurements (x_1, y_1), (x_2, y_2), $\cdots$, (x_n, y_n), usually begins with an attempt to discover the approximate form of the relationship by graphing the data as n points in the x,y plane. Such a graph is called a *scatter diagram*. By means of it one can quickly discern whether there is any pronounced relationship and, if so, whether the relationship may be treated as approximately linear.

160

As an illustration, consider the data of Table 1 consisting of the scores of 30 students on a language test x and a science test y. The maximum possible score on each of these tests was 50 points. The choice of which

TABLE 1

x	y	x	y	x	y
34	37	28	30	39	36
37	37	30	34	33	29
36	34	32	30	30	29
32	34	41	37	33	40
32	33	38	40	43	42
36	40	36	42	31	29
35	39	37	40	38	40
34	37	33	36	34	31
29	36	32	31	36	38
35	35	33	31	34	32

variable to call x and which to call y is arbitrary here. The scatter diagram for these data is shown in Fig. 1.

An inspection of this scatter diagram shows that there is a tendency for small values of x to be associated with small values of y and for large values of x to be associated with large values of y. Furthermore, the general trend of the scatter is that of a straight line. For variables such as these, it would be desirable to be able to measure in some sense the

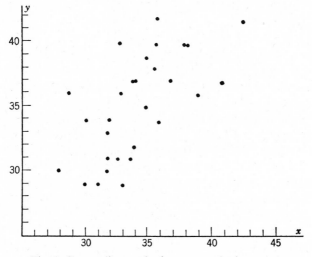

Fig. 1. Scatter diagram for language and science scores.

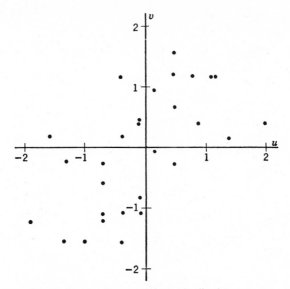

Fig. 2. Scatter diagram for standardized scores.

degree to which the variables are linearly related. For the purpose of devising such a measure, consider what properties would be desirable.

A measure of relationship should certainly be independent of the choice of origin for the variables. The fact that the scatter diagram of Fig. 1 was plotted with the axes conveniently chosen to pass through the point (25, 25) implies that the relationship was admitted to be independent of the choice of origin. This property can be realized by using the variables x_i and y_i in the forms $x_i - \bar{x}$ and $y_i - \bar{y}$ in the construction of the desired measure.

A measure of relationship should also be independent of the scale of measurement used for x and y. Thus, if the x and y scores of Table 1 were doubled in order to make them appear like conventional test scores, the relationship between the variables should be unaffected thereby. This property can be realized by dividing x and y by quantities which possess the same units as x and y. For reasons that will be appreciated presently, the quantities that are chosen here are s_x and s_y. Both properties will therefore be realized if the measure of relationship is constructed by using the variables x_i and y_i in the forms $u_i = (x_i - \bar{x})/s_x$ and $v_i = (y_i - \bar{y})/s_y$. This merely means that the x_i and y_i should be measured in sample standard units.

The scatter diagram of the points (u_i, v_i) for the data of Table 1 is shown in Fig. 2. It will be observed that most of the points are located in the first and third quadrants and that the points in those quadrants tend to have larger coordinates, in magnitude, than those in the second and fourth quadrants. A simple measure of this property of the scatter is the sum $\sum_{i=1}^{n} u_i v_i$. The terms of this sum that are contributed by points in the first and third quadrants will be positive, whereas those corresponding to points in the second and fourth quadrants will be negative. A large positive value of this sum would therefore seem to indicate a strong linear trend in the scatter diagram. This is not strictly true, however, for if the number of points were doubled without changing the nature of the scatter, the value of this sum would be approximately doubled. It is therefore necessary to divide this sum by n, the number of points, before using it as a measure of relationship. The resulting sum, $\sum_{i=1}^{n} u_i v_i / n$, is the desired measure of relationship. It is called the *correlation coefficient* and is denoted by the letter r; hence, in terms of the original measurements, r is defined by the following formula.

(1)   CORRELATION COEFFICIENT: $$r = \frac{\sum_{i=1}^{n} (x_i - \bar{x})(y_i - \bar{y})}{n s_x s_y}$$

Calculations will show that $r = .66$ for the data of Table 1. In order to interpret this result and discover what values of r are likely to be obtained for various degrees and types of relationship between x and y, consider the scatter diagrams of Fig. 3. The first four diagrams correspond to increasing degrees, or strength, of linear relationship. If these diagrams were rotated about the y axis through $180°$ so that the scatters appeared in the second quadrant, the scatters would have downward trends rather than upward trends and the corresponding values of r would be the negatives of the listed values. Thus the magnitude of r determines the strength of the relationship, whereas the sign of r tells one whether y tends to increase, or decrease, with x. The fifth diagram illustrates a scatter in which x and y are closely related but in which the relationship is not linear. This illustration points out that r is a useful measure of the strength of the relationship between two variables only when the variables are linearly related.

The diagrams of Fig. 3, together with the associated values of r, make plausible two properties of r, namely, that the value of r must satisfy the inequality $-1 \leq r \leq 1$ and that the value of r will be equal to ± 1 if, and only if, the points of the scatter lie on a straight line. A demonstration of these properties is somewhat lengthy and therefore will not be undertaken here; however, it is available in the appendix.

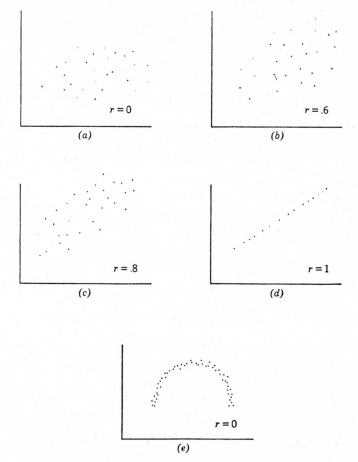

Fig. 3. Scatter diagrams and their associated values of r.

7.1.1   Interpretation of r

The interpretation of a correlation coefficient as a measure of the strength of the linear relationship between two variables is a purely mathematical interpretation and is completely devoid of any cause or effect implications. The fact that two variables tend to increase or decrease together does not imply that one has any direct or indirect effect on the other. Both may be influenced by other variables in a manner that will give rise to a strong mathematical relationship. For example, over a period of years the correlation coefficient between teachers' salaries and the consumption of liquor turned out to be .98. During this period of time there was a steady rise in wages and salaries of all types and a general upward trend of good times. Under such conditions, teachers' salaries would also increase. Moreover, the general upward trend in wages and buying power would be reflected in increased purchases of liquor. Thus this high correlation merely reflects the common effect of the upward trend on the two variables. Correlation coefficients must be handled with care if they are to give sensible information concerning relationships between pairs of variables. Success with correlation coefficients requires familiarity with the field of application as well as with their mathematical properties.

7.1.2 Calculation of r

The formula in (1) that defines r is not always convenient for computational purposes. A better form is obtained by multiplying out factors and inserting values for s_x and s_y:

(2)
$$r = \frac{\sum xy - n\bar{x}\bar{y}}{\sqrt{[\sum x^2 - n\bar{x}^2][\sum y^2 - n\bar{y}^2]}}$$

$$= \frac{n\sum xy - \sum x\sum y}{\sqrt{[n\sum x^2 - (\sum x)^2][n\sum y^2 - (\sum y)^2]}}$$

This last form requires the sums of x, y, x^2, y^2, and xy, all of which are readily calculated with modern electric calculators.

If the data are so numerous that the preceding computations would become unduly lengthy even with a calculating machine, then it may be worthwhile to classify the data with respect to both variables, just as was done for one variable in Chapter 4 in calculating $\bar{x}$. When the data have been so classified, the short method of computation used for finding means may be employed to advantage in computing r. Let

$$x_i = c_x u_i + x_0$$

and

$$y_i = c_y v_i + y_0$$

where c_x and c_y are class intervals and u and v are new integral variables. Then, because of the property of being independent of the choice of origin and choice of scale for x and y, the value of r calculated for the integral variables u and v will be the same as for x and y. This fact may be verified directly by substituting these changes of variables in (1) and simplifying.

7.1.3   Reliability of *r*

In any given problem involving linear correlation, the value of *r* may be thought of as the first sample value of a sequence of sample values $r_1, r_2, r_3, \cdots$ that would be obtained if repeated sets of similar data were obtained. Such sets of data are thought of as having been obtained from drawing random samples of size *n* from some population. For example, the data of Table 1 are assumed to have been obtained from drawing a random sample of size 30 from a population of students.

The population being sampled can be described with respect to the two variables *x* and *y* by means of the frequency function $f(x, y)$ of those variables. Now, suppose that the function $f(x, y)$ contains a parameter ρ whose value serves to measure the extent to which *x* and *y* are linearly related in a probability sense. Then *r* may be used to estimate the value of ρ, just as a sample mean $\bar{x}$ is used to estimate the population mean μ. The parameter ρ would, of course, be called the theoretical, or population correlation coefficient.

Frequency functions of two correlated variables will be studied in Chapter 8. In particular, a frequency function, called the normal frequency function, which contains a parameter ρ of the type described in the preceding paragraph, is introduced. It is shown in the next chapter that *r* is the maximum likelihood estimator of ρ, provided that *x* and *y* possess a normal frequency function. This demonstration constitutes the justification for choosing *r* as given by (1) as a desirable measure of linear correlation.

If it is assumed that *x* and *y* possess a normal frequency function, then it is theoretically possible to derive the frequency function of the random variable *r*, just as it is possible to derive the frequency function of $\bar{x}$ from that of *x*. Both the form and the derivation of this frequency function are too complicated to be considered here. It turns out that the frequency function of *r* depends only on the parameters ρ and *n*, where *n* is the number of points in the scatter diagram. Graphs of the frequency function of *r* for $\rho = 0$ and for $\rho = .8$ when $n = 9$ are shown in Fig. 4.

It is clear from Fig. 4 that the distribution of *r* is decidedly non-normal for large values of ρ; consequently it will not suffice to obtain the standard deviation of *r* and use it to determine the accuracy of *r* as an estimate of ρ. Fortunately, there exists a simple change of variable which transforms the complicated distribution of *r* into an approximately normal distribution. The resulting normal distribution may then be used to determine the accuracy of *r* as an estimate of ρ in the same way that the normal distribution of $\bar{x}$ was used to determine the accuracy of $\bar{x}$ as an estimate of μ. This change of variable is from r to z, where

(3) $$z = \tfrac{1}{2} \log_e \frac{1 + r}{1 - r}$$

It can be shown that when the preceding assumptions are satisfied, z will be approximately normally distributed with mean

$$\mu_z = \tfrac{1}{2} \log_e \frac{1 + \rho}{1 - \rho}$$

and standard deviation

$$\sigma_z = \frac{1}{\sqrt{n - 3}}$$

As an illustration, consider the following problem. Is a correlation of $r = .20$ between the face index and the cephalic index of 50 members of a certain race significant? Set up the hypothesis that $\rho = 0$. Then the variable z will be approximately normally distributed with $\mu_z = 0$ and $\sigma_z = 1/\sqrt{47} = .15$. If a significance level of .05 is taken and if the two tails of this normal distribution are used as a critical region, a sample value of r will be significant if it has a value of z such that $|z| > .30$. Here,

$$z = \tfrac{1}{2} \log_e \frac{1.2}{0.8} = .20$$

Since this value does not exceed the critical value, the value of $r = .20$ is not significant. A value as large as this would be obtained fairly often in random samples from a population in which the two variables are uncorrelated.

As a second illustration, consider the problem of determining an interval of values within which r could reasonably be expected to fall

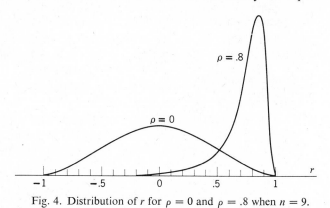

Fig. 4. Distribution of r for $\rho = 0$ and $\rho = .8$ when $n = 9$.

if $\rho = .8$ and if r is based on a sample of size 28. Let reasonably be understood to mean with a probability of .95. The construction of such an interval can be accomplished by first constructing such an interval for z and then transforming it into an interval for r. The simplest interval for z that possesses the desired property is the interval with end points $z_1 = \mu_z - 2\sigma_z$ and $z_2 = \mu_z + 2\sigma_z$. For $\rho = .8$ and $n = 28$, it follows from (3) that these end points are

$$z_1 = \tfrac{1}{2} \log 9 - \frac{2}{\sqrt{25}} = .70$$

$$z_2 = \tfrac{1}{2} \log 9 + \frac{2}{\sqrt{25}} = 1.50$$

If r is expressed as a function of z in relationship (3), it will be found that r is the hyperbolic tangent of z. From tables of this function, or from tables of exponentials, it will be found that $r_1 = .60$ and $r_2 = .91$. Thus it can be stated that the probability is approximately .95 that the sample correlation coefficient will satisfy the inequality $.60 < r < .91$ when r is based on a sample of 28 and $\rho = .8$.

7.2   Linear Regression

In the introduction to section 7.1, it was pointed out that correlation methods are used when one is interested in studying how two or more variables are interrelated. It often happens, however, that one studies the relationship between the variables in the hope that any relationship he finds can be used to assist in making estimates or predictions of one of the variables. Thus, if the two variables for Table 1 had been scores representing college aptitude x and college success y rather than the variables listed there, the relationship between x and y would have been useful for assisting one to predict a student's college success from a knowledge of his score on a college-aptitude test. The correlation coefficient is not capable of solving such prediction problems; therefore, it is necessary to introduce what is known as regression methods for handling those problems. In this section linear regression methods for two variables will be studied, whereas curvilinear regression and regression methods for several variables will be introduced in later sections.

Consider the data of Table 2 on the amount of water applied in inches and the yield of alfalfa in tons per acre on an experimental farm. The graph of these data is given in Fig. 5. From this graph it appears that x and y are approximately linearly related for this range of x values. For

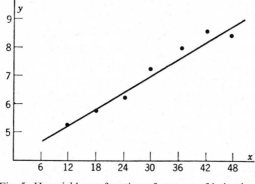

Fig. 5. Hay yield as a function of amount of irrigation.

the purpose of predicting y from x, it should therefore suffice to use a linear function of x. Thus the problem of prediction first requires one to solve the problem of fitting a straight line to a set of points.

7.2.1 Least Squares

The problem of fitting a curve to a set of points in some efficient manner is essentially the problem of estimating the parameters of the curve in an efficient manner. Although there are numerous methods for performing the estimation of such parameters, the best known method is the following, known as the *method of least squares*.

TABLE 2

Water (x)	12	18	24	30	36	42	48
Yield (y)	5.27	5.68	6.25	7.21	8.02	8.71	8.42

Since the desired curve is to be used for estimating, or predicting, purposes, it is reasonable to require that the curve be such that it makes the errors of estimation small. By an error of estimation, or prediction, is meant the difference between an observed value of y and the corresponding fitted curve value of y. If the value of the variable to be estimated is denoted by y and the corresponding curve value by y', then the error of estimation, or prediction, is given by $y - y'$. Since the errors may be positive or negative and might add up to a small value for a poorly fitting curve, it will not do to require merely that the sum of the errors be as small as possible. This difficulty can be avoided by requiring that the sum of the absolute values of the errors be as small as possible. However, sums of absolute values are not convenient to work with mathematically; consequently the difficulty is avoided by requiring that the sum of the squares of the errors be a minimum. The values of the parameters obtained by this minimization determine what is known as the best fitting curve in the sense of least squares.

Consider the application of this principle to the fitting of a straight line to a set of n points. It is convenient to write the equation of any nonvertical line in the form

(4) $$y' = a + b(x - \bar{x})$$

where b is its slope and a is the y intercept on the line $x = \bar{x}$. The y intercept on the y axis is $a - b\bar{x}$. It will be seen shortly why it is so convenient to express the equation of an arbitrary line in this form rather than in the slope-intercept form, $y = a + bx$, of analytical geometry. The problem now is to determine the parameters a and b so that the sum of the squares of the errors of estimation will be a minimum. If the coordinates of the ith point are denoted by (x_i, y_i), this sum of squares will be $\sum_{i=1}^{n} (y_i - y_i')^2$. When y_i' is replaced by its value, as given by (4), it becomes clear that this sum is a function of a and b only. If this function is denoted by $G(a, b)$, then

$$G(a, b) = \sum_{i=1}^{n} [y_i - a - b(x_i - \bar{x})]^2$$

If this function is to have a minimum value, it is necessary that its partial derivatives vanish there; hence a and b must satisfy the equations

(5)
$$\frac{\partial G}{\partial a} = \sum 2[y - a - b(x - \bar{x})][-1] = 0$$

$$\frac{\partial G}{\partial b} = \sum 2[y - a - b(x - \bar{x})][-(x - \bar{x})] = 0$$

where the subscripts and range of summation have been omitted for convenience. When the summations are performed term by term and the sums that involve y are transposed, these equations assume the form

(6)
$$an + b\sum(x - \bar{x}) = \sum y$$

$$a\sum(x - \bar{x}) + b\sum(x - \bar{x})^2 = \sum(x - \bar{x})y$$

Since $\sum(x - \bar{x}) = 0$, the solution of these equations is given by

$$a = \bar{y} \quad \text{and} \quad b = \frac{\sum(x - \bar{x})y}{\sum(x - \bar{x})^2}$$

These values when inserted in (4) yield the desired least squares line. This line is usually called the regression line of y on x; hence the preceding derivation gives the result

(7) REGRESSION LINE: $y' - \bar{y} = b(x - \bar{x})$, where $b = \dfrac{\sum(x_i - \bar{x})y_i}{\sum(x_i - \bar{x})^2}$

A pioneer in the field of applied statistics gave the least squares line this name in connection with some studies he was making on estimating the extent to which the stature of sons of tall parents reverts or regresses toward the mean stature of the population.

For computational purposes, it is convenient to change the form of b slightly in the following manner.

$$b = \frac{\sum xy - \bar{x}\sum y}{\sum x^2 - 2\bar{x}\sum x + \sum \bar{x}^2}$$

(8)

$$= \frac{\sum xy - n\bar{x}\bar{y}}{\sum x^2 - n\bar{x}^2}$$

Table 3 illustrates the computational procedure for the data of Table 2. Here (7) was used to calculate b instead of the suggested computing

TABLE 3

x	y	$x - \bar{x}$	$(x - \bar{x})y$	$(x - \bar{x})^2$
12	5.27	−18	−94.86	324
18	5.68	−12	−68.16	144
24	6.25	−6	−37.50	36
30	7.21	0	0	0
36	8.02	6	48.12	36
42	8.71	12	104.52	144
48	8.42	18	151.56	324
210	49.56		103.68	1008

formula (8) because $\bar{x}$ is so simple. As a result of these computations, the equation of the regression line was found to be

$$y' = .10x + 4.0$$

The graph of this line is shown in Fig. 5.

In fitting a straight line to a set of points, as in the preceding illustration, it is intuitively assumed that the resulting line is an estimate of a theoretical line of regression. The problem of determining the accuracy of the least-squares line as an estimate of the theoretical line of regression is considered in Chapter 11. Chapter 8, however, discusses theoretical lines of regression as models for empirical lines of regression.

There is an important difference between the scatter diagrams of Fig. 1 and Fig. 5 that should be noted. In Fig. 1 the points correspond to a random sample of 30 students; consequently, both x and y are random variables. In Fig. 5, however, the x values were chosen in advance, so that y is the only random variable. Since least squares can be applied whether the x values were fixed in advance or were obtained from random samples, the regression approach to studying the linear relationship between two variables is more flexible than the correlation approach. The interpretation of r as a measure of the strength of the linear relationship between two variables obviously does not apply if the values of x are selected as desired because the value of r will usually depend heavily on the choice of x values. In addition to being more flexible, regression methods also possess the advantage of being the natural methods to use in many experimental situations. The experimenter often wishes to change x by uniform amounts over the range of interest for that variable rather than take a random sample of x values. Thus, if he wanted to study the effect of an amino acid on growth, he would increase the amount of amino acid by a fixed amount, or factor, each time he ran the experiment.

7.3 Multiple Linear Regression

It happens quite often that the method of the preceding section for estimating one variable by means of a related variable yields poor results not because the relationship is far removed from the linear one assumed there but because there is no single variable related closely enough to the variable being estimated to yield good results. However, it may happen that there are several variables that, when taken jointly, will serve as a satisfactory basis for estimating the desired variable. Since linear functions are so simple to work with and experience shows that many sets of variables are approximately linearly related, it is reasonable to attempt to estimate the desired variable by means of a linear function of the remaining variables. For this purpose let $Y, X_1, X_2, \cdots, X_k$ represent the available variables and consider the problem of estimating the variable Y by means of a linear function of the remaining variables. If the variable used to estimate Y is denoted by Y', the linear estimating function may be expressed as

$$(9) \qquad Y' = c_0 + c_1 X_1 + c_2 X_2 + \cdots + c_k X_k$$

where the c's are to be determined by means of available data.

As in the case of two variables, the unknown coefficients are estimated by the method of least squares. This implies that n sets of values of the

$k + 1$ variables are available for obtaining the estimates. Geometrically, the problem is one of finding the equation of the plane which fits best, in the sense of least squares, a set of n points in $k + 1$ dimensions.

The problem now is to find the set of c's in (9) that will minimize the sum $\sum_{i=1}^{n} (Y_i - Y_i')^2$. As in the case of two variables, it is more convenient to work with variables measured from their sample means than with the variables themselves; hence first let

$$y = Y - \bar{Y}$$
$$x_j = X_j - \bar{X}_j, \quad j = 1, 2, \cdots, k$$

If y' is defined by $y' = Y' - \bar{Y}$, then

(10) $$Y - Y' = y + \bar{Y} - (y' + \bar{Y}) = y - y'$$

If now the capital X's and Y in (9) are expressed in terms of the small x's and y, that equation can be written in the form

(11) $$y' = a_0 + a_1 x_1 + a_2 x_2 + \cdots + a_k x_k$$

where the a's could be expressed in terms of $\bar{Y}$, the c's, and the $\bar{X}$'s if so desired. However, from (10) it is clear that minimizing $\sum (Y - Y')^2$ is equivalent to minimizing $\sum (y - y')^2$; consequently one can just as well determine the a's to minimize the latter sum, which because of (11) may be written

(12) $$G(a_0, a_1, \cdots, a_k) = \sum [y - a_0 - a_1 x_1 - \cdots - a_k x_k]^2$$

If this function is to have a minimum value, it is necessary that its partial derivatives vanish there; hence the a's must satisfy the equations

$$\frac{\partial G}{\partial a_0} = \frac{\partial G}{\partial a_1} = \cdots = \frac{\partial G}{\partial a_k} = 0$$

Differentiation of (12) produces the equations

$$\sum 2[y - a_0 - a_1 x_1 - \cdots - a_k x_k] [-1] = 0$$
$$\sum 2[y - a_0 - a_1 x_1 - \cdots - a_k x_k] [-x_1] = 0$$
$$\cdots\cdots\cdots\cdots\cdots\cdots\cdots\cdots\cdots\cdots\cdots$$
$$\sum 2[y - a_0 - a_1 x_1 - \cdots - a_k x_k] [-x_k] = 0$$

If these equations are multiplied by $\frac{1}{2}$, the summations performed term by term, and the first sum transferred to the right side, these equations will assume the form

(13)
$$a_0 n + a_1 \sum x_1 + \cdots + a_k \sum x_k = \sum y$$
$$a_0 \sum x_1 + a_1 \sum x_1^2 + \cdots + a_k \sum x_1 x_k = \sum x_1 y$$
$$\cdots\cdots\cdots\cdots\cdots\cdots\cdots\cdots\cdots\cdots\cdots$$
$$a_0 \sum x_k + a_1 \sum x_k x_1 + \cdots + a_k \sum x_k^2 = \sum x_k y$$

Since $\sum x_i = \sum (X_i - \bar{X}_i) = 0$ and $\sum y = \sum (Y - \bar{Y}) = 0$, all terms in the first equation, except the first term, vanish. This implies that $a_0 = 0$, and thus the number of equations to be solved has been reduced by 1. The advantage of using variables measured from their sample means to simplify the notation and solution of equations like (13) should be clear from this result. The problem is now reduced to solving the equations

$$
\begin{aligned}
a_1 \sum x_1{}^2 + a_2 \sum x_1 x_2 + \cdots + a_k \sum x_1 x_k &= \sum x_1 y \\
a_1 \sum x_2 x_1 + a_2 \sum x_2{}^2 + \cdots + a_k \sum x_2 x_k &= \sum x_2 y \\
\cdots\cdots\cdots\cdots\cdots\cdots\cdots\cdots\cdots\cdots\cdots\cdots \\
a_1 \sum x_k x_1 + a_2 \sum x_k x_2 + \cdots + a_k \sum x_k{}^2 &= \sum x_k y
\end{aligned}
$$

(14)

Equations such as (13) or (14), which are obtained by the method of least squares, are commonly called *normal equations*.

These equations are easily solved, provided that the number of equations is small. For large sets of equations much time is saved by using one of the compact computing schemes available for such problems. The most widely known is probably the Doolittle method, to which references are given at the end of this chapter.

The derivation of (14) did not require that all the n values of X_1, nor of the remaining variables, be different. It is necessary only that there be a sufficient number of distinct values of the variables $X_1, X_2, \cdots, X_k$ to determine uniquely the least-squares plane. Ordinarily, this means that $k + 1$ distinct values will suffice because a plane in $k + 1$ dimensions is determined by $k + 1$ points, provided that the $k + 1$ points do not lie in a lower dimensional plane. For example, a plane in three dimensions is determined by three points, provided that the three points do not lie on a straight line.

As an illustration of the preceding methods, consider the problem of estimating the amount of hay from a knowledge of the spring rainfall and temperature, based on the following data. Here Y denotes the amount of hay in units of 100 pounds per acre, X_1 the spring rainfall in inches, and X_2 the accumulated temperature above 42°F in the spring. The data gave the values

$$\bar{Y} = 28.0, \quad \bar{X}_1 = 4.91, \quad \bar{X}_2 = 594$$

$$\frac{1}{n}\sum x_1 y = 3.872, \quad \frac{1}{n}\sum x_2 y = -149.6, \quad \frac{1}{n}\sum x_1 x_2 = -52.36$$

$$\frac{1}{n}\sum x_1{}^2 = 1.21, \quad \frac{1}{n}\sum x_2{}^2 = 7225$$

The normal equations (14) then become, after multiplying through by n,

$$1.21 a_1 - 52.36 a_2 = 3.872$$
$$52.36 a_1 - 7225 a_2 = 149.6$$

The solution of these equations is $a_1 = 3.3$ and $a_2 = .004$; consequently (11) becomes

$$y' = 3.3x_1 + .004x_2$$

This result when expressed in terms of the capital letters of formula (9) yields

$$Y' = 9.4 + 3.3X_1 + .004X_2$$

This equation indicates that if X_2 is held fixed the amount of hay will increase about 330 pounds per acre with each inch increase in spring rainfall. On the other hand, if spring rainfall is held fixed, the accumulated spring temperature would have to increase about 250 units, which will be observed to be about three standard deviations for variable X_2, in order to increase the amount of hay by 100 pounds per acre. Thus it appears that the spring temperature is relatively unimportant compared with spring rainfall. Such conclusions, of course, are only approximately true. They depend on the variables being approximately linearly related, and they express only average relationships. They also assume that the function in (9) is a satisfactory estimate of a "true" linear regression function for those variables. As in the case of linear regression for one independent variable, the problem of the accuracy of the coefficients in the least squares regression function as estimates of the coefficients in a theoretical regression function is postponed to Chapter 11.

7.4 Curvilinear Regression

If a scatter diagram in the x,y plane indicates that a straight line will not fit a set of points satisfactorily because of the nonlinearity of the relationship, it may be possible to find some simple curve that will yield a satisfactory fit. Since an investigator always strives to explain relationships as simply as possible, with the restriction that his explanation be consistent with previous knowledge, he will prefer to use a simple type of curve. It follows, therefore, that the type of curve to use will depend largely on the amount of theoretical information one has concerning the relationship and thereafter on convenience

7.4.1 Polynomial Regression

If there are no theoretical reasons for expecting a curve of a certain type to represent the relationship, polynomials are usually selected because of their simplicity and flexibility. The lowest degree polynomial that will suffice can often be determined by an inspection of the scatter diagram. After the degree has been determined, the best-fitting polynomial of that degree may then be fitted by the method of least squares.

Let the degree of the polynomial be k and let the equation of the polynomial be written in the form

(15) $$y = a_0 + a_1 x + a_2 x^2 + \cdots + a_k x^k$$

The normal equations here need not be derived because they can be obtained from the normal equations (13) of multiple regression by using the original variables rather than the variables measured from their sample means and letting $X_i = x^i$. This is permissible because the derivation of equations (13) did not place any restriction on the nature of the variables $X_1, X_2, \cdots, X_k$, and therefore they may be related in any manner desired. With this choice of the X's, the normal equations for polynomial regression become

(16)
$$a_0 n + a_1 \sum x + \cdots + a_k \sum x^k = \sum y$$
$$a_0 \sum x + a_1 \sum x^2 + \cdots + a_k \sum x^{k+1} = \sum xy$$
$$\cdots\cdots\cdots\cdots\cdots\cdots\cdots\cdots\cdots\cdots\cdots\cdots$$
$$a_0 \sum x^k + a_1 \sum x^{k+1} + \cdots + a_k \sum x^{2k} = \sum x^k y$$

As in the case of multiple linear regression, if the number of equations is large, the equations should be solved by one of the compact computing schemes for such problems. From the discussion following (14), it follows that all n points of the scatter diagram for polynomial curve fitting need not have distinct x values. It will suffice to have $k + 1$ distinct x values, since a polynomial of degree k is uniquely determined by $k + 1$ points. In evaluating sums such as $\sum x^m$ it is understood that the sum is over all the x values and not over just the distinct x values.

If the investigator is not certain what degree polynomial should be used in a given problem and wishes to compare different degree polynomials for their adequacy, he would prefer a fitting technique that requires little additional labor to increase the degree of the fitted polynomial by one unit. Such a technique is available if one uses *orthogonal polynomials*. These polynomials possess the desirable property of leaving unchanged the coefficients of the previously fitted polynomial when a higher degree term is added. If orthogonal polynomials are not used, the entire set of coefficients would have to be recomputed. Orthogonal polynomials are particularly convenient when there is but one value of y to each value of x and the x values are equally spaced. In the latter case, however, the ordinary normal equations will simplify considerably if x is replaced by $x - \bar{x}$ in (15) because then $\sum(x - \bar{x})^m = 0$ for m odd. The normal equations (16) will then reduce to two sets of equations. Thus, if $k = 5$, the six normal equations will reduce to two sets of three equations each.

The odd-numbered equations will involve only the unknowns a_0, a_2, and a_4, whereas the even-numbered equations will involve only the unknowns a_1, a_3, and a_5. The technique of how to use orthogonal polynomials may be found in one of the references at the end of this chapter.

7.4.2 Other Regression Functions

In the preceding section it was pointed out that when there are no theoretical reasons for preferring a certain type of regression function polynomials are selected because of their simplicity and convenience. There are numerous situations, however, in which the nature of the relationship between two variables is known from theoretical considerations. In such situations the fundamental regression problem is to obtain estimates of the parameters that are needed to determine the equation of the curve that represents the relationship. For example, the equation

$$pv^{\gamma} = \text{constant}$$

represents the relation between the pressure and volume of an ideal gas undergoing adiabatic change. Here γ is a parameter whose value depends on the particular gas and for which an estimate may be obtained from experimental data.

Another example of a nonpolynomial regression function is the function often used in studying simple growth phenomena. If it is assumed that the rate of growth of a biological population is proportional to its size, then the regression function is a simple exponential function. To verify this fact, let y denote the size of the population at time t. Then the assumption concerning the rate of growth can be written in the form

$$\frac{dy}{dt} = cy$$

where c is the constant of proportionality. This equation is equivalent to

$$\frac{dy}{y} = c \, dt$$

Integration of both sides will yield

$$\log y = ct + k$$

where k is the constant of integration. Letting $k = \log b$, this equation simplifies to

(17) $$y = be^{ct}$$

Suppose, now, that one is given a set of n points (t_1, y_1), (t_2, y_2), $\cdots$, (t_n, y_n) representing the size of a growing population at the times t_1, t_2, $\cdots$, t_n. If the parameters b and c are to be estimated by least squares, it is necessary to minimize the function

$$G(b, c) = \sum_{i=1}^{n} [y_i - be^{ct_i}]^2$$

Calculating the partial derivatives with respect to b and c and equating them to 0 will yield the normal equations

$$\sum [y_i - be^{ct_i}] [-e^{ct_i}] = 0$$
$$\sum [y_i - be^{ct_i}] [-be^{ct_i}t_i] = 0$$

These equations simplify to

(18)
$$b\sum e^{2ct_i} = \sum y_i e^{ct_i}$$
$$b\sum t_i e^{2ct_i} = \sum y_i t_i e^{ct_i}$$

The solution of these equations is very difficult and requires tedious numerical methods. This example illustrates what frequently occurs, namely, that the method of least squares for nonpolynomial regression often gives rise to normal equations that are difficult to solve.

There are numerous other methods of fitting a curve to a set of points that can be employed when least squares gives rise to computational difficulties. One such method is to introduce new variables that are functions of the old variables in an effort to obtain a more tractable relationship. Thus, in the preceding illustration, it is convenient to work with the variable $Y = \log y$ rather than with y itself. If logarithms, to the base e, of both sides of (17) are taken, then (17) becomes

$$\log y = \log b + ct$$

Then, letting $Y = \log y$ and $a = \log b$, this relationship reduces to the linear relationship

$$Y = a + ct$$

The problem has now been reduced to the problem of fitting a straight line to a set of points in the t, Y plane and thus to a simple problem in least squares. These least squares estimates for c and a may then be used to yield estimates for c and b. The estimates for c and b obtained in this manner differ, of course, from those obtained by solving the original least squares equations (18); however, the differences are usually quite small.

In studying the problem of determining the accuracy of estimates of regression parameters, it is essential to know how the errors of estimation are distributed. The type of assumption made about their distribution will often determine whether to use direct least squares or to use least squares on a modification of the relationship. The problem of the accuracy of least squares estimates is considered in later chapters; however, it is mentioned here to point out that least squares applied to a modification of a regression relationship may sometimes be preferred to least squares applied to the original relationship and therefore that such a modification does not necessarily yield inferior estimates.

For some types of regression functions it is not possible to introduce changes of variables that will reduce the problem to one for which the least squares equations become tractable. For example, in studying growth phenomena of a somewhat more complex nature than those implied by (17), the modified exponential function $y = a + be^{ct}$ is often used as a regression model. Taking logarithms will not help here because of the parameter a. For functions such as this, other fitting procedures are often used. The simplest procedure is to select three points which appear to represent the trend of the data-points and pass the curve through those points. The three equations resulting from having the coordinates of the points satisfy the equation would suffice to determine the three parameters. There are other more refined methods that could also be used here.

7.5   Linear Discriminant Functions

A problem that arises quite often in certain branches of science is that of discriminating between two groups of individuals or objects on the basis of several properties of those individuals or objects. For example, a botanist might wish to classify a set of plants, some of which belong to one species and the rest to a second species, into their proper species by means of three or four measurements taken on each plant. If the two species were fairly similar with respect to all those measurements, it might not be possible to classify the plants correctly by means of any single measurement because of a fairly large amount of overlap in the distributions of this measurement for the two species; however, it might be possible to find a linear combination of those various measurements whose distributions for the two species would possess very little overlap. This linear combination could then be used to yield a type of index number by means of which plants of two species could be differentiated with a high percentage of success. The procedure for discriminating would consist in finding a critical value of the index such that any plant whose index value fell below the critical value would be classified as belonging to one species, otherwise to the other species.

The principal difference between a *linear discrimination function* and an ordinary linear regression function arises from the nature of the dependent variable. A linear regression function uses values of the dependent variable to determine a linear function that will estimate the values of the dependent variable, whereas the discriminant function possesses no such values or variable but uses instead a two-way classification of the data to determine the linear function.

Consider a set of k variables $x_1, x_2, \cdots, x_k$, by means of which it is desired to discriminate between two groups of individuals. Let

(19)
$$z = \lambda_1 x_1 + \lambda_2 x_2 + \cdots + \lambda_k x_k$$

represent a linear combination of these variables. The problem then is to determine the λ's by means of some criterion that will enable z to serve as an index for differentiating between members of the two groups. For the purpose of simplifying the geometrical discussion of the problem, consider two variables with n_1 and n_2 individuals, respectively, in the two groups. The equation

$$z = \lambda_1 x_1 + \lambda_2 x_2$$

then represents a plane in three dimensions passing through the origin and having direction numbers λ_1, λ_2, and -1. If the two sets of points

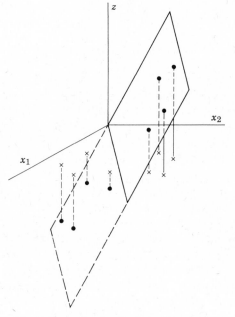

Fig. 6. Example of a discriminating plane.

corresponding to the two groups of individuals are such that they can be separated by means of a plane through the origin, as shown in Fig. 6, it is clear that the values of z corresponding to the two groups will assume increasingly large negative and positive values as the separating plane approaches perpendicularity to the x_1,x_2 plane. At the same time, however, the variations of the values of z within a group becomes increasingly large for both groups; consequently the increase in the separation of the values of z for the two groups occurs at the expense of an increase in the separation of the values of z within each group. This situation corresponds to that in which the means of two distributions are separating but for which the standard deviations are increasing to such an extent that greater discrimination between the two distributions does not necessarily result. It would be desirable, therefore, to choose a plane that separates the values of z for the two groups as widely as possible relative to the variation of the values of z within the two groups. As a measure of the separation of the two groups, it is convenient to use $(\bar{z}_1 - \bar{z}_2)^2$, where $\bar{z}_1$ and $\bar{z}_2$ are the means of the two groups. As a measure of the variation of the values of z within the two groups, it is convenient to use $\sum\limits_{i=1}^{2} \sum\limits_{j=1}^{n_i} (z_{ij} - \bar{z}_i)^2$. Here z_{ij} denotes the z value of the jth individual in the ith group, where $i = 1$ or 2. Then the desired plane will be that plane for which the λ's are determined to maximize the function

$$(20) \qquad G = \frac{(\bar{z}_1 - \bar{z}_2)^2}{\sum\limits_{i=1}^{2} \sum\limits_{j=1}^{n_i} (z_{ij} - \bar{z}_i)^2}$$

Although the arguments leading to (20) were elucidated by means of two variables and three-dimensional geometry, they hold equally well for k variables; consequently the solution of the problem will be carried out for the general case.

Let x_{pij} represent the value of x_p for the jth individual in the ith group and let $\bar{x}_{pi}$ represent the mean value of x_p for the n_i individuals in that group. Then from (19) it follows that

$$(21) \qquad \bar{z}_1 - \bar{z}_2 = \lambda_1(\bar{x}_{11} - \bar{x}_{12}) + \cdots + \lambda_k(\bar{x}_{k1} - \bar{x}_{k2}),$$

and

$$(22) \qquad z_{ij} - \bar{z}_i = \lambda_1(x_{1ij} - \bar{x}_{1i}) + \cdots + \lambda_k(x_{kij} - \bar{x}_{ki})$$

If $d_p = \bar{x}_{p1} - \bar{x}_{p2}$, it follows from (21) that

$$(\bar{z}_1 - \bar{z}_2)^2 = (\lambda_1 d_1 + \cdots + \lambda_k d_k)^2$$

$$= \sum\limits_{p=1}^{k} \sum\limits_{q=1}^{k} \lambda_p \lambda_q d_p d_q$$

If $S_{pq} = \sum\limits_{i=1}^{2} \sum\limits_{j=1}^{n_i} (x_{pij} - \bar{x}_{pi})(x_{qij} - \bar{x}_{qi})$, it follows from (22) that

$$
\begin{aligned}
\sum_{i=1}^{2} \sum_{j=1}^{n_i} (z_{ij} - \bar{z}_i)^2 &= \sum_{i=1}^{2} \sum_{j=1}^{n_i} [\lambda_1(x_{1ij} - \bar{x}_{1i}) + \cdots + \lambda_k(x_{kij} - \bar{x}_{ki})]^2 \\
&= \sum_{i=1}^{2} \sum_{j=1}^{n_i} \sum_{p=1}^{k} \sum_{q=1}^{k} \lambda_p \lambda_q (x_{pij} - \bar{x}_{pi})(x_{qij} - \bar{x}_{qi}) \\
&= \sum_{p=1}^{k} \sum_{q=1}^{k} \lambda_p \lambda_q \sum_{i=1}^{2} \sum_{j=1}^{n_i} (x_{pij} - \bar{x}_{pi})(x_{qij} - \bar{x}_{qi}) \\
&= \sum_{p=1}^{k} \sum_{q=1}^{k} \lambda_p \lambda_q S_{pq}
\end{aligned}
$$

When these values are inserted in (20), it reduces to

(23)
$$
G = \frac{\sum\limits_{p=1}^{k} \sum\limits_{q=1}^{k} \lambda_p \lambda_q d_p d_q}{\sum\limits_{p=1}^{k} \sum\limits_{q=1}^{k} \lambda_p \lambda_q S_{pq}} = \frac{A}{B}
$$

Since the λ's are to be determined to make G a maximum, it is necessary that $\partial G/\partial \lambda_r = 0$ for $r = 1, \cdots, k$ at the maximizing point. This requirement may be expressed in the form

$$
\frac{\partial G}{\partial \lambda_r} = \frac{B \dfrac{\partial A}{\partial \lambda_r} - A \dfrac{\partial B}{\partial \lambda_r}}{B^2} = 0, \qquad r = 1, \cdots, k
$$

which is equivalent to

(24)
$$
\frac{\partial B}{\partial \lambda_r} = \frac{1}{G} \frac{\partial A}{\partial \lambda_r}, \qquad r = 1, \cdots, k
$$

For ease of differentiating, it is convenient to write out B in the form

$$
\begin{aligned}
B = \lambda_1 \lambda_1 S_{11} + \cdots + \lambda_1 \lambda_r S_{1r} + \cdots + \lambda_1 \lambda_k S_{1k} \\
\cdots\cdots\cdots\cdots\cdots\cdots\cdots\cdots\cdots\cdots\cdots \\
\lambda_r \lambda_1 S_{r1} + \cdots + \lambda_r \lambda_r S_{rr} + \cdots + \lambda_r \lambda_k S_{rk} \\
\cdots\cdots\cdots\cdots\cdots\cdots\cdots\cdots\cdots\cdots\cdots \\
\lambda_k \lambda_1 S_{k1} + \cdots + \lambda_k \lambda_r S_{kr} + \cdots + \lambda_k \lambda_k S_{kk}
\end{aligned}
$$

It will be observed that λ_r occurs as a common factor of both the rth row and the rth column. Since $S_{ij} = S_{ji}$, it therefore follows that

$$
\frac{\partial B}{\partial \lambda_r} = 2(\lambda_1 S_{r1} + \cdots + \lambda_k S_{rk})
$$

Similarly,

$$\frac{\partial A}{\partial \lambda_r} = 2(\lambda_1 d_r d_1 + \cdots + \lambda_k d_r d_k)$$

$$= 2(\lambda_1 d_1 + \cdots + \lambda_k d_k) d_r$$

If these expressions are inserted in (24), it will reduce to

(25) $\qquad \lambda_1 S_{r1} + \lambda_2 S_{r2} + \cdots + \lambda_k S_{rk} = c d_r, \qquad r = 1, \cdots, k$

where $c = [\lambda_1 d_1 + \cdots + \lambda_k d_k]/G$ is independent of r.

Since

(26) $$S_{pq} = \sum_{i=1}^{2} \sum_{j=1}^{n_i} (x_{pij} - \bar{x}_{pi})(x_{qij} - \bar{x}_{qi})$$

and

(27) $$d_p = \bar{x}_{p1} - \bar{x}_{p2}$$

are numerical quantities in any given problem, the necessary conditions (25) constitute a set of k linear equations in the λ's. The solution of these equations determines the λ's except for the unknown factor c. Although c is actually a function of the λ's here, so that the solution of these equations expresses each λ_i as a constant times this function, the factor c

TABLE 4

Race A	x_1	6.36	5.92	5.92	6.44	6.40	6.56	6.64	6.68	6.72	6.76	6.72
	x_2	5.24	5.12	5.36	5.64	5.16	5.56	5.36	4.96	5.48	5.60	5.08
Race B	x_1	6.00	5.60	5.64	5.76	5.96	5.72	5.64	5.44	5.04	4.56	5.48	5.76
	x_2	4.88	4.64	4.96	4.80	5.08	5.04	4.96	4.88	4.44	4.04	4.20	4.80

cancels out from numerator and denominator of G when these values are substituted in (23). Thus there is no unique set of λ's maximizing G, and any multiple of a set of λ's satisfying equations (25) will do just as well. From (19) it is clear that such a multiple can be ignored because the two sets of z's would merely be multiplied by this constant factor and thus would be equivalent as far as discriminating between the two groups is concerned. As a matter of fact, it is usually convenient to choose $c = 1$, solve the equations, and then reduce (19) to the form in which one of the λ's, say λ_1, is unity.

As an illustration of the use of this function, consider the data of Table 4 on the mean numbers of teeth found on the proximal (x_1) and distal (x_2) combs of two races of insects. The problem here is to discriminate between members of the two races by means of the two indicated variables.

Computations give $S_{11} = 2.68$, $S_{12} = 1.29$, $S_{22} = 1.75$, $d_1 = 0.915$, $d_2 = 0.597$; consequently if c is chosen equal to 1, (25) becomes

$$2.68\lambda_1 + 1.29\lambda_2 = 0.915$$
$$1.29\lambda_1 + 1.75\lambda_2 = 0.597$$

The solution of these equations is $\lambda_1 = 0.274$ and $\lambda_2 = 0.139$. If these values are used, the linear discriminant function (19) becomes

$$z = 0.274x_1 + 0.139x_2$$

For the purpose of computing values of z, it is more convenient to choose c so that either λ_1 or λ_2 equals 1. If c is chosen to make λ_1 equal 1, this discriminant function reduces to

$$z = x_1 + 0.507x_2$$

The values of z corresponding to the various members of the two races given in Table 4 are as follows:

Race A	9.02	8.52	8.64	9.30	9.02	9.38	9.36	9.19	9.50	9.60	9.30
Race B	8.47	7.95	8.15	8.19	8.54	8.28	8.15	7.91	7.29	6.61	7.61	8.19

It will be noted that the two races are segregated by means of z except for the slight overlap found in the second entry for Race A and the fifth entry for Race B.

As presented in this section, a linear discriminant function is constructed for the purpose of classifying future observations into their proper group. Thus the problem is essentially one of estimating the λ's. This function could be used as a device for testing the hypothesis that the two groups differ in the manner described earlier; however, there are other more natural methods for treating the latter problem.

REFERENCES

Additional material on correlation and in particular on the z transformation may be found in R. A. Fisher, *Statistical Methods for Research Workers*, Oliver and Boyd.

The Doolittle method for solving a set of linear equations may be found in the preceding reference or in Croxton and Cowden, *Applied General Statistics*, Prentice-Hall.

The technique of orthogonal polynomials is explained in the first reference above or in Anderson and Bancroft, *Statistical Theory in Research*, McGraw-Hill Book Co.

EXERCISES

1. Calculate the value of r for the following data on the heights (x) and weights (y) of 12 college students.

x	63	72	70	68	66	69	74	70	63	72	65	71
y	124	184	161	164	140	154	210	164	126	172	133	150

2. What interpretation would you make if told that the correlation between the number of automobile accidents per year and the age of the driver is $r = -.60$ if only drivers with at least 1 accident are considered?

3. What explanation would you give if told that the correlation between fertilizer added and profit made in raising vegetables on a certain experimental farm was only .20?

4. What would be the effect on the value of r for the correlation between height and weight of males of all ages if only males in the 20–25 age group were sampled? Observe what effect this restriction would have on the scatter diagram.

5. Explain why it would not be surprising to find a high correlation between the density of traffic on Wall Street and the height of the tide in Maine if observations were taken every hour from 6:00 A.M. to 10:00 P.M. and high tide occurred at 8:00 A.M. Plot a scatter diagram to assist in the explanation.

6. How large a correlation coefficient is needed for a sample of size 25 before one is justified in claiming that $\rho \neq 0$?

7. Test the hypothesis that $\rho = .7$ if a sample of 50 gave $r = .6$.

8. Prove that $r_{uv} = r_{xy}$ where u and v are the integral variables introduced in 7.1.2.

9. For the data of problem 1, find the equation of the regression line of y on x.

10. Derive the least-squares equations for fitting a curve of the type $y = \alpha x + \beta/x$ to a set of n points.

11. Derive the least-squares equations for fitting $y = axe^{-b(x-c)^2}$ to a set of n points.

12. The following data are for tensile strength (100 lb/in.^{2}) and hardness (Rockwell E) of die-cast aluminum. Find the equation of the regression line with y chosen as tensile strength.

Tensile strength (y)	293	349	368	301	340	308	354	313	322	334
Hardness (x)	53	70	84	55	78	64	71	53	82	67

Tensile strength (y)	377	247	348	298	287	292	345	380	257	258
Hardness (x)	70	56	86	60	72	51	88	95	51	75

Tensile strength (y)	265	281	246	258	237	286	324	282	340
Hardness (x)	54	78	52	69	54	64	83	56	70

13. Show that the equation of the simple regression line can be written in the form $y' - \bar{y} = r(s_y/s_x)(x - \bar{x})$.

14. Use the formula in problem 13 to show that the correlation coefficient between the regression line values y_i' and the observed values y_i is equal to r.

15. The following data are for the 3 variables honor points (Y), general intelligence scores (X_1), and hours of study (X_2). Find the equation of the regression plane of y on x_1 and x_2, given

$$\sum x_1^2 = 250, \quad \sum x_1 x_2 = 33, \quad \sum x_2^2 = 36, \quad \sum x_1 y = 106, \quad \sum x_2 y = 22$$

16. Prove that $s_{x-y}^2 = s_x^2 + s_y^2 - 2rs_x s_y$.

17. Find an expression for s^2 for the first n positive integers by using a familiar formula for the sum of the squares of those integers.

18. If x and y denote the ranks of an individual with respect to two characters for a group of n individuals, derive the formula $r = 1 - 6\Sigma(x - y)^2/n(n^2 - 1)$ for the correlation of the 2 ranked variables by using the results in problems 16 and 17. Calculate r by means of this formula for the data of Table 1 and compare with the regular r value of .66. Replace tied ranks by the mean of the ranks involved.

19. The following data are for intelligence-test scores, grade-point averages, and reading-rates of students.

(a) Calculate r between I.T. scores and G.P.A.

(b) Find the equation of the regression line of G.P.A. on I.T. scores.

(c) Find the equation of the regression plane of G.P.A. on I.T. scores and R.R.

(d) By comparing errors of estimation, determine whether (c) is considerably better than (b) for estimating G.P.A.

I.T.	295	152	214	171	131	178	225	141	116	173
G.P.A.	2.4	.6	.2	0	1	.6	1	.4	0	2.6
R.R.	41	18	45	29	28	38	25	26	22	37

I.T.	230	195	174	177	210	236	198	217	143	186
G.P.A.	2.6	0	1.8	0	.4	1.8	.8	1	.2	2.8
R.R.	39	38	24	32	26	29	34	38	40	27

I.T.	233	136	183	223	106	184	134	211	151	231
G.P.A.	1.4	.2	.4	1.4	0	.8	.8	.8	.4	2.2
R.R.	44	32	26	50	24	32	48	18	20	26

I.T.	135	146	227	204	223	142	176	238	268	163
G.P.A.	1.4	1.2	1.4	1.4	1.4	.8	.8	2.6	2.6	.2
R.R.	26	19	35	26	18	22	23	27	40	33

20. The following data give the velocity of the Mississippi River in feet per second corresponding to various depths expressed in terms of the ratio D of the measured depth to the depth of the river. (a) Fit a parabola $V = a + bD + cD^2$ to the data, choosing a convenient origin. (b) Find V when $D = .9$ (observed $V = 2.976$). (c) When would you consider extrapolation as used in (b) a valid procedure?

D	0	.1	.2	.3	.4	.5	.6	.7	.8
V	3.195	3.230	3.253	3.261	3.252	3.228	3.181	3.127	3.059

21. The following data are for a growing plant. (a) Plot the data on ordinary, semilog, and log-log paper and verify that it is most nearly linear on semilog paper. (b) Fit a simple exponential to the data by first taking logarithms of the exponential equation.

Day	0	1	2	3	4	5	6	7	8
Height	.75	1.20	1.75	2.50	3.45	4.70	6.20	8.25	11.50

22. The pressure of a gas and its volume are related by an equation of the form $pv^a = b$. In a certain experiment the following values were obtained. Determine a and b by least squares on the logarithmic equation.

p	.5	1	1.5	2	2.5	3
v	1.62	1	.75	.62	.52	.46

23. Suppose that the exponential $y = ae^{bx}$ is the proper curve to fit to a set of points. If the parameters a and b are determined by least squares applied to the logarithm of this equation and also by least squares directly, which method is more likely to be heavily influenced by a point with an unusually large value of x?

24. Derive the least-squares equations for fitting a modified exponential $y = c + ae^{bx}$ to a set of n points and indicate why these equations would be difficult to solve.

25. Explain how the least-squares equations for multiple linear regression are also applicable if second-degree terms in addition to the first-degree terms in the k variables are introduced in the regression equation.

26. Derive the equations that would need to be solved if one were to estimate a and b in the equation of the regression line by requiring that the sum of the squares of the perpendicular distances to the regression line be a minimum.

27. Classify the individuals of problem 19 into 1 of 2 groups on the basis of having a G.P.A. less than or greater than .9. (a) Using the remaining variables, find the equation of the discriminant function for classifying individuals into the proper G.P.A. group. (b) Calculate the values of z for the individuals and note whether the discriminant function does appreciably better than either variable alone.

28. Two polynomials $P_i(x)$ and $P_j(x)$ of degrees i and j, respectively, are said to be orthogonal on a set of points $x_1, x_2, \cdots, x_n$, provided that $\sum_{k=1}^{n} P_i(x_k)P_j(x_k) = 0$, $i \neq j$. A polynomial $P_i(x)$ is said to be normalized on the set if $\sum_{k=1}^{n} P_i^2(x_k) = 1$. For the points $x = 0, 1, 2, 3, 4$, find an orthogonal normalized (orthonormal) set of polynomials $P_0(x)$, $P_1(x)$, $P_2(x)$.

29. Assuming the properties defined in problem 28, obtain the least-squares equations for the coefficients of the polynomial $y = a_0P_0(x) + a_1P_1(x) + \cdots + a_kP_k(x)$ and show that their solution for a particular coefficient a_i is the same regardless of the degree of the polynomial, provided, of course, that $i < k$.

30. For linear regression involving more than 2 variables, the multiple correlation coefficient is defined as the correlation between the observed values y_i and their estimates y_i'. It is designed to measure the extent to which the linear regression function is capable of predicting the dependent variable y. Calculate the value of the multiple correlation for the data of problem 19 if the answer to 19(c) is $y' = .012x_1 - .007x_2 - .97$.

31. The partial correlation coefficient between variables x_i and x_j is defined as the correlation between the values $x_i - x_i'$ and $x_j - x_j'$, where x_i' is the regression value of x_i on all variables except x_j and x_j' is the regression value of x_j on all variables except x_i. It is designed to measure the correlation between the variables x_i and x_j when the effects of the remaining variables have been eliminated. Calculate the partial correlation between G.P.A. and R.R. for problem 19, if the answer to 19(b) is $y' = .0116x_1 - 1.11$. It will first be necessary to work 19(b) for R.R. and I.T.

CHAPTER 8

Theoretical Frequency Distributions For Correlation and Regression

Frequency functions of two variables were defined in Chapter 2 for both discrete and continuous variables. Although a number of their properties were discussed there, it is now necessary to consider additional properties if mathematical models for empirical frequency distributions of two variables, such as those encountered in Chapter 7 under correlation, are to be constructed. These properties will turn out to be essential in the construction of regression models as well.

8.1 Continuous Distributions of Two Variables

Since correlation and regression as defined in the preceding chapter involve pairs of continuous variables, it will be necessary to study properties of joint frequency functions for such variables. In this connection, it will be found that theoretical moments are particularly useful for a theory of correlation, whereas the notions of marginal and conditional distributions are needed for a theory of regression. These two types of distributions have already been defined for discrete variables in Chapter 2.

The geometrical representation of $f(x, y)$ as a surface in three dimensions as displayed in Fig. 12, Chapter 2, is convenient for interpreting probability as a volume under the surface; however, in discussing correlation, and marginal and conditional distributions, it is more convenient to think of $f(x, y)$ as giving the density distribution of probability mass over the x,y plane, with the total mass being equal to 1. This was easy to do in 2.12 for discrete variables because only a finite number of mass points was involved. Here, however, it is necessary to conceive of a continuous distribution of mass such as in a sheet of metal. The density of the metal

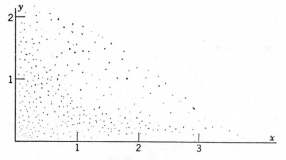

Fig. 1. Probability density distribution.

sheet at a point (x, y) is given by $f(x, y)$ and the mass of the entire sheet is equal to 1. Figure 1 attempts to portray this density interpretation for the frequency function that is graphed as a surface in Fig. 12, Chapter 2.

From the density point of view, the probability that a single sample will yield a point (x, y) lying in a given rectangle is equal to the mass of the rectangle. This interpretation of probability, as well as the volume interpretation, clearly holds for regions other than rectangles in the x,y plane.

8.1.1   Marginal Distributions

Models for regression will be discussed before those for correlation because correlation models require some of the material needed for regression. A general theoretical regression curve can be defined by means of a conditional distribution. It in turn can be defined by means of a marginal distribution; therefore consider such distributions for continuous variables next.

For the purpose of obtaining a formula for continuous variables corresponding to (28), Chapter 2, let $f(x, y)$ be the joint frequency function of any two continuous random variables and consider the following inequalities.

$$P\{\alpha < x < \beta\} = P\{\alpha < x < \beta, -\infty < y < \infty\}$$
$$= \int_{\alpha}^{\beta} \int_{-\infty}^{\infty} f(x, y) \, dy \, dx$$
$$= \int_{\alpha}^{\beta} h(x) \, dx$$

where, as indicated,

(1) $$h(x) = \int_{-\infty}^{\infty} f(x, y) \, dy$$

Now, if x is considered independently of y, then by definition

$$P\{\alpha < x < \beta\} = \int_{\alpha}^{\beta} f(x)\, dx$$

where $f(x)$ is the frequency function of x alone. If these two expressions for $P\{\alpha < x < \beta\}$ are equated,

(2) $$\int_{\alpha}^{\beta} h(x)\, dx = \int_{\alpha}^{\beta} f(x)\, dx$$

Since this equality is to hold for all intervals (α, β), α may be held fixed and β allowed to vary, in which event these integrals may be treated as functions of β. By the well-known calculus formula that has been used before, if

$$F(\beta) = \int_{\alpha}^{\beta} f(x)\, dx$$

then

$$\frac{dF(\beta)}{d\beta} = f(\beta)$$

If both sides of (2) are differentiated with respect to β, this formula will give

$$h(\beta) = f(\beta)$$

Since this is an identity in β, it follows that the function $h(x)$ defined by (1) is the frequency function $f(x)$. These arguments therefore show that the marginal frequency function $f(x)$ is given by the following formula.

(3) MARGINAL DISTRIBUTION: $f(x) = \int_{-\infty}^{\infty} f(x, y)\, dy$

This formula is the continuous analogue of formula (28), Chapter 2, for the discrete case. In a similar manner the integration of $f(x, y)$ with respect to x from $-\infty$ to $+\infty$ will yield the y marginal frequency function $g(y)$. From the density point of view $f(x)$ may be thought of as giving the probability density distribution along the x axis after the entire probability mass in the x,y plane has been projected perpendicularly onto the x axis.

As a simple illustration of how formula (3) applies, consider the joint frequency function

(4) $$f(x, y) = \begin{cases} 2 - x - y, & 0 < x < 1, 0 < y < 1 \\ 0 & , \quad \text{elsewhere} \end{cases}$$

Here, formula (3) gives

(5) $$f(x) = \int_0^1 (2 - x - y)\, dy = \tfrac{3}{2} - x$$

and

$$g(y) = \int_0^1 (2 - x - y)\, dx = \tfrac{3}{2} - y$$

As a second illustration, consider the following frequency function:

$$f(x, y) = \begin{cases} \tfrac{1}{2}xy, & 0 < x < 2, 0 < y < x \\ 0, & \text{elsewhere} \end{cases}$$

In this problem the sample space is the triangle bounded by the lines $x = 2$, $y = x$, and $y = 0$. Although the limits in formula (3) are written $-\infty$ and ∞, this is merely for notational convenience and it is understood that when the limits are not infinite one must determine the limits from the sample space boundaries. The limits of integration in this problem certainly depend on the chosen value of x. Formula (3) gives

$$f(x) = \tfrac{1}{2} \int_0^x xy\, dy = \frac{x^3}{4}, \quad 0 < x < 2$$

Similarly,

$$g(y) = \tfrac{1}{2} \int_y^2 xy\, dx = \tfrac{1}{4}y(4 - y^2), \quad 0 < y < 2$$

8.1.2 Conditional Distributions

Now that marginal distributions have been determined, it is possible to proceed with the problem of defining conditional distributions for continuous variables. For the purpose of obtaining a formula for continuous variables corresponding to (29), Chapter 2, consider the function defined by

(6) $$\frac{f(x, y)}{f(x)}$$

If x is held fixed and is such that $f(x) > 0$, then (6) defines a non-negative function of y for which, in view of (3),

$$\int_{-\infty}^{\infty} \frac{f(x, y)}{f(x)}\, dy = \frac{1}{f(x)} \int_{-\infty}^{\infty} f(x, y)\, dy = 1$$

Thus, according to (31), Chapter 2, $f(x, y)/f(x)$ has properties that enable it to serve as a frequency function for y when x is fixed as indicated.

Because of this property, $f(x, y)/f(x)$ is called the conditional frequency function of y for fixed x and is denoted by $f(y \mid x)$. This definition may be expressed as follows.

(7)   CONDITIONAL DISTRIBUTION: $f(y \mid x) = \dfrac{f(x, y)}{f(x)}$

By going back to the definition of conditional probability for events as given by (6), Chapter 2, and working with integrals, it is possible to derive (7) directly in a natural manner; however (7) is treated here as a definition. Formula (7) is identical with the corresponding formula for the discrete case. As in the case of discrete variables, the conditional distribution of y as given by $f(y \mid x)$ is sometimes called the x array distribution. The conditional frequency function of x for y fixed is defined in a similar manner.

From a density point of view $f(y \mid x)$ may be thought of as giving the probability density distribution along the vertical line in the x,y plane corresponding to the fixed value of x, the total mass of this line being equal to 1. The frequency function $f(x, y)$ as it stands could not be used as a probability density function along such a line because by (3) it would not give a total probability mass of one for the entire line unless $f(x)$ happened to be equal to 1. The factor $1/f(x)$ insures that the total mass of the line will be 1.

In the surface representation of $f(x, y)$ the conditional distribution of y for $x = x_0$, say, is represented by a modification of the curve of inter-section of the surface and the plane whose equation is $x = x_0$. Since the area under the curve is ordinarily not equal to 1, the ordinates of the curve must be multiplied by the proper number to make the area equal 1 before the curve will be the graph of a frequency function. The proper number, of course, is $1/f(x_0)$. Figure 2 indicates this geometrical interpretation for the frequency function given by (4).

For the problem discussed in (4), the equation for the conditional frequency function is obtained by applying (7) to (4) and (5); hence for this problem

(8) $$f(y \mid x) = \frac{2 - x - y}{\frac{3}{2} - x}$$

For a fixed value of x this is a linear function of y; hence the graph of $f(y \mid x)$ must be a straight line, which of course is obvious from Fig. 2 and the geometrical interpretation of $f(y \mid x)$. It will be observed that the only curve of intersection of the type being considered on the surface $z = f(x, y)$ that has unit area under it is the one for which $x = \frac{1}{2}$. All other curves of intersection must have their ordinates multiplied by $1/(\frac{3}{2} - x)$ before they will possess unit area.

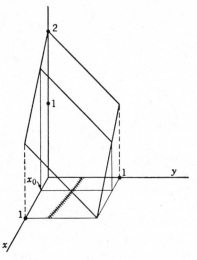

Fig. 2. Geometrical representation of a conditional distribution.

8.1.3   Curve of Regression

This section is concerned with defining a theoretical regression curve that will serve as a model for empirical regression curves. The preceding material on marginal and conditional distributions was merely introductory for use in this section. A theoretical regression curve is basically the graph of the mean of a conditional distribution $f(y \mid x)$. Here it is convenient to use the density interpretation of $f(y \mid x)$. Let x have the fixed value x_0. Then along the line $x = x_0$ the mean value of y will determine a point whose ordinate is denoted by $\mu_{y \mid x_0}$. As different values of x are selected, different mean points along the corresponding vertical lines will be obtained. Thus the ordinate $\mu_{y \mid x_0}$ of the mean point for any such line is a function of the value of x selected. The locus of such mean points, that is, the graph of $\mu_{y \mid x}$ as a function of x, will be a curve that is called the curve of regression of y on x. Analytically, the equation of the curve of regression is given by the following formula.

(9)   CURVE OF REGRESSION: $\displaystyle \mu_{y \mid x} = \int_{-\infty}^{\infty} y f(y \mid x)\, dy$

Because of (7), this formula may also be expressed in the form

(10) $\displaystyle \mu_{y \mid x} = \int_{-\infty}^{\infty} y \frac{f(x, y)}{f(x)}\, dy$

The curve of regression of x on y is defined in an analogous manner.

Figure 3 indicates the geometrical nature of the preceding definition of the curve of regression for a general density distribution.

The frequency function given in (4) will be used to illustrate the preceding definition. From the result obtained in (8), a direct application of (9) gives

$$\mu_{y\,|\,x} = \int_0^1 y\,\frac{2 - x - y}{\frac{3}{2} - x}\,dy$$

$$= \frac{1}{\frac{3}{2} - x}\int_0^1 [(2 - x)y - y^2]\,dy$$

$$= \frac{3x - 4}{6x - 9}$$

This is the equation of a hyperbola. The graph of this curve of regression is shown as the crossed line in Fig. 2.

The second illustration in 8.1.1 will be used here to illustrate the technique of finding the equation of a regression curve when the limits are variable. From the results obtained there, it follows that

$$f(y\,|\,x) = \frac{\frac{1}{2}xy}{\dfrac{x^3}{4}} = \frac{2y}{x^2}$$

In view of the triangular nature of the sample space, when x is fixed y can range over the values from 0 to x only; consequently (9) becomes

$$\mu_{y\,|\,x} = \frac{2}{x^2}\int_0^x y^2\,dy = \tfrac{2}{3}x$$

The fact that the regression curve is a straight line with slope $\tfrac{2}{3}$ might have been anticipated because of the nature of the density function and the sample space.

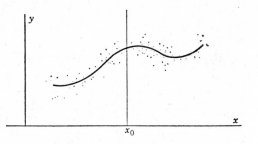

Fig. 3. Curve of regression.

8.1.4   Moments

The type of moments needed for correlation differ slightly from moments that have been defined previously. Although only low-order moments are required, a general definition is given. These moments are known as *product moments* and are defined as follows.

(11)   PRODUCT MOMENT: $\mu_{pq}' = E(x^p y^q) = \int_{-\infty}^{\infty} \int_{-\infty}^{\infty} x^p y^q f(x, y) \, dy \, dx$

Here p and q are any non-negative integers. The corresponding product moment about the mean is defined by the formula

(12)

$$\mu_{pq} = E[(x - \mu_x)^p (y - \mu_y)^q] = \int_{-\infty}^{\infty} \int_{-\infty}^{\infty} (x - \mu_x)^p (y - \mu_y)^q f(x, y) \, dy \, dx$$

It will be observed that these definitions are special cases of the general definition for expected values given in (5), Chapter 6, in which $g(x_1, x_2, \cdots, x_n)$ is chosen as either the function $x_1^p x_2^q$ or $(x_1 - \mu_1)^p (x_2 - \mu_2)^q$, and $n = 2$.

The particular product moment μ_{11}, which is called the *covariance* of the two variables, is of special interest because the *theoretical correlation coefficient* ρ between the two variables is defined in terms of it.

(13)   THEORETICAL CORRELATION COEFFICIENT: $\rho = \dfrac{\mu_{11}}{\sigma_x \sigma_y}$

If (12) is compared with $\Sigma(x - \bar{x})(y - \bar{y})/n$ in (1), Chapter 7, it will be observed that (12) with $p = q = 1$ is the theoretical counterpart of this sum and that (13) is the theoretical counterpart of r.

By using formula (3) it is easily seen that the kth moment of x, say, can be obtained from (11) by choosing $p = k$ and $q = 0$. Thus it follows that

(14) $\mu_{00}' = 1, \mu_{10}' = \mu_x, \mu_{01}' = \mu_y, \mu_{20} = \sigma_x^2, \mu_{02} = \sigma_y^2$

As an illustration of how to calculate the theoretical correlation coefficient, consider the application of formula (13) to the problem first considered in (4). By symmetry and (5), it follows that

$$\mu_x = \mu_y = \int_0^1 x \left(\frac{3}{2} - x \right) dx = \frac{5}{12}$$

Formula (12) yields

$$\mu_{20} = \mu_{02} = \int_0^1 \left(x - \frac{5}{12} \right)^2 \left(\frac{3}{2} - x \right) dx = \frac{11}{144}$$

Formula (12) applied to (4) gives

$$\mu_{11} = \int_0^1 \int_0^1 \left(x - \frac{5}{12}\right)\left(y - \frac{5}{12}\right)(2 - x - y) \, dy \, dx$$

$$= \int_0^1 \left(x - \frac{5}{12}\right) \int_0^1 \left(y - \frac{5}{12}\right)(2 - x - y) \, dy \, dx$$

$$= \int_0^1 \left(x - \frac{5}{12}\right)\left(\frac{1}{24} - \frac{x}{12}\right) dx$$

$$= -\frac{1}{144}$$

Formula (13) applied to these results gives

$$\rho = \frac{-1/144}{11/144} = -\frac{1}{11}$$

An inspection of Fig. 2 shows that the regression curve has a slight negative slope throughout its range and therefore it is not surprising that ρ, which measures linear correlation, turned out to be negative.

8.2 Normal Distribution of Two Variables

The preceding sections have introduced theoretical counterparts of empirical regression and correlation and to that extent have presented mathematical models for those two statistical quantities. It is not possible, however, to work problems of statistical inference with respect to them unless one is supplied with a frequency function for doing so. From the point of view of correlation the frequency function must be such that the density distribution of points in the x,y plane will indicate a linear type relation between x and y because the correlation coefficient is useful as a measure of relationship only when the relationship is approximately linear. This places a considerable restriction on the type of frequency function that can be selected as a model. Unless one wants a model for linear regression only, there is no such restriction on the frequency function necessary for regression models.

Now, since the normal frequency function has been shown to be a useful mathematical model for distributions of a single continuous variable, it is to be expected that a joint normal frequency function for two continuous variables will also prove to be a useful model. If two random variables x and y are normally distributed but in addition are independently distributed, then their joint frequency function is easily written down because, from (24), Chapter 2, the joint frequency function is then the product of the two marginal frequency functions. In this case, therefore,

$$(15) \qquad f(x, y) = \frac{e^{-\frac{1}{2}\left(\frac{x-\mu_x}{\sigma_x}\right)^2}}{\sqrt{2\pi}\sigma_x} \cdot \frac{e^{-\frac{1}{2}\left(\frac{y-\mu_y}{\sigma_y}\right)^2}}{\sqrt{2\pi}\sigma_y} = \frac{e^{-\frac{1}{2}\left[\left(\frac{x-\mu_x}{\sigma_x}\right)^2 + \left(\frac{y-\mu_y}{\sigma_y}\right)^2\right]}}{2\pi\sigma_x\sigma_y}$$

If the variables x and y are not independently distributed, it is necessary to modify (15) to take account of the relationship between x and y. This is done by introducing a cross-product term in the exponent of (15) which is such that its coefficient will be equal to 0 when x and y are independent. The desired modification is accomplished by means of the following definition.

(16) DEFINITION: *The normal frequency function of two variables is given by the following formula, where* $-1 < \rho < 1$,

$$f(x, y) = \frac{e^{-\frac{1}{2(1-\rho^2)}\left[\left(\frac{x-\mu_x}{\sigma_x}\right)^2 - 2\rho\left(\frac{x-\mu_x}{\sigma_x}\right)\left(\frac{y-\mu_y}{\sigma_y}\right) + \left(\frac{y-\mu_y}{\sigma_y}\right)^2\right]}}{2\pi\sigma_x\sigma_y\sqrt{1-\rho^2}}$$

If the same approach had been used here as for a normal distribution of one variable, one would have defined a joint normal frequency function as an exponential function of two variables in which the exponent is a quadratic function of those variables, and then one would have proceeded to show that the parameters defining the function can be expressed in terms of familiar statistical parameters. The result of such an approach is the expression given in (16). As a consequence, the function defined in (16) possesses the properties of a joint frequency function and its parameters are consistent with the general moment properties given in (14) and (13). This implies, for example, that the parameter ρ in (16) is actually the theoretical correlation coefficient here, as defined in (13). These facts can be verified by evaluating the necessary integrals.

8.2.1   Marginal Distribution

The marginal distributions of a joint normal distribution are obtained by applying formula (3), and its y version, to (16). For example, the x marginal frequency function is given by

$$(17) \qquad\qquad f(x) = \int_{-\infty}^{\infty} f(x, y) \, dy$$

where $f(x, y)$ is given in (16). In order to simplify the integration, let $u = (x - \mu_x)/\sigma_x$ and introduce the change of variable $v = (y - \mu_y)/\sigma_y$. Then $dy = \sigma_y \, dv$ and (17) reduces to

$$f(x) = \frac{1}{2\pi\sigma_x\sqrt{1 - \rho^2}}\int_{-\infty}^{\infty} e^{-\frac{1}{2(1-\rho^2)}(u^2 - 2\rho uv + v^2)} \, dv$$

Adding and subtracting $\rho^2 u^2$ to the exponent in order to complete the square in v gives

$$f(x) = \frac{1}{2\pi\sigma_x\sqrt{1 - \rho^2}}\int_{-\infty}^{\infty} e^{-\frac{1}{2(1-\rho^2)}(v^2 - 2\rho uv + \rho^2 u^2 - \rho^2 u^2 + u^2)} \, dv$$

$$= \frac{e^{-\frac{u^2}{2}}}{2\pi\sigma_x\sqrt{1 - \rho^2}}\int_{-\infty}^{\infty} e^{-\frac{1}{2(1-\rho^2)}(v - \rho u)^2} \, dv$$

Now make the change of variable $z = (v - \rho u)/\sqrt{1 - \rho^2}$. Then $dv = \sqrt{1 - \rho^2} \, dz$ and $f(x)$ reduces to

$$f(x) = \frac{e^{-\frac{u^2}{2}}}{2\pi\sigma_x}\int_{-\infty}^{\infty} e^{-\frac{z^2}{2}} \, dz$$

Substituting back the value of u in terms of x and inserting the value $\sqrt{2\pi}$ for this familiar integral, $f(x)$ finally reduces to

(18)
$$f(x) = \frac{e^{-\frac{1}{2}\left(\frac{x - \mu_x}{\sigma_x}\right)^2}}{\sqrt{2\pi}\sigma_x}$$

Since the corresponding result for y follows from symmetry, (18) shows that the marginal distributions of a joint normal distribution are normal. This result was to be expected, because one would certainly have been unhappy with the definition of a joint normal distribution if the individual variables had not been normally distributed.

The result obtained in (18) is very convenient for demonstrating the consistency of definition (16) with several of the general moment properties given in (14). For example, in order to demonstrate that the constant in (16) has been properly chosen, it is necessary to show that the volume under the surface whose equation is given by (16) is equal to 1. Hence it is necessary to evaluate the double integral.

(19)
$$\int_{-\infty}^{\infty} \int_{-\infty}^{\infty} f(x, y) \, dy \, dx$$

where $f(x, y)$ is given by (16). But from (17) the result of integrating with respect to y is given by (18); therefore, the evaluation of (19) is reduced to the integration of (18) with respect to x over all values of x. The value of this integral, of course, is 1.

If one sets $\rho = 0$ in (16), it will be observed that (16) reduces to (15), which is the frequency function of two independent normal variables. This shows that if two normal variables are uncorrelated, they are independently distributed. From the discussion of correlation given in section 7.1, particularly with respect to diagram (e) of Fig. 3, in Chapter 7, it should be clear that a lack of linear correlation does not ordinarily guarantee a lack of relationship of every kind between the two variables.

8.2.2 Conditional Distribution

A joint normal distribution of two variables possesses conditional distributions with interesting properties. In order to study these properties, it will suffice to examine the conditional frequency function $f(y \mid x)$.

For ease of writing, let $u = (x - \mu_x)/\sigma_x$ and $v = (y - \mu_y)/\sigma_y$. Then, a direct application of definition (7) to (16) and (18), together with a few algebraic reductions, will give

$$f(y \mid x) = \frac{e^{-\frac{1}{2(1-\rho^2)}(u^2 - 2\rho uv + v^2)}}{2\pi\sigma_x\sigma_y\sqrt{1 - \rho^2}} \div \frac{e^{-\frac{u^2}{2}}}{\sqrt{2\pi}\sigma_x}$$

$$= \frac{e^{-\frac{1}{2(1-\rho^2)}(v^2 - 2\rho uv + \rho^2 u^2)}}{\sqrt{2\pi}\sigma_y\sqrt{1 - \rho^2}}$$

$$= \frac{e^{-\frac{1}{2}\left(\frac{v - \rho u}{\sqrt{1-\rho^2}}\right)^2}}{\sqrt{2\pi}\sigma_y\sqrt{1 - \rho^2}}$$

If the values of u and v in terms of x and y are inserted and if the value of y is denoted by y_x to show its dependence on the selected value of x, $f(y \mid x)$ will reduce to

$$(20) \qquad f(y \mid x) = \frac{e^{-\frac{1}{2}\left[\frac{y_x - \mu_y - \rho\frac{\sigma_y}{\sigma_x}(x - \mu_x)}{\sigma_y\sqrt{1-\rho^2}}\right]^2}}{\sqrt{2\pi}\sigma_y\sqrt{1 - \rho^2}}$$

Since x has a fixed value and y_x is the random variable here, (20) shows that y_x possesses a normal distribution with mean $\mu_y + \rho(\sigma_y/\sigma_x)(x - \mu_x)$

and standard deviation $\sigma_y \sqrt{1 - \rho^2}$. By symmetry a similar result holds for x and y interchanged. Thus the conditional distributions of a joint normal distribution are also normal.

Since by definition (9) a curve of regression is the locus of the means of a conditional distribution, it follows from (20) that the curve of regression of y on x for x and y jointly normally distributed is the straight line whose equation is

$$(21) \qquad \mu_{y \mid x} = \mu_y + \rho \frac{\sigma_y}{\sigma_x} (x - \mu_x)$$

This property of a joint normal distribution, namely, that the curve of regression of y on x is a straight line, helps to justify the frequent use of linear regression because variables that are approximately normally distributed are encountered frequently.

8.2.3 Normal Surface

Instead of thinking in terms of probability density in the plane, consider now the geometry of (16), treating it as the equation of a surface in three dimensions. If (7) and the particular results (18) and (20) are applied, the equation of this surface may be written

$$(22) \qquad z = f(x) \frac{e^{-\frac{1}{2}\left[\frac{y - \mu_y - \rho\frac{\sigma_y}{\sigma_x}(x - \mu_x)}{\sigma_y\sqrt{1 - \rho^2}}\right]^2}}{\sqrt{2\pi}\sigma_y\sqrt{1 - \rho^2}}$$

For the purpose of studying this surface consider its intersections with planes perpendicular to the x axis. The equations of the intersecting curves are obtained by replacing x with the constant values corresponding to the cutting planes. From (22) it will be observed that these curves are normal curves, although not the graphs of normal frequency functions because the area under any such curve is not usually equal to one, with their means lying on the regression line (21), all having the same standard deviation $\sigma_y\sqrt{1 - \rho^2}$ and varying in maximum height according to the factor $f(x)$. The tallest such normal curve is the one lying in the cutting plane $x = \mu_x$, since this value makes $f(x)$ a maximum. By symmetry, planes perpendicular to the y axis will intersect the surface in normal curves with corresponding properties. A sketch of a normal correlation surface which shows these various geometrical properties is given in Fig. 4.

Further information is obtained by considering the intersection of the surface by planes perpendicular to the z axis. In this connection it is

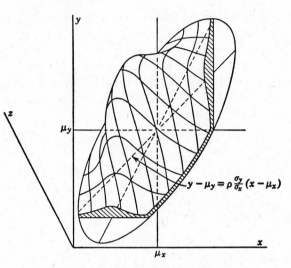

Fig. 4. Normal correlation surface.

more convenient to use the original form (16) with $f(x, y)$ replaced by z. If z assumes different constant values, the quantity in brackets in the exponent will assume corresponding values that can be calculated from the constant values assigned to z. Hence the equations of such intersecting curves may be written in the form

$$\left(\frac{x - \mu_x}{\sigma_x}\right)^2 - 2\rho\left(\frac{x - \mu_x}{\sigma_x}\right)\left(\frac{y - \mu_y}{\sigma_y}\right) + \left(\frac{y - \mu_y}{\sigma_y}\right)^2 = k$$

where k corresponds to the selected value of z. Since this is a quadratic function in x and y, these curves of intersection must be conic sections. Furthermore, since the type of conic section depends only on the quadratic terms, the discriminant for testing conic sections may be applied directly to give

$$B^2 - 4AC = \left(\frac{2\rho}{\sigma_x\sigma_y}\right)^2 - 4\frac{1}{\sigma_x{}^2}\frac{1}{\sigma_y{}^2}$$

$$= \frac{4(\rho^2 - 1)}{\sigma_x{}^2\sigma_y{}^2} < 0$$

This result shows that the intersecting curves are ellipses, because by definition (16) $\rho^2 < 1$. Allowing k to assume different values will merely change the sizes of these ellipses; consequently, these ellipses have the same centers and the same orientation of principal axes. It will be found, when rotating axes properly to eliminate the x,y term, that the principal axis of these ellipses is not parallel to a line of regression as might be supposed. The line of regression turns out to be parallel to the diameter of the ellipses obtained by considering chords parallel to the y axis.

8.3 Normal Correlation

The normal frequency function defined in (16) appears to be a satisfactory model for correlation problems because it yields a probability density distribution in the x,y plane for which the regression is linear and because it possesses a parameter that measures the theoretical correlation present. In addition, experience shows that many pairs of real-life variables possess distributions of approximately this type.

In Chapter 7 the sample correlation coefficient r was introduced as a measure of the degree to which two variables are linearly related. It was stated there that the justification for choosing r as the preferred measure rested upon the fact that it is the maximum likelihood estimator of the theoretical correlation coefficient ρ when the two variables possess a joint normal distribution. This property of r will now be verified.

Let (x_1, y_1), (x_2, y_2), $\cdots$, (x_n, y_n) represent a random sample of size n from a normal population whose frequency function is given by (16). The likelihood function for this sample is

$$L = \prod_{i=1}^{n} f(x_i, y_i)$$

$$= \frac{e^{-\frac{1}{2(1-\rho^2)}\sum_{i=1}^{n}\left[\left(\frac{x_i-\mu_x}{\sigma_x}\right)^2 - 2\rho\left(\frac{x_i-\mu_x}{\sigma_x}\right)\left(\frac{y_i-\mu_y}{\sigma_y}\right) + \left(\frac{y_i-\mu_y}{\sigma_y}\right)^2\right]}}{(2\pi\sigma_x\sigma_y\sqrt{1-\rho^2})^n}$$

For ease of differentiating, the logarithms of both sides are taken. Then

$$\log L = -n \log 2\pi\sigma_x\sigma_y\sqrt{1-\rho^2}$$

$$- \frac{1}{2(1-\rho^2)} \sum \left[\left(\frac{x_i-\mu_x}{\sigma_x}\right)^2 - 2\rho\left(\frac{x_i-\mu_x}{\sigma_x}\right)\left(\frac{y_i-\mu_y}{\sigma_y}\right) + \left(\frac{y_i-\mu_y}{\sigma_y}\right)^2 \right]$$

In order to find the maximum likelihood estimators of the parameters, it is necessary to differentiate $\log L$ with respect to μ_x, μ_y, σ_x, σ_y, and ρ, and then to solve the five equations that are obtained by setting these five derivatives equal to 0. It will be found on solving the first two of these equations that the maximum likelihood estimators for μ_x and μ_y are, as was to be expected, $\bar{x}$ and $\bar{y}$. It is not possible to solve the third and fourth equations alone for the estimators for σ_x and σ_y because they involve ρ; therefore, the remaining three equations need to be solved simultaneously.

Differentiating $\log L$ with respect to σ_x gives

$$\frac{\partial \log L}{\partial \sigma_x} = -\frac{n}{\sigma_x} - \frac{1}{2(1 - \rho^2)} \left[\frac{-2\sum(x_i - \mu_x)^2}{\sigma_x{}^3} + \frac{2\rho\sum(x_i - \mu_x)(y_i - \mu_y)}{\sigma_x{}^2\sigma_y} \right]$$

A similar formula results from differentiating with respect to σ_y. Setting these two derivatives equal to 0 will yield the equations

$$\frac{\sum(x_i - \mu_x)^2}{\sigma_x{}^2} = \frac{\rho\sum(x_i - \mu_x)(y_i - \mu_y)}{\sigma_x\sigma_y} + n(1 - \rho^2)$$

$$\frac{\sum(y_i - \mu_y)^2}{\sigma_y{}^2} = \frac{\rho\sum(x_i - \mu_x)(y_i - \mu_y)}{\sigma_x\sigma_y} + n(1 - \rho^2)$$

If now μ_x and μ_y are replaced by $\bar{x}$ and $\bar{y}$, which are the solutions of the first two of the maximum likelihood equations, and if the notation $\sum(x_i - \bar{x})(y_i - \bar{y}) = nrs_xs_y$ is used, these equations will simplify to

$$\frac{s_x{}^2}{\sigma_x{}^2} = \rho r \frac{s_x s_y}{\sigma_x\sigma_y} + (1 - \rho^2)$$

$$\frac{s_y{}^2}{\sigma_y{}^2} = \rho r \frac{s_x s_y}{\sigma_x\sigma_y} + (1 - \rho^2)$$

This shows that

$$\frac{s_y}{\sigma_y} = \frac{s_x}{\sigma_x}$$

and therefore, substituting into the first equation, that

$$\frac{s_x}{\sigma_x} = \sqrt{\frac{1 - \rho^2}{1 - \rho r}}$$

The fifth maximum likelihood equation is obtained by differentiating $\log L$ with respect to ρ. This differentiation, followed by some algebraic simplification, yields the result

$$\frac{\partial \log L}{\partial \rho} = \frac{n\rho}{1 - \rho^2} + \frac{1}{1 - \rho^2} \sum \left(\frac{x_i - \mu_x}{\sigma_x} \right)\left(\frac{y_i - \mu_y}{\sigma_y} \right)$$
$$- \frac{\rho}{(1 - \rho^2)^2} \sum \left[\left(\frac{x_i - \mu_x}{\sigma_x} \right)^2 - 2\rho\left(\frac{x_i - \mu_x}{\sigma_x} \right)\left(\frac{y_i - \mu_y}{\sigma_y} \right) + \left(\frac{y_i - \mu_y}{\sigma_y} \right)^2 \right]$$

Setting this derivative equal to 0 and performing some simplifications yields the equation

$$n\rho(1 - \rho^2) + (1 + \rho^2) \sum \left(\frac{x_i - \mu_x}{\sigma_x} \right)\left(\frac{y_i - \mu_y}{\sigma_y} \right)$$
$$= \rho\sum \left[\left(\frac{x_i - \mu_x}{\sigma_x} \right)^2 + \left(\frac{y_i - \mu_y}{\sigma_y} \right)^2 \right]$$

Now, replacing μ_x and μ_y by $\bar{x}$ and $\bar{y}$ and s_x/σ_x and s_y/σ_y by

$$\sqrt{(1 - \rho^2)/(1 - \rho r)},$$

this equation reduces to

$$\rho(1 - \rho^2) + r(1 + \rho^2)\frac{1 - \rho^2}{1 - \rho r} = 2\rho \frac{1 - \rho^2}{1 - \rho r}$$

Since $1 - \rho^2$ may be factored out, this equation is easily seen to possess the solution $\hat{\rho} = r$; consequently this proves that the maximum likelihood estimator of ρ when x and y are jointly normally distributed is the sample correlation coefficient r.

Incidentally, when ρ is replaced by r in the expression for s_x/σ_x, it will be observed that the maximum likelihood estimator of σ_x reduces to s_x. Thus the joint maximum likelihood estimators of μ_x, μ_y, σ_x, σ_y, and ρ are $\bar{x}$, $\bar{y}$, s_x, s_y, and r.

8.4 Normal Regression

In Chapter 7 the study of the relationship between two or more variables was considered from two points of view, namely, that of correlation and that of regression. Correlation methods were considered appropriate when interest is centered on measuring the degree to which two variables are linearly related and when both variables are randomly sampled. The theory presented thus far in this chapter has been principally theory for correlation because it has been the theory of two correlated random variables. Some of this theory, however, is also useful in the construction of mathematical models for regression. Such a model is considered next.

In all the regression problems of Chapter 7 the independent variables were considered to be fixed so that y was the only random variable present. For example, in the illustration of linear regression given in Table 2, Chapter 7, the values of x were selected by the experimenter to be equally spaced over the range of x values of interest to him. Repeated experiments of this type would require that the experimenter use the same x values each time. It is clear that the joint distribution of two variables is not needed for a regression problem such as this.

Although the joint distribution of x and y is not needed for regression, the conditional distribution of y for x fixed is needed if the accuracy of the least-squares estimates of the regression coefficients obtained in Chapter 7 is to be determined. In the notation of (7) this means that the conditional frequency function $f(y \mid x)$ must be known for all the fixed x values. In the case of multiple regression x will be understood to represent all the independent variables.

Consider, first, the problem of deciding what type of conditional frequency function $f(y \mid x)$ would make a satisfactory model for simple linear regression of y on x. Although the x values are fixed in regression, x usually possesses a continuous distribution under random sampling. If x and y possess a joint normal distribution, the regression curve will be a straight line and $f(y \mid x)$ will be given by (20). For two variables that are approximately normally distributed one would therefore choose $f(y \mid x)$ to be a function having the properties of the function given by (20). Hence $f(y \mid x)$ is chosen to be a normal frequency function with its mean, as a function of x, lying on a straight line and with its variance independent of x.

Since the x's are to be fixed, the conditional distribution of y for fixed x is needed only for the y's corresponding to the fixed x values. Thus, denoting the set of sample values by (x_1, y_1), (x_2, y_2), $\cdots$, (x_n, y_n), the conditional frequency function $f(y \mid x)$ is needed only for these n pairs of values. If the equation of the straight line on which the means of the conditional distributions lie is written in the form

$$y = \alpha + \beta(x - \bar{x})$$

and the variance is denoted by σ^2, the desired conditional frequency

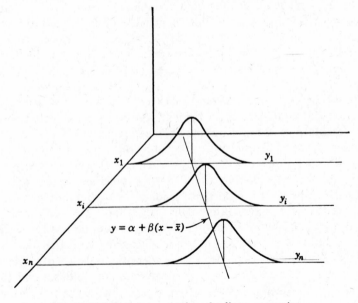

Fig. 5. Distribution assumptions for linear regression.

function is then given by

(23) $$f(y_i \mid x_i) = \frac{e^{-\frac{1}{2\sigma^2}[y_i - \alpha - \beta(x_i - \bar{x})]^2}}{\sqrt{2\pi}\sigma}$$

A sketch illustrating the preceding assumption concerning the conditional distribution of the y's is given in Fig. 5.

A second assumption is that the random variables $y_1, y_2, \cdots, y_n$ are independently distributed. This assumption is satisfied, for example, in the regression problem discussed in Section 7.2. It is not satisfied, however, for regression problems in which $y_1, y_2, \cdots, y_n$ represent, say, the heights of a growing plant on n consecutive days.

8.4.1 Estimation of α, β, and σ

The model selected in the preceding section for simple linear regression contains the three parameters α, β, and σ. In order to be able to apply this model to a given problem, it is necessary to estimate these parameters by means of available data. This is done by the method of maximum likelihood.

Since the random variables $y_1, y_2, \cdots, y_n$ were assumed to be independently distributed, the likelihood function L for the sample (x_1, y_1), $(x_2, y_2), \cdots, (x_n, y_n)$ is given by

$$L = \prod_{i=1}^{n} \frac{e^{-\frac{1}{2\sigma^2}[y_i - \alpha - \beta(x_i - \bar{x})]^2}}{\sqrt{2\pi}\sigma}$$

$$= \frac{e^{-\frac{1}{2\sigma^2}\sum_{i=1}^{n}[y_i - \alpha - \beta(x_i - \bar{x})]^2}}{\sigma^n(2\pi)^{\frac{n}{2}}}$$

Taking logarithms and differentiating with respect to α, β, and σ, respectively, and setting the derivatives equal to 0, one obtains

(24)
$$\frac{\partial \log L}{\partial \alpha} = \frac{1}{\sigma^2} \sum_{i=1}^{n} [y_i - \alpha - \beta(x_i - \bar{x})] = 0$$

$$\frac{\partial \log L}{\partial \beta} = \frac{1}{\sigma^2} \sum_{i=1}^{n} [y_i - \alpha - \beta(x_i - \bar{x})][x_i - \bar{x}] = 0$$

$$\frac{\partial \log L}{\partial \sigma} = -\frac{n}{\sigma} + \frac{1}{\sigma^3} \sum_{i=1}^{n} [y_i - \alpha - \beta(x_i - \bar{x})]^2 = 0$$

Now, a comparison of the first two of these equations with the equations of least squares as given by (5), Chapter 7, demonstrates the fact that the least-squares estimates of the regression coefficients are precisely the same as the estimates obtained by the method of maximum likelihood under the stipulated normality and independence assumptions. Since estimation by the method of least squares does not require the restrictive assumptions made in the maximum likelihood approach, it would seem to be a more desirable method for estimating α and β. However, as soon as one tries to determine the accuracy of the estimates or to test hypotheses about the parameters being estimated, he will discover that it is necessary to make some distribution assumptions about the y's. The normality and independence assumptions made earlier are assumptions that enable one to work such problems, in addition to estimating the regression parameters. Least squares alone is capable of estimating the parameters only. The problems of determining the accuracy of the estimates and testing hypotheses about the parameters being estimated are considered in Chapter 11.

If the estimates of α and β obtained from (24) and given by (7), Chapter 7 are denoted by $\hat{\alpha}$ and $\hat{\beta}$, the third equation in (24) will yield the following estimate for σ^2:

$$\hat{\sigma}^2 = \frac{1}{n} \sum_{i=1}^{n} [y_i - \hat{\alpha} - \hat{\beta}(x_i - \bar{x})]^2$$

A mathematical model for multiple linear regression can be constructed in the same manner as simple linear regression. If there are k independent variables $x_1, x_2, \cdots, x_k$ and all the x's have fixed values, so that the only random variables are $y_1, y_2, \cdots, y_n$, then the conditional frequency function of y_i corresponding to (23) will become

$$(25) \quad f(y_i \mid x_{1i}, \cdots, x_{ki}) = \frac{e^{-\frac{1}{2\sigma^2}[y_i - \alpha - \beta_1(x_{1i} - \bar{x}_1) - \cdots - \beta_k(x_{ki} - \bar{x}_k)]^2}}{\sqrt{2\pi}\sigma}$$

The maximum likelihood estimates of the regression coefficients $\beta_1, \cdots, \beta_k$ are the same as those obtained by least squares and are given by solving the normal equations (13) of Chapter 7.

REFERENCES

Additional discussion and problems on the material of this chapter may be found in A. M. Mood, *Introduction to the Theory of Statistics*, McGraw-Hill Book Co.

EXERCISES

1. If $f(x, y) = 1$, $0 \leq x \leq 1$, $0 \leq y \leq 1$, find the probability that (a) $x > .5$ and $y > .7$; (b) $x > .5$; (c) $x > y$; (d) $x = y$; (e) $x > .5$, given that $y = .5$; (f) $x > y$, given that $y < .5$; (g) $x + y < 1$; and (h) $x^2 + y^2 < 1$.

2. If $f(x, y) = e^{-(x+y)}$, $x \geq 0$, $y \geq 0$, find the probability that (a) $x < 1$; (b) $x < 1$, given that $y = 1$; (c) $x > y$; (d) $x + y < 1$; and (e) $x > y$, given that $y < 1$.

3. If $f(x, y) = 2$, $0 \leq x \leq 1$, $0 \leq y \leq x$, find (a) the marginal frequency functions; (b) the conditional frequency functions; and (c) the curve of regression of y on x.

4. Given $f(x, y) = c(xy + e^x)$, $0 \leq x \leq 1$, $0 \leq y \leq 1$, (a) find the value of c; (b) find $f(x)$; and (c) determine whether x and y are independently distributed.

5. Given $f(x, y) = xe^{-x(y+1)}$, $x \geq 0$, $y \geq 0$, find (a) the marginal frequency functions; (b) the conditional frequency functions; and (c) the curve of regression of y on x.

6. Find the equation of the regression curve of y on x, given that $f(x, y) = \frac{9}{2}(1 + x + y)/(1 + x)^4(1 + y)^4$, $x > 0, y > 0$.

7. Given $f(x, y) = 1$, $0 \leq x \leq 1$, $0 \leq y \leq 1$, find (a) $\mu_{pq}{}'$; (b) ρ; and (c) $\mu_{y \mid x}$.

8. Given $f(x, y) = 2/a^2$, $0 \leq x \leq a$, $0 \leq y \leq x$, find (a) $\mu_{pq}{}'$; (b) ρ; and (c) $\mu_{y \mid x}$.

9. Given $f(x, y) = c$ in the two triangular regions bounded by the lines $x = -1$, $y = 0$, $y = -x$ and $x = 1$, $y = 0$, $y = x$, find (a) the value of c; (b) the equation of the regression curve of y on x; and (c) the value of ρ.

10. Given $f(x, y) = c(x^2 + y^2)$, $x^2 + y^2 < 1$, and zero elsewhere, find (a) the value of c; (b) the equation of the regression curve of y on x; and (c) the equation of the regression curve of x on y.

11. Find a nontrivial joint distribution of two variables x and y such that the regression curve of y on x is the parabola $y = x^2$.

12. Given $f(x, y) = 8xy$, $0 \leq x \leq 1$, $0 \leq y \leq x$, show that x and y are not independent random variables.

13. If the exponent in the normal frequency function of x and y is

$$-\tfrac{5}{8}[4(x - 1)^2 - 9.6(x - 1)(y + 2) + 16(y + 2)^2]$$

find (a) μ_x, μ_y, σ_x, σ_y, ρ; (b) the marginal frequency function of x; and (c) the regression line of y on x.

14. Assume that a bomber is making a bombing run in the direction along the positive y axis at a square target 200 feet by 200 feet, whose center is at the origin and whose sides are parallel to the coordinate axes. Assume further that the x and y errors in repeated bombing runs are normally distributed about 0. (a) If the x and y errors are also independently distributed with $\sigma_x = \sigma_y = 400$ feet, find the probability that the target will be hit on the first run. (b) Under the conditions of (a), find the probability of getting at least 1 hit in 10 runs. (c) Under these same conditions, how many runs would be needed to make the probability at least .9 of getting at least 1 hit on the target? (d) Show why it would be difficult to work (a) if the x and y errors were correlated with, say, $\rho = \tfrac{1}{5}$.

15. How must the frequency function of a normal variable x be modified if x is restricted to (a) values larger than μ and (b) positive values?

16. If x and y are independently and normally distributed with $\mu_x = \mu_y = 0$ and $\sigma_x = \sigma_y = 1$, (a) find the probability that $x^2 + y^2 < 1$ and (b) determine what size circle with the center at the origin is such that the probability is .95 that the sample point (x, y) will fall inside it.

17. If x and y are independently distributed, show that the curve of regression will be a horizontal straight line.

18. If x and y are independent variables, find expressions for the mean and variance of $z = xy$ in terms of the means and variances of x and y.

19. Let n independent trials be made of an experiment for which p is the probability of success in a single trial. Let x equal the number of successes and let y equal the sum of the numbers of the trials at which successes occur. Write $x = x_1 + \cdots + x_n$ where $x_i = 1$ or 0, depending on success or failure, and write $y = y_1 + \cdots + y_n$ where $y_i = i$ or 0, depending on success or failure. Calculate $E(x)$, $E(y)$, $E(xy)$, and μ_{11}.

20. Suppose that a binomial distribution is to be truncated by agreeing to discard the value $x = 0$ whenever it occurs. Find the resulting frequency function of x, that is, find the conditional frequency function of binomial x when $1 \leq x \leq n$.

21. Suppose it is known that x and y are jointly normally distributed with means $\mu_x = 4$, $\mu_y = 2$, $\sigma_x = \sigma_y = 1$, and $\rho = \frac{3}{4}$. If you wish to estimate the value of y for an individual whose x value is equal to 6, how will the size of the variance of the error of this estimate differ from that when nothing is known about his x value?

22. In problem 14 suppose the x and y errors are normally distributed about the point of aiming rather than about the center of the target and that the x and y coordinates of the aiming point are independently normally distributed about the center of the target with $\sigma_x = \sigma_y = 100$ feet. Letting $x = z + u$ and $y = w + v$, where z and w are the aiming errors and u and v are the bombing errors, solve part (a) of problem 14 by using the fact that x and y are independently normally distributed because they are the sums of such variables.

23. Verify by integration that definition (16) is consistent with the general moment properties given in (14) and (13).

24. Construct or describe a joint non-normal distribution of 2 variables whose marginal distributions are both normal.

25. Find a nontrivial joint distribution of 2 variables such that both regression curves are straight lines.

26. Prove that all vertical plane sections of a normal correlation surface are normal curves.

27. Prove that $\bar{x}$ and $\bar{y}$ are the maximum likelihood estimators of μ_x and μ_y for the bivariate normal frequency function.

28. Assume that $\mu_x = \mu_y = 0$ and $\sigma_x = \sigma_y = 1$ for x and y jointly normally distributed. Find an equation whose solution gives the maximum likelihood estimate of ρ for a sample of size n. How does this result compare with that when the means and variances are unknown?

29. Show that the maximum likelihood estimates of the β's in (25) are the same as the least-squares estimates given by (13), Chapter 7.

30. Given the conditional distribution $f(y \mid x) = x^y e^{-x}/y!$, where y is discrete and can assume the values $y = 0, 1, 2, \cdots$, and given $f(x) = e^{-x}$, $x > 0$, show that the marginal distribution of y is given by $g(y) = (\frac{1}{2})^{y+1}$. Use the factorial property of the gamma function integral.

31. The length of life x of a physical particle is a random variable whose distribution depends on a parameter α. This parameter characterizes the type of particle. A population of particles is made up of various types of particles with the proportion having parameter value α given by $g(\alpha) = e^{-\alpha}$, $\alpha > 0$. If the distribution of length of life for fixed α is given by $f(x \mid \alpha) = \alpha e^{-\alpha x}$, $x > 0$, find the unconditional frequency function $f(x)$.

CHAPTER 9

General Principles For Testing
Hypotheses and For Estimation

9.1 Testing Hypotheses

A large part of the material presented in the preceding chapters has
been concerned with testing various statistical hypotheses. These hypotheses were tested by means of random variables such as $\bar{x}$, or p', which
seemed appropriate for the particular problem being considered. Thus
$\bar{x}$ was introduced because it appeared to be a satisfactory variable to use
for testing a theoretical mean. A random variable such as this, which is a
function of sample values, is often called a *statistic*. Now, not only was
the statistic for a given type of problem selected on intuitive grounds, but
the critical region for the statistic was also selected on an intuitive basis
rather than on any logical principle. Although such intuitive arguments
often yield highly efficient tests for testing the hypothesis in question,
some logical principle for selecting the proper test is necessary if one is to
be certain of always designing a good test. Such a principle was introduced in Chapter 3 for testing a hypothesis H_0 against an alternative
hypothesis H_1. In this chapter the ideas introduced in Chapter 3 will be
studied more thoroughly and extended somewhat to include more general
problems.

9.1.1 Test of a Hypothesis

From (2) and (4), Chapter 3, it will be recalled that a statistical hypothesis is defined as an assumption about the frequency function of a
random variable and that a test of a hypothesis is a procedure for deciding
whether to accept or reject the hypothesis.

In all the problems of testing hypotheses that have been considered thus far the procedure for deciding whether to accept or reject the hypothesis has consisted in selecting a statistic based on a sample of fixed size n, calculating the value of the statistic for the sample, and then rejecting the hypothesis if and only if the value of the statistic corresponded to a point in the chosen critical region.

A more general procedure that possesses striking advantages in many situations is one in which the random sample is obtained by selecting one individual at a time until a sufficiently large sample has been accumulated to arrive at a reliable decision. This method of sampling, called sequential sampling, often arrives at a decision some time before the fixed-size sample, with the same size type I and type II errors, is exhausted, and thus it often decreases the cost of sampling. In the sequential procedure one must decide at every stage of the sampling whether to accept the hypothesis, to reject the hypothesis, or to continue sampling. The fixed-size sample procedure does not permit any conclusions to be drawn until the entire sample has been taken and does not permit additional sampling. A sequential method for testing hypotheses is discussed in Chapter 14; hence only fixed-size sample procedures are considered in this chapter.

9.1.2 Kinds of Tests

Most of the statistical hypotheses that one encounters are assumptions about the parameters of a frequency function. The hypotheses tested in the preceding chapters have been of this kind. For the purpose of describing them, let $f(x; \theta_1, \theta_2, \cdots, \theta_k)$ denote a known frequency function that depends on k parameters. A statistical hypothesis then becomes an assumption about the k parameters. In studying hypotheses of this kind it is convenient to classify them into one of two types by means of the following definition.

(1) DEFINITION: *If a hypothesis specifies the values of all the parameters of a frequency function, it is called a simple hypothesis; otherwise, it is called a composite hypothesis.*

As an illustration, suppose the frequency function is

$$f(x; \theta_1, \theta_2) = \frac{e^{-\frac{1}{2}\left(\frac{x-\theta_1}{\theta_2}\right)^2}}{\sqrt{2\pi}\theta_2}$$

If the hypothesis is $H_0: \theta_1 = 10$, $\theta_2 = 2$, then H_0 is a simple hypothesis. If, however, the hypothesis is $H_0: \theta_1 = 10$, $\theta_2 < 2$, then H_0 is composite.

The theory of how to design good tests for simple hypotheses is much simpler than that for composite hypotheses. In the next two sections two methods for constructing good tests are discussed. The first method is directly applicable to simple hypotheses only, although it sometimes solves composite problems also, whereas the second method is applicable to both simple and composite hypotheses.

9.1.3   Best Tests for Simple Hypotheses

In this section a method is given for constructing best tests, in the sense of principle (7), Chapter 3, for simple hypotheses. In discussing the relative merits of different tests, this principle requires that only tests with an agreed upon type I error size, denoted by α, be considered. Then a best test is defined as a test in this set that minimizes the size of the type II error, denoted by β. The method of constructing a best test depends on the use of a theorem that was first proved and used by the two statisticians after whom it is named. The theorem, called the Neyman-Pearson lemma, will be proved for a frequency function, $f(x; \theta)$, of a single continuous variable and a single parameter; however, by merely thinking of x and θ as vectors, the proof will be seen to hold for any number of random variables and parameters. The variables $x_1, x_2, \cdots, x_n$ occurring in the theorem are understood to represent a random sample of size n from the population whose frequency function is $f(x; \theta)$. The theorem is concerned with a simple hypothesis $H_0: \theta = \theta_0$ and a simple alternative $H_1: \theta = \theta_1$. This is the type of problem discussed and illustrated in Chapter 3 beginning with the illustration following (4), Chapter 3. One should review that material before studying the following. In particular one should recall that the phrase "critical region of size α" means that the critical region is one for which the size of the type I error is α. In terms of this language, the theorem may be expressed as follows.

(2)   NEYMAN-PEARSON LEMMA: *If there exists a critical region A of size α and a constant k such that*

$$\frac{\prod\limits_{i=1}^{n} f(x_i; \theta_1)}{\prod\limits_{i=1}^{n} f(x_i; \theta_0)} \geq k \text{ inside } A$$

and

$$\frac{\prod\limits_{i=1}^{n} f(x_i; \theta_1)}{\prod\limits_{i=1}^{n} f(x_i; \theta_0)} \leq k \text{ outside } A$$

then A is a best critical region of size α.

To prove this lemma, let A^* be any other critical region of size α. The regions A and A^* may be represented geometrically as the regions interior to the indicated closed surfaces in Fig. 1. For simplicity of notation, let

$$L_0 = \prod_{i=1}^{n} f(x_i; \theta_0)$$

denote the frequency function for the variables $x_1, x_2, \cdots, x_n$ when H_0 is true, and let L_1 denote this function when H_1 is true. Further, write

$$\int_A \cdots \int \prod_{i=1}^{n} f(x_i; \theta_0)\, dx_1 \cdots dx_n = \int_A L_0\, dx$$

with a similar expression for L_1.

Since A and A^* are both critical regions of size α,

(3) $$\int_A L_0\, dx = \int_{A^*} L_0\, dx$$

But from Fig. 1 it is clear that the integral over b, which is the common part of A and A^*, will cancel from both sides of (3) and reduce it to the form

(4) $$\int_a L_0\, dx = \int_c L_0\, dx$$

Now, calculate the size of the type II error for both A and A^*. Since the size of the type II error is the probability that the sample point will fall outside the critical region when H_1 is true, which in turn is equal to 1 minus the probability that it will fall inside the critical region when H_1 is true, these errors may be written in the form

$$\beta^* = 1 - \int_{A^*} L_1\, dx$$

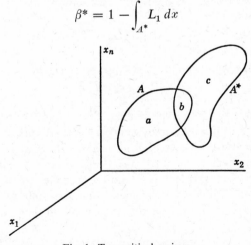

Fig. 1. Two critical regions.

and

$$\beta = 1 - \int_A L_1 \, dx$$

Consequently

$$\beta^* - \beta = \int_A L_1 \, dx - \int_{A^*} L_1 \, dx$$

If the integral over the common part b is canceled, this difference will reduce to

(5) $$\beta^* - \beta = \int_a L_1 \, dx - \int_c L_1 \, dx$$

Since region a lies in A, it follows from the definition of A given in (2) that every point of a satisfies the inequality

$$kL_0 \leq L_1$$

hence

$$\int_a L_1 \, dx \geq k \int_a L_0 \, dx$$

Similarly, since c lies outside A, every point of c satisfies the second inequality in (2), namely,

$$kL_0 \geq L_1$$

hence

$$\int_c L_1 \, dx \leq k \int_c L_0 \, dx$$

When these two results are used in (5), it follows that

$$\beta^* - \beta \geq k \int_a L_0 \, dx - k \int_c L_0 \, dx$$

But from (4) the right side must be equal to zero; hence

$$\beta^* \geq \beta$$

Since β^* is the size of the type II error for any critical region of size α, other than A, the preceding analysis proves that A is a best critical region of size α, where best is understood to mean a critical region with a minimum size type II error.

The constant k of this lemma is chosen to make A a critical region of size α. In most problems, as k goes from 0 to infinity, the size of A decreases from 1 to 0, thus making it possible to determine the proper value of k.

The usefulness and meaning of this lemma is best explained by means of illustrations: consider first the problem that was discussed in Chapter 3, beginning with (3). For that problem

$$f(x; \theta) = \theta e^{-\theta x}, \ x \geq 0$$

In order to discuss a somewhat more general problem let the hypothesis be $H_0 : \theta = \theta_0$ and the alternative be $H_1 : \theta = \theta_1 < \theta_0$ and assume that a sample of size n is to be taken. The corresponding likelihood functions are

$$L_0 = \prod_{i=1}^{n} f(x_i; \theta_0) = \theta_0{}^n e^{-\theta_0 \sum\limits_{i=1}^{n} x_i}$$

and

$$L_1 = \prod_{i=1}^{n} f(x_i; \theta_1) = \theta_1{}^n e^{-\theta_1 \sum\limits_{i=1}^{n} x_i}$$

According to (2), the region A is the region in which

$$\frac{\theta_1{}^n e^{-\theta_1 \Sigma x_i}}{\theta_0{}^n e^{-\theta_0 \Sigma x_i}} \geq k$$

This inequality may be written in the form

$$e^{(\theta_1 - \theta_0) \Sigma x_i} \leq \frac{1}{k} \left(\frac{\theta_1}{\theta_0} \right)^n$$

Taking logarithms, the inequality becomes

$$(\theta_1 - \theta_0) \sum x_i \leq \log \frac{1}{k} \left(\frac{\theta_1}{\theta_0} \right)^n$$

Since H_1 specifies that $\theta_1 < \theta_0$, dividing both sides by $\theta_1 - \theta_0$ will reverse the inequality and yield

$$(6) \qquad \sum x_i \geq \frac{\log \dfrac{1}{k} \left(\dfrac{\theta_1}{\theta_0} \right)^n}{\theta_1 - \theta_0}$$

Now the problem of Chapter 3 has $n = 1$, $\theta_0 = 2$, and $\theta_1 = 1$; hence for that problem the best critical region, as given by (6), would be that part of the x axis to the right of the point

$$x_0 = \frac{\log \dfrac{\theta_1}{k \theta_0}}{\theta_1 - \theta_0} = \log 2k$$

where k is chosen to make the probability .135 that x will exceed x_0. Thus the right tail, which was shown in Chapter 3 to be better than the left tail for that problem, is now shown to be the best possible critical region for that problem.

The derivation that led to (6) does not depend on the particular value of θ_1, provided that $\theta_1 < \theta_0$. Thus the same critical region is used whatever the value of θ_1, as long as $\theta_1 < \theta_0$. The value of k necessary to produce the same x_0 for (6) will, of course, depend on the value of θ_1. This discussion shows that (6) gives the best critical region for testing the hypothesis $H_0 : \theta = \theta_0$ against the composite alternative $H_1 : \theta < \theta_0$. Thus the Neyman-Pearson lemma, although designed to test a simple hypothesis against a simple alternative, can sometimes be used to solve a problem in which the alternative hypothesis is composite. From this result it follows that the critical region selected for the problem discussed in Chapter 3 is the best critical region for testing $H_0 : \theta = 2$ against $H_1 : \theta < 2$. This form of the alternative hypothesis would undoubtedly be much more realistic and satisfying to the experimenter than the original alternative $H_1 : \theta = 1$.

As a second illustration, consider the problem of testing whether a normal population with unit variance has a mean $\theta = \theta_0$ or a mean $\theta = \theta_1 < \theta_0$. Here

$$f(x; \theta) = \frac{e^{-\frac{1}{2}(x-\theta)^2}}{\sqrt{2\pi}}$$

Then

$$L_0 = \prod_{n=1}^{n} f(x_i; \theta_0) = (2\pi)^{-\frac{n}{2}} e^{-\frac{1}{2}\sum_{i=1}^{n}(x_i - \theta_0)^2}$$

and

$$L_1 = \prod_{i=1}^{n} f(x_i; \theta_1) = (2\pi)^{-\frac{n}{2}} e^{-\frac{1}{2}\sum_{i=1}^{n}(x_i - \theta_1)^2}$$

The region A in (2) is therefore the region in which

$$\frac{e^{-\frac{1}{2}\sum(x_i - \theta_1)^2}}{e^{-\frac{1}{2}\sum(x_i - \theta_0)^2}} = e^{\frac{1}{2}[\sum(x_i - \theta_0)^2 - \sum(x_i - \theta_1)^2]} \geq k$$

If logarithms are taken, this inequality will reduce to

$$\sum(x_i - \theta_0)^2 - \sum(x_i - \theta_1)^2 \geq 2 \log k$$

Simplification of the left side will produce the form

$$2(\theta_1 - \theta_0)\sum x_i \geq 2 \log k + (\theta_1{}^2 - \theta_0{}^2)n$$

If both sides are divided by $2n(\theta_1 - \theta_0)$, which is a negative number because it was assumed that $\theta_1 < \theta_0$, this inequality will finally reduce to

$$(7) \qquad \bar{x} \leq \frac{2 \log k + (\theta_1{}^2 - \theta_0{}^2)n}{2n(\theta_1 - \theta_0)}$$

By choosing k properly, the quantity on the right can be made to have a value $\bar{x}_0$ such that the probability that $\bar{x}$ will be less than $\bar{x}_0$ when H_0 is true will be equal to, say, $\alpha = .05$. Thus the best critical region here is the left tail of the $\bar{x}$ distribution. This is the region that was chosen on an intuitive basis for the problem of this type discussed in 6.5.1.

As in the first illustration of this section, it will be observed that the critical region obtained by applying (2) is the same for all alternative values θ_1, provided that $\theta_1 < \theta_0$, and is the best critical region for the more general composite alternative $H_1 : \theta < \theta_0$.

If $\theta_1 > \theta_0$, inequality (7) will be reversed; consequently the best critical region will consist of the right tail of the $\bar{x}$ distribution. This critical region will also be best for the composite alternative $H_1 : \theta > \theta_0$.

If one wished to test $H_0 : \theta = \theta_0$ against $H_1 : \theta \neq \theta_0$, there would be no best critical region for all possible alternative values θ_1 because when $\theta_1 < \theta_0$ the left tail will be best, whereas when $\theta_1 > \theta_0$ the right tail will be best. The preceding result is typical; best critical regions usually exist only if the alternative values of the parameter are suitably restricted.

As a final illustration, consider a discrete variable problem. Although lemma (2) was proved for continuous variables, the same proof will apply to discrete variables if one replaces integrals by sums. A certain difficulty arises with discrete variable problems in that there may be very few, or no other, critical regions having the same value of α as that for a selected critical region. If this were true, it would be academic to say that a certain critical region is a best critical region of size α. These possibilities are considered in the following illustration.

Let x possess a Poisson distribution with mean μ and let the hypothesis $H_0 : \mu = \mu_0$ be tested against the alternative hypothesis $H_1 : \mu = \mu_1 < \mu_0$. By proceeding as for continuous variables,

$$\frac{L_1}{L_0} = \frac{\prod_{i=1}^{n} e^{-\mu_1} \dfrac{\mu_1{}^{x_i}}{x_i!}}{\prod_{i=1}^{n} e^{-\mu_0} \dfrac{\mu_0{}^{x_i}}{x_i!}} = e^{n(\mu_0 - \mu_1)} \left(\frac{\mu_1}{\mu_0}\right)^{\Sigma x_i}$$

The inequality

$$e^{n(\mu_0 - \mu_1)} \left(\frac{\mu_1}{\mu_0}\right)^{\Sigma x_i} \geq k$$

is equivalent to the inequality

$$\sum x_i \log \frac{\mu_1}{\mu_0} \geq \log k + n(\mu_1 - \mu_0)$$

Since $\log \mu_1/\mu_0 < 0$ because it was assumed that $\mu_1 < \mu_0$, the preceding inequality can be written

$$\sum x_i \leq \frac{\log k + n(\mu_1 - \mu_0)}{\log \mu_1 - \log \mu_0}$$

It was shown in Chapter 6 that the sum of independent Poisson variables is a Poisson variable with its mean equal to the sum of the means; it therefore follows that the variable $z = \sum x_i$ is a Poisson variable with mean $n\mu$. The critical region determined by the preceding inequality is therefore equivalent to a critical region of the type $z \leq z_0$ for the Poisson variable z where z_0 is chosen to make the region one of size α.

This is where the difficulty with discrete variable problems arises. Since the sample space for a Poisson variable consists of the points $z = 0, 1, 2, \cdots$, the critical region $z \leq z_0$ is constructed by starting with the point $z = 0$ and adding successive points $z = 1$, $z = 2$, etc., until the sum of the probabilities for those points under H_0 is equal to α. But it is unlikely that this sum will exactly equal a previously specified α value. This unsatisfactory state of affairs can be overcome by employing what is known as a *randomization* device. Suppose, for example, that $\alpha = .05$ and that the Poisson probabilities under H_0 corresponding to $z = 0, 1, 2, \cdots$ are .018, .072, .144, $\cdots$. Choosing $z = 0$ as the critical region makes $\alpha = .018$, whereas choosing it to consist of the two points $z = 0$ and $z = 1$ makes $\alpha = .018 + .072 = .091$. The randomization device that will yield a value of $\alpha = .05$ consists in agreeing to reject H_0 when $z = 0$ but to reject H_0 only a certain proportion of the time when $z = 1$. The proper proportion here is p, where p satisfies the equation $.018 + .072p = .05$. The solution of this equation is $p = \frac{4}{9}$; consequently, in carrying out the test, one would consult a table of random numbers, or use some game of chance that would yield successes $\frac{4}{9}$ of the time, to determine whether to place $z = 1$ in the critical region when the value $z = 1$ is obtained. By using such randomization devices, it is possible to discuss best tests and to apply lemma (2) to discrete variable problems in much the same manner as for continuous variables. In practical applications with discrete variables one usually dispenses with these devices and chooses a critical region whose size is possible and close to the desired α value.

9.1.4 Likelihood Ratio Tests

When the Neyman-Pearson lemma fails to yield a best test, or when the hypothesis is composite rather than simple, it is necessary to place further restrictions on the class of tests and then attempt to find a best test in this restricted class or to introduce some other principle for obtaining good tests. In this section a second principle for constructing good tests is introduced and discussed. Since any method for testing composite hypotheses will include the testing of simple hypotheses as a special case, this principle is introduced from the point of view of composite hypotheses.

Suppose that the variable x has a frequency function $f(x; \theta_1, \cdots, \theta_k)$ that depends on k parameters. Let the composite hypothesis to be tested be denoted by $H_0 : \theta_i = \theta_i'(i = 1, 2, \cdots, k)$, where θ_i' may or may not denote a numerical value. Thus, if there are two parameters, H_0 might be the hypothesis that $\theta_1 = 10$ with θ_2 unspecified; then $\theta_1' = 10$ and $\theta_2' = \theta_2$. As a second illustration, H_0 might be the hypothesis that $\theta_1 = \theta_2$; then $\theta_1' = \theta_1$ and $\theta_2' = \theta_1$. With the aid of this notation, $f(x; \theta_1', \cdots, \theta_k')$ will denote the frequency function of x when H_0 is true.

Let $\hat{\theta}_i$ denote the maximum likelihood estimator of θ_i for the likelihood function $L(\theta) = \prod_{i=1}^{n} f(x_i; \theta_1, \cdots, \theta_k)$, where the likelihood function is treated as a function of the parameters and the x_i are fixed. Similarly, let $\hat{\theta}_i'$ denote the maximum likelihood estimator of θ_i when H_0 is true; that is, for the likelihood function $L(\theta') = \prod_{i=1}^{n} f(x_i; \theta_1', \cdots, \theta_k')$. Now, form the ratio

$$(8) \qquad\qquad \lambda = \frac{L(\hat{\theta}')}{L(\hat{\theta})}$$

This is the ratio of the two likelihood functions $L(\theta')$ and $L(\theta)$ when their parameters have been replaced by their maximum likelihood estimators. Since the maximum likelihood estimators are functions of the random variables $x_1, x_2, \cdots, x_n$, the ratio λ is a function of $x_1, x_2, \cdots, x_n$ only and is therefore an observable random variable.

The denominator of λ is the maximum of the likelihood function with respect to all the parameters, whereas the numerator is the maximum only after some or all of the parameters have been restricted by H_0; consequently it is clear that the numerator cannot exceed the denominator in value and therefore that λ can assume values between 0 and 1 only. Now the likelihood function gives the probability density (or probability in case x is a discrete variable) at the sample point $x_1, x_2, \cdots, x_n$. Therefore, if λ is close to 1, it follows that the probability density (or probability) of the sample point could not be increased much by allowing the parameters to assume values other than those possible under H_0; consequently, a value of λ near 1 corresponds intuitively to considerable belief in the reasonableness of the hypothesis H_0. If, however, the value of λ is close to 0, it implies that the probability density (or probability) of the sample point is very low under H_0 as contrasted to its value under certain other possible values of the parameters not permitted under H_0, and therefore a value of λ near 0 corresponds to considerable belief in the unreasonableness of the hypothesis. If increasing values of λ are treated as corresponding to increasing degrees of belief in the truth of the hypothesis, then λ may serve as a statistic for testing H_0, with small values of λ leading to the rejection of H_0.

Now suppose that H_0 is true and the frequency function of the random variable λ, say $g(\lambda)$, has been found. This is theoretically possible if the explicit form of $f(x; \theta_1', \cdots, \theta_k')$ is known. Suppose, further, that $g(\lambda)$ does not depend on any unknown parameters. Then one can find a value of λ, call it λ_0, such that

$$(9) \qquad \int_0^{\lambda_0} g(\lambda)\, d\lambda = \alpha$$

The critical region of size α for testing H_0 by means of the statistic λ then is chosen to be the interval $0 \leq \lambda \leq \lambda_0$.

The preceding explanation of how likelihood ratio tests are constructed may be summarized in the following form.

(10) LIKELIHOOD RATIO TESTS: *To test a hypothesis H_0, simple or composite, use the statistic λ given by (8) and reject H_0 if, and only if, the sample value of λ satisfies the inequality $\lambda \leq \lambda_0$, where λ_0 is given by (9).*

There is a great deal of similarity between the techniques used to obtain a best test and a likelihood ratio test. They both use the ratio of the two likelihood functions as a basis for making decisions. This similarity may be observed by comparing (2) and (8).

Although the use of λ as a statistic for testing hypotheses has been justified largely on intuitive grounds, it can be shown that such tests possess several very desirable properties. These properties will be discussed briefly after a few illustrations have been given on how to construct likelihood ratio tests.

Consider the second illustration of the preceding section, namely, the problem of testing the hypothesis $H_0: \theta = \theta_0$, where

$$f(x; \theta) = \frac{e^{-\frac{1}{2}(x-\theta)^2}}{\sqrt{2\pi}}$$

Here

$$L(\theta) = (2\pi)^{-\frac{n}{2}} e^{-\frac{1}{2} \sum_{i=1}^{n} (x_i - \theta)^2}$$

Since $L(\theta)$ will be maximized if $\log L(\theta)$ is maximized, it will suffice to maximize $\log L(\theta)$. But

$$\frac{\partial \log L(\theta)}{\partial \theta} = \sum_{i=1}^{n} (x_i - \theta)$$

hence $\hat{\theta} = \bar{x}$, and therefore

$$L(\hat{\theta}) = (2\pi)^{-\frac{n}{2}} e^{-\frac{1}{2}\sum_{i=1}^{n}(x_i-\bar{x})^2}$$

Since there are no parameters to be estimated under H_0,

$$L(\hat{\theta}') = L(\theta') = (2\pi)^{-\frac{n}{2}} e^{-\frac{1}{2}\sum_{i=1}^{n}(x_i-\theta_0)^2}$$

Then λ, as given by (8), becomes

$$\lambda = e^{-\frac{1}{2}\left[\sum_{i=1}^{n}(x_i-\theta_0)^2 - \sum_{i=1}^{n}(x_i-\bar{x})^2\right]}$$

Upon simplifying the exponent, λ reduces to

(11) $$\lambda = e^{-\frac{n}{2}(\bar{x}-\theta_0)^2}$$

Now n and θ_0 are known constants; hence (11) expresses a relationship between λ and $\bar{x}$. By means of this relationship the critical value λ_0 can be determined without finding $g(\lambda)$. The nature of the relationship expressed by (11) is most easily seen graphically, as in Fig. 2. To each value of λ correspond two values of $\bar{x}$, which are symmetrical with respect to $\bar{x} = \theta_0$. There are therefore two critical values of $\bar{x}$ corresponding to the critical value of $\lambda = \lambda_0$. Figure 2 also shows that increasingly small values of λ correspond to increasingly large values of $|\bar{x} - \theta_0|$. Therefore the 5 per cent critical region for λ, consisting of the interval $0 \leq \lambda \leq \lambda_0$, will correspond to the two $2\frac{1}{2}$ per cent tails of the normal $\bar{x}$ distribution. Thus the 5 per cent critical region for the likelihood ratio test is equivalent to the two equal tails of the $\bar{x}$ distribution given by the familiar inequality

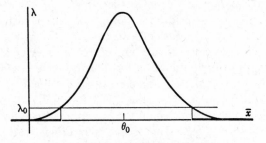

Fig. 2. Relationship between λ and $\bar{x}$.

$|\bar{x} - \theta_0| \sqrt{n} > 1.96$. For this problem the likelihood ratio test is precisely the same test as the two-tailed test selected on intuitive grounds in preceding chapters.

The preceding illustration was concerned with testing a simple hypothesis and was selected for the purpose of comparing the result of applying the Neyman-Pearson lemma for best tests with that obtained by the likelihood ratio approach. It will be recalled that a best test exists for this problem only for one-sided alternatives, $\theta_1 > \theta_0$ or $\theta_1 < \theta_0$; hence the likelihood ratio test cannot be a best test. It serves as a compromise test when there is no restriction placed on the alternative values of θ.

In the preceding illustration it was not necessary to find the distribution of λ because it turned out that λ was a simple function of $\bar{x}$ whose distribution is known. In general, however, there is no assurance that some such nice relationship to a familiar variable will exist. Then one must use whatever tools he has available in an effort to find the distribution of λ. Fortunately, for large samples there is a good approximation to the distribution of λ which eliminates the necessity for finding the exact distribution. This result from the advanced theory of statistics may be expressed in the form of a theorem.

(12) THEOREM: *Under certain regularity conditions, the random variable* $-2 \log_e \lambda$, *where λ is given by* (8), *has a distribution that approaches that of a χ^2 variable as n becomes infinite, with its degrees of freedom equal to the number of parameters that are determined by the hypothesis H_0.*

Since small values of λ correspond to large values of $-2 \log_e \lambda$, it follows that the critical region for a test based on $-2 \log_e \lambda$ will consist of large values of this variable. If the borderline of a critical region for the χ^2 variable $-2 \log_e \lambda$ is denoted by χ_0^2, then χ_0^2 must be a number such that $P\{\chi^2 > \chi_0^2\} = \alpha$. Thus, in order to determine the critical region for this approximate likelihood ratio test, it is necessary to have a table of critical values, χ_0^2. Table III in Appendix 2 enables one to find such critical values. Since the χ^2 distribution as given in (20), Chapter 6, depends on the parameter ν, called the number of degrees of freedom, any critical value will depend on ν. Graphs of the χ^2 frequency function corresponding to several values of ν are given in Fig. 7, Chapter 6.

According to theorem (12), the number of degrees of freedom in the approximating χ^2 distribution for the illustration considered earlier is $\nu = 1$ because only a single parameter was determined by H_0. Furthermore, from (11) the value of $-2 \log_e \lambda$ is $n(\bar{x} - \theta_0)^2$. From (12) it therefore follows that the critical region for this approximate test is the region in which $n(\bar{x} - \theta_0)^2 > \chi_0^2$. This is the same critical region as that obtained from the exact likelihood ratio test. It should be noted that

$\sqrt{n}(\bar{x} - \theta_0)$ is a standard normal variable because the standard deviation of $\bar{x}$ is $1/\sqrt{n}$ here; therefore from 5.4.3.1 its square is a χ^2 variable with 1 degree of freedom. Thus this theorem is seen to check with the known exact distribution here.

9.1.4.1 Testing the Equality of Variances. Consider an illustration involving the testing of a composite hypothesis. Let $x_1, x_2, \cdots, x_k$ be k independent normally distributed variables with means $\mu_1, \mu_2, \cdots, \mu_k$ and variances $\sigma_1{}^2, \sigma_2{}^2, \cdots, \sigma_k{}^2$. Let random samples of sizes $n_1, n_2, \cdots, n_k$ be drawn from these populations and let the hypothesis to be tested be

$$H_0: \sigma_1{}^2 = \sigma_2{}^2 = \cdots = \sigma_k{}^2$$

The random variable corresponding to the jth observation for the variable x_i is represented by x_{ij}. Thus there are altogether $\sum_1^k n_i = n$ random variables. Since

$$f(x_{ij}; \mu_i, \sigma_i) = \frac{e^{-\frac{1}{2}\left(\frac{x_{ij} - \mu_i}{\sigma_i}\right)^2}}{\sqrt{2\pi}\sigma_i}$$

the likelihood function may be written as

$$(13) \qquad L(x; \mu, \sigma) = \frac{e^{-\frac{1}{2}\sum\limits_{i=1}^{k}\sum\limits_{j=1}^{n_i}\left(\frac{x_{ij}-\mu_i}{\sigma_i}\right)^2}}{(2\pi)^{\frac{n}{2}}\sigma_1{}^{n_1}\cdots\sigma_k{}^{n_k}}$$

When H_0 is true, (13) reduces to

$$(14) \qquad L(x; \mu', \sigma') = \frac{e^{-\frac{1}{2}\sum\limits_{i=1}^{k}\sum\limits_{j=1}^{n_i}\left(\frac{x_{ij}-\mu_i}{\sigma}\right)^2}}{(2\pi)^{\frac{n}{2}}\sigma^n}$$

where σ on the right side of (14) represents the common value of the σ_i. In order to calculate λ, it is necessary to maximize (13) and (14) with respect to their parameters. This is accomplished by first taking logarithms of both sides and then maximizing the logarithms. If (13) and (14) are denoted by L and L_0, respectively, then it will be found that

$$\frac{\partial \log L}{\partial \mu_i} = \frac{1}{\sigma_i{}^2}\sum_{j=1}^{n_i}(x_{ij} - \mu_i)$$

$$\frac{\partial \log L}{\partial \sigma_i} = -\frac{n_i}{\sigma_i} + \frac{1}{\sigma_i{}^3}\sum_{j=1}^{n_i}(x_{ij} - \mu_i)^2$$

$$\frac{\partial \log L_0}{\partial \mu_i} = \frac{1}{\sigma^2}\sum_{j=1}^{n_i}(x_{ij} - \mu_i)$$

$$\frac{\partial \log L_0}{\partial \sigma} = -\frac{n}{\sigma} + \frac{1}{\sigma^3}\sum_{i=1}^{k}\sum_{j=1}^{n_i}(x_{ij} - \mu_i)^2$$

From the first and third of these derivatives it follows that the maximum likelihood estimators for μ_i are in each case given by $\hat{\mu}_i = \bar{x}_i$. From the second and fourth of these derivatives, together with the results just obtained, it follows that the respective maximum likelihood estimators for the standard deviations are given by

$$\hat{\sigma}_i^2 = \sum_{j=1}^{n_i} \frac{(x_{ij} - \bar{x}_i)^2}{n_i} = s_i^2$$

and

$$\hat{\sigma}^2 = \sum_{i=1}^{k} \sum_{j=1}^{n_i} \frac{(x_{ij} - \bar{x}_i)^2}{n} = \sum_{i=1}^{k} \frac{n_i s_i^2}{n}$$

If these estimators are substituted in (13) and (14), respectively, L and L_0 will become

$$\hat{L} = \frac{e^{-\frac{n}{2}}}{(2\pi)^{\frac{n}{2}} s_1^{n_1} \cdots s_k^{n_k}}$$

and

$$\hat{L}_0 = \frac{e^{-\frac{n}{2}}}{(2\pi)^{\frac{n}{2}} \left(\dfrac{n_1 s_1^2 + \cdots + n_k s_k^2}{n} \right)^{\frac{n}{2}}}$$

The likelihood ratio given by (8) will then reduce to

(15)
$$\lambda = \frac{s_1^{n_1} \cdots s_k^{n_k}}{\left(\dfrac{n_1 s_1^2 + \cdots + n_k s_k^2}{n} \right)^{\frac{n}{2}}}$$

If now the frequency function $g(\lambda)$ were available under H_0 and $g(\lambda)$ did not depend on any unknown parameters, it would be possible to find a critical value λ_0 for deciding whether to accept or reject the hypothesis that the k populations possess equal variances. However, because of the complexity of the problem, it is necessary to resort to the approximation for the distribution of λ given in (12).

If H_0 had specified that the variances all had a certain known value, then the degrees of freedom here would have been k; however, the variances are only assumed to be equal in value; therefore the number of degrees of freedom is $k - 1$.

Studies made on the accuracy of the χ^2 approximation when applied to (15) have shown that a more accurate test, particularly for small values of the n_i, can be constructed by altering (15) somewhat. Although this chapter is concerned with the general theory of testing hypotheses and estimation, the problem of testing the homogeneity of variances arises so frequently and is so important that it may be worthwhile to display the more refined test here. The altered form of (15) consists in treating

(16)
$$\frac{-2 \log_e \mu}{1 + \dfrac{1}{3(k-1)} \left(\sum_{i=1}^{k} \dfrac{1}{n_i - 1} - \dfrac{1}{n-k} \right)}$$

as a variable having a χ^2 distribution with $k - 1$ degrees of freedom, where μ is given by

$$\mu = \frac{\displaystyle\prod_{i=1}^{k} \left(\frac{n_i s_i^2}{n_i - 1} \right)^{\frac{n_i-1}{2}}}{\left(\dfrac{\sum n_i s_i^2}{\sum (n_i - 1)} \right)^{\sum \frac{n_i-1}{2}}}$$

As a numerical illustration of this test, consider the problem of testing whether the variability of a manufactured product which is assumed to be normally distributed has remained constant over a period of five weeks as judged by the following five weekly sample variances based on samples of five each: $s_1^2 = 237, s_2^2 = 320, s_3^2 = 853, s_4^2 = 296, s_5^2 = 141$. Here $n_i = 5 \ (i = 1, \cdots, 5)$;   hence

$$\mu = \frac{\prod (\frac{5}{4} s_i^2)^2}{\left(\dfrac{5 \sum s_i^2}{20} \right)^{10}} = \frac{5^{10} \prod (s_i^2)^2}{(\sum s_i^2)^{10}}$$

Then

$$\log_e \mu = 2 \sum \log_e s_i^2 - 10 \log_e \frac{\sum s_i^2}{5}$$
$$= -1.844$$

Further computations yield the value of 3.35 for (16). Since the 5 per cent critical value of χ^2 for $k - 1 = 4$ degrees of freedom is $\chi_0^2 = 9.5$, this result shows that the hypothesis of homogeneity is a reasonable one as far as these data are concerned. The unimproved likelihood ratio test given by (15) would have yielded a value of $-2 \log_e \lambda = 4.6$. The fairly large difference in the numerical values of these two variables, which are assumed to possess the same approximate χ^2 distribution, is due to the small values of the n_i.

Although the problem of testing hypotheses, both simple and composite, would appear to be completely solved for large samples, the question whether likelihood ratio tests are good tests from the point of view of type II errors still remains. Studies show that when best tests as given by the Neyman-Pearson lemma do not exist, likelihood ratio tests are often equivalent to tests that are known to be very desirable from the type II error point of view, particularly for large samples. Thus, when best tests do not exist, it is usually safe to employ a likelihood ratio test, provided that the samples are fairly large.

9.2 Estimation

An introduction to the problem of estimating parameters of frequency functions was given in Chapter 3. In that chapter maximum likelihood estimation was introduced as a favorite method of many statisticians for obtaining point estimates of parameters. In this chapter properties to be desired in point estimates are considered, and estimation by means of intervals is introduced.

9.2.1 Unbiased Estimates

Perhaps the first property of an estimate that one would think of as being desirable is the property of the estimate converging, in some sense, to the value of the parameter as the sample size becomes increasingly large. Since almost any reasonable estimate will possess such a property, a closely related property that is somewhat more restrictive is often considered instead. This is the property of being unbiased. For the purpose of defining this term, consider a random variable x whose frequency function depends on a parameter θ. Let $x_1, x_2, \cdots, x_n$ represent a sample of size n from the corresponding population and let $t(x_1, x_2, \cdots, x_n)$ be any statistic being contemplated as an estimator of θ. Then the property of being unbiased may be defined as follows.

(17) DEFINITION: *The statistic* $t = t(x_1, x_2, \cdots, x_n)$ *is called an unbiased estimate (or estimator) of the parameter* θ *if* $E[t] = \theta$.

This property merely states that the random variable t possesses a distribution whose mean is the parameter θ being estimated. This property was shown in section 6.6 to hold, for example, for $t = \bar{x}$ when estimating the mean μ of a distribution.

As an illustration of how the bias in a statistic may sometimes be determined by means of expected value formulas, consider the expected value of a sample variance based on a random sample of size n. From properties of E, and the definition of σ^2, it follows that

$$(18) \qquad E[s^2] = E\left[\frac{1}{n}\sum_{i=1}^{n}(x_i - \bar{x})^2\right]$$

$$= E\left\{\frac{1}{n}\sum_{i=1}^{n}[(x_i - \mu) - (\bar{x} - \mu)]^2\right\}$$

$$= E\left[\frac{1}{n}\sum_{i=1}^{n}(x_i - \mu)^2 - (\bar{x} - \mu)^2\right]$$

$$= \frac{1}{n}\sum_{i=1}^{n}E(x_i - \mu)^2 - E(\bar{x} - \mu)^2$$

$$= \frac{1}{n}\sum_{i=1}^{n}\sigma^2 - \sigma_{\bar{x}}^2$$

$$= \sigma^2 - \frac{\sigma^2}{n}$$

$$= \frac{n-1}{n}\sigma^2$$

This shows that s^2 is not an unbiased estimate of σ^2, which means that if repeated samples of size n are taken and the resulting sample variances are averaged the average will not approach the true variance in value but will be consistently too small by the factor of $(n-1)/n$. For small samples this factor becomes important; consequently, one must be careful how he combines samples in making an estimate of the true variance when an unbiased estimate is desired. In order to overcome the bias in s^2, it is merely necessary to multiply s^2 by $n/(n-1)$ and use the resulting quantity as the estimate of σ^2. Then, because of (18),

$$E\left(\frac{n}{n-1}s^2\right) = \frac{n}{n-1}E[s^2] = \sigma^2$$

Since

$$\frac{n}{n-1}s^2 = \frac{\displaystyle\sum_{i=1}^{n}(x_i - \bar{x})^2}{n-1}$$

it is clear that one can avoid the bias in estimating variances by dividing the sum of squares of deviations by $n-1$ rather than by n, as was the practice in the preceding chapters. It is because of this property that some authors define the sample variance as $\sum(x_i - \bar{x})^2/(n-1)$.

As a second illustration, consider the problem of how to combine several sample variances to obtain a single unbiased estimate of the population variance. Such a problem would arise, for example, in quality-control work if one wished to obtain an unbiased estimate of the variability of a manufacturing process as measured by σ^2 and had available a number of daily estimates of the variability. Let $s_1^2, \cdots, s_k^2$ denote k sample variances based on samples of sizes $n_1, \cdots, n_k$, respectively. Then, if each sample variance is weighted with the size of the sample on which it is based, the proper weighted average to use for estimating σ^2 is given by

$$t = \frac{n_1 s_1^2 + \cdots + n_k s_k^2}{a}$$

where a is chosen to make this estimate unbiased. From properties of E and the result in (18), it follows that

$$E[t] = \frac{1}{a}[(n_1 - 1)\sigma^2 + \cdots + (n_k - 1)\sigma^2]$$

$$= \frac{\sigma^2}{a}(n_1 + \cdots + n_k - k)$$

In order that t be unbiased, it is therefore necessary to choose $a = n_1 + \cdots + n_k - k$. Thus the desired estimate of σ^2 is given by

(19)
$$\frac{n_1 s_1^2 + \cdots + n_k s_k^2}{n_1 + \cdots + n_k - k}$$

As an exercise to illustrate the convenience of using the operator E for calculating mean values and at the same time to derive a useful formula, consider the problem of expressing the variance of a linear combination of a set of variables in terms of the variances and correlations of the variables. Let

$$z = a_1 x_1 + \cdots + a_k x_k$$

be the function whose variance is desired. Then

$$E[z] = a_1 \mu_1 + \cdots + a_k \mu_k$$

and

$$z - E[z] = a_1(x_1 - \mu_1) + \cdots + a_k(x_k - \mu_k)$$

Then, from the definition of the variance of a variable and this result,

$$\sigma_z^2 = E[z - E(z)]^2$$

$$= E[a_1(x_1 - \mu_1) + \cdots + a_k(x_k - \mu_k)]^2$$

$$= E\left[\sum_{i=1}^{k} a_i^2(x_i - \mu_i)^2 + 2\sum_{i<j} a_i a_j(x_i - \mu_i)(x_j - \mu_j)\right]$$

$$= \sum_{i=1}^{k} a_i^2 E(x_i - \mu_i)^2 + 2\sum_{i<j} a_i a_j E(x_i - \mu_i)(x_j - \mu_j)$$

Denoting the variance of the variable x_i by σ_i^2 and the correlation coefficient between x_i and x_j by ρ_{ij} it follows from (12) and (13), Chapter 8, that

$$E(x_i - \mu_i)(x_j - \mu_j) = \rho_{ij}\sigma_i\sigma_j$$

hence that

(20)
$$\sigma_z^2 = \sum_{i=1}^{k} a_i^2\sigma_i^2 + 2\sum_{i<j} a_i a_j \rho_{ij}\sigma_i\sigma_j$$

When the variables $x_1, \cdots, x_k$ are uncorrelated, this formula reduces to the well-known formula

(21)
$$\sigma_z^2 = \sum_{i=1}^{k} a_i^2\sigma_i^2$$

which is essentially equivalent to formula (14), Chapter 6. Formulas (20) and (21) are very useful for determining the accuracy of estimates of means of populations when these estimates are constructed as linear combinations of other estimates.

9.2.2 Best Unbiased Estimates

Although the property of being unbiased is a desirable one to seek in an estimate, it is not nearly so important as the property of an estimate being close in some sense to the parameter being estimated. Thus, if an estimate t is consistently closer to θ than another estimate t' in repeated samples of the same size, then t would certainly be preferred to t', even if t were biased and t' were unbiased. Because of the difficulty or impossibility of determining whether one of two estimates is closer than the other to θ for any reasonable definition of closeness, it is customary to substitute a measure of the variability of t about θ in place of closeness. Since the variance, or the standard deviation, has been used to measure variability throughout the preceding chapters, one would naturally think of selecting one or the other of these measures; however, unless θ happens to be the mean of the distribution of t, the variance will not measure the variability about θ. This difficulty can be overcome by using the second moment about θ as the desired measure. When θ is the mean of t, that is, when t is an unbiased estimate of θ, this measure reduces to the variance of t.

If now t_1 and t_2 are two estimates of θ that are to be compared, this can be done by comparing their second moments about θ. In this connection, a statistic t_1 will be said to be better than the statistic t_2 for estimating θ, provided that $E(t_1 - \theta)^2 \leq E(t_2 - \theta)^2$ for all possible values of θ and provided that the strict inequality holds for at least one value of θ.

The problem of deciding whether an estimate is a good one in comparison with all other possible estimates is not quite so simple. The difficulty is that a trivial estimate such as $t = c$, where c is some constant, will be better as an estimate of the mean θ of a normal population than $\bar{x}$ when θ happens to be equal to c. Thus one cannot expect to find a reasonable estimate such as $\bar{x}$ to possess a second moment about θ that is a minimum for all possible values of θ. In order to avoid such paradoxical results, it is customary to limit the discussion of the goodness of an estimate to unbiased estimates. Since the property of being unbiased is required to hold for all possible values of θ, trivial estimates such as $t = c$ are automatically eliminated from consideration. In view of the preceding discussion, the following definition is introduced as a basis for choosing a good estimate.

(22) DEFINITION: *A statistic $t = t(x_1, x_2, \cdots, x_n)$ will be called a best unbiased estimate (estimator) of the parameter θ if it is unbiased and if it possesses minimum variance among all unbiased estimates (estimators).*

This property must hold for all possible values of θ, that is, regardless of what the true value of the parameter may be. Although there are other definitions of a best estimate in use, the preceding definition is one that is frequently used. It should be realized that the variance was selected in (22) because it was considered to measure the concentration of the distribution of t about θ. Since it is easy to construct an example of a distribution in which most of the distribution is heavily concentrated about θ, yet for which the second moment is extremely large, one must appreciate that the second moment is not foolproof for giving the comparison of estimates that one originally had in mind. Nevertheless, the same type of criticism can be leveled at any other substitute; furthermore, experience and theory have shown that (22) is a very useful definition.

As an application of the preceding ideas, consider the problem of determining whether some weighted average of a random sample from a population can yield a better unbiased estimate of the population mean than the sample mean. Let the two competing estimates be written

$$t_1 = a_1 x_1 + \cdots + a_n x_n$$

and

$$t_2 = \bar{x}$$

The unknown a's in t_1 are selected to make t_1 unbiased and to minimize $E(t_1 - \theta)^2$. In order to determine the bias in t_1, calculate

$$E(t_1) = a_1 E(x_1) + \cdots + a_n E(x_n)$$
$$= a_1 \mu + \cdots + a_n \mu$$
$$= (a_1 + \cdots + a_n)\mu$$

The statistic t_1 will be unbiased if the a's are restricted to satisfy

$$a_1 + \cdots + a_n = 1.$$

This merely states that the sum of the coefficients in t_1 must be 1; hence the restriction can be ignored if t_1 is written in the form

$$t_1 = \frac{c_1 x_1 + \cdots + c_n x_n}{c_1 + \cdots + c_n}$$

Since t_1 is now unbiased, its second moment about μ is merely its variance. Because the variables $x_1, x_2, \cdots, x_n$ are independent and have the same variance, it follows from formula (21) that the variance of t_1 is given by

$$\sigma_{t_1}^{\,2} = \sigma^2 \frac{\sum\limits_{i=1}^{n} c_i^{\,2}}{\left(\sum\limits_{i=1}^{n} c_i \right)^2}$$

Now choose the c's to minimize this expression. Using calculus methods, the c's must satisfy the equations

$$\frac{\partial}{\partial c_k} \frac{\sum c_i^{\,2}}{(\sum c_i)^2} = \frac{(\sum c_i)^2 2c_k - \sum c_i^{\,2} 2 \sum c_i}{(\sum c_i)^4} = 0 \qquad (k = 1, \cdots, n)$$

These equations reduce to

$$c_k = \frac{\sum c_i^{\,2}}{\sum c_i} \qquad (k = 1, \cdots, n)$$

This result shows that the best linear combination to use is the one in which the coefficients are all equal, since c_k does not depend on k, in which case t_1 reduces to $\bar{x}$. Thus no linear combination of the sample can yield a better unbiased estimate than the sample mean $\bar{x}$. If the variable x is normally distributed, it can be shown that $\bar{x}$ is not only the best linear combination of the sample values to use but the best function of any kind to use, that is, $\bar{x}$ minimizes $E(t' - \mu)^2$, where t' is any unbiased estimate of μ. A proof of this fact is given in the appendix as an application of a formula that is derived there to enable one to determine whether a particular estimate satisfies definition (22) for being a best unbiased estimate.

9.2.3   Maximum Likelihood Estimates

In Chapter 3 maximum likelihood estimation was introduced on the grounds that it is a popular method for finding point estimates. This popularity rests on the ease with which such estimates are usually obtained and with the desirable properties that they possess.

Among the desirable features of maximum likelihood estimates is their property of often yielding best estimates. Examples can be found for which the maximum likelihood estimate is a poor one; however, for most applications it is either a best estimate or very nearly so.

A second desirable feature of maximum likelihood estimates is their excellent large sample properties. If $\hat{\theta}$ denotes such an estimate, and if some mild restrictions are placed upon the frequency function $f(x; \theta)$, it can be shown that the variable

$$(23) \qquad \frac{\hat{\theta} - \theta}{\dfrac{a}{\sqrt{n}}}$$

possesses a distribution approaching that of a standard normal variable as $n \to \infty$. The constant a in the denominator depends on $f(x; \theta)$. The situation here is very similar to that in 6.6, where it was shown that $(\bar{x} - \mu) \sqrt{n}/\sigma$ possesses a distribution approaching that of a standard normal variable. It is customary to call such limiting distributions *asymptotic distributions*. Thus the maximum likelihood estimate $\hat{\theta}$ is said to be asymptotically normally distributed. The quantity $a/\sqrt{n}$ in the denominator of (23) is called the asymptotic standard deviation of $\hat{\theta}$. Now it can be shown that among all estimates that are asymptotically normally distributed, the maximum likelihood estimate possesses minimum asymptotic variance. Thus, in the sense of possessing minimum asymptotic variance, one can say that among all asymptotically normally distributed estimates the maximum likelihood estimate is a best estimate.

It will be found that maximum likelihood estimates are often biased; hence, if an unbiased estimate is desired, it may be necessary to multiply the maximum likelihood estimate by a constant that depends on n, such as was done with s^2, in order to obtain an unbiased estimate. In some problems it is not possible to adjust a maximum likelihood estimate in this manner.

The preceding properties are the principal ones that justify the popularity of maximum likelihood estimation.

9.2.4 Confidence Intervals

Thus far, only point estimates of parameters have been considered. In many problems of estimation, however, one prefers an interval estimate that will express the accuracy of the estimate as well. If the sample is sufficiently large and the estimate is a maximum likelihood estimate, one can use normal curve methods as indicated in the preceding section to find such an interval; however, in order to be able to treat more general problems, a more general method is needed for constructing interval estimates. Such a method, known as the method of *confidence intervals*, is now described by means of a particular example.

Suppose that a random sample of size 100 has been taken from a population that is known to be normal and whose variance is known to be equal to 16. Suppose, further, that the mean of this sample is 30. Then the problem is to estimate the population mean μ by the use of an interval of values of x. Since $\sigma^2 = 16$, $\sigma_{\bar{x}} = \sigma/\sqrt{n} = .4$. Although the value of μ is unknown, it is known from the theory of Chapter 6 that for repeated samples of the type being considered $\bar{x}$ will be normally distributed about this value of μ with a standard deviation of .4; consequently, the fixed but unknown interval given by $\mu \pm .8$ will contain 95 per cent of such sample means in the long run. Since μ is unknown and is to be estimated, one would be tempted to replace μ by $\bar{x}$ to obtain the interval $\bar{x} \pm .8$ and to make the claim that the probability is .95 that this interval will contain μ. Such a claim actually is correct if one interprets this probability in the following manner.

If the interval $\bar{x} \pm .8$ is treated as a variable interval, changing with each sample of 100, then in repeated sampling 95 per cent of such intervals in the long run will contain μ. This follows from the fact that if 95 per cent of sample means $\bar{x}$ lie within .8 unit of μ, in 95 per cent of such samples μ must lie within .8 unit of the corresponding $\bar{x}$. The situation is represented geometrically in Fig. 3.

Each point represents an $\bar{x}$ based on a sample of 100. The upper diagram corresponds to the case in which μ is assumed known and a probability statement is made concerning $\bar{x}$'s. The lower diagram corresponds to the case in which μ is assumed unknown and the variable intervals $\bar{x} \pm .8$ are plotted. If a point lies inside the 95 per cent band of the upper diagram, its interval in the lower diagram must necessarily cover μ, and not otherwise.

In practice, only one such $\bar{x}$ is available, so that only the first point and

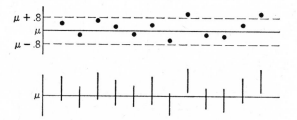

Fig. 3. Illustration of confidence interval methods.

its corresponding interval of $30 \pm .8$ is available. On the basis of this one experiment, the claim will be made that the interval $30 \pm .8$ contains the population mean μ. If for each such experiment the same claim were made for the interval corresponding to that experiment, then for these experiments 95 per cent of such claims would be true in the long run. It is in this sense that correct probability statements can be made concerning population parameters. The interval $30 \pm .8$ is called a 95 per cent *confidence interval* for μ. The end points of a confidence interval for a parameter are called *confidence limits* for the parameter.

It should be clearly understood that one is merely betting on the correctness of the rule of procedure when applying the confidence interval technique to a given experiment. It is obviously incorrect to make the claim that the probability is .95 that the interval $30 \pm .8$ contains μ. The latter probability is either 1 or 0, depending on whether μ does or does not lie in this fixed interval. It is only when the random interval $\bar{x} \pm .8$ is considered that one can make correct probability statements of the type desired.

The preceding illustration of a confidence interval was discussed from a geometrical point of view. In most problems, however, one obtains confidence intervals by analytical methods. Thus, for the preceding example, one would first write

$$P\{ |\bar{x} - \mu| < .8\} = .95$$

This statement may be written in the form

$$P\{-.8 < \bar{x} - \mu < .8\} = .95$$

If the two inequalities are rearranged, the statement becomes

$$P\{\bar{x} -.8 < \mu < \bar{x} + .8\} = .95$$

Since $\bar{x}$ is the random variable here, this statement must be interpreted as saying that the probability is .95 that the random interval $\bar{x} \pm .8$ will contain μ in its interior. If $\bar{x}$ is replaced by its observed sample value, then the 95 per cent confidence interval $30 \pm .8$ for μ is obtained.

The preceding analytical method for finding confidence intervals is used extensively in the following chapters for finding confidence intervals for the more common statistical parameters. An examination of this illustration and those in the following chapters will reveal that the method for finding confidence intervals consists in first finding a random variable, call it z, that involves the desired parameter θ but whose distribution does not depend on any unknown parameters. Thus $z = \bar{x} - \mu$ is such a variable. Next, two numbers, z_1 and z_2, are chosen such that

$$P\{z_1 < z < z_2\} = 1 - \alpha$$

where $1 - \alpha$ is the desired *confidence coefficient*, such as .95. Then these two inequalities are solved so that this probability statement assumes the form

$$P\{\underline{\theta} < \theta < \bar{\theta}\} = 1 - \alpha$$

where $\underline{\theta}$ and $\bar{\theta}$ are random variables depending on z but not involving θ. Finally, one substitutes the sample values in $\underline{\theta}$ and $\bar{\theta}$ to obtain a numerical interval which is then the desired confidence interval. The preceding technique does not always lead to a confidence interval because the rearrangement of the probability inequality may not yield an interval. It is also clear that any number of confidence intervals can be constructed for a parameter by choosing z_1 and z_2 differently each time or by choosing different random variables of the z type. The problem of determining which confidence interval is the shortest on the average in some sense, hence to be preferred, is closely related to the problem of finding best tests of hypotheses. If one chooses a random variable z that is known to yield a good test for the hypothesis $H_0: \theta = \theta_0$, then the confidence interval based on z will turn out to be a good one also. The random variables discussed in Chapter 11 for testing hypotheses are of this type; hence there will be no discussion concerning the quality of the confidence intervals obtained there.

As pointed out in the preceding discussion, the analytical method for finding confidence intervals requires that the proper type of random variable z be available. When such a variable is not available, a more general method may be employed to construct confidence intervals. The method is explained for the case of a continuous variable x whose frequency function $f(x; \theta)$ depends on a single parameter θ.

Let $\theta^* = \theta^*(x_1, \cdots, x_n)$ be an estimator of θ that is based on a random sample of size n from the population corresponding to $f(x; \theta)$, and let $g(\theta^*; \theta)$ be the frequency function of θ^*. Theoretically, at least, this frequency function can be determined when $f(x; \theta)$ is given. Then a 95 per cent confidence interval for θ may be constructed in the following manner.

Suppose that θ is given any value whatever, say $\theta = \theta_0$. Since $g(\theta^*; \theta_0)$ is now completely specified, it would be possible to find two numbers h_1 and h_2 such that

(24)
$$\int_{-\infty}^{h_1} g(\theta^*; \theta_0) \, d\theta^* = .025$$

and

(25)
$$\int_{h_2}^{\infty} g(\theta^*; \theta_0) \, d\theta^* = .025$$

These two numbers, of course, would depend on the particular value given to θ; therefore, this dependence is indicated by writing h_1 and h_2 as functions of θ, namely, $h_1(\theta)$ and $h_2(\theta)$. Now, consider the graphs of these two functions of θ. A typical pair of such graphs is illustrated in Fig. 4.

After a random sample of size n has been drawn and the value of θ^* calculated, draw a horizontal line θ^* units above the θ axis as indicated in Fig. 4. If the two functions $h_1(\theta)$ and $h_2(\theta)$ are increasing functions, as shown in the sketch, then this horizontal line will cut each curve in only one point. Let θ_1 and θ_2 be the abscissas of these points of intersection. Then the interval from θ_2 to θ_1 on the θ axis is the desired 95 per cent confidence interval for θ because of the following considerations.

Whatever the true value of θ in $f(x; \theta)$ may be, call it θ', it follows from the construction of $h_1(\theta)$ and $h_2(\theta)$ as given by (24) and (25) that

$$P\{h_1(\theta') < \theta^* < h_2(\theta')\} = .95$$

Geometrically, this means that the probability is .95 that the horizontal line of Fig. 4 corresponding to the estimator θ^* will cut the vertical line through θ' somewhere between the two curves. This is the situation illustrated in Fig. 4. If this type of intersection does occur, then θ' must lie inside the interval (θ_2, θ_1), as shown. If this type of intersection does not occur, then θ' must lie outside the interval (θ_2, θ_1). Since the probability is .95 that an intersection of this type will occur, regardless of what the true value, θ', may be, the probability is .95 that an interval (θ_2, θ_1) constructed in this manner will contain the true value θ'.

The preceding derivation assumed that the two functions $h_1(\theta)$ and $h_2(\theta)$ were increasing functions of θ. In most applications this is the case. The arguments, of course, apply equally well to decreasing functions and for confidence coefficients other than 95 per cent. However, if the curves corresponding to $h_1(\theta)$ and $h_2(\theta)$ are intersected in more than single points by horizontal lines, the construction becomes more difficult and the confidence interval becomes a set of intervals.

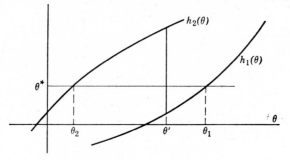

Fig. 4. Construction of confidence intervals.

In many problems it is possible to find the confidence limits θ_2 and θ_1 without explicitly finding the functions $h_1(\theta)$ and $h_2(\theta)$. It is clear from inspecting Fig. 4 that θ_1 is the value of θ for which $h_1(\theta) = \theta^*$ and that θ_2 is the value of θ for which $h_2(\theta) = \theta^*$. Thus, replacing θ^* in (24) and (25) by t, since θ^* is merely a dummy variable of integration there, it follows that θ_1 and θ_2 must be the values of θ satisfying the equations

(26)
$$\int_{-\infty}^{\theta^*} g(t; \theta_1)\, dt = .025$$
$$\int_{\theta^*}^{\infty} g(t; \theta_2)\, dt = .025$$

It is often possible to solve these equations for θ_1 and θ_2 and thus determine the desired confidence interval.

Although this geometrical method of constructing confidence intervals was discussed for the case of a continuous variable, it has proved useful for discrete variables as well. To illustrate the application of the method to a discrete variable, consider the problem of finding a 95 per cent confidence interval for binomial p if a sample of size 50 has yielded the estimate $p' = .4$. Here $\theta = p$ and $\theta^* = p' = .4$. Since the estimator p' is a discrete random variable, the integrals in (26) must be replaced by the appropriate sums; hence the confidence limits p_2 and p_1 must satisfy the equations

(27)
$$\sum_{t=0}^{.4} g(t; p_1) = .025$$
$$\sum_{t=.4}^{1} g(t; p_2) = .025$$

where $g(t; p)$ is the frequency function for the estimator $t = p'$ and the values of t for which terms exist are values given by $t = x/50$ ($x = 0, 1, \cdots, 50$). Now, because of this relationship,

$$P\{x = k\} = P\{t = k/50\} = g(k/50; p)$$

consequently, one can just as well work with the binomial variable x as with the variable p'. If equations (27) are expressed in terms of binomial x, they will become

(28)
$$\sum_{k=0}^{20} \frac{50!}{k!\,(50-k)!}\, p_1{}^k q_1{}^{50-k} = .025$$
$$\sum_{k=20}^{50} \frac{50!}{k!\,(50-k)!}\, p_2{}^k q_2{}^{50-k} = .025$$

It is possible to solve these equations by trial-and-error methods; however, tables are available for sums of binomial probabilities to assist one in the solution. Such tables yield the values $p_2 = .26$ and $p_1 = .55$, which are therefore the desired confidence limits for p.

Although the variable p' is a discrete variable, the problem was solved as though the arguments for a continuous variable that led to equations (26) were applicable to discrete variables also. Since the integrals in (24) and (25) become sums for a discrete variable, it is not possible in general to find numbers $h_1(p)$ and $h_2(p)$ such that these sums exactly equal .025 for all values of p. It is customary, therefore, to choose $h_1(p)$ and $h_2(p)$ in such a manner that the corresponding sums come as close as possible to but do not exceed .025. With this understanding, the arguments for the continuous case will show that the probability will be at least .95 that the confidence interval constructed in the foregoing manner will contain p.

REFERENCES

Additional material on the testing of hypotheses and on estimation may be found in the following books:

Neyman, J., *First Course in Probability and Statistics*, Henry Holt and Co.

Dixon and Massey, *An Introduction to Statistical Analysis*, McGraw-Hill Book Co.

Mood, A. M., *Introduction to the Theory of Statistics*, McGraw-Hill Book Co.

The derivation of the correction to the likelihood ratio test for testing the homogeneity of a set of variances, although difficult, may be found in M. S. Bartlett, "Properties of Sufficiency and Statistical Tests," *Proc. Royal Soc. London, Series A*; **160**, pp. 273 ff.

EXERCISES

1. Suppose that you are testing $H_0:\mu = 2$ against $H_1:\mu = 1$ for the Poisson distribution by means of a sample of size 2. Indicate by means of a sketch in the sample space x_1, x_2 the part of the sample space you would choose for the critical region. Give a justification for your choice.

2. Estimate the size of the type II error if the type I error is chosen to be $\alpha = .16$, if you are testing $H_0:\mu = 7$ against $H_1:\mu = 6$ for a normal distribution with $\sigma = 2$ by means of a sample of size 25, and if the proper tail of the $\bar{x}$ distribution is used as critical region.

3. In testing $H_0:\mu = 20$ for a normal distribution, what is the probability that you will accept H_0 when the mean is actually $\sigma/2$ units above 20, if a sample of size 9 is taken, and the critical region is chosen as the two $2\frac{1}{2}$ per cent tails of the $\bar{x}$ distribution?

4. Under the 3 possible hypotheses H_1, H_2, and H_3, a discrete random variable x has the following distributions:

x	1	2	3	4	5	6	7	8	9	10
$f(x \mid H_1)$	0	.58	.02	.05	.03	.11	.01	.07	.04	.09
$f(x \mid H_2)$	.60	0	.06	.08	.03	.01	.04	.12	.02	.04
$f(x \mid H_3)$	.54	0	.10	.03	.12	.06	.04	.01	.08	.02

(a) Choose $\alpha = .10$ and find a best critical region for testing H_1 against H_2.
(b) Determine whether there is a best critical region of size $\alpha = .10$ for testing H_1 against both H_2 and H_3.

5. Forty pairs of runners have been matched with respect to ability. Each member of a pair is given a pill, with 1 member receiving a stimulant in his pill. Races are run between each pair. Let x denote the number of races won by the individuals who received the stimulant. Construct a best test for testing the hypothesis $H_0:p = \frac{1}{2}$ against $H_1:p > \frac{1}{2}$, where p is the probability that a stimulated runner will win an evenly matched race. Choose a critical region that makes α as close to .10 as possible. Calculate the power of this test for $p = .6$.

6. Graph the power function, by plotting a few points on it, for testing the hypothesis $H_0:\mu = 0$ when using the two $2\frac{1}{2}$ per cent tails of the $\bar{x}$ distribution as critical region, given that x is normally distributed with $\sigma = 1$ and that a sample of size 4 is used.

7. If x is normally distributed with $\sigma = 10$ and it is desired to test $H_0:\mu = 100$ against $H_1:\mu = 110$, how large a sample should be taken if the probability of accepting H_0 when H_1 is true is to be .02 and if a critical region of size .05 is used?

8. By means of the Neyman-Pearson lemma, prove that the best test for testing the hypothesis $H_0:\sigma = \sigma_0$ against $H_1:\sigma = \sigma_1 > \sigma_0$ for x normally distributed with 0 mean is given by choosing as critical region the region where $\sum_1^n x_i^2 > c$, where c is the proper constant.

9. Use the Neyman-Pearson lemma to determine the nature of a best critical region based on a sample of size n for testing $H_0:\theta = \theta_0$ against $H_1:\theta = \theta_1 < \theta_0$ if $f(x; \theta) = (1 + \theta)x^\theta, 0 \leq x \leq 1$.

10. Can the Neyman-Pearson lemma be applied to testing $H_0:\theta = 1$ against $H_1:\theta = 2$ if $f(x; \theta) = 1/\theta, 0 \leq x \leq \theta$ and a sample of one is to be taken?

11. Given $f(x; p) = pq^x, p = 1 - q$, find a best test based on a sample of size n for testing $H_0:q = q_0$ against $H_1:q = q_1 > q_0$. Is this test also best for $H_1:q > q_0$?

12. Given that x is normally distributed with mean 0 and variance σ^2, find the expression for λ for the likelihood ratio test for testing $H_0:\sigma = 1$.

13. Work problem 12 if the mean is μ rather than 0, with μ unknown.

14. Construct a likelihood ratio test for testing $H_0:\theta = 1$, given that $f(x; \theta) = \theta e^{-\theta x}, x \geq 0$. Carry your solution to the stage of obtaining λ as a function of $\bar{x}$.

15. Construct a likelihood ratio test for testing $H_0:p = p_0$ by means of n

observations of a binomial variable with probability p. Is this a best test for some alternative value?

16. Work problem 15 if N such experiments are carried out with numbers of successes $x_1, x_2, \cdots, x_N$.

17. Construct a likelihood ratio test for problem 9.

18. Given the following 5 sample variances based on 10 observations each, test the hypothesis that the 5 population variances are equal. The sample variances are 22, 40, 30, 32, 12. Assume normal samples.

19. Using the fact that $-2 \log_e \lambda$ possesses an approximate χ^2 distribution with 1 degree of freedom for the likelihood ratio test of problem 14, use the result of problem 14 and the following sample values to test the hypothesis $H_0 : \theta = 1$. The sample values are 1.5, 2, .8, 1.3, 2.8, .9, 1.6, .6, 4.2, 3.1, 1.4, 2.2, .7, 1.6, .8.

20. Given that x is normally distributed and given the following 3 sample values, (a) combine these 3 variances to yield an unbiased estimate of σ^2 and (b) show that $(2s_1^2 + 2s_2^2 + s_3^2)/5$ is not an unbiased estimate of σ^2. The sample values are $s_1^2 = 12$, $s_2^2 = 10$, $s_3^2 = 14$, with $n_1 = 10$, $n_2 = 10$, $n_3 = 5$.

21. Using the expected value operator, derive an expression for the correlation between $u = a_1 x_1 + \cdots + a_k x_k$ and $v = b_1 x_1 + \cdots + b_k x_k$, where the a's and b's are constants and the variables $x_1, \cdots, x_k$ are independently distributed.

22. Consider the variable $z = (a_1 x_1 + \cdots + a_k x_k)/(a_1 + \cdots + a_k)$, where the variables $x_1, \cdots, x_k$ are independently distributed with 0 means and variances $\sigma_1^2, \cdots, \sigma_k^2$. Prove that the variance of z will be minimized if the weight a_i is chosen inversely proportional to σ_i^2.

23. Given that $\sigma_1^2 = 1$, $\sigma_2^2 = 2$, $\sigma_3^2 = 3$, $\sigma_4^2 = 4$, $\sigma_5^2 = 5$, calculate the variance of z in problem 22 when (a) a_i is chosen inversely proportional to σ_i^2, (b) a_i is chosen equal to $1/k$. (c) Comment on the advantage of the weighting used in (a).

24. Show that $2\bar{x}$ is an unbiased estimate of θ for $f(x; \theta) = 1/\theta, 0 \leq x \leq \theta$.

25. Show that the distribution function of $z = \max \{x_1, x_2, \cdots, x_n\}$ is given by $(z/\theta)^n$, when x has the distribution given in problem 24. In this connection see problem 41, Chapter 6. Use the preceding result to show that $(1 + 1/n)z$ is also an unbiased estimate of θ in problem 24.

26. Compare the variances of the two estimates of θ obtained in problems 24 and 25.

27. A fisheries investigator catches fish from a lake until he has obtained x fish of a certain species. His total catch then is N. Assuming that the lake has a very large number of fish, show that the frequency function of the variable N is given by $\dbinom{N-1}{x-1} p^x (1-p)^{N-x}$, $N = x, x+1, \cdots$, where p is the proportion of this species in the lake. Use this result to show that $(x-1)/(N-1)$ is an unbiased estimate of p, and that x/N is a biased estimate.

28. Find the maximum likelihood estimator of p for a binomial distribution based on a total of n trials.

29. Find the maximum likelihood estimator of p for a binomial distribution based on N experiments of n trials each and with successes $x_1, x_2, \cdots, x_N$.

30. Find the maximum likelihood estimator of θ for the frequency function
$$f(x;\theta) = (2\pi\theta^2)^{-\frac{1}{2}}e^{-\frac{1}{2}\left(\frac{x-\theta}{\theta}\right)^2}$$

31. Find the joint maximum likelihood estimators of μ and σ for a normal distribution.

32. Given $f(x) = ce^{-(x-\mu)^{2\alpha}}$ where α is a given positive integer and c is a constant depending on α but not μ, what steps would be required to find the maximum likelihood estimator of μ?

33. Find the maximum likelihood estimate of q for $f(x;p) = pq^x$, $p = 1 - q$, $x = 1, 2, \cdots$, if n experiments yielded the observations $x_1, x_2, \cdots, x_n$.

34. Given $f(x;\theta) = \theta e^{-\theta x}$, $x \geq 0$, (a) find the maximum likelihood estimator for θ and (b) find the maximum likelihood estimator for the mean value of x.

35. Show that the situation occurring in problem 34 is typical, namely, that the maximum likelihood estimator for a parameter of a frequency function is the same as the estimator of that parameter when one expresses the parameter in terms of the mean value of x and finds the maximum likelihood estimator of the latter parameter.

36. Show that the maximum likelihood estimator of p_i in a multinomial frequency function is given by $\hat{p}_i = n_i/n$, where n_i is the observed frequency in the ith cell.

37. Find an 80 per cent confidence interval for the mean of a normal distribution if $\sigma = 2$ and if a sample of size 8 gave the values 9, 14, 10, 12, 7, 13, 11, 12.

38. Assuming that n is large enough to justify the use of the normal approximation to the binomial distribution, show that a 95 per cent confidence interval for binomial p is given by $p_1 < p < p_2$, where p_1 and p_2 are solutions of the quadratic equation $(p - p^2)(1.96)^2 = n(p' - p)^2$.

39. A lake contains N fish. A netting experiment yielded x fish, which were marked and released. A second experiment yielded y fish, of which z were found to be marked. If y is small compared with N, show that the maximum likelihood estimate of N is given, approximately, by $\hat{N} = xy/z$.

40. Given that x is normally distributed with $\sigma = 1$, use the general method for finding confidence intervals to find a confidence interval for μ if $\bar{x} = 10$ and $n = 9$; that is, construct a diagram similar to Fig. 4.

41. Assume that x possesses a Poisson distribution with unknown mean μ. If 10 observations yielded the values 20, 23, 17, 16, 21, 22, 19, 19, 25, 18, find an approximate 90 per cent confidence interval for μ. Use a normal approximation, and base your interval on the sample mean only.

42. Apply the general method for finding confidence intervals to find a 90 per cent confidence interval for θ in $f(x;\theta) = (1 + \theta)x^\theta$, $0 \leq x \leq 1$, if only the single observed value $x = .8$ is available.

CHAPTER 10

Testing Goodness of Fit

A problem that arises frequently in statistical work is the testing of the compatibility of a set of observed and theoretical frequencies. For example, if Mendelian inheritance suggests that four kinds of plants should occur in the proportions $9:3:3:1$ and if a sample of 240 plants yielded 120, 40, 55, 25 in the four categories, one would like to know whether these frequencies are compatible with those expected under Mendelian inheritance.

This type of problem has already been discussed and solved for the special case in which there are only two pairs of frequencies to be compared. Then the binomial distribution may be applied as shown in the first illustration of 5.3.4.5. When more than two pairs of frequencies are to be compared, the multinomial distribution, which was derived in 5.4.2, is needed.

10.1 The χ^2 Test

The problem that is being considered here can be formulated quite generally in terms of the notation that was introduced in 5.4.2. In this connection, consider an experiment in which there are k mutually exclusive possible outcomes $A_1, A_2, \cdots, A_k$. Let p_i be the probability that event A_i will occur at a trial of the experiment and let n trials be made. The number of trials producing outcome A_i will be denoted by n_i. Since n_i is a binomial variable with probability p_i with respect to the single outcome A_i, the mean, or expected value, of n_i is given by

$$e_i = E[n_i] = np_i$$

In terms of this notation, the problem is to determine whether the observed frequencies $n_1, n_2, \cdots, n_k$ are compatible with the expected frequencies $e_1, e_2, \cdots, e_k$.

An analysis of the preceding discussion will show that the problem is

244

really one of testing a hypothesis because it is assumed that the multinomial distribution is the proper model here and interest centers on whether the postulated p's are correct. Thus the problem can be treated as a problem of testing the hypothesis

$$(1) \qquad H_0 : p_i = p_{i0}, \qquad i = 1, 2, \cdots, k$$

where the p_{i0}'s are the postulated values of the probabilities of a multinomial distribution.

The hypothesis expressed in (1) is a simple hypothesis, but unless alternative values of the p's are specified the alternative hypothesis is composite. As a result, lemma (2) of Chapter 9 is not applicable; consequently the likelihood ratio test is the natural test to employ here. Now it will be found that the expression for λ in this test is so complicated that it is not feasible to find its distribution; therefore only the large sample approximation given by theorem (12), Chapter 9, for a general likelihood ratio test is ordinarily used.

If the various steps involved in evaluating λ in (8), Chapter 9, are carried out, it will be found that

$$(2) \qquad -2 \log_e \lambda = 2 \sum_{i=1}^{k} n_i \log_e \frac{n_i}{e_i}$$

Now according to theorem (12), Chapter 9, this quantity possesses an approximate χ^2 distribution when n is large. The number of degrees of freedom here is given by $v = k - 1$ because the multinomial distribution is determined by only $k - 1$ parameters in view of the restriction that $\sum_{1}^{k} p_i = 1$. The test of hypothesis H_0 therefore consists in choosing as critical region the right tail of the χ^2 distribution with $k - 1$ degrees of freedom.

Although (2) does yield a valid large sample test for the hypothesis (1), this test is not the one that is customarily employed here. A modification of it, which is based on approximating the right side of (2), is more commonly used. This approximation is obtained by expanding the logarithms and retaining only the dominating terms in much the same manner as in the derivation of Theorem 3, Chapter 6. Since all other terms converge to zero as $n \to \infty$, the results of such manipulations can be expressed in the form of a theorem.

THEOREM: *If* $n_1, n_2, \cdots, n_k$ *and* $e_1, e_2, \cdots, e_k$ *are the observed and expected frequencies, respectively, for the k possible outcomes of an experiment that is performed n times, then, as n becomes infinite, the distribution of the quantity*

$$(3) \qquad \sum_{i=1}^{k} \frac{(n_i - e_i)^2}{e_i}$$

will approach that of a χ^2 variable with $k - 1$ degrees of freedom.

The test procedure here is the same as for the test based on (2). Thus, after calculating the value of the quantity given by (3), one determines whether this value exceeds the critical value $\chi_0{}^2$ that is obtained from the table of critical values of the χ^2 distribution given in Table III in Appendix 2. Although this test was derived here as an approximate likelihood ratio test, it was obtained by other methods many years before likelihood ratio tests were introduced. Since statisticians were already familiar with the preceding theorem when the test based on (2) was introduced, they continued using the test based on (3), known as the χ^2 *test for goodness of fit.*

The derivation of the theorem given in connection with (3) as an application of theorem (12), Chapter 9, is given in the appendix.

As a simple illustration of how to apply this theorem, consider a typical problem. Suppose that a gambler's die is rolled 60 times and a record is kept of the number of times each face comes up. If the die is an "honest" die, each face will have the probability $\frac{1}{6}$ of appearing in a single roll. Therefore, each face would be expected to appear 10 times in an experiment of this kind. Suppose that the experiment produced the following results, where the row labeled n_i represents the observed frequencies and the row labeled e_i represents the expected frequencies.

Face	1	2	3	4	5	6
n_i	15	7	4	11	6	17
e_i	10	10	10	10	10	10

As explained in an earlier paragraph, the problem is one of testing a hypothesis about a multinomial distribution, namely, the hypothesis

$$H_0 : p_1 = \cdots = p_6 = \tfrac{1}{6}$$

Since $\nu = k - 1$ and $k = 6$ here, $\nu = 5$. If a critical region of size .05 is chosen, it will consist of those values of the approximate χ^2 variable given in (3) that exceed the value $\chi_0{}^2$ which cuts off 5 per cent of the right tail of the χ^2 distribution with five degrees of freedom. From Table III it will be found that $\chi_0^2 = 11.1$. Now calculations show that

$$\sum_{i=1}^{6} \frac{(n_i - e_i)^2}{e_i} = \frac{(15 - 10)^2}{10} + \frac{(7 - 10)^2}{10} + \frac{(4 - 10)^2}{10} + \frac{(11 - 10)^2}{10}$$

$$+ \frac{(6 - 10)^2}{10} + \frac{(17 - 10)^2}{10} = 13.6$$

Since this value exceeds the critical value $\chi_0^2 = 11.1$, it lies in the critical region and therefore the hypothesis H_0 is rejected. Thus one would conclude that the gambler's die is "dishonest." The error introduced in using the approximate χ^2 distribution here would be very small because n is fairly large; consequently the χ^2 test based on the theorem in (3) may be applied with confidence to this problem.

10.2 Limitations on the χ^2 Test

Since the χ^2 distribution is only an approximation to the exact distribution of the quantity $\Sigma(n_i - e_i)^2/e_i$, care must be exercised that the χ^2 test is used only when the approximation is good. Experience and theoretical investigations indicate that the approximation is usually satisfactory, provided that the $e_i \geq 5$ and $k \geq 5$. If $k < 5$, it is best to have the e_i somewhat larger than 5. This limitation is similar to that placed on the use of the normal curve approximation to the binomial frequency function in which np and nq were required to exceed 5.

If the expected frequency of a cell does not exceed 5, this cell should be combined with one or more other cells until the above condition is satisfied. For example, suppose that the gambler's die of the preceding section had been rolled only 24 times and the following results had been obtained:

Face	1	2	3	4	5	6
n_i	6	5	2	3	0	8
e_i	4	4	4	4	4	4

Here none of the expected frequencies exceeds 5; therefore, it is necessary to combine each cell with some other cell. If successive pairs of cells are

248   INTRODUCTION TO MATHEMATICAL STATISTICS

combined, the preceding empirical rule will be satisfied and the following table of values will be obtained:

Face	1 or 2	3 or 4	5 or 6
n_i	11	5	8
e_i	8	8	8

The application of the χ^2 test will now yield a value of $\chi^2 = 2.25$ with $\nu = 2$. From a theoretical point of view it is legitimate to combine cells in any desired manner, provided that one is not influenced by the observed frequencies. In many applications, however, there are practical reasons for combining neighboring cells as in the preceding impractical illustration.

10.3 Applications

In experiments on the breeding of flowers of a certain species, an experimenter obtained 120 magenta flowers with a green stigma, 48 magenta flowers with a red stigma, 36 red flowers with a green stigma, and 13 red flowers with a red stigma. Theory predicts that flowers of these types should be obtained in the ratios $9:3:3:1$. Are these experimental results compatible with the theory?

This is a problem of testing the hypothesis

$$H_0: p_1 = \tfrac{9}{16}, \quad p_2 = \tfrac{3}{16}, \quad p_3 = \tfrac{3}{16}, \quad p_4 = \tfrac{1}{16}$$

for a multinomial distribution involving four cells and for which $n = 217$. Under H_0, the expected frequencies, correct to the nearest integer, are those in the second row of the following table.

n_i	120	48	36	13
e_i	122	41	41	14

Calculations give

$$\chi^2 = \frac{(120 - 122)^2}{122} + \frac{(48 - 41)^2}{41} + \frac{(36 - 41)^2}{41} + \frac{(13 - 14)^2}{14} = 1.9$$

From Table III the 5 per cent critical value of χ^2 for three degrees of freedom is $\chi_0^2 = 7.8$; consequently the result is not significant. The hypothesis H_0 is acceptable here and thus there is no reason on the basis of this test for doubting that the theory is applicable to these data.

As a second application, consider the following problem. On the basis of extensive experience with trainees, a training station determined four scores in marksmanship so that equal numbers of trainees would be located in the resulting five categories of skill. A new group of 200 trainees is given the marksmanship test with the following results:

Category	I	II	III	IV	V
n_i	54	44	40	35	27
e_i	40	40	40	40	40

If the five categories are listed according to increasing ability, would you be justified in claiming that the 200 trainees represent an inferior group of trainees with respect to marksmanship? This problem may be treated as a problem of testing the hypothesis

$$H_0 : p_1 = \cdots = p_5 = \tfrac{1}{5}$$

for a multinomial distribution with $n = 200$. Calculations give $\chi^2 = 10.1$. Since $\chi_0^2 = 9.5$ for $\nu = 4$, this result is significant, hence one is justified in claiming that the new group of trainees is not typical of past trainees. Because of the excess frequencies at the lower end of the scale, the new trainees undoubtedly are inferior marksmen.

10.4 Generality of the χ^2 Test

In the preceding applications the expected frequencies for the various cells were known because the cell probabilities were assumed known; however, many applications involve situations in which the cell probabilities are functions of some unknown parameters. For example, suppose that one is interested in studying the sex distribution of children in families having eight children. If it is assumed that the probability is p that a child selected at random from a family with eight children will be a son, and if N such families are selected then the expected frequencies for the nine cells corresponding to $0, 1, 2, \cdots, 8$ sons will be given by the successive terms in the expansion of the binomial $N(q + p)^8$. Here the probabilities for the various cells depend on the unknown parameter p. Except for crude work, the difficulty cannot be overcome by assuming that the two sexes are equally divided because experience has shown that p is slightly larger than $\tfrac{1}{2}$.

Fortunately, the χ^2 test possesses a remarkable property that permits it to be applied even when the cell probabilities depend on unknown parameters as in this problem. This property, although very difficult to prove, is very simple to state. It may be expressed as follows.

(4) PROPERTY: *The χ^2 test is applicable when the cell probabilities depend on unknown parameters, provided that the unknown parameters are replaced by their maximum likelihood estimates and provided that one degree of freedom is deducted for each parameter estimated.*

It is assumed, of course, that the cell frequencies are large enough to justify the use of the regular χ^2 test. Since $\nu = k - 1$ when there are k cells and the cell probabilities are known, it follows that $\nu = k - 1 - l$ when the cell probabilities depend on l parameters. The preceding property enables the χ^2 test to be applied to a wide variety of problems involving the comparison of observed and expected frequencies. Some of these applications are considered in the next few sections.

10.5   Frequency Curve Fitting

If a theoretical frequency function has been fitted to an empirical frequency function, the question whether the fit is satisfactory naturally arises. This question was asked, for example, in the exercise on fitting a normal curve to a histogram in Chapter 5. When a normal curve is fitted to a histogram, it is usually assumed that the data represent a sample selected at random from a normal population and that the fitted normal curve is an approximation to the population curve. Thus, the question whether a fit is satisfactory can be answered only if one knows what sort of histograms will be obtained in random samples from a normal population.

Now, the χ^2 test can be employed to give a partial answer to this question. Since the χ^2 test is concerned only with comparing sets of observed and expected frequencies, it is capable of testing only those features of the fitted distribution that affect a lack of agreement in the compared sets of frequencies. For example, the χ^2 test is not capable of distinguishing between the two curves shown in Fig. 1, in which the x axis has been divided into six intervals to give six cells for the χ^2 test and in which the areas under the two curves for each of the six intervals are equal.

With this understanding of the capabilities of the χ^2 test, consider the problem of testing the adequacy of the normal curve fit in Table 2, Chapter 5. The frequencies labeled theoretical frequencies were

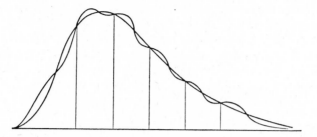

Fig. 1. Two χ^2 equivalent frequency functions.

obtained by integrating the fitted normal curve over the successive class intervals of the histogram. The fitted normal curve was obtained by replacing the parameters μ and σ by their sample estimates $\bar{x}$ and s. If these frequencies are treated as the expected frequencies in the χ^2 test, then the problem of comparing the observed and expected frequencies is the type discussed in the preceding section because the cell probabilities depend on the two parameters μ and σ. Since $\bar{x}$ and s are the maximum likelihood estimates of μ and σ, the property stated in (4) permits the application of the χ^2 test, provided that one chooses $\nu = 10 - 1 - 2 = 7$. Calculations here yield $\chi^2 = 10.4$. Since $\chi_0{}^2 = 14.1$ for $\nu = 7$, the hypothesis that the data were obtained from sampling a normal population is substantiated, as far as compatibility of corresponding pairs of frequencies is concerned, and so the fit in Fig. 6, Chapter 5, would be considered satisfactory from this point of view.

Since $e_{10} = 2.2$ does not satisfy the empirical rule in 10.2, requiring all $e_i \geq 5$, one should combine the last cell with, say, the next to last cell before applying the test; however, it is obvious that this procedure will not alter the conclusions here.

If a binomial distribution is fitted to an empirical frequency distribution by estimating the two parameters p and n in $f(x) = n! / [x! (n - x)!] \times p^x q^{n-x}$ from the data, the number of degrees of freedom in the χ^2 test will be $\nu = k - 1 - 2 = k - 3$ just as in normal curve fitting; however, it often happens in binomial problems that one or more of the parameters will be specified from other considerations. For example, suppose that one were interested in studying the sex distribution in families of eight children. Here $n = 8$ is known; hence it is not obtained as a maximum likelihood estimate from the data. Consequently the number of degrees of freedom would be $k - 2$. If one were to assume that $p = \frac{1}{2}$ rather than estimate p from the observations, the number of degrees of freedom would be $k - 1$.

Since the fitting of a Poisson distribution involves only the parameter

μ, the χ^2 test will possess $k - 2$ or $k - 1$ degrees of freedom, depending on whether μ is replaced by $\bar{x}$ or is known from other considerations.

Property (4) of the χ^2 test requires that the unknown parameters be estimated by the method of maximum likelihood using the likelihood function $p_1{}^{n_1}p_2{}^{n_2} \cdots p_k{}^{n_k}$, corresponding to the multinomial distribution. If one calculates the maximum likelihood estimates of μ and σ from this likelihood function when fitting a normal curve to a histogram, the resulting estimates will not be exactly equal to $\bar{x}$ and s, which are the maximum likelihood estimates of μ and σ for ungrouped data; however, they will ordinarily be very nearly the same. Thus, although theoretically speaking one should calculate the maximum likelihood estimates for the multinomial situation, it suffices to use the well-known maximum likelihood estimates for the continuous situation.

10.6 Contingency Tables

Another very useful application of the χ^2 test occurs in connection with testing the compatibility of observed and expected frequencies in two-way tables. Such two-way tables are usually called *contingency tables*. Table 1, in which are recorded the frequencies corresponding to the indicated classifications for a sample of 400, is an illustration of a contingency table.

A contingency table is usually constructed for the purpose of studying the relationship between the two variables of classification. In particular, one may wish to know whether the two variables are related. By means of the χ^2 test it is possible to test the hypothesis that the two variables are independent. Thus, in connection with Table 1, the χ^2 test can be used to test the hypothesis that there is no relationship between an individual's educational level and his adjustment to marriage.

TABLE 1

MARRIAGE-ADJUSTMENT SCORE

		Very low	Low	High	Very high	Totals
Education	College	18 (27)	29 (39)	70 (64)	115 (102)	232
	High school	17 (13)	28 (19)	30 (32)	41 (51)	116
	Grades only	11 (6)	10 (9)	11 (14)	20 (23)	52
	Totals	46	67	111	176	400

Before considering how the χ^2 test may be applied to this particular problem, consider a general contingency table containing r rows and c columns. Let p_{ij} be the probability that an individual selected at random from the population under consideration will be a member of the cell in the ith row and jth column of the contingency table. Let $p_i.$ be the probability that the individual will be a member of the ith row and let $p._j$ be the probability that the individual will be a member of the jth column. Then the hypothesis that the two variables are independent can be written in the form

$$H_0 : p_{ij} = p_i. p._j, \quad \begin{cases} i = 1, \cdots, r \\ j = 1, \cdots, c \end{cases}$$

If a sample of n individuals is selected and n_{ij} of them are found in the cell in the ith row and jth column, then χ^2 as defined by (3) will assume the form

$$\chi^2 = \sum_{i=1}^{r} \sum_{j=1}^{c} \frac{(n_{ij} - np_{ij})^2}{np_{ij}}$$

But under the hypothesis H_0, this expression will become

(5)
$$\chi^2 = \sum_{i=1}^{r} \sum_{j=1}^{c} \frac{(n_{ij} - np_i.p._j)^2}{np_i.p._j}$$

Since the $p_i.$ and $p._j$ are unknown, it is necessary to estimate them from the sample. If the estimates are maximum likelihood estimates, the theory discussed in 10.4 will permit the χ^2 test to be applied here, provided that one degree of freedom is deducted for each parameter so estimated. Since $\sum_1^r p_i. = 1$ and $\sum_1^c p._j = 1$, there are $r - 1 + c - 1 = r + c - 2$ parameters that need to be estimated; hence the proper number of degrees of freedom for testing independence in a contingency table of r rows and c columns is given by $\nu = k - 1 - l = rc - 1 - (r + c - 2) = (r - 1)(c - 1)$.

In order to complete the discussion, it is necessary to find the maximum likelihood estimates of the $p_i.$ and $p._j$. For this purpose let $n_i.$ denote the sum of the frequencies in the ith row and let $n._j$ denote the sum of the frequencies in the jth column. Since the variables n_{ij} are discrete, the likelihood of the sample is the probability of obtaining the sample in the order in which it occurred. Thus the likelihood of the sample is given by

$$L = \prod_{i=1}^{r} \prod_{j=1}^{c} p_{ij}{}^{n_{ij}}$$

But, because of H_0 and the definitions of $n_{i\cdot}$ and $n_{\cdot j}$, this will reduce to

$$L = \prod_{i=1}^{r} \prod_{j=1}^{c} (p_{i\cdot} p_{\cdot j})^{n_{ij}}$$

$$= \prod_{i=1}^{r} \prod_{j=1}^{c} p_{i\cdot}^{n_{ij}} \prod_{i=1}^{r} \prod_{j=1}^{c} p_{\cdot j}^{n_{ij}}$$

$$= \prod_{i=1}^{r} p_{i\cdot}^{\sum\limits_{j=1}^{c} n_{ij}} \prod_{j=1}^{c} p_{\cdot j}^{\sum\limits_{i=1}^{r} n_{ij}}$$

$$= \prod_{i=1}^{r} p_{i\cdot}^{n_{i\cdot}} \prod_{j=1}^{c} p_{\cdot j}^{n_{\cdot j}}$$

Before differentiating L with respect to $p_{i\cdot}$ for maximizing purposes, it is necessary to express one of the $p_{i\cdot}$'s, say $p_{r\cdot}$, in terms of the remaining ones through the relation $\sum_{i=1}^{r} p_{i\cdot} = 1$. If this is done, L will assume the form

$$L = \left(1 - \sum_{1}^{r-1} p_{i\cdot} \right)^{n_{r\cdot}} \prod_{i=1}^{r-1} p_{i\cdot}^{n_{i\cdot}} \prod_{j=1}^{c} p_{\cdot j}^{n_{\cdot j}}$$

Taking logarithms,

$$\log L = n_{r\cdot} \log \left(1 - \sum_{1}^{r-1} p_{i\cdot} \right) + \sum_{i=1}^{r-1} n_{i\cdot} \log p_{i\cdot} + K$$

where K does not involve the variable $p_{i\cdot}$. Now, differentiating with respect to $p_{i\cdot}$ and setting the derivative equal to 0 for a maximum,

$$\frac{\partial \log L}{\partial p_{i\cdot}} = - \frac{n_{r\cdot}}{1 - \sum\limits_{1}^{r-1} p_{i\cdot}} + \frac{n_{i\cdot}}{p_{i\cdot}} = 0$$

Since $1 - \sum_{1}^{r-1} p_{i\cdot} = p_{r\cdot}$, this equation is equivalent to

$$p_{i\cdot} = \frac{p_{r\cdot}}{n_{r\cdot}} n_{i\cdot} = \lambda n_{i\cdot}.$$

where λ does not depend on the index i. Since this must hold for $i = 1$, $2, \cdots, r$ and since

$$1 = \sum_{1}^{r} p_{i\cdot} = \lambda \sum_{1}^{r} n_{i\cdot} = \lambda n$$

it follows that $\lambda = 1/n$ and that the maximum likelihood estimate of $p_{i\cdot}$ is

$$\hat{p}_{i\cdot} = \frac{n_{i\cdot}}{n}$$

By symmetry the maximum likelihood estimate of $p_{.j}$ is

$$\hat{p}_{.j} = \frac{n_{.j}}{n}$$

If $p_{i.}$ and $p_{.j}$ in (5) are replaced by their maximum likelihood estimates, χ^2 will become

(6)
$$\chi^2 = \sum_{i=1}^{r} \sum_{j=1}^{c} \frac{\left(n_{ij} - \frac{n_{i.}n_{.j}}{n}\right)^2}{\frac{n_{i.}n_{.j}}{n}}$$

According to the theory of 10.4, this quantity may be treated as possessing a χ^2 distribution with $(r-1)(c-1)$ degrees of freedom, provided that n is sufficiently large and H_0 is true.

Now, consider the application of (6) to testing independence in Table 1. To calculate the values of the $n_{i.}n_{.j}/n$ in the ith row, it is merely necessary to multiply the column totals $n_{.j}$ by the fraction $n_{i.}/n$. Thus the values of $n_{i.}n_{.j}/n$ for the first row of Table 1 are obtained by multiplying the column totals by 232/400 and similarly for the remaining rows. These values, correct to the nearest integer, are inserted in parentheses in Table 1. The calculation of χ^2 is now like that for (3), with the values in parentheses treated as the e_i. It will be found that $\chi^2 = 20.7$. Since $\chi_0^2 = 12.6$ for $(3-1)(4-1) = 6$ degrees of freedom, this result is significant and the hypothesis H_0 of independence is therefore rejected. An inspection of Table 1 shows that individuals with some college education appear to adjust themselves to marriage more readily than those with less education.

10.7 Indices of Dispersion

It frequently happens that an experimenter has a set of data that he believes can be treated as having been obtained from sampling a binomial population, or possibly a Poisson population, but which contains so few values that it is useless to attempt to fit a binomial, or Poisson, distribution to the observed distribution. In such situations one can often test the hypothesis that the data came from a population of the assumed type by testing whether the sample variance is compatible with the theoretical variance. This test can be obtained as a slight modification of the χ^2 test for contingency tables.

Let $x_1, x_2, \cdots, x_k$ represent the number of successes for k samples of n trials each taken from the same binomial population. Then $n - x_1$,

$n - x_2, \cdots, n - x_k$ will represent the corresponding failures. These two sets of numbers may be arranged in the following two-way table:

(7)

x_1	x_2	$\cdots$	x_k
$n - x_1$	$n - x_2$	$\cdots$	$n - x_k$

If this table is treated as though it were an ordinary contingency table and if the technique used to arrive at the maximum likelihood estimates for the e_i, as in (6), is used, the estimates for the e_i in the first row will be given by

$$\hat{e}_i = \frac{\sum\limits_1^k x_i}{nk} n = \bar{x}, \quad (i = 1, 2, \cdots, k)$$

As a consequence, the estimates for the e_i in the second row will become $n - \bar{x}$. With these estimates, the value of χ^2 as given by (6) will reduce to

$$\chi^2 = \sum_1^k \frac{(x_i - \bar{x})^2}{\bar{x}} + \sum_1^k \frac{(x_i - \bar{x})^2}{n - \bar{x}}$$

$$= \left(\frac{1}{\bar{x}} + \frac{1}{n - \bar{x}}\right) \sum_1^k (x_i - \bar{x})^2$$

(8)
$$= \frac{\sum\limits_1^k (x_i - \bar{x})^2}{\bar{x}\left(1 - \dfrac{\bar{x}}{n}\right)}$$

The contingency table on which this result is based differs slightly from the ordinary contingency table treated previously. For the ordinary table, successive observations are free to fall in any one of the cells; however, for this table the first n observations must fall in either of the two cells of the first column only, the second n observations must fall in either of the two cells of the second column only, etc. The general theory of 10.4 shows, however, that the χ^2 test as applied in (6) is applicable to this modified type of contingency table also; hence (8) may be assumed to possess a χ^2 distribution with $k - 1$ degrees of freedom.

It will be observed that the numerator in (8) is k times the sample variance. For a binomial distribution the variance may be expressed in the form

$$npq = np(1 - p) = \mu\left(1 - \frac{\mu}{n}\right)$$

If μ is replaced by the sample mean, it will be observed that the denominator in (8) is a second sample estimate of the variance. Thus χ^2 is essentially k times the ratio of two sample estimates of the binomial variance. If the x_i are from different binomial populations rather than from the same binomial population, there will be a tendency for the numerator estimate to be large relative to the denominator estimate and thus to give rise to a significant value of χ^2. Thus the χ^2 test essentially tests the hypothesis that the data came from the same binomial population by the device of checking on the variability of the data. Because of this property of the test, the expression (8) is called the *binomial index of dispersion*.

As an illustration of the application of (8), consider the following data giving the number of infected plants per plot of 90 plants, for 12 plots: 19, 6, 9, 18, 15, 13, 14, 15, 16, 20, 22, 14. The problem here is to determine whether it is reasonable to assume that the rate of infection is the same over the 12 plots. This problem may be treated as the problem of testing the hypothesis

$$H_0 : p_1 = \cdots = p_{12}$$

where p_i denotes the probability that a plant selected at random from the ith plot will be infected. Calculations applied to (8) give, to the indicated accuracy,

$$\bar{x} = 15.1, \quad \sum_1^{12} (x_i - \bar{x})^2 = 223, \quad \chi^2 = 18$$

For 11 degrees of freedom, $\chi_0^2 = 19.7$; consequently, H_0 would be accepted here. Since $\chi^2 = 18$ is so close to the critical value and since the sample is so small, one would be tempted to suspend judgment here until more data became available. For data of this type, it often happens that the infection is localized and gradually spreads from such localized centers of concentration. If such were the case, one would expect the hypothesis of homogeneity to be rejected because some plots would have a high rate of infection whereas others might still be largely untouched by the infection.

If the value of p is very small and the value of n is very large, the value of $\bar{x}/n$, which is the sample estimate of p, will be very small; consequently, the value of $1 - \bar{x}/n$ will be very nearly equal to one. If this approximation is used in (8), the binomial index of dispersion reduces to what is known as the *Poisson index of dispersion*, namely,

$$\sum_1^k \frac{(x_i - \bar{x})^2}{\bar{x}}$$

It would appear that the Poisson index is merely a special case of the standard χ^2 test given in (3) for those situations in which the expected frequencies are equal; however, there is a distinction in the nature of the variables. The sum of the frequencies in the ordinary χ^2 test represents the total number of observations made, whereas in applications of the Poisson index there are but k observations, each observation yielding a result that happens to be an integer. It is important to distinguish between these two types of problems in order to avoid the mistake of applying the ordinary χ^2 test to the first row only of the binomial frequencies in (7). Such an application would be equivalent to assuming that the data came from a Poisson rather than a binomial population.

As an illustration of the application of the Poisson index, consider the problem of testing whether the following data on the number of defective parts found in samples of 1000 parts each are homogeneous: 15, 13, 8, 6, 11, 9, 14, 10, 16, 9, 12. Since the probability of a part being defective is very small and n is very large, these frequencies may be treated as having come from Poisson populations. The problem now is one of testing the hypothesis

$$H_0 : \mu_1 = \cdots = \mu_{11}$$

where μ_i is the mean of the Poisson population corresponding to the ith sample. Calculations give

$$\bar{x} = 11.2, \quad \sum(x_i - \bar{x})^2 = 97.6, \quad \frac{\sum(x_i - \bar{x})^2}{\bar{x}} = 8.7$$

For 10 degrees of freedom $\chi_0^2 = 18.3$; consequently the result is not significant. Thus this test gives no reason for questioning the assumption that the data came from the same Poisson population.

REFERENCES

Investigations have shown that the χ^2 test must be applied with discretion when the e_i are small. An interesting example to illustrate the errors that may arise is given in E. J. Gumbel, "On the Reliability of the Classical Chi-Square Test," *Annals of Mathematical Statistics*, **14**, 253–263.

For 2 × 2 contingency tables there is available a correction to χ^2 called Yates' correction that makes the χ^2 test slightly more accurate when some of the e_i are small. This correction is illustrated in P. Rider, *An Introduction to Modern Statistical Methods*, John Wiley and Sons.

A proof of the property of the χ^2 test that permits it to be applied to problems in which parameters are replaced by their maximum likelihood estimates is very difficult and requires advanced mathematical techniques. It may be found in H. Cramér, *Mathematical Methods of Statistics*, Princeton University Press.

EXERCISES

1. By integration, verify the .05 critical value of χ^2 given in Table III for $v = 2$.

2. Toss a coin 100 times and apply the χ^2 test to see whether the coin is unbiased.

3. In a breeding experiment it was expected that ducks would be hatched in the ratio of 1 duck with a white bib to every 3 ducks without bibs. Of 86 ducks hatched, 17 had white bibs. Are these data compatible with expectation?

4. According to Mendelian inheritance, offspring of a certain crossing should be colored red, black, or white in the ratios $9:3:4$. If an experiment gave 72, 35, and 38 offspring in those categories, is the theory substantiated?

5. The number of individuals possessing the 4 blood types should be in the proportions $q^2:p^2 + 2pq:r^2 + 2qr:2pr$ where $p + q + r = 1$. Given the observed frequencies 180, 360, 132, 98, test for compatibility with $p = .4$, $q = .4$, and $r = .2$.

6. According to the Hardy-Weinberg formula, the number of flies resulting from certain crossings should be in the proportions $q^2:2pq:p^2$, where $q + p = 1$. If an experiment gave the frequencies 42, 52, 22, would the results be compatible with this formula (a) if $q = .5$, (b) if q is estimated from the data by using the maximum likelihood estimate $\hat{q} = \dfrac{n_1 + n_2/2}{n_1 + n_2 + n_3}$, where n_1, n_2, and n_3 are the observed frequencies in the three categories?

7. Apply the χ^2 test to the normal curve fit for the following 500 determinations of the width of a spectral band of light. Here e denotes the fitted normal curve frequencies obtained by estimating all the parameters.

o	5	12	43	61	105	103	89	54	19	7	2
e	5	14	36	71	102	109	85	50	21	7	2

8. Given the following data,

x	0	1	2	3	4	5	6	7	8
f	2	4	10	15	19	12	8	7	1

state how many degrees of freedom you would probably use in the χ^2 test if you attempted to fit the histogram with (a) a normal frequency function, (b) Poisson frequency function, and (c) binomial frequency function with theory suggesting that $n = 10$.

9. Apply the χ^2 test for goodness of fit to the results of problem 44, Chapter 5.

10. Apply the χ^2 test for goodness of fit to the results of problem 68, Chapter 5.

11. Apply the χ^2 test for goodness of fit to the results of problem 69, Chapter 5.

12. A certain drug is claimed to be effective in curing colds. In an experiment

on 164 people with colds, half were given the drug and half were given sugar pills. The patients' reactions to the treatment are recorded in the following table. Test the hypothesis that the drug is no better than sugar pills for curing colds.

	Helped	Harmed	No Effect
Drug	52	10	20
Sugar	44	12	26

13. In an epidemic of a certain disease 927 children contracted the disease. Of these, 408 received no treatment, and, of those, 104 suffered aftereffects. Of the remainder who did receive treatment, 166 suffered aftereffects. Test the hypothesis that the treatment was not effective and comment about the conclusion.

14. Is there any relation between the mentality and weight of criminals as judged by the following data?

Mentality	90–120	120–130	Weight 130–140	140–150	150–
Normal	21	51	94	106	124
Weak	15	18	34	15	15

15. The following data are for school children in a city in Scotland. Test to see whether hair color and eye color are independently distributed.

Eye \ Hair	Fair	Red	Medium	Dark	Black
Blue	1368	170	1041	398	1
Light	2577	474	2703	932	11
Medium	1390	420	3826	1842	33
Dark	454	255	1848	2506	112

16. Show that for a 2×2 contingency table with cell frequencies a, b, c, and d, respectively,

$$\chi^2 = \frac{(a + b + c + d)(ad - bc)^2}{(a + b)(c + d)(b + d)(a + c)}$$

17. The number of automobile accidents per week in a certain city were 12, 8, 20, 2, 14, 10, 15, 6, 9, 4. Assuming that such frequencies follow a Poisson distribution, test the homogeneity of these frequencies with the Poisson index of dispersion.

18. Five boxes of different brands of canned salmon containing 24 cans each were examined for high-quality specifications. The number of cans below specification were, respectively, 4, 10, 6, 2, 8. Can one conclude that the 5 brands are of comparable quality?

19. The following data give the number of colonies of bacteria that developed on 15 different plates from the same dilution. Is one justified in claiming that the dilution technique is satisfactory in the sense that the bacteria behave as though they were randomly distributed in the dilution? The number of colonies were 193, 168, 161, 153, 183, 152, 171, 156, 159, 140, 151, 152, 133, 164, 157.

20. Given the following set of frequencies, 10, 2, 5, 4, 13, 11, 7, 12, 8, (a) test to see if they may be treated as Poisson frequencies from the same population and (b) determine whether the assumption that they are binomial frequencies would be more plausible.

21. Prove that the estimate used in problem 6 for q is the maximum likelihood estimate based on the multinomial distribution.

22. On the basis of a given hypothesis, indicate why, if an experiment yields a value of $\chi^2 = \chi_1^2$ slightly less than the critical value for ν degrees of freedom and if the experiment is repeated with approximately the same results, the two experiments combined will yield a degree of confidence in the hypothesis different from that given by the first experiment alone.

23. Show that the method of Chapter 6 for testing the difference of percentages is equivalent to the χ^2 test when applied to the 2 × 2 contingency table of successes and failures. It is assumed that p is estimated from the combined sample in the difference of percentages method.

24. Use the table of random numbers to sample from the population given by

x	0	1	2
f	.4	.4	.2

Take samples of 25 each and perform 20 (or more) such sampling experiments. For each sample of 25, calculate the value of χ^2 for observed and expected frequencies in the 3 cells. Classify the 20 (or more) values of χ^2 into a frequency table. Compare the resulting histogram with the χ^2 curve for $\nu = 2$. As a class exercise, this is intended to make the χ^2 theory concerning the use of the continuous χ^2 distribution for the discrete χ^2 variable more plausible.

CHAPTER 11

Small Sample Distributions

Many of the statistical techniques considered in the preceding chapters are applicable only when large samples are available. For example, the method used in 6.7.1 for testing the hypothesis that two population means are equal assumes that the samples are so large that population variances may be replaced by their sample estimates without appreciably affecting the validity of the test. In this chapter methods are developed that do not require the assumption of large samples. Although such methods are called small sample methods, they obviously apply to large samples as well and might better have been called exact methods. Some small sample methods require more information or assumptions than the corresponding large sample methods; consequently, small sample techniques cannot completely displace the techniques designed for large samples.

11.1 Distribution of a Function of Random Variables

In developing small sample techniques it is often necessary to find the distribution of a function of a single basic random variable or the distribution of a function of several basic random variables. The technique for solving the first of these two problems was developed in 5.4.3. In this section methods are presented for solving the second problem.

Let x and y be two continuous variables with the frequency function $f(x, y)$ and consider the problem of finding the frequency function of the variable $z = t(x, y)$, where t is some function of interest. The particular functions that are of interest in this chapter are $t(x, y) = y - x$ and $t(x, y) = y/x$; however, it is desirable to have available a general method of attack for such problems.

One method of approach is to adapt the change of variable technique of 5.4.3 to functions of two variables by holding one of the variables fixed. Toward this end, suppose the value of x is fixed so that the relation

262

$z = t(x, y)$ becomes a relation between the random variables z and y only. Assume that $t(x, y)$ is an increasing, or decreasing, function of y. Then, for x fixed, the relation $z = t(x, y)$ represents a change of variable from y to z to which formula (42), Chapter 5, applies. If $g(y \mid x)$ and $k(z \mid x)$ are used to denote the conditional frequency functions of y and z, respectively, for x fixed, then by that formula

$$(1) \qquad k(z \mid x) = \frac{g(y \mid x)}{\left| \dfrac{\partial z}{\partial y} \right|}$$

Next, write $f(x, y)$ in the factored form

$$f(x, y) = f(x)g(y \mid x)$$

Similarly, if $h(x, z)$ denotes the joint frequency function of x and z, one can write

$$h(x, z) = f(x)k(z \mid x)$$

Taking the ratio of these two joint frequency functions and using (1) will then yield the formula

$$(2) \qquad h(x, z) = \frac{f(x, y)}{\left| \dfrac{\partial z}{\partial y} \right|}$$

In this formula it is necessary to replace y by its value in terms of x and z by means of the relation $z = t(x, y)$.

Formula (2) gives the joint frequency function of x and z in terms of that of x and y. In order to obtain the frequency function of z, it is therefore merely necessary to integrate $h(x, z)$ with respect to x over the entire range of x values for z fixed. This follows from formula (3), Chapter 8, for marginal distributions.

As an application of this technique, consider the problem of finding the frequency function of the ratio $z = y/x$ when x and y are independently distributed. Since $f(x, y) = f(x) g(y)$ and $\partial z/\partial y = 1/x$ here, it follows directly from formula (2) that

$$h(x, z) = |x| f(x) g(y)$$
$$= |x| f(x) g(zx)$$

The frequency function of z, say $q(z)$, is therefore given by

$$(3) \qquad q(z) = \int |x| f(x) g(zx) \, dx$$

where the integration is over the range of x values for z fixed.

As a special case of (3), let $f(x) = e^{-x}$, $x > 0$, and $g(y) = e^{-y}$, $y > 0$. Then (3) yields

$$q(z) = \int_0^\infty xe^{-x}e^{-xz}\,dx$$

The substitution $w = x(1 + z)$ will lead to the result

$$q(z) = (1 + z)^{-2}, \qquad z > 0$$

As a second application of this general technique, consider the problem of finding the frequency function of the difference $z = y - x$. Here $\partial z/\partial y = 1$; consequently (2) reduces to

$$h(x, z) = f(x, y) = f(x, x + z)$$

The frequency function of z is therefore given by

(4) $$q(z) = \int f(x, x + z)\,dx$$

where the integration is over the range of x values for z fixed.

The only real difficulty in finding the frequency function of a variable $z = t(x, y)$ by means of the preceding technique lies in selecting the proper limits of integration when integrating the function $h(x, z)$ with respect to x. The following problem illustrates the nature of such difficulties.

Let $f(x, y) = 8xy$, $0 < x < 1$, $0 < y < x$, and let $z = x + y$. Then $\partial z/\partial y = 1$ and (2) reduces to

$$h(x, z) = f(x, y) = f(x, z - x) = 8x(z - x)$$

Now when z is fixed, x can range over only those values that correspond to points of the sample space lying on the line whose equation is $x + y = z$ and whose graph is shown in Fig. 1. The sample space here is the triangle bounded by the lines $y = x$, $x = 1$, and $y = 0$. If z is fixed at any value satisfying $z < 1$, as indicated by line l_1 in Fig. 1, then the range of possible x values is $x = z/2$ to $x = z$. However, if $z > 1$, as shown by line l_2, then the range is $x = z/2$ to $x = 1$. As a consequence, the frequency function of z is given by the two formulas

$$k(z) = \int_{\frac{z}{2}}^{z} 8x(z - x)\,dx = \tfrac{2}{3}z^3, \qquad 0 < z \leq 1$$

$$= \int_{\frac{z}{2}}^{1} 8x(z - x)\,dx = -\tfrac{2}{3}z^3 + 4z - \tfrac{8}{3}, \qquad 1 < z < 2$$

The graph of this frequency function is shown in Fig. 2.

A somewhat more general problem arises when the joint distribution of

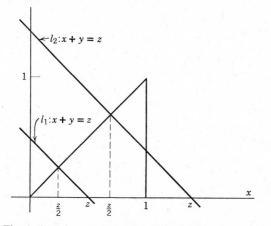

Fig. 1. Sample space corresponding to $z = x + y$.

two functions of the basic variables, say $u = u(x, y)$ and $v = v(x, y)$, is desired. This corresponds to a change from the coordinate system x,y to the coordinate system u,v. This is a familiar procedure in calculus, for example, when performing a double integration and accomplishing it by shifting to polar coordinates. The functions in that case are given by $r = \sqrt{x^2 + y^2}$ and $\theta = \tan^{-1} y/x$. Here the problem would be to find out how r and θ are distributed when given the distribution of x and y.

There exists a simple formula for finding the frequency function of such transformed variables. It is obtained by applying probability considerations to an advanced calculus formula for integration and involves the Jacobian function. This formula can be extended to any number of variables as well. The theory that is developed in this book does not

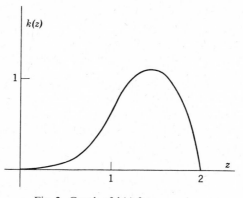

Fig. 2. Graph of $k(z)$ for $z = x + y$.

require the use of these more general methods; however, a brief discussion of them is given in the appendix for the benefit of those who are familiar with advanced calculus methods and wish to become acquainted with the general methods.

The methods that have been explained in this section are now used to develop some of the theory of small samples.

11.2   The χ^2 Distribution

One of the most widely used continuous frequency functions in statistical work is the χ^2 function that arose in connection with radial error problems in Chapter 6 and with the problem of testing goodness of fit in Chapter 10. This function has many other applications as well. In this section it is used to assist in finding the frequency function of the sample variance when random samples are drawn from a normal population.

11.2.1   Distribution of s^2

Let x be normally distributed with mean μ and variance σ^2 and let $\bar{x}$ and s^2 be the usual sample estimates of these parameters based on a random sample of size n.

Now if the mean μ were known, one would use the estimate $\Sigma(x_i - \mu)^2/n$ for σ^2. It would be a simple matter to find the distribution of this estimate because the quantity

$$(5) \qquad \sum_{i=1}^{n} \left(\frac{x_i - \mu}{\sigma}\right)^2 = \sum_{i=1}^{n} y_i^2$$

is the sum of squares of n random sample values of a normal variable y with zero mean and unit variance and therefore by Theorem 6, Chapter 6, possesses a χ^2 distribution with n degrees of freedom. Then by the change of variable technique developed in 5.4.3 one could find the frequency function of $\Sigma(x_i - \mu)^2/n$.

The difficulty in finding the distribution of s^2 arises from the presence of $\bar{x}$ in place of μ. In order to make allowance for $\bar{x}$, it is necessary to carry out certain manipulations. After these have been made, it can be shown by moment generating function methods that the χ^2 distribution is still applicable.

Obvious algebraic operations will show that

$$ns^2 = \sum(x_i - \bar{x})^2 = \sum[(x_i - \mu) - (\bar{x} - \mu)]^2$$
$$= \sum(x_i - \mu)^2 - n(\bar{x} - \mu)^2$$

Because of the convenience of working with standard units, this relationship is divided by σ^2 and then written in the form

$$\frac{ns^2}{\sigma^2} + \left(\frac{\bar{x} - \mu}{\sigma/\sqrt{n}}\right)^2 = \sum\left(\frac{x_i - \mu}{\sigma}\right)^2$$

or symbolically as

$$J + K = L$$

If the moment generating function of both sides is taken,

$$(6) \qquad M_{J+K}(\theta) = M_L(\theta)$$

Now it can be shown that $\bar{x}$ and s^2 are independently distributed when the basic variable x is normally distributed. A proof of this property is given in the appendix. This fact is therefore assumed here. Since J is a function of s^2 and K is a function of $\bar{x}$, it follows from the independence of $\bar{x}$ and s^2 that J and K are independently distributed. The independence of J and K permits the left side of (6) to be factored; therefore (6) may be written in the form

$$M_J(\theta)M_K(\theta) = M_L(\theta)$$

Since s^2 is the variable of interest here, this relationship is written in the form

$$(7) \qquad M_J(\theta) = \frac{M_L(\theta)}{M_K(\theta)}$$

From the discussion following (5), it follows that L possesses a χ^2 distribution with n degrees of freedom. Now the variable $(\bar{x} - \mu)\sqrt{n}/\sigma$ is a normal variable with zero mean and unit variance; therefore it constitutes a random sample of size 1 from such a variable. The same reasoning as before shows that K possesses a χ^2 distribution with one degree of freedom.

The moment generating function of a χ^2 variable with ν degrees of freedom is given by formula (21), Chapter 6, namely

$$(8) \qquad M_{\chi^2}(\theta) = (1 - 2\theta)^{-\frac{\nu}{2}}$$

Application of this formula to (7) will yield

$$M_J(\theta) = \frac{(1 - 2\theta)^{-\frac{n}{2}}}{(1 - 2\theta)^{-\frac{1}{2}}} = (1 - 2\theta)^{-\frac{1}{2}(n-1)}$$

Because a frequency function is uniquely determined by its moment generating function, this result together with (8) proves the following theorem.

THEOREM 1: *If x is normally distributed with variance σ^2 and s^2 is the sample variance based on a random sample of size n, then ns^2/σ^2 has a χ^2 distribution with $n - 1$ degrees of freedom*

Although the name "degrees of freedom" is merely a name given to the parameter ν in the χ^2 distribution, it is well chosen because the parameter ν represents the number of independent variables whose sum of squares is a χ^2 variable. Thus (5) has $\nu = n$ because the n variables being squared and summed are independent, whereas the n variables being squared and summed in s^2 contain only $n - 1$ independent variables because the sum of the variables is 0.

11.2.2   Additive Nature of χ^2

An interesting and useful property of the χ^2 distribution is that the sum of two or more independent χ^2 variables possesses a χ^2 distribution also. This property is demonstrated now because it is needed in the next section.

Let χ_1^2 and χ_2^2 possess independent χ^2 distributions with ν_1 and ν_2 degrees of freedom, respectively. Consider the variable $w = \chi_1^2 + \chi_2^2$. From moment generating function properties and (8), it follows that

$$M_w(\theta) = M_{\chi_1^2}(\theta)M_{\chi_2^2}(\theta)$$
$$= (1 - 2\theta)^{-\frac{\nu_1}{2}}(1 - 2\theta)^{-\frac{\nu_2}{2}}$$
$$= (1 - 2\theta)^{-\frac{1}{2}(\nu_1 + \nu_2)}$$

But this is of the same form as (8); therefore, the following theorem holds.

THEOREM 2: *If χ_1^2 and χ_2^2 possess independent χ^2 distributions with ν_1 and ν_2 degrees of freedom, respectively, then $\chi_1^2 + \chi_2^2$ will possess a χ^2 distribution with $\nu_1 + \nu_2$ degrees of freedom.*

11.3   Applications of the χ^2 Distribution

In this section Theorems 1 and 2 are used to test hypotheses about, and obtain confidence limits for, the variance of a normal variable.

As a first illustration, consider a problem of testing a hypothetical value of σ. If past experience with the quality of a manufactured product has shown that $\sigma = 7.5$ for the quality variable in question, and if the latest sample of size 25 gave a value of $s = 10$, would there be justification for believing that the variability of the quality had increased? This problem may be treated as a problem of testing the hypothesis

$$H_0 : \sigma = 7.5$$

against the alternative hypothesis

$$H_1 : \sigma > 7.5$$

From Theorem 1, ns^2/σ^2 possesses a χ^2 distribution with 24 degrees of freedom. If the right tail of the χ^2 distribution is chosen as the critical region for testing H_0 against H_1, it will be found from Table III that the critical value of χ^2 is given by $\chi_0{}^2 = 36.4$. Since

$$\frac{ns^2}{\sigma^2} = \frac{25 \cdot 10^2}{(7.5)^2} = 44$$

the hypothesis H_0 is rejected in favor of H_1, which implies that there is justification for believing that the variability has increased.

The solution of problem 8, Chapter 9, shows that the right tail of the χ^2 distribution is the best critical region for testing H_0 against H_1, provided that the mean of x is 0. If the mean were μ rather than 0, one would use $\Sigma(x_i - \mu)^2 > c$ in place of $\Sigma x_i{}^2 > c$ to define the best critical region. When the mean is not known, as in the problem just solved, it can be shown by methods somewhat more complicated than those used to solve problem 8 that $\Sigma(x_i - \bar{x})^2 > c$, where c is chosen properly, defines a restricted type of best critical region for the problem being discussed. Since $ns^2/\sigma^2 > \chi_0{}^2$ is equivalent to $\Sigma(x_i - \bar{x})^2 > c$, where $c = \sigma^2 \chi_0{}^2$, it follows that the test employed in solving this problem is a restricted type of best test.

If one were to test the hypothesis $H_0 : \sigma = \sigma_0$ against the alternative $H_1 : \sigma < \sigma_0$, one would use the left tail of the χ^2 distribution to obtain a best test; however, if the problem were one of testing $H_0 : \sigma = \sigma_0$ against $H_1 : \sigma \neq \sigma_0$, then methods like those of Chapter 9 will show that there does not exist a best critical region in this case. For this last type of alternative it is customary to use the two equal tails of the χ^2 distribution as the critical region.

As a second application of the χ^2 distribution, consider the problem of finding confidence limits for σ^2. Let x be normally distributed with variance σ^2, and let s^2 be the sample variance based on a random sample of size n. Then 95 per cent confidence limits for σ^2 may be obtained by using the analytical methods explained in 9.2.4 in the following manner.

From Table III for $n - 1$ degrees of freedom find two values of χ^2, namely, $\chi_1{}^2$ and $\chi_2{}^2$, such that the probability is .975 that $\chi^2 > \chi_1{}^2$ and such that the probability is .025 that $\chi^2 > \chi_2{}^2$. Then it follows from Theorem 1 that the probability is .95 that

$$\chi_1{}^2 < \frac{ns^2}{\sigma^2} < \chi_2{}^2$$

or that

(9) $$\frac{ns^2}{\chi_2{}^2} < \sigma^2 < \frac{ns^2}{\chi_1{}^2}$$

These two numbers yield 95 per cent confidence limits for σ^2. From the discussion in the section on confidence intervals it follows that in the long run 95 per cent of the inequalities of this type that are computed will be true inequalities. This method, of course, is not restricted to 95 per cent limits.

As a numerical illustration of the use of formula (9), consider once more the data for the first illustration of this section. Since the hypothetical value of $\sigma = 7.5$ was rejected, one would use the sample value $s = 10$, or the unbiased version of it, as the point estimate of σ; however, if one were interested in an interval estimate, (9) would be used. Here $n = 25$ and $ns^2 = 2500$. A direct application of (9) and Table III will show that 96 per cent confidence limits for σ^2 are given by

$$\frac{2500}{40.27} < \sigma^2 < \frac{2500}{11.99}$$

This inequality is equivalent to

$$7.9 < \sigma < 14.4$$

It is clear from this result that σ cannot be estimated with much precision for such a small sample and such variable data.

As a third illustration, consider the problem of finding confidence limits for σ^2 when several sample variances are available. In particular, consider the data given just after (16), Chapter 9, namely, $s_1{}^2 = 237$, $s_2{}^2 = 320$, $s_3{}^2 = 853$, $s_4{}^2 = 296$, and $s_5{}^2 = 141$. Since each of these variances is based on a random sample of size 5, Theorem 1 shows that the variables $n_i s_i{}^2/\sigma^2$, $(i = 1, \cdots, 5)$, will possess independent χ^2 distributions with four degrees of freedom each. By Theorem 2 their sum, $\Sigma n_i s_i{}^2/\sigma^2$, will therefore possess a χ^2 distribution with 20 degrees of freedom. Since $\Sigma n_i s_i{}^2 = 9235$, formula (9) and Table III will then yield the following 96 per cent confidence limits for σ^2:

$$\frac{9235}{35.02} < \sigma^2 < \frac{9235}{9.237}$$

or

$$264 < \sigma^2 < 1000$$

For data of the type just considered, the technique of combining several sample variances to obtain an estimate of σ^2 has certain advantages over the customary method of combining all the data to obtain a single direct estimate of σ^2. In the problem considered it may be that the variability of the product is unchanged from day to day but that the mean has changed. If all the data were combined, the change in the mean would tend to increase the value of s^2 over what it would be if the mean were stable from day to day. The sum of the daily values of s^2, however, would not be affected by such changes in the mean. Thus, by using the sums of daily variances, one may be able to obtain a valid estimate of σ^2, even though the product is not strictly under control. Here σ^2 is understood to be the population variance of the product when shifts in the mean do not occur.

11.4   Student's t Distribution

Consider the data of Table 1 on the additional hours of sleep gained by

TABLE 1

Patient	1	2	3	4	5	6	7	8	9	10
Hours gained	0.7	−1.1	−0.2	1.2	0.1	3.4	3.7	0.8	1.8	2.0

10 patients in an experiment with a certain drug. The problem is to determine whether these data justify the claim that the drug does produce additional sleep.

Assume that these patients may be treated as a random sample of size 10 from a population of such patients. Furthermore, assume that the number of additional hours of sleep that a patient obtains from the use of this drug is a normally distributed variable. The problem may then be treated as a problem of testing the hypothesis

$$H_0: \mu = 0$$

against the alternative

$$H_1: \mu > 0$$

If this problem were treated in the traditional large-sample manner of Chapter 6, the experimenter would use the data of Table 1 to obtain

$$\bar{x} = 1.24 \quad \text{and} \quad s = 1.45$$

Then he would calculate

$$\tau = \frac{\bar{x} - \mu}{\sigma_{\bar{x}}} = \frac{\bar{x} - 0}{\sigma}\sqrt{n}$$

and approximate its value by replacing σ by s to obtain

$$\tau \doteq \frac{1.24\sqrt{10}}{1.45} = 2.70$$

From Table II, the probability of obtaining a value of $\tau > 2.70$ is .0035; consequently the hypothesis that $\mu = 0$ would be rejected here in favor of the alternative that $\mu > 0$. The drug undoubtedly has a beneficial effect with respect to sleep, even though it may be due to psychological factors affecting the patient.

This method of solving the problem is subject to one serious objection. For a sample as small as this, the sample standard deviation, s, will not be an accurate estimate of σ; consequently a serious error may be introduced in the value of τ in replacing σ by its sample estimate. In most applied problems the true standard deviation is unknown. In order to overcome this defect in the test, it is necessary to replace the random variable τ by a new random variable which involves the sample standard deviation rather than the population standard deviation. Such considerations will lead to what is known as *Student's t distribution.*

Although the t distribution is being introduced here to solve a particular problem, it has many other important applications. In its most general form a Student t variable is a variable of the type

(10) $$t = \frac{u\sqrt{\nu}}{v}$$

where u is a standard normal variable and v^2 is a χ^2 variable with ν degrees of freedom distributed independently of u.

The frequency function of t can be obtained by finding the frequency functions of the numerator and denominator of t and then applying formula (3).

The numerator variable $u\sqrt{\nu}$, which is denoted by y, is a normal variable with mean zero and variance ν because u is a standard normal variable; consequently the frequency function of y, which is denoted by $k(y)$, is given by

(11) $$k(y) = \frac{e^{-\frac{y^2}{2\nu}}}{\sqrt{2\pi\nu}}$$

The denominator variable v is the square root of a χ^2 variable; therefore its distribution can be found by using the change of variable technique that was explained in 5.4.3. Toward this end, let the variables x and y of that section be set equal to $x = v^2$ and $y = v$. Then the required change of variable is given by the relationship $y = \sqrt{x}$. Application of formula (42), Chapter 5, then yields

$$g(v) = f(v^2)2v$$

But v^2 is a χ^2 variable with v degrees of freedom whose frequency function is given by (20), Chapter 6; consequently

$$(12) \qquad g(v) = a(v^2)^{\frac{v}{2}-1} e^{-\frac{v^2}{2}} \cdot 2v$$

$$= 2av^{v-1} e^{-\frac{v^2}{2}}$$

Here a is the χ^2 distribution constant $1/2^{v/2}\Gamma(v/2)$.

In order to apply formula (3) to (10), it is necessary to associate the variable v with x and the variable $u\sqrt{v}$ with y. The function $f(x)$ of (3) is therefore given by replacing v by x in (12). The function $g(y)$ of (3) is given by $k(y)$ in (11). Finally, it is necessary to associate the variable t with the variable z. After these substitutions in notation have been made, formula (3) when applied to (10) will yield

$$q(t) = \int_0^\infty x \cdot 2ax^{v-1} e^{-\frac{x^2}{2}} \cdot \frac{e^{-\frac{(tx)^2}{2v}}}{\sqrt{2\pi v}} \, dx$$

$$= \frac{2a}{\sqrt{2\pi v}} \int_0^\infty x^v e^{-\frac{1}{2}x^2\left(1+\frac{t^2}{v}\right)} \, dx$$

Now let $w = x^2(1 + t^2/v)/2$; then $dx = dw/\sqrt{2w}\sqrt{1 + t^2/v}$ and

$$q(t) = \frac{2^{\frac{v}{2}}a}{\sqrt{\pi v}}\left(1 + \frac{t^2}{v}\right)^{-\frac{1}{2}(v+1)} \int_0^\infty w^{\frac{1}{2}(v-1)} e^{-w} \, dw$$

From the derivation in 6.9 it will be observed that this last integral is equal to $\Gamma[(v + 1)/2]$; consequently

$$q(t) = c\left(1 + \frac{t^2}{v}\right)^{-\frac{1}{2}(v+1)}$$

where c is the constant

$$(13) \qquad c = \frac{2^{\frac{v}{2}}a}{\sqrt{\pi v}}\Gamma\left(\frac{v+1}{2}\right) = \frac{\Gamma\left(\dfrac{v+1}{2}\right)}{\sqrt{\pi v}\,\Gamma\left(\dfrac{v}{2}\right)}$$

The preceding derivation proves the following theorem.

THEOREM 3: *If u is normally distributed with zero mean and unit variance and v^2 has a χ^2 distribution with ν degrees of freedom, and u and v are independently distributed, then the variable*

$$t = \frac{u\sqrt{\nu}}{v}$$

has a Student's t distribution with ν degrees of freedom given by

$$f(t) = c\left(1 + \frac{t^2}{\nu}\right)^{-\frac{1}{2}(\nu+1)}$$

where c is the constant given in (13).

Now consider once more the problem that was introduced at the beginning of this section in order to see how this theorem can remedy the defect in the large sample method of solution. Since x is normally distributed with 0 mean, the variable

$$u = \frac{\bar{x}}{\sigma_{\bar{x}}} = \frac{\bar{x}\sqrt{n}}{\sigma}$$

possesses the properties of u in Theorem 3. From Theorem 1 it follows that

$$v^2 = \frac{ns^2}{\sigma^2}$$

possesses the properties of v^2 in Theorem 3 with $\nu = n - 1$. Since it is known that $\bar{x}$ and s^2 are independently distributed, Theorem 3 may be applied to give

$$t = \frac{\bar{x}\sqrt{n-1}}{s} = \frac{1.24\sqrt{9}}{1.45} = 2.57, \quad \nu = 9$$

From Table IV it will be found that the probability is approximately .017 of obtaining a value of $t > 2.57$. This result is therefore significant at the 5 per cent significance level.

A comparison of the probability of $P = .017$ with that of $P = .0035$ obtained by the use of large sample methods shows that the large sample method is not accurate for a sample as small as 10. It will be found that the large sample method gives probabilities that are consistently too small; consequently large sample methods will claim significant results more often than is justified. The explanation for this bias on the part of large sample methods is that the t distribution has a slightly larger dispersion than the standard normal distribution. The situation is shown

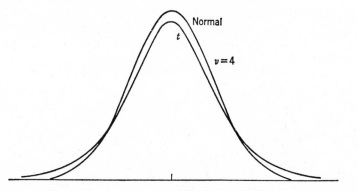

Fig. 3. Standard normal and Student's t distributions.

graphically in Fig. 3, which gives the graphs of the standard normal distribution and Student's t distribution for four degrees of freedom.

The important feature of the t distribution is that it does not depend on any unknown population parameters, hence there is no necessity for replacing parameter values by questionable sample estimates as there is in the large sample normal curve method.

11.5 Applications of the t Distribution

11.5.1 Confidence Limits for a Mean

Let x be normally distributed with mean μ and variance σ^2. Let $\bar{x}$ and s^2 be their sample estimates based on a random sample of size n. Then, as before,

$$u = \frac{\bar{x} - \mu}{\sigma/\sqrt{n}}$$

and

$$v^2 = \frac{ns^2}{\sigma^2}$$

satisfy the requirements of u and v in Theorem 3; consequently,

$$(14) \qquad t = \frac{(\bar{x} - \mu)\sqrt{n - 1}}{s}$$

possesses a t distribution with $n - 1$ degrees of freedom. If $t_{.05}$ represents the value of t such that the probability is .05 that $|t| > t_{.05}$, then the probability is .95 that

$$\left| \frac{(\bar{x} - \mu)\sqrt{n - 1}}{s} \right| < t_{.05}$$

or that

(15)
$$\bar{x} - t_{.05}\frac{s}{\sqrt{n-1}} < \mu < \bar{x} + t_{.05}\frac{s}{\sqrt{n-1}}$$

This inequality determines a 95 per cent confidence interval for μ. Since the probabilities heading the columns of Table IV are for one tail only, it is necessary to look in the column headed .025 in order to find the value of $t_{.05}$ needed in (15). If some probability other than .95 is desired, it is merely necessary to replace $t_{.05}$ by the corresponding value of t from Table IV, once more looking in the column headed with half the probability attached to t. The entries in the last row of Table IV, which are those for a standard normal variable, enable one to observe how rapidly Student's t distribution approaches that of a standard normal variable as the sample size increases. They also enable one to select the correct column in looking up critical values of t because of familiarity with large sample normal curve critical values such as 1.64 and 1.96.

11.5.2   Difference of Two Means

The t distribution may be used to eliminate the error in large sample methods when testing the difference of two means in the same manner as for testing one mean. Let x and y be normally distributed with means μ_x and μ_y and with the same variance σ^2. Let random samples of sizes n_x and n_y be taken from these two populations. Denote the sample means and variances by $\bar{x}$, $\bar{y}$, s_x^2, and s_y^2. Then

$$u = \frac{(\bar{x} - \bar{y}) - (\mu_x - \mu_y)}{\sigma_{\bar{x}-\bar{y}}}$$

$$= \frac{(\bar{x} - \bar{y}) - (\mu_x - \mu_y)}{\sigma\sqrt{\frac{1}{n_x} + \frac{1}{n_y}}}$$

will possess the required properties of u in Theorem 3. Furthermore

$$v^2 = \frac{n_x s_x^2 + n_y s_y^2}{\sigma^2}$$

with $\nu = n_x + n_y - 2$ degrees of freedom, is easily seen to possess the properties of v^2 in Theorem 3. This follows from Theorems 1 and 2 because

$$\frac{n_x s_x^2}{\sigma^2} \quad \text{and} \quad \frac{n_y s_y^2}{\sigma^2}$$

possess independent χ^2 distributions with $n_x - 1$ and $n_y - 1$ degrees of freedom, respectively. Consequently

$$(16) \qquad t = \frac{(\bar{x} - \bar{y}) - (\mu_x - \mu_y)}{\sqrt{n_x s_x^2 + n_y s_y^2}} \sqrt{\frac{n_x n_y (n_x + n_y - 2)}{n_x + n_y}},$$

$$\nu = n_x + n_y - 2$$

will have Student's t distribution with $n_x + n_y - 2$ degrees of freedom. Then, to test the hypothesis that $\mu_x = \mu_y$, it is merely necessary to calculate the value of t and use Table IV to see whether the sample value of t numerically exceeds the critical value.

It will be noted that the value of t does not depend on any population parameters as in the large sample method explained in 6.7.1. It will also be noted, however, that the t test is less general than the large sample method because here it is necessary to assume equality of the variances, which was not true for the large sample approach.

Formula (16) may also be used to determine confidence limits for $\mu_x - \mu_y$. If it has been shown that the hypothesis $\mu_x = \mu_y$ is not a reasonable one, it may be of interest to know how large or how small a difference is reasonable. For a given probability, confidence limits for $\mu_x - \mu_y$ will give the desired answer.

As a numerical illustration, consider the data of Table 2 on the yield of corn in bushels per plot on 20 experimental plots of ground, half of which were treated with phosphorus as a fertilizer.

TABLE 2

Treated	6.2	5.7	6.5	6	6.3	5.8	5.7	6	6	5.8
Untreated	5.6	5.9	5.6	5.7	5.8	5.7	6	5.5	5.7	5.5

The problem is to decide whether the addition of phosphorus will improve the yield of corn. It may be treated as a problem of testing the hypothesis

$$H_0 : \mu_x = \mu_y$$

against the alternative

$$H_1 : \mu_x > \mu_y$$

where x and y denote the yield on a treated and untreated plot, respectively. It will be assumed that all the plots were treated alike, except for the addition of phosphorus to half of them selected at random, and that the yield of corn on a plot may be treated as a normal variable. It will

INTRODUCTION TO MATHEMATICAL STATISTICS

also be assumed that $\sigma_x = \sigma_y$. These assumptions are sufficient to permit formula (16) to be applied to this problem. Calculations here give

$$\bar{x} = 6, \quad n_x s_x^2 = .64$$
$$\bar{y} = 5.7, n_y s_y^2 = .24$$

When (16) is applied,

$$t = \frac{.3}{\sqrt{.64 + .24}} \sqrt{\frac{100(18)}{20}} = 3.03, \quad \nu = 18$$

From Table IV the .005 critical value of t is $t = 2.878$, using only the right tail because of H_1; consequently, this result is certainly significant, and the hypothesis of no increase in mean yield will be discarded.

If the assumptions of normality and equality of variances are reasonable so that the experimenter can justifiably claim that this significant difference is caused by a real difference in the population means, he will undoubtedly want confidence limits for $\mu_x - \mu_y$. The same calculations as before give

$$t = \frac{.3 - (\mu_x - \mu_y)}{.0989}$$

Then, 95 per cent confidence limits are given by

$$\left| \frac{.3 - (\mu_x - \mu_y)}{.0989} \right| < 2.101$$

which reduces to

$$.092 < \mu_x - \mu_y < .508$$

From this result it is clear that for a sample as small as 10 one cannot promise with any great degree of certainty more than about .092 unit increase in yield, which is only about a 2 per cent increase in the mean yield of $\bar{y} = 5.7$ because of the addition of this amount of phosphorus.

The preceding methods are valid only under the assumption that $\sigma_x = \sigma_y$. If $\sigma_x \neq \sigma_y$ but the values of σ_x and σ_y are known, one can test the hypothesis $\mu_x = \mu_y$ by means of the standard normal variable

$$\tau = \frac{(\bar{x} - \bar{y}) - (\mu_x - \mu_y)}{\sigma_{\bar{x} - \bar{y}}}$$
$$= \frac{(\bar{x} - \bar{y}) - (\mu_x - \mu_y)}{\sqrt{\dfrac{\sigma_x^2}{n_x} + \dfrac{\sigma_y^2}{n_y}}}$$

The values of the two variances are seldom known; therefore it is usually necessary to replace them by their sample estimates, just as was done for the large-sample method in 6.7. The difficulty here is that only small samples are assumed to be available.

If $\sigma_x{}^2$ and $\sigma_y{}^2$ are replaced by their unbiased sample estimates,

$$\hat{\sigma}_x{}^2 = \frac{\sum_{i=1}^{n_x} (x_i - \bar{x})^2}{n_x - 1} \quad \text{and} \quad \hat{\sigma}_y{}^2 = \frac{\sum_{i=1}^{n_y} (y_i - \bar{y})^2}{n_y - 1}$$

the resulting variable

$$(17) \qquad t = \frac{(\bar{x} - \bar{y}) - (\mu_x - \mu_y)}{\sqrt{\dfrac{\hat{\sigma}_x{}^2}{n_x} + \dfrac{\hat{\sigma}_y{}^2}{n_y}}}$$

can be shown to possess an approximate Student t distribution. This is not surprising in view of the fact that Student's t is obtained by replacing the unknown variance by its unbiased sample estimate in the corresponding expression for a single variable. The number of degrees of freedom necessary to make (17) an approximate t variable is given by a rather elaborate formula, namely,

$$\nu = \frac{\left(\dfrac{\hat{\sigma}_x{}^2}{n_x} + \dfrac{\hat{\sigma}_y{}^2}{n_y}\right)^2}{\dfrac{\left(\dfrac{\hat{\sigma}_x{}^2}{n_x}\right)^2}{n_x + 1} + \dfrac{\left(\dfrac{\hat{\sigma}_y{}^2}{n_y}\right)^2}{n_y + 1}} - 2$$

Although ν is not likely to be an integer, it usually suffices to choose the nearest integer value in looking up critical values of t.

The foregoing problem is known as the Behrens-Fisher problem. There has been much controversy over how it should be solved, and the approximate solution here is but one version.

11.5.3 Confidence Limits for a Regression Coefficient

The problem to be considered in this section is that of determining whether the difference between the slopes of a sample and a theoretical regression line might reasonably be caused by sampling variation. Let X and Y denote the two variables, and let X_i and Y_i $(i = 1, 2, \cdots, n)$ denote their sample values for a random sample of size n. The corresponding small letter is used to represent the variable measured from its mean. With this notation, the equation of the least-squares, or maximum likelihood, regression line as given by (7), Chapter 7, is $y' = bx$, where

$$b = \frac{\sum\limits_{1}^{n} x_i Y_i}{\sum\limits_{1}^{n} x_i^2}$$

The assumptions made in 8.4 are made here also. They consist in assuming that repeated samples of size n are selected in such a manner that the same set of X values as the original set is obtained each time and that the Y_i are independently normally distributed about a true regression line whose equation may be written in the form

$$Y' = \alpha + \beta x$$

with the same variance σ^2, for all Y_i. Since the same set of X's, hence the same set of x's, is obtained in each sample of n, the x's may be treated as constants with respect to the sampling. The value of Y_i corresponding to X_i, however, varies with each sample of n in the manner just described. Although the X's and Y's were assumed to be chosen at random, the X's need not be so chosen. In practice, one usually chooses them in advance to cover adequately the range of X of interest and then selects the Y's corresponding to these values of X in a random manner. This is discussed more fully in 8.4.

For simplicity of notation let

(18)
$$w_i = \frac{x_i}{\sum\limits_{j=1}^{n} x_j^2}$$

Then

$$b = \sum\limits_{i=1}^{n} w_i Y_i$$

Since the x_i may be treated as constants with respect to the sampling, the w_i may also be so treated; hence b may be treated as a random variable that is a linear function of the random variables $Y_1, Y_2, \cdots, Y_n$. Now the solution of problem 38 of Chapter 6 shows that a linear combination of independent normal variables is also a normal variable; hence b is a normal variable. Since the mean and variance of b will be needed, consider their evaluations next.

Using expected values,

$$E[b] = E[\sum w_i Y_i] = \sum w_i E[Y_i]$$

But from the assumption that the means of the Y_i lie on the true regression line,

$$E[Y_i] = \alpha + \beta x_i$$

Hence

$$E[b] = \sum w_i(\alpha + \beta x_i) = \alpha \sum w_i + \beta \sum w_i x_i$$

Since $\Sigma x_i = 0$ because $x_i = X_i - \bar{X}$, it follows from (18) that

$$E[b] = \beta \sum w_i x_i = \beta$$

This shows that the mean value of the slope of the sample regression line is equal to the slope of the population regression line, or in the language of Chapter 9, that b is an unbiased esimator of β.

Since the Y_i are statistically independent and have the same variances, it follows from formula (21), Chapter 9, that

$$\sigma_b^2 = \sum w_i^2 \sigma_{Y_i}^2 = \sigma^2 \sum w_i^2$$

Substituting (18),

$$\sigma_b^2 = \frac{\sigma^2}{\sum x_i^2}$$

From the preceding results, it follows that the variable

$$u = \frac{b - \beta}{\sigma_b} = \frac{b - \beta}{\sigma} \sqrt{\sum x_i^2}$$

possesses the properties of the variable u in Theorem 3. In order to be able to apply Theorem 3 to this problem, it is necessary to find an independent χ^2 variable to serve as v^2. In the preceding applications of this theorem such a variable was obtained by recognizing that ns^2/σ^2 possesses a χ^2 distribution. Since σ^2 for this problem is the variance of the deviations of the Y_i from the true regression line, the quantity to use in place of ns^2, the sample estimate of $n\sigma^2$, is $\sum(Y_i - Y_i')^2$. With this choice, one would expect the variable

$$v^2 = \frac{\sum_{i=1}^{n} (Y_i - Y_i')^2}{\sigma^2}$$

to possess a χ^2 distribution. It can be shown with considerable difficulty that v^2 does possess a χ^2 distribution, but with $n - 2$, not $n - 1$, degrees of freedom, and that u and v^2 are independently distributed. These facts are assumed here. A direct application of Theorem 3 to the preceding u and v variables will then show that

$$(19) \qquad t = (b - \beta)\sqrt{\frac{(n - 2)\sum(X_i - \bar{X})^2}{\sum(Y_i - Y_i')^2}}, \quad v = n - 2$$

possesses a Student's t distribution with $n - 2$ degrees of freedom. By means of (19) one can test hypothetical values of regression slopes and find confidence limits for them.

As an illustration of how (19) is applied, consider the data of Table 3 on the relationship between the thickness of coatings of galvanized zinc as measured by a standard stripping method Y and a magnetic method X.

If the magnetic method were reliable for measuring the thickness of such coatings, it would be preferred to the standard stripping method because it does not destroy the sample being measured and the standard

TABLE 3

Y	116	132	104	139	114	129	720	174	312	338	465
X	105	120	85	121	115	127	630	155	250	310	443

method does. Now suppose that the magnetic method yields the same mean thickness as the standard method for thicknesses in the normal range. Then the true regression line of Y on X will be the line $Y = X$. Thus, under this assumption of the consistency of the two methods, $\beta = 1$. If, contrary to the preceding supposition, the magnetic method were biased in giving, say, too small a reading for thin coatings, then the true regression line, provided that the regression curve is a straight line, would have a slope greater than 1.

In view of the preceding discussion, consider the problem of testing the consistency of the two methods for measuring the thicknesses of coatings. The problem may be treated as a problem of testing the hypothesis

$$H_0 : \beta = 1$$

against the alternative hypothesis

$$H_1 : \beta \neq 1$$

If it is assumed that the necessary conditions for applying (19) are satisfied, then the data of Table 3 may be used to yield the information needed in (19). It will be found that the equation of the least squares line fitted to the data is

$$Y' = 1.12X - 1.79$$

It will also be found that

$$\sum (X_i - \bar{X})^2 = 301,826$$

and

$$\sum (Y_i - Y_i')^2 = 2766$$

If these values are used in (19), then

$$t = .12\sqrt{\frac{9(301,826)}{2766}} = 3.76. \quad \nu = 9$$

From Table IV in Appendix 2 the 5 per cent critical value of t is 2.26; consequently this value is significant. It appears that there is a slight bias in the magnetic method of the type suggested earlier.

In the preceding problem interest was centered exclusively on the consistency of the two methods. No attempt was made to consider the precision of the magnetic method as a substitute for the standard method. This problem can be solved by studying the variance of the errors of estimation. If the magnetic method were sufficiently precise to justify its use, then the preceding discussion and test would suggest that a larger sample be taken to obtain an accurate estimate of β so that the bias could be estimated accurately and a correction made for it.

The preceding method for finding confidence limits for the slope of a regression line can be generalized to find confidence limits for the regression coefficients in multiple and curvilinear regression. It can also be adapted to finding confidence limits for the ordinate of a regression curve corresponding to any fixed value of x. All of these problems give rise to the t distribution. References for these applications are given at the end of the chapter.

Thus far, Student's t distribution has been justified only on the grounds that it eliminates an inaccuracy of certain large sample methods. It is conceivable that there are other tests which overcome this inaccuracy and which at the same time are better tests than the t test in the sense of Chapter 9. It can be shown, however, that the tests using the t distribution that have been considered possess optimum properties from this point of view.

11.6 The F Distribution

It will be recalled that it was necessary to assume that $\sigma_x = \sigma_y$ in order to apply the t distribution to testing the difference between two means. In order to check on this assumption, it is necessary to derive a frequency function that can be used for testing the equality of two variances. It will be found that such a frequency function has many other uses as well.

Let u and v possess independent χ^2 distributions with ν_1 and ν_2 degrees of freedom, respectively. Then consider the problem of finding the frequency function of the variable

(20) $$F = \frac{u/\nu_1}{v/\nu_2}$$

Formula (3) can be used to solve this problem in much the same manner as it was used to find the frequency function of Student's t variable. Since u possesses a χ^2 distribution with ν_1 degrees of freedom, the distribution of the numerator variable u/ν_1 in (20) can be found by using the change of variable technique given in (42), Chapter 5. For this purpose let $x = u$ and $y = u/\nu_1$; then the change of variable is given by $y = x/\nu_1$, and formula (42), Chapter 5, gives

$$g(y) = f(x)\nu_1 = \frac{\nu_1}{2^{\frac{\nu_1}{2}}\,\Gamma\!\left(\dfrac{\nu_1}{2}\right)}\, x^{\frac{\nu_1}{2}-1}\, e^{-\frac{x}{2}}$$

$$= a y^{\frac{\nu_1}{2}-1}\, e^{-\frac{1}{2}y\nu_1}$$

where the constant a is given by

$$a = \nu_1^{\frac{\nu_1}{2}}/2^{\frac{\nu_1}{2}}\,\Gamma\!\left(\frac{\nu_1}{2}\right)$$

The denominator variable v/ν_2 in (20) will possess a corresponding frequency function with a constant b that is obtained from the constant a by replacing ν_1 by ν_2.

Formula (3) may now be applied, provided z is replaced by F, to give

$$q(F) = \int_0^\infty x \cdot b x^{\frac{\nu_2}{2}-1}\, e^{-\frac{1}{2}x\nu_2} \cdot a(xF)^{\frac{\nu_1}{2}-1}\, e^{-\frac{1}{2}xF\nu_1}\, dx$$

$$= ab F^{\frac{\nu_1}{2}-1} \int_0^\infty x^{\frac{1}{2}(\nu_1+\nu_2-2)}\, e^{-\frac{x}{2}(\nu_2+\nu_1 F)}\, dx$$

Let $w = x(\nu_2 + \nu_1 F)/2$; then $dx = 2dw/(\nu_2 + \nu_1 F)$ and

$$q(F) = \frac{ab F^{\frac{\nu_1}{2}-1}\, 2^{\frac{1}{2}(\nu_1+\nu_2)}}{(\nu_2 + \nu_1 F)^{\frac{1}{2}(\nu_1+\nu_2)}} \int_0^\infty w^{\frac{1}{2}(\nu_1+\nu_2)-1}\, e^{-w}\, dw$$

It will be observed that the value of this integral is $\Gamma[(\nu_1 + \nu_2)/2]$; consequently $q(F)$ reduces to

$$q(F) = c\, \frac{F^{\frac{\nu_1}{2}-1}}{(\nu_2 + \nu_1 F)^{\frac{1}{2}(\nu_1+\nu_2)}}$$

where

(21)
$$c = \frac{\nu_1^{\frac{\nu_1}{2}} \nu_2^{\frac{\nu_2}{2}}\, \Gamma\!\left(\dfrac{\nu_1 + \nu_2}{2}\right)}{\Gamma\!\left(\dfrac{\nu_1}{2}\right)\Gamma\!\left(\dfrac{\nu_2}{2}\right)}$$

This derivation proves the following theorem.

THEOREM 4: *If u and v possess independent χ^2 distributions with ν_1 and ν_2 degrees of freedom, respectively, then*

$$F = \frac{u/\nu_1}{v/\nu_2}$$

has the F distribution with ν_1 and ν_2 degrees of freedom given by

$$f(F) = cF^{\frac{1}{2}(\nu_1 - 2)}(\nu_2 + \nu_1 F)^{-\frac{1}{2}(\nu_1 + \nu_2)}$$

where c is given by (21).

11.7 Applications of the F Distribution

Since the F distribution was derived partly in order to justify the assumption of the equality of variances which is needed in the t test when that test is applied to testing the difference between two means, consider the problem of testing the hypothesis

$$H_0 : \sigma_x = \sigma_y$$

against the alternative

$$H_1 : \sigma_x \neq \sigma_y$$

under the assumption that x and y are normally distributed.

Let s_x^2 and s_y^2 be sample variances based on random samples of sizes n_x and n_y, respectively, from these two populations. Then, since $n_x s_x^2/\sigma_x^2$ and $n_y s_y^2/\sigma_y^2$ possess independent χ^2 distributions,

$$\frac{u}{\nu_1} = \frac{n_x s_x^2}{(n_x - 1)\sigma_x^2}$$

and

$$\frac{v}{\nu_2} = \frac{n_y s_y^2}{(n_y - 1)\sigma_y^2}$$

will satisfy the requirements for u/ν_1 and v/ν_2 in Theorem 4. Under the hypothesis H_0, $\sigma_x = \sigma_y$; therefore, by Theorem 4,

$$F = \frac{n_x s_x^2/(n_x - 1)}{n_y s_y^2/(n_y - 1)}$$

$$= \frac{\hat{\sigma}_x^2}{\hat{\sigma}_y^2}$$

will possess the F distribution with $n_x - 1$ and $n_y - 1$ degrees of freedom. Here $\hat{\sigma}_x^2$ and $\hat{\sigma}_y^2$ denote the unbiased estimates of σ_x^2 and σ_y^2. This notation is introduced to point out the fact that the value of F to use in testing $\sigma_x^2 = \sigma_y^2$ is the ratio of the unbiased estimates of the two variances. This test, like the t test, possesses the desirable feature of being independent of population parameters.

As a numerical illustration, consider the problem that illustrated the application of the t distribution to the testing of the difference between two normal means. From Table 2 and immediately following it,

$$\hat{\sigma}_x^2 = \frac{n_x s_x^2}{n_x - 1} = .071$$

and

$$\hat{\sigma}_y^2 = \frac{n_y s_y^2}{n_y - 1} = .027$$

Therefore $F = 2.63$ with $\nu_1 = \nu_2 = 9$ degrees of freedom. It is necessary to consult tables of critical values of the F distribution in order to decide whether this value of F is unreasonably large or small. Such values are to be found in Table V in Appendix 2.

Since the F distribution depends on the two parameters ν_1 and ν_2, a three-way table would be needed to tabulate the values of F corresponding to different probabilities and values of ν_1 and ν_2. As a consequence, only the 5 and 1 per cent right-tail area points are tabulated corresponding to various values of ν_1 and ν_2. The technique in the use of Table V is explained by means of the graph in Fig. 4, which illustrates the graph of $f(F)$ for a typical pair of values of ν_1 and ν_2. Let F_1 denote the value of F for which $P\{F < F_1\} = .025.$ and F_2 the value for which $P\{F > F_2\} = .025$. If the sample value of F falls outside the interval (F_1, F_2), the hypothesis of a common σ^2 will be rejected. For convenience of notation,

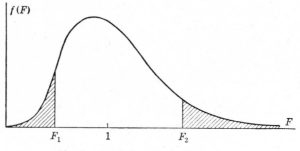

Fig. 4. A typical F distribution.

let $F' = 1/F$. Since $F = \hat{\sigma}_x{}^2/\hat{\sigma}_y{}^2$ with ν_1 and ν_2 degrees of freedom, $F' = \hat{\sigma}_y{}^2/\hat{\sigma}_x{}^2$ with ν_2 and ν_1 degrees of freedom. By means of the reciprocal function F', the probability of $F < F_1$ can be evaluated as follows:

$$.025 = P\{F < F_1\} = P\left\{\frac{1}{F} > \frac{1}{F_1}\right\} = P\left\{F' > \frac{1}{F_1}\right\}$$

This result shows that the left critical value of the F distribution corresponds to the right critical value of the F' distribution. As a result, it is necessary to find only right critical values for F and F' to determine F_2 and F_1. The reciprocal of the right critical value for F' gives the left critical value for F. Because of this property of F, only right critical points for F are tabulated. Unfortunately, only the 5 and 1 per cent critical points have been tabulated in Table V; consequently, it is necessary to interpolate between these two values in order to obtain an approximate $2\frac{1}{2}$ per cent critical point.

In view of this reciprocal property, the procedure to be followed is always to place the larger of the two unbiased variance estimates in the numerator of F; consequently, $\hat{\sigma}_x{}^2$ will always denote the larger of the two estimates. If the hypothesis of a common σ^2 is rejected whenever the sample value of this F exceeds its $2\frac{1}{2}$ per cent point, the hypothesis will be rejected whenever the original F falls outside the interval (F_1, F_2), for, when $F > 1$, F_2 will serve as the critical value, and, when $F < 1$, F' will be used instead and F_2' will serve as the critical value. But, as demonstrated in the preceding paragraph, F_2' for F' corresponds to F_1 for F.

If this procedure is applied to the numerical problem being discussed, it will be found from Table V that the 5 per cent critical value is, by interpolation,

$$F_2 = 4.5, \qquad \nu_1 = \nu_2 = 9$$

The sample value of $F = 2.63$ is therefore not significant. This result implies that the assumption of equal variances is a reasonable one and that the significant value of t obtained in connection with this problem when testing the hypothesis $\mu_x = \mu_y$ may not be reasonably attributed to a lack of the assumption $\sigma_x = \sigma_y$ being satisfied. This check on the reasonableness of the assumption that $\sigma_x = \sigma_y$ is usually carried out whenever the t test is used to test the difference between two means. It does not follow, however, that if the hypothesis $\sigma_x = \sigma_y$ is not substantiated a significant value of t will be due to a lack of this assumption's being satisfied.

The preceding test is not a best test in the sense of Chapter 9, because it can be shown that there does not exist a best test for this problem; however, it is known that this is a good test from the type II error point of view.

Further applications of the F distribution are made in Chapter 12 on what is known as analysis of variance techniques. Because of the importance of such techniques in designing experiments, they have been incorporated in a separate chapter.

11.8   Distribution of the Range

In certain fields of applied statistics the amount of routine computation becomes burdensome unless methods are chosen that involve only a small amount of it. In industrial quality-control work, for example, the repeated computation of standard deviations as measures of the variability of a product is undesirable. It is customary in such work to take the range as the measure of variability. Not only is the range easy to compute, but it is also simple to explain as a measure of variation to individuals without a statistical background. For small samples from a normal population, it can be shown that the range is nearly as efficient for estimating σ as is the sample standard deviation; consequently for small samples the range is a highly useful statistic.

Consider a random sample, $x_1', x_2', \cdots, x_n'$, drawn from the population whose frequency function is $f(x)$, which is assumed to be continuous. Let these sample values be arranged in order of increasing magnitude and denote the ordered set by $x_1, x_2, \cdots, x_n$. Now, consider the problem of finding the probability that the smallest value x_1 and the largest value x_n will fall within specified intervals. The frequency function of the range can be found quite easily by means of this probability.

Let the x axis be divided into the five intervals $(-\infty, u)$, $(u, u + \Delta u)$, $(u + \Delta u, v)$, $(v, v + \Delta v)$, $(v + \Delta v, \infty)$, where $u < v$ are any two values of x. The probability that x will fall in any particular one of these intervals is given by the integral of $f(x)$ over that interval; hence the probabilities corresponding to these five intervals can be written down even though they cannot be evaluated unless the form of $f(x)$ is known. In this connection, let

$$(22) \quad p_2 = \int_u^{u+\Delta u} f(x)\,dx, \quad p_3 = \int_{u+\Delta u}^v f(x)\,dx, \quad p_4 = \int_v^{v+\Delta v} f(x)\,dx$$

and determine the probability that in a sample of n values of x one will obtain no value in the first interval, 1 value in the second interval, $n - 2$ values in the third interval, 1 value in the fourth interval, and no value in the fifth interval. This procedure is equivalent to finding the probability that the smallest value in the sample will fall between u and $u + \Delta u$, whereas the largest value will fall between v and $v + \Delta v$. The desired probability can be obtained directly from the multinomial distribution given by (39), Chapter 5, by treating x as a discrete variable which can assume only one of five possible values corresponding to the five intervals. If p_1 and p_5 denote the probabilities that x will fall in the first and fifth intervals, respectively, the desired probability is given by

$$\frac{n!}{0!\,1!\,(n-2)!\,1!\,0!}\,p_1^{\,0}p_2^{\,1}p_3^{\,n-2}p_4^{\,1}p_5^{\,0}$$

which reduces to

(23) $$n(n-1)p_2 p_4 p_3^{n-2}$$

Expression (23) can be simplified somewhat by simplifying the integrals of (22). Since $f(x)$ is assumed to be a continuous function, the mean value theorem for integrals may be applied here. This theorem states that if $f(x)$ is continuous on the interval (α, β), then

$$\int_{\alpha}^{\beta} f(x)\,dx = (\beta - \alpha)f(X)$$

where X is some number in the interval (α, β). A direct application of this theorem to (22) shows that

$$p_2 = \Delta u \cdot f(u + \theta_1 \Delta u), \quad 0 \le \theta_1 \le 1$$

and

$$p_4 = \Delta v \cdot f(v + \theta_2 \Delta v), \quad 0 \le \theta_2 \le 1$$

The first of these two results when applied to p_3 yields

$$p_3 = \int_{u+\Delta u}^{v} f(x)\,dx = \int_{u}^{v} f(x)\,dx - \int_{u}^{u+\Delta u} f(x)\,dx$$

$$= \int_{u}^{v} f(x)\,dx - \Delta u f(u + \theta_1 \Delta u)$$

If these values for p_2, p_3, and p_4 are inserted in (23), it becomes

(24) $$n(n-1)f(u + \theta_1 \Delta u)f(v + \theta_2 \Delta v)$$
$$\times \left[\int_{u}^{v} f(x)\,dx - \Delta u f(u + \theta_1 \Delta u)\right]^{n-2} \Delta u\,\Delta v$$

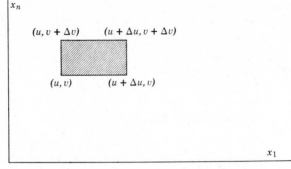

Fig. 5. Sample space for smallest and largest values.

This expression is the probability that the smallest value of the sample x_1 will lie between u and $u + \Delta u$ and at the same time that the largest value of the sample x_n will be between v and $v + \Delta v$. Geometrically, this expression gives the probability that the point (x_1, x_n) will lie inside the rectangle sketched in Fig. 5. In order to find the probability density of the two variables x_1 and x_n at the point (u, v), it is necessary to divide the preceding probability by the area of the rectangle, namely $\Delta u \, \Delta v$, and take the limit of the resulting quotient as Δu and Δv approach 0. If this probability density is denoted by $f(u, v)$, it follows from (24) that

$$(25) \qquad f(u, v) = n(n - 1)f(u)f(v)\left[\int_{u}^{v} f(x)\, dx\right]^{n-2}$$

‘Since $f(u, v)$ is the probability density of the variables x_1 and x_n at the arbitrary point (u, v), (25) gives the desired joint frequency function of the smallest and largest values of a sample of size n. These results may be stated in the following theorem.

THEOREM 5: *If u and v denote the smallest and largest values, respectively, in a random sample of size n from the population with the continuous frequency function f(x), then the joint distribution of u and v is given by*

$$f(u, v) = n(n - 1)f(u)f(v)\left[\int_{u}^{v} f(x)\, dx\right]^{n-2}$$

The frequency function for the range can be obtained very easily from this result by means of formula (4). For this purpose it is necessary to let $y = v$, $x = u$, and $z = R$. Then

$$q(R) = \int f(u, u + R)\, du$$

where the range of integration is over possible values of u when R is fixed. If the variable x ranges over the interval (a, b), the range of u with R fixed will be from a to $b - R$. This upper limit arises from the fact that the smallest measurement, u, must be R units smaller than the largest measurement, v, and v cannot exceed the upper limit b for x. An expression for $q(R)$ may now be obtained by inserting the value of $f(u, v)$ given in Theorem 5 and using the limits of integration that were just found. The results of these operations are expressed in the form of a theorem.

THEOREM 6: *If the continuous variable x has the frequency function $f(x)$ and if x assumes values in the interval (a, b) only, then the frequency function of the range $q(R)$ for a random sample of size n is given by the formula*

$$q(R) = n(n - 1) \int_a^{b-R} f(u)f(u + R) \left[\int_u^{u+R} f(x)\, dx \right]^{n-2} du$$

Unless the integral of $f(x)$ is quite simple, this expression is likely to be difficult to work with, even numerically. As an illustration of a simple problem, consider the range for a sample of size n from the rectangular distribution that is defined for $0 \le x \le 1$ by $f(x) = 1$. Here

$$\int_u^{u+R} f(x)\, dx = \int_u^{u+R} dx = R$$

Therefore, by Theorem 6,

$$q(R) = n(n - 1) \int_0^{1-R} R^{n-2}\, du$$
$$= n(n - 1)R^{n-2}(1 - R)$$

11.9   Applications of the Range

In the introduction to the last section it was remarked that the range was useful as a substitute for the standard deviation as a measure of variability in certain routine operations. It should therefore be of interest to know what the relationship is between the range and the standard deviation for, say, a normal distribution. This relationship may be found by calculating the mean of R. Since

$$E(R) = \int_0^{b-a} R q(R)\, dR$$

it is clear from Theorem 6 that the evaluation of the desired relationship will give rise to a complicated double integral. Unfortunately, when $f(x)$ is a normal frequency function, these integrations cannot be performed directly for general n; therefore numerical methods of integration are required. In spite of the complicated nature of the integral defining $E(R)$, it can be shown that $E(R)$ is a constant, depending on n, times σ. Tables are available for the normal variable case that expresses $E(R) = \mu_R$ in terms of σ_x for various values of n. Table 4 gives a few entries from a table to indicate the nature of the relationship.

TABLE 4

n	2	3	4	5	10	50	100
$d_n = \dfrac{\mu_R}{\sigma_x}$	1.128	1.693	2.059	2.326	3.078	4.498	5.015

As an illustration of the use of such tables, consider once more the technique of constructing a quality-control chart for $\bar{x}$ as given in 6.6.1. There a $3\sigma_{\bar{x}}$ band was constructed for controlling $\bar{x}$. If the range is taken as the measure of variability, $3\sigma_{\bar{x}} = 3\sigma_x/\sqrt{n}$ will be replaced by $3\mu_R/d_n\sqrt{n}$, where d_n is the value obtained from the table, that is, the value of the ratio μ_R/σ_x corresponding to the given value of n. Now the value of μ_R can be estimated by using the sample mean of the R values obtained for the various samples of n each. For such charts n is usually chosen to be an integer near 4 and a fairly large number of samples of this size is obtained before the chart is drawn; consequently, μ_R is usually estimated quite accurately.

If n is chosen less than 10, the estimation of σ_x by means of the range rather than the standard deviation of a sample is quite efficient. Investigations have shown, for example, that the variance of the estimate of σ_x based on the range of a sample of size 6 is only about 15 per cent larger than the variance of the sample standard deviation for a sample of size 6. From the point of view of Chapter 9, one can therefore conclude that the range is nearly as good as the standard deviation as an estimator for σ_x for small samples.

REFERENCES

A proof of the χ^2 distribution of $\Sigma(y_i - y_i')^2/\sigma^2$ which is needed to justify the use of the t distribution on regression coefficients may be found in S. S. Wilks, *Mathematical Statistics*, Princeton University Press, pp. 157–159.

The tables for ranges from which Table 4 was extracted may be found in L. H. C.

Tippett, "On the Extreme Individuals and the Range of Samples Taken from a Normal Population," *Biometrika*, **17**, 364–387.

The application of the range to quality control charts may be found in E. L. Grant, *Statistical Quality Control*, McGraw-Hill Book Co.

The application of the *t* distribution to the problem of finding confidence limits for multiple regression coefficients and related problems may be found in H. Cramér, *Mathematical Methods of Statistics*, Princeton University Press, pp. 551–554.

EXERCISES

1. Given $f(x) = e^{-x}$, $x > 0$, find, by moment generating function techniques, the frequency function of $z = 2n\bar{x}$.

2. Given that x is normally distributed and given the sample values $\bar{x} = 42$, $s = 5$, $n = 20$, (a) test the hypothesis that $\sigma = 8$, (b) find 98 per cent confidence limits for σ^2.

3. Work problem 2(b) for $n = 40$, using the normal approximation suggested in Table III in Appendix 2.

4. A sample of size 8 from a normal population gave the values 9, 14, 10, 12, 7, 13, 11, 12. Find 90 per cent confidence limits for σ.

5. Given the following sample values from a normal population, find 96 per cent confidence limits for σ^2 based on combining these sample values properly. The sample variances are $s_1^2 = 25$, $s_2^2 = 36$, $s_3^2 = 16$, with $n_1 = 5$, $n_2 = 5$, $n_3 = 10$.

6. Given that x is normally distributed with mean μ and variance σ^2, show that the likelihood ratio test of the hypothesis $H_0: \sigma^2 = \sigma_0^2$ reduces to a χ^2 test.

7. Find formulas for the mean and variance of a χ^2 variable with ν degrees of freedom by integration.

8. Show that $\sigma_{s^2}^2 = 2\sigma^4/n$, where $s^2 = \Sigma x_i^2/n$ and x is normally distributed with 0 mean and variance σ^2. Note that s^2 here is not the customary sample variance because the true mean is known. Use the results of problem 7.

9. Find what value of k will make $E(ks^2 - \sigma^2)^2$ a minimum, where s^2 is defined as in problem 8. What does this result imply about the unbiased estimate s^2 of σ^2 with respect to best estimates? Use the results of problem 7.

10. Determine what value of k will minimize $E[k\Sigma(x_i - \bar{x})^2 - \sigma^2]^2$ if x is normally distributed with mean μ and variance σ^2.

11. For the data of problem 2, (a) test the hypothesis $H_0: \mu = 45$ and (b) find 99 per cent confidence limits for μ.

12. Given $\bar{x} = 20$, $s = 4$, $n = 10$, with x normally distributed, find 95 per cent confidence limits for μ.

13. Compare the confidence limits obtained in problem 12 with those that would have been obtained if s had been treated as the true value of σ and normal curve methods of Chapter 6 had been employed.

14. Work problem 4 for μ rather than σ.

15. Show that $E[t] = 0$ for Student's *t* distribution.

16. The following data give the corrosion effects in various soils for coated

and uncoated steel pipe. Taking differences of pairs of values, test the hypothesis that the mean of such differences is 0.

Uncoated	42	37	61	74	55	57	44	55	37	70
Coated	39	43	43	52	52	59	40	45	47	62

Uncoated	52	55	60	48	52	44	56	44	38	47
Coated	40	27	50	33	56	36	54	32	39	40

17. Given 2 random samples of sizes 10 and 12 from 2 normal populations with $\bar{x}_1 = 20$, $\bar{x}_2 = 24$, $s_1 = 5$, $s_2 = 6$, (a) test the hypothesis $H_0 : \mu_1 = \mu_2$ and (b) find 95 per cent confidence limits for $\mu_1 - \mu_2$, assuming that $\sigma_1 = \sigma_2$.

18. Work problem 17(a) without assuming that $\sigma_1 = \sigma_2$ and compare your result with that for problem 17(a).

19. Treating the data of problem 16 as random sample values from 2 normal populations rather than as paired values, test the hypothesis $H_0 : \mu_1 = \mu_2$. Explain why it is probably incorrect to apply this test to this problem.

20. The following data give the gains of 20 rats, half of which received their protein from raw peanuts and half of which received their protein from roasted peanuts. Test to see whether roasting the peanuts had any effect on their protein value.

Raw	61	60	56	63	56	63	59	56	44	61
Roasted	55	54	47	59	51	61	57	54	62	58

21. In an industrial experiment a job was performed by 30 workmen according to method I and by 40 workmen according to method II. The following data give the results of the experiment. Determine by means of 95 per cent confidence limits for $\mu_1 - \mu_2$ how much time on the average could be expected to be saved by using method I.

Time	50	51	52	53	54	55	56	57	58	59	60
I	1	3	5	4	7	5	3	1	1	0	0
II	0	1	2	5	8	9	6	3	3	1	2

22. In estimating the mean of a normal population by means of a confidence interval, how large a sample is needed so that the length of a 95 per cent confidence interval will be less than $\sigma/10$ if σ is known.

23. Prove that the likelihood ratio test of the hypothesis $\mu = \mu_0$ for a normal population of unknown variance σ^2 is equivalent to Student's t test for this hypothesis.

24. Prove that the frequency function of the variable t approaches the frequency function of the standard normal variable as the number of degrees of freedom ν becomes infinite. Assume that the constant approaches $1/\sqrt{2\pi}$.

25. Find a likelihood ratio test for testing the hypothesis $H_0:\mu_1 = \mu_2$ for two normal populations with a common variance σ^2. Assume equal size samples are taken from the two populations.

26. For the data of problem 9, Chapter 7, find 95 per cent confidence limits for the slope β of the theoretical regression line.

27. Samples of sizes 10 and 20 taken from two normal populations gave $s_1 = 12$ and $s_2 = 18$. Test the hypothesis $H_0:\sigma_1 = \sigma_2$.

28. The following table gives data on the hardness of wood stored outside and inside. Test to see whether the variability of hardness is affected by weathering.

	Outside	Inside
Sample size	40	100
Mean	117	132
Sum of squares about the mean	8,655	27,244

29. If one desires to have $\alpha = .05$ and $\beta = .05$ in testing the equality of 2 normal variances when actually one variance is twice the other, how large an equal size sample from each population should be taken if the right tail of the F distribution is chosen as the critical region?

30. Verify the .05 value of F for $\nu_1 = 2$ and $\nu_2 = 2$ by direct integration of the frequency function of F.

31. Derive a formula for obtaining confidence limits for σ_1^2/σ_2^2, where σ_1^2 and σ_2^2 are the variances of 2 normal populations, if samples of sizes n_1 and n_2, respectively, are taken from those populations.

32. Find 90 per cent confidence limits for σ_x/σ_y if 20 samples are taken from each of 2 normal populations and if $s_x/s_y = 3$.

33. The time x between recordings of certain types of radiation activity is known to have the frequency function $f(x) = \alpha e^{-\alpha x}$, $x > 0$. How would you proceed to construct a test of the hypothesis that the values of α for two different experiments are the same?

34. Prove that the variable t^2 with ν degrees of freedom is a special case of the variable F with $\nu_1 = 1$ and $\nu_2 = \nu$.

35. Given samples of sizes n_1 and n_2, respectively, from 2 normal populations with zero means and variances σ_1^2 and σ_2^2, construct a likelihood ratio test for testing $H_0:\sigma_1^2 = \sigma_2^2$ and show that it is equivalent to an F test for this problem.

36. Show that $E[F] = \nu_2/(\nu_2 - 2)$ for the F distribution.

37. If $f(x, y) = e^{-(x+y)}$, $x \geq 0$, $y \geq 0$, find the frequency function of (a) $z = x + y$, (b) $z = e^{-(x+y)}$. Sketch the sample space to obtain the proper limits of integration.

38. Given $f(x, y) = 2(1 + x + y)^{-3}, x > 0, y > 0$, find the frequency function of $z = x + y$.

39. Prove that if x and y are independent standard normal variables, then $z = y/x$ has a Cauchy distribution.

40. If $f(x, y) = 1$, $0 \leq x \leq 1$, $0 \leq y \leq 1$, find the frequency function of (a) $z = x^2$, (b) $z = x + y$, (c) $z = y/x$. Sketch the sample space to obtain the proper limits of integration.

41. If x and y are independent standard normal variables, derive the frequency function of $z = \sqrt{x^2 + y^2}$. The variable z represents a radial error in gunnery problems in which x and y represent independent coordinate axes errors with equal variability.

42. Find boundaries for a quality-control chart for controlling variability if samples of size 5 are taken every hour and if it is known from past experience that $\sigma^2 = 10$. Use boundaries that will include 98 per cent of the sample values of the variable $\sum_{1}^{5} (x_i - \bar{x})^2$.

43. Find the frequency function of R if x has the frequency function $f(x) = e^{-x}, x \geq 0$.

44. Find the probability that in a sample of size 10 from the horizontal distribution $f(x) = 1, 0 \leq x \leq 1$, the range will exceed .8.

45. Determine how large a random sample must be taken from the horizontal distribution $f(x) = 1, 0 \leq x \leq 1$ in order that the probability will exceed .95 that the range will exceed .90.

46. Suppose that samples of size 4 are taken from the distribution $f(x) = e^{-x}$, $x \geq 0$. (a) Calculate the mean value of R. (b) Calculate σ and then compare the ratio $E(x)/\sigma$ with that given by Table 4 for a normal variable. (c) Determine limits R_1 and R_2 for R such that $P\{R < R_1\} = .025$ and $P\{R > R_2\} = .025$.

47. For a control chart for the sample mean of a normal variable with $\mu = 40$, based on samples of size 5, find control boundaries in terms of the range.

48. For problem 33, Chapter 6, find control boundaries in terms of the mean of the sample ranges.

49. The random samples $x_1, x_2, \cdots, x_{n_1}$ and $y_1, y_2, \cdots, y_{n_2}$ are taken from two standard normal populations. Find the frequency function of the variable z where $z = \sum_{1}^{n_1} x_i^2 \Big/ \left(\sum_{1}^{n_1} x_i^2 + \sum_{1}^{n_2} y_i^2 \right)$.

50. For a fixed value of x, find the distribution of the random variable $Y_x' = \bar{y} + b(x - \bar{x})$ in 11.5.3.

51. Use the results in problem 50 to construct a Student t variable for Y_x' by means of which one can obtain confidence limits for $E[Y_x']$. Assume independence of certain variables if necessary.

52. Use the general method for finding the distribution function of a function of random variables to obtain a formula for the frequency function of $z = x^2/(x^2 + y^2)$, given that x and y are independent continuous variables with the same frequency function f and can assume any real value.

CHAPTER 12

Statistical Design in Experiments

It is a common occurrence for experimenters who are unacquainted with statistical principles to seek statistical assistance when their experiments fail to produce the results anticipated by them. In some experiments the data were obtained in such a manner as to exclude any valid conclusions of the type desired; in others, there is little that can be done to extract further information from the data because the experiment was not designed with a statistical analysis in mind. Only rarely are the experiments that give valid conclusions as sensitive as they would have been if a standard statistical design had been employed. Too many experimenters do not seem to appreciate the obvious injunction that the time to design an experiment is before the experiment is begun.

In this chapter, after a brief discussion of a few of the general principles involved in the design of experiments, some of the common techniques used in the design and analysis of experiments will be studied.

12.1 Randomization, Replication, and Sensitivity

In most experiments there are several variables in addition to the one or more being investigated that need to be controlled if the experiment is to give valid conclusions. In some cases these interfering variables can be controlled by laboratory techniques; in others such control may be possible only by statistical design. As a simple illustration, consider an agricultural experiment in which two different seed varieties are to be tested on a piece of land. If the piece of land were divided into two equal pieces and one variety planted on each, the difference in yields could not be used as a valid estimate of the differential effect of the two seed varieties because of the possible difference in the soil fertility of the two pieces.

Experiments can often be made valid by applying the principles of *randomization* and *replication*. Thus, in the present illustration, if the piece of land were divided into a number of small plots of equal size and if one variety of seed were planted on half of these plots and the other variety on the remaining half, with the selection of the plots for each variety determined by a random process, then the varying fertility of the land would affect the two varieties approximately equally and therefore the difference in varietal yields would represent a valid estimate of the differential effects of the two seed varieties.

Randomization by itself is not necessarily sufficient to yield a valid experiment. For example, if one merely tossed a coin to determine which half of the original piece of land should be planted with one of the seed varieties, the selection would be random but it would not permit the two seed varieties to be equally affected by any varying soil fertility. If the two seed varieties were equally productive but the two halves of land were markedly different in fertility, then regardless of the seed variety selected for each half the conclusion would invariably be that the seed varieties differed in productivity. In order to insure validity, it would be necessary that the piece of land be divided into a sufficiently large number of similar plots so that the probability of having one of the seed varieties largely located on the more fertile plots would be very small. This repetition of an experiment or experimental unit is called replication. Thus, to insure validity in an experiment, randomization should be accompanied by sufficient replication.

Not only are randomization and replication useful techniques for assisting in the construction of valid experiments, but they are often essential to certain classes of experiments whose conclusions depend on the use of statistical techniques. Since the frequency functions of the various statistics considered in the preceding chapters were derived on the basis of random sampling, it follows that the methods employed in the preceding chapters are applicable to such samples only; consequently, any experiment whose conclusions depend on these methods requires randomization. Replication is also necessary for the application of any method that obtains its measure of variability directly from the data because at least two observations are needed to measure variation. For example, the illustrative experiment just discussed requires randomization and replication if the difference between mean yields is to be tested by means of Student's t distribution because the t distribution is based on random sampling and because sample variances are needed to evaluate t.

The requirement of random samples for the applicability of most statistical methods is not always easy to satisfy. For example, if the product of a machine is sampled every hour for several days, it may easily happen that the product of the machine changes during the day because of the operator's working pattern and also from day to day because of machine wear. For situations such as this, in which observations are ordered with respect to time, one of the methods for testing randomness, such as the method of runs discussed in Chapter 13, should be applied before methods based on random samples are used.

In the preceding illustration the techniques of randomization and replication removed much of the danger of obtaining biased results; however, these techniques did not remove the effect of differences in soil fertility on the variability of yields. If the variation in fertility is increased, the variation in yield is thereby increased. As a consequence, if Student's t distribution for testing the difference between two means were applied, a considerably larger sample might be needed to produce a significant difference if large fertility differences existed between plots than if the plots were of uniform fertility because of the larger estimate of variance involved in the denominator of t. Such an experiment could therefore be made more sensitive by selecting plots of uniform fertility. Very often, however, it is not feasible to control the fertility in this manner. Now, by arranging the plots into small homogeneous groups and applying statistical design, it is often possible to eliminate statistically the greater share of the fertility variability effects in the t test and thereby make the experiment more sensitive.

12.2 Analysis of Variance

One of the most useful techniques for increasing the sensitivity of an experiment is designing it in such a way that the total variation of the variable being studied can be separated into components that are of experimental interest or importance. Splitting up the total variation in this manner enables the experimenter to utilize statistical methods to eliminate the effects of certain interfering variables and thus to increase the sensitivity of his experiment. The analysis of variance is a technique for carrying out the analysis of an experiment designed from this point of view.

In designing an experiment, the experimenter usually has in mind the testing of a hypothesis or the estimation of some parameters. Although the analysis of variance technique enables the experimenter to design sensitive experiments for either of these basic problems, the explanation of the technique is made largely from the point of view of testing hypotheses.

As an illustration of the type of problem for which the analysis of variance is useful, consider a gunnery experiment in which four different brands of shells are to be tested to see whether they are equally satisfactory in quality. The experiment consists of having six different marksmen fire

an equal number of rounds with each brand of shells and recording the
scores made by each marksman for each of the brands. These scores
may be arranged in a rectangular array containing six rows and four
columns; however, for the purpose of considering other problems also,
let the scores be displayed in a rectangular array containing a rows and
b columns as shown in Table 1.

TABLE 1

$$
\begin{array}{cccccc|c}
x_{11} & x_{12} & \cdots & x_{1j} & \cdots & x_{1b} & \bar{x}_{1\cdot} \\
x_{21} & x_{22} & \cdots & x_{2j} & \cdots & x_{2b} & \bar{x}_{2\cdot} \\
\multicolumn{6}{c|}{\cdots\cdots\cdots\cdots\cdots\cdots\cdots} & \cdot \\
x_{i1} & x_{i2} & \cdots & x_{ij} & \cdots & x_{ib} & \bar{x}_{i\cdot} \\
\multicolumn{6}{c|}{\cdots\cdots\cdots\cdots\cdots\cdots\cdots} & \cdot \\
x_{a1} & x_{a2} & \cdots & x_{aj} & \cdots & x_{ab} & \bar{x}_{a\cdot} \\
\hline
\bar{x}_{\cdot1} & \bar{x}_{\cdot2} & \cdots & \bar{x}_{\cdot j} & \cdots & \bar{x}_{\cdot b} & \bar{x}
\end{array}
$$

The entries in the margins of the table represent the means of the corresponding rows and columns. The location of the dot in the index
shows whether the mean is a row mean or a column mean.

Two well-known mathematical models are available for application
to experiments of the type being discussed. One of them is called the
"linear hypothesis" model; the other is known as the "components of
variance" model. The essential difference between the two models lies
in the assumptions made concerning the population of experiments of
which the given experiment is considered to be a random sample. Thus
the x_{ij} in Table 1 are treated as a set of ab random variables, for which
the observed values are the values resulting from a single random
experiment.

12.2.1 Linear Hypothesis Model

This model assumes that the random variable x_{ij} has a mean μ_{ij} which
can be written in the form

(1) $$\mu_{ij} = a_i + b_j + c$$

where c denotes the expected value of $\bar{x}$, a_i denotes the expected value of
$\bar{x}_{i\cdot} - \bar{x}$, and b_j denotes the expected value of $\bar{x}_{\cdot j} - \bar{x}$. Since $\bar{x}$ is the
sample mean of both $\bar{x}_{i\cdot}$ and $\bar{x}_{\cdot j}$,

$$\sum_{i=1}^{a} (\bar{x}_{i\cdot} - \bar{x}) = 0 \quad \text{and} \quad \sum_{j=1}^{b} (\bar{x}_{\cdot j} - \bar{x}) = 0$$

Upon taking the expected value of each of these sums, it therefore follows that

$$(2) \qquad \sum_{i=1}^{a} a_i = 0 \quad \text{and} \quad \sum_{j=1}^{b} b_j = 0$$

Assumption (1) essentially states that the mean of the variable x_{ij} is the sum of a general mean c, a row effect a_i, and a column effect b_j. Thus, in the gunnery experiment, if the ith marksman were a superior marksman, his mean score would be expected to exceed the mean score for all six marksmen by a positive amount, a_i, whereas if he were an inferior marksman, a_i would be negative. Similarly, b_j is a number, positive or negative, that measures the superiority or inferiority of brand j with respect to the brands being tested. Assumption (1) is more restrictive than might appear at first glance, because in many practical problems it is unrealistic to assume that the two variables of classification have their effects additive in this simple fashion. For example, if the rows of Table 1 corresponded to different amounts of a chemical compound added to the soil, whereas the columns corresponded to different amounts of a second chemical compound added, one would not expect the effects of these compounds on crop productivity to operate independently in this manner.

In addition to assumption (1), the linear hypothesis model assumes that the variables x_{ij} are independently and normally distributed with the same variances σ^2.

Since the analysis of variance is being introduced as a technique for increasing the sensitivity of an experiment for testing hypotheses, consider the problem of testing the hypothesis that the theoretical column means of Table 1 are equal. For the illustration of marksmen and shell brands, this would mean testing the hypothesis that the four brands of shells are equally good, that is, that $b_1 = b_2 = \cdots = b_b$. This hypothesis is a generalization of the hypothesis $\mu_x = \mu_y$ considered in Chapter 11. In terms of the notation introduced in (1), it follows from (2) that the hypothesis can be written in the form

$$(3) \qquad H_0 : b_j = 0 \quad (j = 1, 2, \cdots, b)$$

Under the foregoing assumptions and notation, the analysis of variance technique proceeds as follows. Write the total sum of squares of deviations of the variables x_{ij} from their sample mean $\bar{x}$ in the following form:

$$\sum_{i=1}^{a} \sum_{j=1}^{b} (x_{ij} - \bar{x})^2$$
$$= \sum_{i=1}^{a} \sum_{j=1}^{b} [(\bar{x}_{i\cdot} - \bar{x}) + (\bar{x}_{\cdot j} - \bar{x}) + (x_{ij} - \bar{x}_{i\cdot} - \bar{x}_{\cdot j} + \bar{x})]^2$$

If the trinomial on the right is squared and summed term by term, it will be found that the sums involving cross-product terms vanish, hence that

$$(4) \quad \sum_{i=1}^{a} \sum_{j=1}^{b} (x_{ij} - \bar{x})^2 = \sum_{i=1}^{a} \sum_{j=1}^{b} (\bar{x}_{i.} - \bar{x})^2$$

$$+ \sum_{i=1}^{a} \sum_{j=1}^{b} (\bar{x}_{.j} - \bar{x})^2 + \sum_{i=1}^{a} \sum_{j=1}^{b} (x_{ij} - \bar{x}_{i.} - \bar{x}_{.j} + \bar{x})^2$$

As a partial verification of the fact that the cross-product terms do vanish, consider the evaluation of the second cross-product term. It is convenient to sum with respect to j first; thus

$$\sum_{i=1}^{a} \sum_{j=1}^{b} (\bar{x}_{i.} - \bar{x})(x_{ij} - \bar{x}_{i.} - \bar{x}_{.j} + \bar{x})$$

$$= \sum_{i=1}^{a} (\bar{x}_{i.} - \bar{x}) \sum_{j=1}^{b} (x_{ij} - \bar{x}_{i.} - \bar{x}_{.j} + \bar{x})$$

But, summing term by term, it is clear from Table 1 that

$$\sum_{j=1}^{b} (x_{ij} - \bar{x}_{i.} - \bar{x}_{.j} + \bar{x}) = b\bar{x}_{i.} - b\bar{x}_{i.} - b\bar{x} + b\bar{x} = 0$$

Formula (4) shows that the total sum of squares can be broken down into three components, the first component measuring the variation of row means, the second component measuring the variation of column means, and the third component measuring the variation in the variables x_{ij} after the row and column effects have been eliminated.

The purpose of the breakdown in (4) was to separate the total variation into components that are of experimental interest and that can be used in a significance test using the F distribution of Chapter 11. It will turn out that the F value to use involves the ratio of two of the three sums of squares on the right side of (4). It is clear that the second sum of squares on the right should be used in the test because it measures the variation of column means and this variation is likely to be excessively large when H_0 is not true as compared to its value when H_0 is true. The last sum of squares should also be selected because it measures the variation of the x_{ij} after the variation due to row differences and column differences has been eliminated, and therefore it should prove useful as a basis for comparison for the second sum of squares. This technique of finding a measure of variation that has eliminated the effect of an interfering variable, such as plot fertility, and using it as a basis for comparison with the variation of experimental interest, is a technique that often increases the sensitivity of the experiment remarkably. With the selection of these two sums of squares, the problem of testing H_0 is reduced to the problem of determining how to apply the F distribution to these two sums of squares.

Consider, therefore, the method of converting these sums of squares into χ^2 variables.

The variable $\bar{x}_{.j}$ is a normal variable because it is a linear combination of the basic variables x_{ij} which are assumed to be normal. The mean of $\bar{x}_{.j}$, because of (1) and (2), is given by

$$E(\bar{x}_{.j}) = E\left(\frac{1}{a}\sum_{i=1}^{a} x_{ij}\right)$$

$$= \frac{1}{a}\sum_{i=1}^{a} E(x_{ij})$$

$$= \frac{1}{a}\sum_{i=1}^{a} (a_i + b_j + c)$$

$$= b_j + c$$

But when H_0 is true, it follows from (3) that $E(\bar{x}_{.j}) = c$. The variance of $\bar{x}_{.j}$ may be found by realizing that $\bar{x}_{.j}$ is the mean of a independent variables having the same variances σ^2. Thus the variance of $\bar{x}_{.j}$ is equal to σ^2/a. The variables $\bar{x}_{.j}$ are independent because the x_{ij} are independent; therefore, these results show that the variables $\bar{x}_{.j}$ are independently and normally distributed with the same means, c, and the same variances, σ^2/a, when H_0 is true. By Theorem 1, Chapter 11, it therefore follows that

$$(5) \qquad \sum_{j=1}^{b} \frac{(\bar{x}_{.j} - \bar{x})^2}{\sigma^2/a} = \sum_{i=1}^{a}\sum_{j=1}^{b} \frac{(\bar{x}_{.j} - \bar{x})^2}{\sigma^2}$$

will possess a χ^2 distribution with $b - 1$ degrees of freedom. This proves that the second sum of squares on the right of (4), when divided by σ^2, possesses a χ^2 distribution with $b - 1$ degrees of freedom, provided that H_0 is true.

The demonstration that the last sum of squares of (4) can be converted into a χ^2 variable is considerably more difficult than that just given for the second sum of squares. Because of the length and difficulty of the demonstration, the desired result is accepted without proof. Thus it is accepted that

$$(6) \qquad \frac{1}{\sigma^2}\sum_{i=1}^{a}\sum_{j=1}^{b} (x_{ij} - \bar{x}_{i.} - \bar{x}_{.j} + \bar{x})^2$$

possesses a χ^2 distribution with $(a - 1)(b - 1)$ degrees of freedom. The reason for this number of degrees of freedom is that in the derivation showing that (6) has a χ^2 distribution it is shown that the degrees of freedom on the left of (4) equal the sum of the degrees of freedom on the right. Since the left side of (4), when divided by σ^2, would possess a χ^2 distribution with $ab - 1$ degrees of freedom if the μ_{ij} were equal and since the first sum on the right has $a - 1$ degrees of freedom, it follows by subtraction that the last sum on the right must have

$$ab - 1 - [(a - 1) + (b - 1)] = (a - 1)(b - 1)$$

degrees of freedom.

Finally, in order to be able to apply Theorem 4, Chapter 11, to (5) and (6), it is necessary to know that (5) and (6) are independently distributed. The demonstration of this fact is quite difficult; hence the independence of (5) and (6) is also accepted without proof.

In view of the preceding discussion and Theorem 4, Chapter 11, if (5) is divided by $(b - 1)$ and (6) is divided by $(a - 1)(b - 1)$, the ratio of the resulting quantities will possess an F distribution. This result may be summarized in the following manner.

(7) LINEAR HYPOTHESIS F TEST: *If the variables x_{ij} are independently and normally distributed with means $\mu_{ij} = a_i + b_j + c$ and variances σ^2, the hypothesis $H_0: b_j = 0$ $(j = 1, \cdots, b)$ may be tested by using the right tail of the F distribution as critical region, where*

$$F = \frac{(a - 1) \sum_{i=1}^{a} \sum_{j=1}^{b} (\bar{x}_{.j} - \bar{x})^2}{\sum_{i=1}^{a} \sum_{j=1}^{b} (x_{ij} - \bar{x}_{i.} - \bar{x}_{.j} + \bar{x})^2}$$

and where $v_1 = b - 1$ and $v_2 = (a - 1)(b - 1)$.

The right tail of the F distribution is selected as the critical region because the numerator of F is likely to be excessively large when H_0 is false. With this choice of critical region, the F test is known to be very good from the type II error point of view.

The equality of row means can be tested in a similar manner by using the first sum of squares on the right of (4) in the numerator of F and changing the degrees of freedom accordingly. Although the numerator in (7) can be written as a single sum, it is written as a double sum to remind one of the simple manner in which F can be written down. All that one needs to do is to write out the fundamental identity (4), divide the sums of squares by their degrees of freedom, and take the proper ratio of two such quantities. The proper ratio depends on whether one is testing the equality of column means or the equality of row means.

12.2.2 Application of the Linear Hypothesis Model

For the purpose of illustrating the use of (7), consider the data of Table 2 on the yield of potatoes. Four plots of land were divided into five subplots each. For each plot, the five treatments were assigned at random to the five subplots. The problem here is to test whether the five treatments are equally effective with respect to mean yield.

TABLE 2

Treatment

	A	B	C	D	E
1	310	353	366	299	367
2	284	293	335	264	314
3	307	306	339	311	377
4	267	308	312	266	342

(Plot on left margin of table)

The numerator sum of squares in (7) is readily computed directly from the means of the columns and the grand mean; however, the denominator sum of squares is most easily computed indirectly by computing the other sums of squares in (4) and then solving for this sum of squares. Calculations here yield the values

$$\sum_{j=1}^{5} (\bar{x}_{.j} - \bar{x})^2 = 3178$$

$$\sum_{i=1}^{4} (\bar{x}_{i.} - \bar{x})^2 = 1286$$

$$\sum_{i=1}^{4} \sum_{j=1}^{5} (x_{ij} - \bar{x})^2 = 21{,}530$$

Therefore, by formula (4), it follows that

$$\sum_{i=1}^{4} \sum_{j=1}^{5} (x_{ij} - \bar{x}_{i.} - \bar{x}_{.j} + \bar{x})^2 = 2388$$

As a result, the F value in (7) becomes

$$F = \frac{3 \cdot 4(3178)}{2388} = 16.0, \quad \nu_1 = 4, \quad \nu_2 = 12$$

From Table V in Appendix 2 it is clear that this result is significant; therefore, the five treatments undoubtedly differ in their effect on yield.

Since the preceding computations give the necessary sums of squares for testing the hypothesis that the row means are equal, that is, for testing the hypothesis

$$H_0: a_i = 0, \quad (i = 1, \cdots, a)$$

this hypothesis will also be tested. The value of F now becomes

$$F = \frac{4 \cdot 5(1286)}{2388} = 10.8, \quad \nu_1 = 3, \quad \nu_2 = 12$$

This result is also significant, which means that the four plots undoubtedly differ in fertility.

The computational results for analysis of variance problems are usually displayed in table form. Table 3 illustrates this type of summary for the problem just discussed.

TABLE 3

Source of variation	Sum of squares	d. f.	Mean square	F Value
Columns	12,712	4	3178	16.0
Rows	6,430	3	2143	10.8
Remainder	2,388	12	199	
Totals	21,530	19		

The entries in the second column are the sums of squares in the fundamental identity (4). The third column lists the corresponding degrees of freedom, and the fourth column gives each sum of squares divided by its degrees of freedom. These entries are the χ^2 values needed for the F ratios, which are displayed in the last column.

In order to observe the increased sensitivity obtained by eliminating the variation due to differences in plot fertility when testing the hypothesis that the treatment means are equal, consider how the hypothesis would have been tested if the row classification were not available. This would be the situation, for example, if the five treatments had been assigned to the 20 subplots at random.

The fundamental identity (4) now reduces to

$$\sum_{i=1}^{a} \sum_{j=1}^{b} (x_{ij} - \bar{x})^2 = \sum_{i=1}^{a} \sum_{j=1}^{b} (\bar{x}_{\cdot j} - \bar{x})^2 + \sum_{i=1}^{a} \sum_{j=1}^{b} (x_{ij} - \bar{x}_{\cdot j})^2$$

It is easy to show that the second sum on the right, when divided by σ^2, has a χ^2 distribution with $b(a-1)$ degrees of freedom. Then accepting the fact that this χ^2 variable and the χ^2 variable given by (5) are independently distributed, it follows that the F distribution may be applied to give

$$(8) \quad F = \frac{b(a-1) \sum_{i=1}^{a} \sum_{j=1}^{b} (\bar{x}_{\cdot j} - \bar{x})^2}{(b-1) \sum_{i=1}^{a} \sum_{j=1}^{b} (x_{ij} - \bar{x}_{\cdot j})^2}, \quad \nu_1 = b-1, \quad \nu_2 = b(a-1)$$

The earlier calculations for Table 2 may be used to give the necessary values here. It will be found that

$$F = \frac{5 \cdot 3(12{,}712)}{4(8{,}818)} = 5.4, \quad \nu_1 = 4, \quad \nu_2 = 15$$

The 5 per cent and 1 per cent critical values are 3.06 and 4.89; hence this F value is still significant at the 1 per cent significance level but only barely so. A comparison of this result with the earlier result in which $F = 16.0$ shows that the segregation of plot differences in (4) gave rise to a much more sensitive experiment than that obtained by ignoring them.

The preceding illustration may give one the impression that the experimenter can choose either one of the two F tests applied there to determine whether a set of column means is equal. This is not strictly true, however, because the two models differ somewhat. The earlier problem concerning men and machines is a good one to illustrate the difference. The test based on (7) assumes that six men are selected and each performs four experiments, one with each brand of shells. The test based on (8) assumes that 24 men are selected and each performs one experiment with the brand of shells assigned him. In the first model the six men could have been selected at random, or otherwise, from a population of workers; however, it is assumed that in repetitions of the experiment the same six men are used. In the second model it is assumed that a fresh set of 24 men is selected at random from a population of workers every time the experiment is performed.

12.2.3 Components of Variance Model

This model makes a linearity assumption about the basic variable x_{ij} rather than about its mean, μ_{ij}, as was done in the linear hypothesis model. In place of assumption (1), it is assumed that x_{ij} can be expressed in the form

(9) $$x_{ij} = u_i + v_j + w_{ij}$$

where the u_i, v_j, and w_{ij} are independent normal variables. The u_i are assumed to possess the same normal distribution with mean μ_a and variance σ_a^2, the v_j are assumed to possess the same normal distribution with mean μ_b and variance σ_b^2, and the w_{ij} are assumed to possess the same normal distribution with mean μ_c and variance σ_c^2. From these assumptions, it follows that

$$E(x_{ij}) = \mu_a + \mu_b + \mu_c$$

and

$$\sigma_{x_{ij}}^2 = \sigma_a^2 + \sigma_b^2 + \sigma_c^2$$

These results, together with (9), show that the variables x_{ij} are normally, but not independently, distributed with the same means and variances. The lack of independence is obvious if one compares, say, the variables $x_{11} = u_1 + v_1 + w_{11}$ and $x_{12} = u_1 + v_2 + w_{12}$. Since x_{11} and x_{12} contain the common variable u_1, with the remaining variables on the right being independent, they must be correlated.

In the linear hypothesis model considered earlier, the variables x_{ij} were assumed to be normally, and independently, distributed with the same variances but with different means.

The analysis of variance technique for the components of variance model proceeds in much the same manner as for the linear hypothesis model. One starts with the same breakdown of the basic sum of squares given by (4) and shows that the second and third sums of squares on the right can be incorporated into an F test for the hypothesis that there are no column effects. However, in the components of variance model this hypothesis assumes the form

(10) $$H_0 : \sigma_b^2 = 0$$

For the purpose of demonstrating that (5) possesses a χ^2 distribution in this model also, use (9) to obtain

$$\bar{x}_{.j} - \bar{x} = \frac{1}{a} \sum_{i=1}^{a} x_{ij} - \frac{1}{ab} \sum_{i=1}^{a} \sum_{j=1}^{b} x_{ij}$$

$$= \bar{u} + v_j + \bar{w}_{.j} - (\bar{u} + \bar{v} + \bar{w})$$

$$= (v_j + \bar{w}_{.j}) - (\bar{v} + \bar{w})$$

Letting $y_j = v_j + \bar{w}_{.j}$, it follows that

$$\bar{y} = \frac{1}{b} \sum_{j=1}^{b} (v_j + \bar{w}_{.j}) = \bar{v} + \bar{w}$$

hence that

(11) $$\bar{x}_{.j} - \bar{x} = y_j - \bar{y}$$

Since y_j is a linear combination of the variables $v_j, w_{1j}, \cdots, w_{aj}$, which are independent normal variables, it follows that y_j is a normal variable. Furthermore, since each of the variables $y_1, y_2, \cdots, y_b$ is a linear combination of a different set of independent normal variables, it follows that the y_j ($j = 1, \cdots, b$) are independently normally distributed. The mean of y_j is given by

$$E(y_j) = E(v_j) + E(\bar{w}_{.j}) = \mu_b + \mu_c$$

The variance of y_j is given by

$$\sigma_{y_j}^2 = \sigma_{v_j}^2 + \sigma_{\bar{w}.j}^2$$

$$= \sigma_b^2 + \frac{\sigma_{\bar{w}_{ij}}^2}{a}$$

$$= \sigma_b^2 + \frac{\sigma_c^2}{a}$$

The preceding results show that the y_j are independently normally distributed with the same means, $\mu_b + \mu_c$, and the same variances, $\sigma_b^2 + \sigma_c^2/a$; therefore, by Theorem 1, Chapter 11, it follows that the quantity corresponding to ns^2/σ^2 for $y_1, y_2, \cdots, y_b$ will possess a χ^2 distribution. Because of (11), this quantity is

$$(12) \qquad \frac{\sum_{j=1}^{b}(y_j - \bar{y})^2}{\sigma_b^2 + \sigma_c^2/a} = \frac{\sum_{j=1}^{b}(\bar{x}._j - \bar{x})^2}{\sigma_b^2 + \sigma_c^2/a} = \frac{\sum_{i=1}^{a}\sum_{j=1}^{b}(\bar{x}._j - \bar{x})^2}{a\sigma_b^2 + \sigma_c^2}$$

The preceding derivation proves that (12) possesses a χ^2 distribution with $b - 1$ degrees of freedom. This corresponds to (5) for the linear hypothesis model. As with the linear hypothesis model, it is considerably more difficult to convert the last sum of squares of (4) into a χ^2 variable and to show that it is distributed independently of (12). The results of such a demonstration are accepted here without proof. Thus, it can be shown that

$$(13) \qquad \frac{1}{\sigma_c^2}\sum_{i=1}^{a}\sum_{j=1}^{b}(x_{ij} - \bar{x}_{i.} - \bar{x}._j + \bar{x})^2$$

possesses a χ^2 distribution with $(a - 1)(b - 1)$ degrees of freedom and that (12) and (13) are independently distributed. From Theorem 4, Chapter 11, it therefore follows that the F distribution may be applied to (12) and (13) to give

$$(14) \qquad F = \frac{\sigma_c^2(a - 1)\sum_{i=1}^{a}\sum_{j=1}^{b}(\bar{x}._j - \bar{x})^2}{(a\sigma_b^2 + \sigma_c^2)\sum_{i=1}^{a}\sum_{j=1}^{b}(x_{ij} - \bar{x}_{i.} - \bar{x}._j + \bar{x})^2}$$

with $\nu_1 = b - 1$ and $\nu_2 = (a - 1)(b - 1)$.

It is clear from (14) that the value of F can never be calculated in a given problem unless σ_b^2/σ_c^2 is known. But, when H_0 is true, it follows from (10) that this ratio is equal to 0 and that the value of F in (14) can be evaluated from the data of the experiment. This result may be summarized in the following manner.

(15) COMPONENTS OF VARIANCE F TEST: *If the variables x_{ij} are express-
ible in the form $x_{ij} = u_i + v_j + w_{ij}$, where the u_i, v_j, and w_{ij} are three
sets of random samples from three normal populations, the hypothesis
$H_0 : \sigma_b^2 = 0$, where σ_b^2 is the variance for the second normal population,
may be tested by using the right tail of the F distribution as critical region,
where*

$$F = \frac{(a-1) \sum\limits_{i=1}^{a} \sum\limits_{j=1}^{b} (\bar{x}_{.j} - \bar{x})^2}{\sum\limits_{i=1}^{a} \sum\limits_{j=1}^{b} (x_{ij} - \bar{x}_{i.} - \bar{x}_{.j} + \bar{x})^2}$$

and where $v_1 = b - 1$ and $v_2 = (a-1)(b-1)$.

A comparison of (7) and (15) shows that the test for the hypothesis
that there are no column effects is the same for the two models; however,
the mathematical formulation of this hypothesis is quite different in the
two schemes, as is evident on comparing (3) and (10). In order to see
what these mathematical differences in formulation imply experimentally,
consider once more the experiment suggested in 12.2 of testing four brands
of shells with six marksmen.

The linear hypothesis model assumes that the experiment in question
is a random sample of similar experiments in which the same four brands
of shells and the same six marksmen are used. As a consequence, if H_0
is accepted, it implies that there is no real difference in the quality of the
four brands as far as these six marksmen are concerned. It might happen,
however, that a different set of marksmen would show up differences in
the four brands. Thus in the linear hypothesis model the conclusions
drawn from the F test are strictly applicable only for the given marksmen.

The components of variance model assumes that the experiment in
question was obtained by selecting six marksmen at random from a
population of marksmen and by selecting four brands of shells at random
from a population of brands. As a consequence, if H_0 is accepted, it
implies that the population of brands consists essentially of one brand
only, because $\sigma_b^2 = 0$. In the components of variance model the conclusions drawn from the F test apply to the population of marksmen and
the population of brands.

In the present illustration neither model seems to be entirely appropriate. It would be desirable to have a test that is concerned with the four
chosen brands of shells only, since they alone are of interest, but it would
also be desirable to have the test applicable to a population of marksmen.
Thus a mixture of the two models would appear to be the most realistic
model for this illustration. The preceding methods can be extended to
cover mixed cases also, but such an extension is not considered here.

12.2.4 Analysis of Variance Estimation

Although the analysis of variance technique was presented as a technique for testing hypotheses, it is also a very useful tool for obtaining estimates of the various parameters, or functions of the parameters, involved in the two models.

Consider, first, the problem of estimating the parameters involved in the linear hypothesis model. From (1) the parameters c, a_i, and b_j were defined as the expected values of the corresponding random variables $\bar{x}, \bar{x}_{i\cdot} - \bar{x}$, and $\bar{x}_{\cdot j} - \bar{x}$; hence these random variables yield unbiased estimates of those parameters. Thus, using a circumflex to denote an unbiased estimate,

$$\hat{c} = \bar{x}, \quad \hat{a}_i = \bar{x}_{i\cdot} - \bar{x}, \quad \hat{b}_j = \bar{x}_{\cdot j} - \bar{x}$$

An unbiased estimate of σ^2 is given by

$$(16) \qquad \hat{\sigma}^2 = \frac{\sum\limits_{i=1}^{a} \sum\limits_{j=1}^{b} (x_{ij} - \bar{x}_{i\cdot} - \bar{x}_{\cdot j} + \bar{x})^2}{(a-1)(b-1)}$$

A demonstration of the fact that this estimator is unbiased can be based on (6). It was accepted that (6) possesses a χ^2 distribution with $(a-1)$ $(b-1)$ degrees of freedom. From problem 7, Chapter 11, it is known that the expected value of a χ^2 variable is equal to its degrees of freedom; hence the expected value of (16) must be σ^2. The fact that (16) is an unbiased estimator of σ^2 could be demonstrated without the aid of (6) by using expected value operator methods.

The preceding estimators may be used to give unbiased estimates of interesting functions of the parameters. For example, an experimenter interested in estimating the difference between two treatment effects corresponding, say, to the first and second column effects, could use the estimator $\bar{x}_{\cdot 1} - \bar{x}_{\cdot 2}$.

Consider, next, the problem of estimating the parameters involved in the components of variance model. The parameters here are μ_a, μ_b, μ_c, σ_a^2, σ_b^2, and σ_c^2. In most applications of this model the experimenter's estimation interests are usually centered on the total mean and the individual variances and not on individual means. The total mean, namely $E(x_{ij}) = \mu_a + u_b + \mu_c$, obviously can be estimated by $\bar{x}$. Estimates for the individual variances can be obtained by using the appropriate sums of squares listed in Table 4.

The last column gives the expected values of the entries in the fourth column. These values can be verified by using expected value operator

TABLE 4

Source of variation	Sum of squares	d. f.	Mean square	Expected mean square
Rows	$\Sigma\Sigma(\bar{x}_{i.}-\bar{x})^2 = S_1$	$a-1$	$S_1/(a-1)$	$\sigma_c{}^2 + b\sigma_a{}^2$
Columns	$\Sigma\Sigma(\bar{x}_{.j}-\bar{x})^2 = S_2$	$b-1$	$S_2/(b-1)$	$\sigma_c{}^2 + a\sigma_b{}^2$
Remainder	$\Sigma\Sigma(x_{ij}-\bar{x}_{i.}-\bar{x}_{.j}+\bar{x})^2$ $= S_3$	$(a-1)(b-1)$	$S_3/(a-1)(b-1)$	$\sigma_c{}^2$

methods. For example, the second entry in the last column can be obtained as follows:

$$E(S_2) = E \sum_{i=1}^{a} \sum_{j=1}^{b} (\bar{x}_{.j} - \bar{x})^2$$
,
$$= aE \sum_{j=1}^{b} (\bar{x}_{.j} - \bar{x})^2$$

But from (11) this is equivalent to

(17) $$E(S_2) = aE \sum_{j=1}^{b} (y_j - \bar{y})^2$$

From the discussion following (11) it is clear that the y_j are independent normal variables with the same means and variances, namely, $\mu_b + \mu_c$ and

$$\sigma_{y_j}{}^2 = \sigma_b{}^2 + \frac{\sigma_c{}^2}{a}$$

As a consequence, $\sum_{j=1}^{b} (y_j - \bar{y})^2/(b-1)$ will be an unbiased estimate of this variance; that is,

$$E \sum_{j=1}^{b} \frac{(y_j - \bar{y})^2}{b-1} = \sigma_b{}^2 + \frac{\sigma_c{}^2}{a}$$

Using this result in (17) yields

$$E(S_2) = a(b-1)\left(\sigma_b{}^2 + \frac{\sigma_c{}^2}{a}\right)$$

The expected value of the second entry in the fourth column of Table 4 is therefore given by

$$E \frac{S_2}{(b-1)} = a\sigma_b{}^2 + \sigma_c{}^2$$

The first entry in the last column of Table 4 follows by symmetry, whereas the last entry can be verified by methods similar to those employed in the preceding demonstration.

From Table 4 it now follows that unbiased estimates of σ_c^2, σ_a^2, and σ_b^2 are given by

$$\hat{\sigma}_c^2 = \frac{S_3}{(a-1)(b-1)}$$

$$\hat{\sigma}_a^2 = \frac{S_1 - S_3/(b-1)}{b(a-1)}$$

$$\hat{\sigma}_b^2 = \frac{S_2 - S_3/(a-1)}{a(b-1)}$$

The accuracy of the various estimates obtained in this section has not been discussed because some of the theory relating to accuracy is somewhat incomplete and lengthy.

12.2.5 Generalizations

Both the linear hypothesis model and the components of variance model can be generalized to cover situations in which there are more than two variables of classification. Thus, if there were three variables of classification, the fundamental identity (4) would assume the form

$$
\begin{aligned}
(18) \quad \sum\sum\sum(x_{ijk} - \bar{x})^2 &= \sum\sum\sum(\bar{x}_{i..} - \bar{x})^2 + \sum\sum\sum(\bar{x}_{.j.} - \bar{x})^2 \\
&+ \sum\sum\sum(\bar{x}_{..k} - \bar{x})^2 + \sum\sum\sum(\bar{x}_{ij.} - \bar{x}_{i..} - \bar{x}_{.j.} + \bar{x})^2 \\
&+ \sum\sum\sum(\bar{x}_{i.k} - \bar{x}_{i..} - \bar{x}_{..k} + \bar{x})^2 + \sum\sum\sum(\bar{x}_{.jk} - \bar{x}_{.j.} - \bar{x}_{..k} + \bar{x})^2 \\
&+ \sum\sum\sum(x_{ijk} - \bar{x}_{ij.} - \bar{x}_{i.k} - \bar{x}_{.jk} + \bar{x}_{i..} + \bar{x}_{.j.} + \bar{x}_{..k} - \bar{x})^2
\end{aligned}
$$

The general theory for the linear hypothesis model shows that one proceeds in the same manner as before. Thus it is merely necessary to divide each of the preceding sums of squares by its degrees of freedom and then take the proper ratio, depending on the hypothesis to be tested, to obtain an F variable. For example, if the equality of row means were being tested, one would choose the first and last sums of squares on the right of (18) to form the F ratio. The new feature in (18), not found in (4), is that now there are sums of squares that measure the *interaction* between two variables. Thus the fourth sum of squares on the right measures the extent to which the first and second variables interact on each other. If, for example, different amounts of two different chemicals were applied to experimental plots of ground, it might happen that increased amounts of each chemical alone would increase yield but that when both chemicals were applied equally no appreciable increase in yield would result.

For the purpose of seeing how the fourth sum of squares is capable of measuring the interaction of the first two variables, consider the expression

$$(x_{ij} - \bar{x}_{i.}) - (\bar{x}_{.j} - \bar{x}) = y_{ij} - \bar{y}_{.j}$$

This quantity is the typical term, before squaring and with the third variable dots omitted, in the sum of squares being discussed. If the row effects were strictly additive, then subtracting the row mean $\bar{x}_{i.}$ from every cell entry, x_{ij}, in a two-way table would yield a set of observational values, y_{ij}, that are random except for column effects. The sample variance of these adjusted values in any given column would therefore yield an estimate of the basic variance σ^2. Since $\bar{y}_{.j}$ is the column mean of the y_{ij}, it follows that $\sum_{i=1}^{a} (y_{ij} - \bar{y}_{.j})^2$, when divided by the appropriate number of degrees of freedom, would be expected to be a valid estimate of σ^2 and therefore that the double sum when divided by the proper number would yield such an estimate also.

Now suppose that the two variables do not act independently of each other in this additive fashion and that, say, the first row variable is beneficial in conjunction with the first column variable but harmful otherwise. Then the value of $y_{11} = x_{11} - \bar{x}_{1.}$ would be expected to be larger than under independence, whereas the values of the y_{1j} for $j = 2, \cdots, b$ would be expected to be smaller (larger negatively) than under independence. If the other row variables also interact in various ways with the column variables, the net effect will be to produce sets of y_{ij} in the various columns that are more variable than under independence. As a result, the sum of squares being discussed will tend to be larger when interaction is present than when it is absent. The general theory of analysis of variance shows that a valid test of the hypothesis that there is no interaction between the first and second variables is given by applying the F test to the fourth and last sums of squares in the usual manner.

An analysis of variance design in which there are two variables of classification but in which there are k observations in each cell can be treated as a special case of a three-variable problem. Since the index k on x_{ijk} corresponds to a kth replication rather than to a third variable, the fundamental identity (18) would be rewritten to eliminate terms involving a segregation for the third variable. Thus the third, fifth, and sixth terms on the right would be combined with the seventh term to give a new remainder term. The breakdown would then become

$$(19) \quad \sum\sum\sum(x_{ijk} - \bar{x})^2 = \sum\sum\sum(\bar{x}_{i..} - \bar{x})^2 + \sum\sum\sum(\bar{x}_{.j.} - \bar{x})^2$$
$$+ \sum\sum\sum(\bar{x}_{ij.} - \bar{x}_{i..} - \bar{x}_{.j.} + \bar{x})^2 + \sum\sum\sum(x_{ijk} - \bar{x}_{ij.})^2$$

The analysis then proceeds as usual. It is now possible to test for inter-action between the two variables, whereas when there was but one obser-vation per cell, as in (4), this was not possible.

The general theory for the components of variance model shows that the nice generalization, just discussed, that holds for the linear hypoth-esis model does not apply to the components of variance model. When there are three or more variables of classification, it is not possible to apply the F test as usual to testing, say, that there are no row differences. The F test is applicable to this problem only if it can be assumed that one of the theoretical interactions involving the row variable is zero; other-wise, it is necessary to estimate an unknown parameter from the data and thus use an inexact method.

The material presented here on the analysis of variance is only an introduction to this important topic. Books on experimental design discuss many other models and generalizations and give detailed discus-sions of applications.

12.3 Stratified Sampling

The technique of breaking down the variation of a variable into useful components in order to decrease the experimental variation, as done in the analysis of variance, can also be used to advantage in designing experiments for estimating means of populations. It turns out that a more accurate estimate of the mean can often be obtained by taking restricted random samples than by using completely random samples. For example, suppose that an accurate estimate of the mean weight of fifth grade pupils is desired by a school system. By taking the proper size random samples in the various age groups, or in the various schools of the system, a more accurate estimate of the population mean can usually be obtained than by taking the same total sample at random in the system. In order to determine the proper size subsamples, consider the following general problem.

Let a population be divided into k distinct subpopulations. Further, let the mean and variance of this population be μ and σ^2 and of the ith subpopulation, μ_i and σ_i^2. Then consider as estimates of μ the quantities $\bar{x}$ and $\bar{x}_R$, where $\bar{x}$ is the mean of a random sample of size n and where

$$(20) \qquad \bar{x}_R = \frac{n_1}{n}\bar{x}_1 + \cdots + \frac{n_k}{n}\bar{x}_k$$

in which $\bar{x}_i$ is the mean of a random sample of size n_i drawn from the ith subpopulation and $\sum_1^k n_i = n$. This restricted type of random sampling is called *stratified sampling*.

For the purpose of comparing the relative precision of these two estimates of μ, consider their respective variances. The variance of $\bar{x}$ is given by $\sigma_{\bar{x}}^2 = \sigma^2/n$. Since the $\bar{x}_i$ are independent, the variance of (20) is given by

$$(21) \qquad \sigma_{\bar{x}_R}^2 = \sum_1^k \left(\frac{n_i}{n}\right)^2 \sigma_{\bar{x}_i}^2 = \sum_1^k \left(\frac{n_i}{n}\right)^2 \frac{\sigma_i^2}{n_i} = \sum_1^k \frac{n_i \sigma_i^2}{n^2}$$

In order to express the variance of $\bar{x}$ in terms of the σ_i^2, it is necessary to express the frequency function of the population in terms of those of the subpopulations. This may be done by applying the two basic rules of probability to the problem of determining the probability that x will assume a value within any specified interval. If p_i denotes the probability that x will come from the ith subpopulation and $f_i(x)$ denotes the frequency function for this subpopulation,

$$p_i \int_\alpha^\beta f_i(x)\,dx$$

represents the probability that x will come from the ith subpopulation and will assume a value between α and β. Since these subpopulations are mutually exclusive, the probability that x will assume a value between α and β is the sum of all such probabilities; hence

$$\int_\alpha^\beta f(x)\,dx = p_1 \int_\alpha^\beta f_1(x)\,dx + \cdots + p_k \int_\alpha^\beta f_k(x)\,dx$$

But α and β are arbitrary; consequently by the same reasoning followed in (2), Chapter 8,

$$f(x) = p_1 f_1(x) + \cdots + p_k f_k(x)$$

Now

$$(22) \qquad \mu = \int_a^b x f(x)\,dx = p_1 \int_a^b x f_1(x)\,dx + \cdots + p_k \int_a^b x f_k(x)\,dx$$

$$= p_1 \mu_1 + \cdots + p_k \mu_k$$

Furthermore

$$\sigma^2 + \mu^2 = \int_a^b x^2 f(x)\,dx$$

$$= p_1 \int_a^b x^2 f_1(x)\,dx + \cdots + p_k \int_a^b x^2 f_k(x)\,dx$$

$$= p_1(\sigma_1^2 + \mu_1^2) + \cdots + p_k(\sigma_k^2 + \mu_k^2)$$

If the value of μ^2 is eliminated by means of (22) and the fact that $\sum_1^k p_i = 1$, this reduces to

$$\sigma^2 = \sum_1^k p_i[\sigma_i^2 + (\mu_i - \mu)^2]$$

From this result it follows that the variance of $\bar{x}$ can be written in the form

(23)
$$\sigma_{\bar{x}}^2 = \frac{1}{n}\sum_1^k p_i[\sigma_i^2 + (\mu_i - \mu)^2]$$

Now consider a special type of sampling called *representative sampling* in which the subpopulation sample sizes n_i are chosen so that $n_i/n = p_i$. For a finite population this means that the relative sizes of the subpopulation samples are chosen equal to the relative sizes of the subpopulations. For representative sampling, (23) may be reduced by means of (21) to the form

(24)
$$\sigma_{\bar{x}}^2 = \sigma_{\bar{x}_R}^2 + \sum_1^k \frac{n_i}{n^2}(\mu_i - \mu)^2$$

This shows that $\sigma_{\bar{x}}^2 > \sigma_{\bar{x}_R}^2$, unless the subpopulations have equal means. Representative sampling is of particular advantage for populations whose subpopulations have widely differing means.

Public opinion polls are familiar examples of representative sampling. For such polls it is customary to stratify the population in several ways. For example, it may be divided into several income groups, into several vocational groups, etc. Then, within strata, random samples are taken proportional to the relative sizes of those strata.

Various other types of restricted random sampling are available, most of which have been developed by governmental and industrial agencies for their particular needs.

As an illustration of the increased precision of estimating μ by the use of representative sampling, suppose for the sake of simplicity that a district is made up of 45 per cent Democrats and 55 per cent Republicans and that 70 per cent of the Democrats will vote for a certain "nonpartisan" candidate in a primary election but only 20 per cent of the Republicans will do so. Now suppose that a sample of size 200 is taken by each method. Although experience indicates that the precision of poll percentages is not so great as that given by binomial theory, the precisions here will be compared on a theoretical basis; consequently

$$\sigma_{\bar{x}}^2 = \sigma_{p'}^2 = \frac{pq}{n} = \frac{(.425)(.575)}{200} = .00122$$

and

$$\sum_1^k \frac{n_i}{n^2}(\mu_i - \mu)^2 = \frac{90}{(200)^2}(.70 - .425)^2 + \frac{110}{(200)^2}(.20 - .425)^2$$

$$= .00031$$

Therefore, from (24)

$$\sigma_{\bar{x}_R}^{\ 2} = .00091$$

Since $\sigma_{\bar{x}_R}^{\ 2}/\sigma_{\bar{x}}^{\ 2} = .75$ here, a considerable increase in precision would result from using representative sampling in preference to pure random sampling. Formulas (23) and (24) are valid for discrete variables.

12.4 Sampling Inspection

The discussion thus far in this chapter has been concerned with techniques for designing valid experiments and for increasing the sensitivity of such experiments. In the remainder of this chapter the emphasis will be on a method that directly tries to minimize the amount of sampling needed to attain a desired sensitivity in the experiment. Since a smaller size analysis of variance experiment usually suffices to attain the same sensitivity as a corresponding more elementary design, the analysis of variance can be considered indirectly as a technique for decreasing the amount of sampling needed to attain a desired sensitivity. Thus all the techniques of this chapter can be thought of as techniques for decreasing the amount of sampling needed to attain the desired objective.

One of the most useful applications of the design of experiments to minimize the amount of sampling occurs in industrial sampling inspection. If a certain type of sampling procedure is agreed on, the notion of the two types of error can be used to advantage to design a good inspection procedure.

It is a common practice in industry to accept or reject lots of merchandise on the basis of a sample drawn from the lot. This practice arises from the fact that it is often more economical to tolerate a small percentage of defectives than to bear the cost of 100 per cent inspection. The basis for accepting a lot of merchandise usually consists in specifying the maximum number of defective pieces that will be tolerated in a random sample of a given size. By means of such samples and specifications the purchaser is protected against receiving bad lots of merchandise.

Sampling inspection is quite different from quality control. It is a method for protecting the purchaser against poor quality after the product has been manufactured rather than a method for finding and correcting flaws in the manufacturing process, as in quality-control methods.

When sampling inspection methods are applied to continuous manufacturing processes, however, they are often useful in helping to control the quality of the product.

From the consumer's point of view, there is a maximum percentage of defectives that he will tolerate. This percentage when expressed as a decimal is known as the *lot tolerance fraction defective* and is denoted by p_t. Without almost 100 per cent inspection, it may be impossible to be certain that the quality is better than p_t; however, it is possible to set up a sampling procedure that will insure this quality with a certain probability. To this end consider a lot of N pieces from which a random sample of n pieces is to be selected. Let c denote the maximum number of defective pieces that will be tolerated in the sample if the lot is to be accepted.

Although numerous sampling schemes are available, only one common type of sampling procedure, known as *single sampling*, is considered here. This scheme proceeds as follows:

(25)   (i) Inspect a sample of n pieces.
    (ii) If the number of defective pieces does not exceed c, accept the lot; otherwise, inspect the entire lot.
    (iii) Replace all defective pieces found by nondefective pieces.

Now consider the computation of the probability that the consumer will receive a bad lot under this sampling procedure, where bad is defined to be quality worse than p_t. Suppose that the lot being submitted for inspection is of p fraction defective so that it contains exactly Np defective and $N - Np$ nondefective items. Then the probability of obtaining exactly x defectives in a sample of size n is given by the ratio of the number of ways of choosing x things from Np things and $n - x$ things from $N - Np$ things to the number of ways of choosing n things from N things. Using the hypergeometric distribution given in (36), Chapter 5, this probability, $P\{x\}$, may be expressed in the form

$$
(26) \qquad P\{x\} = \frac{\dbinom{Np}{x}\dbinom{N - Np}{n - x}}{\dbinom{N}{n}}
$$

Under the sampling scheme (25), the consumer will accept a bad lot provided that $p > p_t$ and that $x \leq c$. Assuming, therefore, that $p > p_t$, the probability that the consumer will accept a bad lot is given by summing the probabilities, $P\{x\}$, given by (26) for $x = 0, 1, \cdots, c$. Now it can be shown that $\sum_{x=0}^{c} P\{x\}$ decreases as p increases; consequently the probability that the consumer will accept a bad lot will be a maximum when p is as small as possible. But p cannot be less than p_t if the lot is to be judged as bad; hence the probability that the consumer will accept a bad lot cannot exceed the value

$$(27) \qquad P_c = \frac{\sum_{x=0}^{c} \binom{Np_t}{x} \binom{N - Np_t}{n - x}}{\binom{N}{n}}$$

This value is given a special name.

(28) DEFINITION: *The probability P_c that a consumer will accept a lot of fraction defective p_t, where p_t is his lot tolerance fraction defective, is called the consumer's risk.*

By demanding a small value of P_c, the consumer is protected against poor quality. If the actual fraction defective p is smaller than p_t, the consumer will be satisfied with the lot, whereas if it is larger than p_t he will wish to reject the lot, and the probability that he will fail to do so will not exceed P_c. Thus P_c is a conservative estimate of the probability that he will accept a bad lot.

From the producer's point of view any sampling scheme for deciding on the quality of a lot possesses the disadvantage of occasionally rejecting a lot of satisfactory quality. Most producers, however, are concerned principally with the percentage of the lots that are likely to be rejected, whether those lots deserve to be rejected or not. Thus the producer is interested in knowing what the probability is that a lot of N selected at random from his production line will be rejected. In order to calculate this probability, assume that the manufacturing process is under control with a process fraction defective p. This means that individual items coming off the production line may be considered to be random samples from a binomial population for which the probability that an item will be defective is p. From this point of view selecting a random sample of size N from the production process and then selecting a subsample of size n from the sample of N already selected is equivalent to selecting a random sample of size n directly from the production process. Since a lot will be rejected only if $x > c$, it follows that the probability that a lot will be rejected is equivalent to the probability of getting more than c successes in n trials of an experiment for which p is the probability of success in a single trial. The desired probability is therefore given by

$$(29) \qquad P_p = \sum_{x=c+1}^{n} \frac{n!}{x! \, (n - x)!} \, p^x q^{n-x}$$

This value is also given a special name.

(30) DEFINITION: *The probability P_p that a producer will have a lot rejected when his production process is under control is called the producer's risk.*

The producer's risk is sometimes defined with respect to a single lot of size N, similar to the consumer's risk, in which case the binomial term being summed in (29) would be replaced by (26). The definition given by (30) is more realistic from the producer's point of view because he is interested in the long-run percentage of lots that will be rejected rather than in a particular lot of given quality. It should be observed that the consumer's risk does not depend on the process fraction defective p, whereas the producer's risk does.

12.4.1 Minimum Single Sampling

Thus far nothing has been said concerning the method of selecting values of n and c. The consumer's requirements fix the values of p_t and P_c in (27). Since N is specified, (27) places a single restriction on n and c. Now from the producer's point of view one desirable method of approach is to select that pair of values which minimizes the amount of inspection. Since a sample of size n is always inspected and the remainder of the lot is inspected with a probability given by (29), the mean number of pieces inspected per lot under the sampling scheme (25) will be given by

$$(31) \qquad I = n + (N - n)P_p$$

In order to satisfy the consumer's demands and also minimize the amount of inspection, it is necessary to find that pair of values of n and c which satisfies (27) and minimizes (31). These quantities are difficult to manipulate; consequently the minimizing solution is obtained numerically for different values of the parameters involved. Extensive tables are available for the minimizing values of n and c for various values of the parameters and for P_c chosen equal to .10.

As an illustration, consider a lot of 1000 pieces for which the fraction defective is $p = .01$ and for which the consumer is willing to assume a risk of $P_c = .10$ of accepting a lot with a fraction defective of $p_t = .05$. By allowing c to assume small integral values and working numerically by trial and error methods, it will be found that the minimum amount of inspection will occur if a sample of 130 is taken and if the maximum allowable number of defectives is 3. With these values of n and c, it will also be found that the mean number of pieces inspected will be 164 as long as production remains in control. These results are easily obtained by consulting the Dodge and Romig tables referred to at the end of this chapter.

12.4.2 Average Outgoing Quality Limit

A somewhat different approach to the problem of protecting the consumer from an inferior product is to attempt to guarantee him a certain quality level of the product after inspection, regardless of what quality level is being maintained by the producer. Toward this end, consider the problem of determining the mean value of the fraction defective after inspection if the producer's fraction defective is p.

First, it is necessary to derive a formula for calculating the expected value of a variable y in terms of conditional expected values of y when the population is split into two groups by means of a related variable x. For example, suppose the mean grade-point average of students in a given college is desired. It might be interesting to obtain the mean grade-point averages of students whose intelligence-quotient scores are less than 110 and of those whose scores are at least 110 and then combine the two means properly to give the desired mean.

Suppose that each member of a finite population is measured with respect to two variables x and y. Let the population be split into two parts by the criterion that $x \leq c$ or $x > c$ and let $y_1, y_2, \cdots, y_k$ denote the possible values of y. The mean value of y is given by

$$(32) \qquad E[y] = \sum_{i=1}^{k} y_i P\{y_i\}$$

Now, the probability $P\{y_i\}$ that y will assume the value y_i can be obtained by considering the two mutually exclusive ways in which this event can occur. Either the individual selected at random will belong to the first group $(x \leq c)$ and possess this value or he will belong to the second group $(x > c)$ and possess this value. The sum of the probabilities of these two possibilities will yield $P\{y_i\}$; hence

$$P\{y_i\} = P\{x \leq c\}P\{y_i \mid x \leq c\} + P\{x > c\}P\{y_i \mid x > c\}$$

If this formula is substituted in (32), it will follow that

$$(33) \quad E[y] = P\{x \leq c\} \sum_{i=1}^{k} y_i P\{y_i \mid x \leq c\}$$

$$+ P\{x > c\} \sum_{i=1}^{k} y_i P\{y_i \mid x > c\}$$

But each of the two sums on the right, when compared with (32), is seen to be a conditional expected value of y. As a result, (33) may be written in the form

(34) $$E[y] = P\{x \le c\}E[y \mid x \le c] + P\{x > c\}E[y \mid x > c]$$

In order to use this formula to determine the mean value of the fraction defective after inspection, let y be the number of defectives left in a lot when the procedure given in (25) is followed. When $x > c$, the entire lot will be inspected and all defective pieces will be replaced by nondefective pieces; hence the value of y will be 0 and therefore the value of $E[y \mid x > c]$ will be 0. When $x \le c$, there will be $N - n$ uninspected pieces; hence the value of y can range from 0 to $N - n$. But, since these $N - n$ pieces constitute a random sample of this size from a binomial population with probability p, the mean number of defectives will be $(N - n)p$; hence this is the value of $E[y \mid x \le c]$. If these values are inserted in (34), it will reduce to

(35) $$E[y] = P\{x \le c\}(N - n)p$$

In order to obtain the mean fraction defective after inspection, rather than the mean number of defectives as given by (35), it is merely necessary to divide both sides of (35) by N. If $\tilde{p}$ denotes the mean fraction defective after inspection, it therefore follows that

(36) $$\tilde{p} = E\left[\frac{y}{N}\right] = P\{x \le c\}\left(1 - \frac{n}{N}\right)p$$

Since x is the binomial variable discussed in connection with (29), $P\{x \le c\}$ may be expressed as the sum of the corresponding binomial probabilities; hence (36) can be written

(37) $$\tilde{p} = \left(1 - \frac{n}{N}\right)p \sum_{x=0}^{c} \frac{n!}{x!\,(n-x)!}\, p^x q^{n-x}$$

This formula gives the mean fraction defective after inspection when following the inspection procedure (25); however, it is more commonly called the *average outgoing quality*.

When the sampling procedure given by (25) has been specified, the values of N, n, and c may be treated as given. Although (37) was calculated on the assumption that the producer's fraction defective is p and is known, the consumer is not likely to accept the producer's claim that p is the actual process fraction defective; hence p may not be treated as given. If $\tilde{p}$ is considered as a function of p only, it will be found that $\tilde{p}$ ordinarily possesses a maximum value that is assumed for a single value of p. This maximum value of $\tilde{p}$, denoted by $\tilde{p}_L$, is given the following special name.

(38) DEFINITION: *The maximum value, $\tilde{p}_L$, of the mean fraction defective after inspection, as a function of p, is called the average outgoing quality limit.*

The average outgoing quality limit is a number such that, regardless of what the producer's fraction defective may be, the mean fraction after inspection will not exceed it. This does not prevent a particular lot from containing worse quality, but in the long run the average value of the fraction defective in the inspected lots will not exceed $\tilde{p}_L$. Since these calculations are based on the assumption that the binomial distribution may be applied to defective parts coming off the production line, it is necessary that the production process be under control at some quality level p, even though the particular value of p being maintained is irrelevant.

The average outgoing quality limit has a certain appeal to many consumers that is not possessed by the protection afforded by a specified consumer's risk. For this reason, it is widely used as a basis for consumer protection.

It is usually possible to select several pairs of values of c and n that will yield functions, $\tilde{p}$, having approximately the same value of $\tilde{p}_L$. Figure 1 illustrates a typical situation. Since it is immaterial to the consumer which pair of values of c and n is chosen for a specified value of $\tilde{p}_L$, the producer is at liberty to choose them to his advantage. From his point of view it would be highly desirable to select that pair of values which minimizes the amount of inspection given by (31). As in the minimum single sampling scheme of the preceding section, the minimizing pair of values of c and n is obtained numerically. Tables are also available for determining these minimizing values corresponding to useful ranges of values of N, $\tilde{p}_L$ and p. It should be noted that the value of the process fraction defective p is required in order to minimize I, just as it was in the case of minimum single sampling.

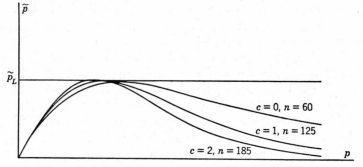

Fig. 1. Sampling plans with approximately equal p_L values.

As an illustration of the preceding ideas, consider the problem that was used as an illustration for minimum single sampling. There $N = 1000$ and $p = .01$. If the consumer requests an average outgoing quality limit of, say, $\tilde{p}_L = .03$, the Dodge and Romig tables referred to previously will give $c = 2$ and $n = 44$ as the values that will minimize the amount of inspection.

REFERENCES

An extensive discussion of fundamental principles such as randomization and replication may be found in R. A. Fisher, *The Design of Experiments*, Oliver and Boyd.

A mathematical proof that the F distribution may be applied to the analysis of variance problems as indicated in the text may be found in D. S. Fraser, *Statistics: An Introduction*, John Wiley and Sons.

A discussion of the difficulties that arise in the two analysis of variance models when there are three or more variables may be found in A. M. Mood, *Introduction to the Theory of Statistics*, McGraw-Hill Book Co.

Tables for assisting in the design of efficient sampling inspection schemes may be found in Dodge and Romig, *Sampling Inspection Tables*, John Wiley and Sons.

EXERCISES

1. Given the following analysis of variance breakdown and the corresponding numerical values of the sums of squares, test the hypothesis that the column means are equal.

$$\sum_{i=1}^{4} \sum_{j=1}^{5} (x_{ij} - \bar{x})^2 = \sum_{i=1}^{4} \sum_{j=1}^{5} (\bar{x}_{.j} - \bar{x})^2 + \sum_{i=1}^{4} \sum_{j=1}^{5} (x_{ij} - \bar{x}_{.j})^2$$

$$400 \qquad\qquad 160 \qquad\qquad 240$$

2. Suppose that the last sum of squares in problem 1 had been further analyzed to measure the row variability and had yielded the indicated numerical values. Now test the hypothesis that the column means are equal.

$$\sum_{i=1}^{4} \sum_{j=1}^{5} (x_{ij} - \bar{x}_{.j})^2 = \sum_{i=1}^{4} \sum_{j=1}^{5} (x_{i.} - \bar{x})^2 + \sum_{i=1}^{4} \sum_{j=1}^{5} (x_{ij} - \bar{x}_{i.} - \bar{x}_{.j} + \bar{x})^2$$

$$240 \qquad\qquad 100 \qquad\qquad 140$$

3. Assuming that the row means of problem 1 are equal, use the last sum of squares in that problem to construct an unbiased estimate of σ^2.

4. Use the last sum of squares in problem 2 to find 98 per cent confidence limits for σ^2.

5. The following table gives the gains of 4 different types of hogs fed 3 different

rations. Test to see whether the rations or the hog types differ in their effect on mean weight.

Type

	I	II	III	IV
A	7	16	10.5	13.5
B	14	15.5	15	21
C	8.5	16.5	9.5	13.5

(Ration is the row label.)

6. The following data represent the number of units of production per day turned out by 5 different workmen using 4 different types of machines. (*a*) Test to see whether the mean productivity is the same for the 4 different machine types. (*b*) Test to see whether the 5 men differ with respect to mean productivity.

Machine Type

	1	2	3	4
1	44	38	47	36
2	46	40	52	43
3	34	36	44	32
4	43	38	46	33
5	38	42	49	39

(Workman is the row label.)

7. Suppose that an analysis of variance experiment involving 10 rows and 4 columns gave a significant result when testing the hypothesis that the column means are equal and that 2 of the sample column means appeared to be larger than the rest. The error sum of squares occurring in the denominator of the F test, based on 36 degrees of freedom, was equal to 180. If you wished to test the new hypothesis $H_0 : \mu_1 = \mu_2$ against $H_1 : \mu_1 > \mu_2$ for the 2 columns of interest, approximately how large a sample of equal size should you expect to take from each if you wanted to be certain with a probability of about .90 of detecting a difference of $\mu_1 - \mu_2 = 1$?

8. For the components of variance model, derive an expression for the expected value of the second sum of squares on the right side of the identity

$$\sum_{i=1}^{a} \sum_{j=1}^{b} (x_{ij} - \bar{x})^2 = \sum_{i=1}^{a} \sum_{j=1}^{b} (\bar{x}_{.j} - \bar{x})^2 + \sum_{i=1}^{a} \sum_{j=1}^{b} (x_{ij} - \bar{x}_{.j})^2$$

First, express it in terms of the variables v_j and w_{ij} $(i = 1, \cdots, a; j = 1, \cdots, b)$, where it is assumed that $x_{ij} = v_j + w_{ij}$, and then calculate the necessary expected values.

9. For the data of problem 1 use the formula obtained in problem 8 and Table 4 to obtain an unbiased estimate of σ_w^2 and of σ_v^2.

10. Describe an analysis of variance experiment for which it is clear that the linear hypothesis model is the natural model for testing row or column variability. Describe an experiment for which the components of variance model is the natural model to use.

11. Using the Poisson approximation

$$\sum_{x=0}^{c} \frac{e^{-np}(np)^x}{x!}$$

with p equal to .05 and .01, respectively, to obtain the values of P_c and P_p given by (27) and (29), respectively, verify that the values of c and n given in the illustration on minimum single sampling are approximately correct to yield $P_c = .10$ and $I = 164$.

12. Using the Poisson approximation of problem 11, determine by numerical methods the values of c and n that minimize the amount of inspection for $N = 400$, $P_c = .10$, $p_t = .05$, and $p = .02$. Proceed by assigning c a value, beginning with 2, then by determining the value of n to satisfy (27), and finally by selecting that pair of values which makes (31) a minimum.

13. Explain why you should prefer to calculate the producer's risk from formula (29) than from the corresponding formula based on the hypergeometric distribution used in (26).

14. Consult the Dodge and Romig tables to verify that your results in problem 12 are approximately correct. Use these same tables to determine the average outgoing quality limit for this problem.

15. Show that $P\{x \mid p\} \geq P\{x \mid p'\}$, where $Np' = Np + 1$, if $x < n(Np + 1)/(N + 1)$. This shows that $\sum_{x=0}^{c} P\{x \mid p\} \geq \sum_{x=0}^{c} P\{x \mid p'\}$, provided that $c < np$, and that $\sum_{x=0}^{c} P\{x \mid p\}$ is a decreasing function of p as assumed in the discussion following formula (26) in the text.

16. A sample of size n is to be taken from a population made up of the k strata consisting of $N_i (i = 1, 2, \cdots, k)$ members. If n_i denotes the size sample to be taken from the ith stratum and c_i the cost per sample from this stratum, and if a total of $c = \sum_{1}^{k} c_i n_i$ dollars can be spent for the sample, show that the variance of the estimate of the population mean will be a minimum if n_i is chosen proportional to $N_i \sigma_i / \sqrt{c_i}$, where σ_i^2 is the variance for the ith stratum population.

17. A population is made up of k subpopulations. The probabilities of success for an experiment for these subpopulations are $p_1, p_2, \cdots, p_k$, respectively. A set of n experiments is conducted by first drawing one of the k subpopulations at random and then performing the n experiments with it. If x denotes the number

of successes obtained, show that the variance of x is given by $V(x) = n\mu_p(1 - \mu_p) + n(n - 1) V(p)$, where μ_p is the mean of the p's and $V(p)$ is their variance. Explain what this means with respect to sampling from a population made up of highly different subpopulations.

18. If infected plants tend to occur in groups that are randomly distributed over an area and if p is the proportion of sampling areas that contain at least 1 group of infected plants, show that an estimate of the plant density of infected plants is $-\mu \log (1 - p)$, where μ is the mean number of infected plants per group.

19. Suppose a population consists of 2 subpopulations with means 20 and 30, respectively, and a common variance of 5. If the two subpopulations are equally probable in random sampling, calculate the advantage in estimating the mean in taking 2 samples of 50 each from the 2 subpopulations over taking a random sample of 100 from the entire population.

20. Let p denote a cost factor that represents what a single sample costs when it is necessary to sample from 1 of the subpopulations in problem 19 as contrasted to 1 unit of cost for a single random sample from the entire population. Thus, if $p = 1.2$, it follows that 120 random samples will cost the same as 100 samples from a subpopulation. Determine the largest value of p such that the 2 methods in problem 19 will cost the same and yield the same precision in estimating μ.

21. Why is it reasonable to take the ratio of the variances rather than the ratio of the standard deviations of 2 estimates to compare the estimates?

CHAPTER 13

Nonparametric Methods

Most of the statistical methods that have been considered so far have possessed two features in common. They have assumed that the functional form of the basic frequency function is known and have been concerned with testing hypotheses about parameters of this frequency function or with estimating its parameters. For example, all the small sample methods developed in Chapter 11, with the exception of the material on the range, require that the basic variable be normally distributed and are concerned with testing or estimating means and variances of those variables. The χ^2 distribution of Chapter 10, however, was not restricted to problems of this type and is a striking exception to the general pattern of methods found in other chapters.

For situations in which very little is known about the distribution of the basic variable or for which it is known that the distribution is not of the required type, it is necessary to develop methods that do not depend on the particular form of the basic frequency function. A number of methods of this type have been designed. The only assumption that is needed for most of these methods is that the frequency function be continuous. A few of them, however, require that the frequency function possess low order moments.

Since the methods being described are not concerned with testing or estimating the parameters of a frequency function of a given type, they are usually called *nonparametric methods*. Such methods are also called *distribution-free methods* because they do not require a knowledge of how the basic variables are distributed. Since neither name is strictly correct for all of the methods usually listed under these names, the first name is used here because of tradition. Although a large number of nonparametric techniques are available to solve certain types of problems, only a few of the more important ones that are fairly easy to discuss are considered in this chapter. All of the techniques to be discussed are concerned with testing hypotheses, except for one, which was designed for estimating a distribution function.

13.1   Sign Test

In this and the next section the problem to be considered is that of testing whether two unknown frequency functions are identical. This problem arises, for example, when the same population is sampled on two different occasions and there is reason to believe that the population may be changing. If it were known that the two populations were normal, then one could use the methods developed in Chapter 11 for testing the equality of means and variances to solve the problem; however, since the population distribution is assumed to be unknown here, a nonparametric method is needed. The method that is about to be discussed was designed for experiments in which the same size sample is taken from each of the populations and in which the experimental values are paired. For example, in determining whether two types of coating for soil pipe are equally resistant to corrosion, the experimenter would ordinarily subject each type of coating to the same set of soil types and thus obtain a pair of experimental values for each soil type.

Let $f_1(x)$ and $f_2(x)$ be the two continuous frequency functions under discussion and let $(x_1, y_1), (x_2, y_2), \cdots, (x_n, y_n)$ denote n paired sample values to be drawn from the two populations. Consider the hypothesis

$$(1) \qquad\qquad H_0 : f_1(x) = f_2(x)$$

For the purpose of testing this hypothesis, it is convenient to consider the differences $x_i - y_i$, $(i = 1, 2, \cdots, n)$. When H_0 is true, x_i and y_i constitute a random sample of size two from the same population. Since the probability that the first of two sample values will exceed the second is the same as the probability that the second will exceed the first and since, theoretically, the probability of a tie is zero, it follows that the probability that $x_i - y_i$ will be positive is $\frac{1}{2}$. Thus, if only the signs of the differences are considered, a nonparametric test for H_0 can be constructed. Toward this end, let

$$z_i = \begin{cases} 1, & \text{if } x_i - y_i > 0 \\ 0, & \text{if } x_i - y_i < 0 \end{cases}$$

Then the variable z_i is a binomial variable corresponding to a single trial of an experiment for which $p = \frac{1}{2}$. Since the z_i are independent, their sum $u = \sum_{i=1}^{n} z_i$ will be a binomial variable corresponding to n independent trials of an experiment for which $p = \frac{1}{2}$.

In order to use this last result for testing H_0, consider as an alternative to H_0 the hypothesis

(2) $$H_1:f_1(x) = f_2(x - c)$$

where c is some positive constant. H_1 states that the second frequency function is merely the first frequency function shifted to the left a distance of c units. Figure 1 illustrates the relationship between $f_1(x)$ and $f_2(x)$.

Under H_1, the x_i will tend to be larger than the y_i and the variable u will tend to exceed its expected value of $n/2$. One would therefore choose as critical region the right tail of the binomial distribution. If c had been negative, the left tail would have been chosen; however, if H_1 were the alternative that a translation of unknown direction had occurred, both tails would be used.

The test that has just been described is known as the *sign test*. It is an extremely simple test to apply. A useful feature of the test is that it is applicable to situations in which the frequency functions $f_1(x)$ and $f_2(x)$, although identical under H_0 for each pair of samples, change from sample pair to sample pair. For example, in the illustration of soil-pipe coatings it might happen that for one type of soil there is very little corrosion for either coating, whereas for another type there is a great deal of corrosion for both coatings. One would expect the variation in the amount of corrosion for the first soil type to be considerably smaller than the variation for the second. Thus not only the mean but also the standard deviation would differ for the two soil types.

As an illustration of how the sign test is applied, consider the data found in Table 1.

These data were obtained by taking random samples of 30 from two normal populations with means 14 and 16 and standard deviations 2 and 2, respectively. The reason for choosing normal data is that it is interesting to compare this and other nonparametric methods with standard methods based on normality.

If the differences $x_i - y_i$ are taken, it will be found that there are 10 positive and 20 negative differences; hence $u = 10$. Since the normal

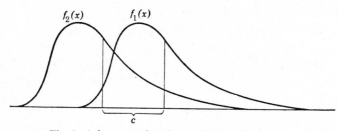

Fig. 1. A frequency function and its translation.

TABLE 1

x	13.3	14.6	13.6	17.2	14.1	10.6	15.9	14.7	14.2	14
y	14.1	15.1	9.9	14.5	17.9	16.1	16.8	15.1	13.2	18

x	17.4	15.6	8.2	13.8	15.4	16.3	17.7	15	13.4	13.4
y	16.3	13.3	15.8	18	20.4	15.7	21.5	14.5	16.7	13.7

x	16	13.3	14.9	12.9	14	16.2	11.5	10.4	12.6	18.1
y	13.6	17	15.7	16.8	18.8	18.8	16	14.6	12.3	17.7

approximation to a binomial distribution with $p = \frac{1}{2}$ is excellent for n as large as 30, u may be treated as a normal variable here.

Because it is known that the alternative given by (2) holds here with $c = -2$, let the hypothesis to be tested be that given by (1) and let the alternative be that given by (2), where $c < 0$. The left tail of the u distribution will therefore be chosen as the critical region for the test. In order to test the hypothesis, it suffices to calculate the probability that $u \leq 10.5$. Thus

$$(3) \qquad \tau = \frac{10.5 - 15}{\sqrt{30\frac{1}{2}\frac{1}{2}}} = -1.643$$

hence $P\{u \leq 10.5\} \doteq .050$. Since this probability is the borderline value for making a decision, one might toss a coin or compute P more accurately; however, the hypothesis is known to be false here.

If this problem is worked on the assumption that the differences of the paired values can be treated as random sample values of a normal variable and if Student's t is calculated for the differences, it will be found that

$$t = -3.16$$

For 29 degrees of freedom, the .005 point for the t distribution is 2.76; hence the probability of obtaining a value less than -3.16 is much smaller than .005. A comparison of this result with that above using the sign test shows that the t test was able to demonstrate the real difference existing in the two populations with greater assurance than the sign test. This, of course, is to be expected when the normality assumption holds because the t test is known to be an optimum test for this type of problem.

The sign test can also be used to test the hypothesis that the median of a distribution has a given value. Since the median point on a distribution is one such that the probability is $\frac{1}{2}$ that a sample value will exceed it, the median is essentially a nonparametric property of a distribution. Testing the hypothesis that the median has a given value is a nonparametric analogue of testing whether the mean has a given value. Instead of observing the signs of the differences $x_i - y_i$, as in the preceding problem, one works with the signs of the quantities $x_i - \xi$, where ξ is the postulated median value. The test procedure is then the same as before.

Although the sign test may appear to be rather weak, it can be shown that it possesses certain optimum properties for testing a hypothetical median when nothing is known about the underlying distribution. It is only when one compares the sign test with a test based on a given distribution, such as the normal distribution, that the sign test suffers.

13.2 Rank Sum Test

If the data for testing the hypothesis $f_1(x) = f_2(x)$ do not consist of matched pairs, the sign test is not the natural test to apply. This is particularly true if the sizes of the samples from the two populations differ considerably because then the sign test will waste some of the data. A simple nonparametric test for this more general situation can be obtained by studying the possible ordered arrangements of the combined sample values.

Let $x_1', x_2', \cdots, x_{n_1}'$ and $y_1', y_2', \cdots, y_{n_2}'$ denote random samples of sizes n_1 and n_2 taken from the populations with the continuous frequency functions $f_1(x)$ and $f_2(x)$, respectively. Let these two sets of sample values be arranged in order of increasing magnitude and denote the ordered sets by $x_1, x_2, \cdots, x_{n_1}$ and $y_1, y_2, \cdots, y_{n_2}$. If the two ordered sets are combined into a single ordered set, a typical arrangement such as

(4) $$y_1, y_2, x_1, y_3, x_2, y_4, y_5, x_3, \cdots$$

will be obtained. When $f_1(x) = f_2(x)$ the x_i' and y_j' represent random samples from the same population. The combined set $x_1', \cdots, x_{n_1}', y_1', \cdots, y_{n_2}'$ therefore represents a random sample of size $n_1 + n_2$ from this common population. Since the sampling is random, any particular order of these sample values should have the same probability of occurring as any other order. For example, the first sample to be drawn, x_1', has the same probability of being, say, the largest value obtained as the second sample x_2'. Thus each of the $(n_1 + n_2)!$ possible permutations of the variables $x_1', \cdots, x_{n_1}', y_1, \cdots, y_{n_2}'$ has the same probability of being the ordered set of values. In calculating the probability that a particular type of ordered set will be obtained, it is therefore necessary to count the number of the $(n_1 + n_2)!$ permutations that give rise to the desired order type and divide this number by $(n_1 + n_2)!$

Although it makes no difference which variable is labeled x and which y, it is convenient when consulting the tables that have been constructed for the test to be presented here to have $n_1 \leq n_2$ and therefore to label the variables accordingly.

After this joint ordering, as in (4), has been performed, write down the ranks of the x values and let T denote the sum of those ranks. For example, in (4) one would write down beneath the consecutive x values displayed there the numbers 3, 5, 8, $\cdots$ because those are the ranks of the x values in the combined set. The value of T would then be the sum of those numbers.

Now the sampling distribution of T under the assumption that $f_1(x) = f_2(x)$, and therefore based on the resulting assumption that all $(n_1 + n_2)!$ permutations of the combined set of values have the same probability of being the ordered set, has been worked out by combinatorial methods. The distribution of T depends, of course, on the sizes, n_1 and n_2, of the two samples. Table VII in Appendix 2 gives the necessary critical values corresponding to various sample sizes for $n_2 \leq 10$. For larger sample sizes the distribution of T can be approximated satisfactorily by the proper normal distribution. This is the normal distribution with mean and variance given by the formulas

(5)
$$E(T) = \frac{n_1(n_1 + n_2 + 1)}{2}$$
$$\sigma_T^2 = \frac{n_1 n_2 (n_1 + n_2 + 1)}{12}$$

The problem used to illustrate the sign test is also used to illustrate the rank sum test. If the 30 values of x and the 30 values of y from Table 1 are ordered in magnitude, the following combined ordering will be obtained. The y values are the italicized values. The tied values of x and y were alternated in the ordering for all tied pairs.

(6)
8.2, *9.9*, 10.4, 10.6, 11.5, *12.3*, 12.6, 12.9, *13.2*, 13.3,
13.3, 13.3, 13.4, 13.4, *13.6*, 13.6, *13.7*, 13.8, 14.0, 14.0,
14.1, *14.1*, 14.2, *14.5*, 14.5, *14.6*, 14.6, 14.7, 14.9, 15.0,
15.1, 15.1, 15.4, 15.6, *15.7*, *15.7*, *15.8*, 15.9, *16.0*, 16.0,
16.1, 16.2, 16.3, *16.3*, 16.7, *16.8*, *16.8*, 17.0, 17.2, 17.4,
17.7, 17.7, *17.9*, 18.0, *18.0*, 18.1, *18.8*, *18.8*, 20.4, *21.5*,

In order to calculate the value of T, it is necessary to write down the ranks of the x values in (6).

1, 3, 4, 5, 7, 8, 10, 12, 13, 14, 16, 18, 19, 20, 21, 23, 27, 28, 29, 30, 33, 34, 38, 40, 42, 43, 49, 50, 52, 56

The sum of these ranks is $T = 745$. Since $n_1 = n_2 = 30$, application of formulas (5) will show that

$$E(T) = 915, \quad \sigma_T{}^2 = 4575$$

Consequently

$$\tau = \frac{T - E(T)}{\sigma_T} = \frac{745 - 915}{67.6} = -2.51$$

Since τ is an approximate standard normal variable, it follows from Table II that $P\{\tau \le -2.51\} \doteq .006$. A comparison of this result with that of the sign test shows that the rank sum test is superior to the sign test for this problem. The value of $t = -3.16$ for the Student's t test shows, however, that the t test is still somewhat better than either of the nonparametric tests for this problem, as was to be expected.

When testing the hypothesis $f_1(x) = f_2(x)$ against the alternative hypothesis that the first population is situated to the left of the second population, the left tail of the T distribution should obviously be chosen as the critical region. One should, of course, use the right tail if the shift has been to the right. The rank sum test is known to be an excellent test for the type of problem being considered here. It can be shown, for example, that even when the variables are normal, the rank sum test based on 100 observations is approximately as good as Student's t test based on 95 observations.

13.3 Runs

Most of the statistical methods that have been considered in the preceding chapters were designed to be applied to data for which no useful information was gained by preserving the time order of the observations. It was assumed that the observations constitute a random sample from a fixed population, in which case the time order can be ignored. If there is reason to believe that the observations may not behave like a random set when they are taken over some time interval, then it is necessary to test the randomness of the sequence before the usual statistical methods based on randomness can be applied.

A second reason for studying methods that attempt to detect a lack of randomness in sequences of observations is that such methods may be superior to the usual static methods for testing certain hypotheses. The advantage of preserving the time order of observations in testing hypotheses is demonstrated in Chapter 14 in the material on sequential analysis.

Although a few of the statistical methods in the preceding chapters have been based on the order of observations, they assume that the distribution of the basic variable is known. For example, the quality-control chart technique was applied to such variables as normal and binomial variables. In this section a nonparametric method is discussed for testing the randomness of sequences of observations.

Suppose samples are taken every morning and afternoon from a production line to check on a quality characteristic of the product, say, the diameter of a part, and suppose that the following diameters are obtained: .220, .213, .221, .222, .219, .214, .222, .216, .212, .221, .223, .214, .221, .216, .217, .215. If each value is assigned the letter a, provided that it is above the median, which will be found to be .218, and the letter b, provided that it is below .218, this set of values will yield the following sequence of letters:

(7) $a, b, a, a, a, b, a, b, b, a, a, b, a, b, b, b$

Now, a sequence of i identical letters that is preceded and followed by a different letter or no letter is called a run of length i. The runs of a's and b's in this example have the lengths 1, 1, 3, 1, 1, 2, 2, 1, 1, 3.

By studying how runs behave for random sequences, it is possible to derive tests for randomness that are based on runs. One of the simplest statistics to study in this manner is the total number of runs in the sequence. In the preceding illustration the total number of runs is 10. Now, intuitively, one might feel that there are too many runs in a sequence of this length, compared to the number of runs expected in a randomly selected sequence of the same length. An excessive number of runs might occur, for example, if there were a tendency for machines to turn out parts slightly too large in the morning and slightly too small in the afternoon because then there would be a tendency toward the sequence $a, b, a, b, a,$ $\cdots$. Too few runs might occur if there were a tendency for the machines gradually to produce larger parts from day to day because then the early diameters would be mostly below the median, whereas the later diameters would be mostly above the median. Several very long runs will, of course, reduce the total number of runs possible for a sequence of given length.

In order to obtain the frequency function of a statistic such as the total number of runs, it is necessary to obtain the joint frequency function of the number of runs of a's and the number of runs of b's. Toward this end, consider a sequence of n letters consisting of n_a a's and n_b b's. Let

r_a and r_b denote the number of runs of a's and b's, respectively. Now consider the basic problem of finding the probability that the number of runs of a's and of b's will have specified values.

Let x_1', x_2', $\cdots$, x_n' denote the random variables whose values are to be converted to a's or b's, depending on whether the value is above or below the median of the set. These variables are assumed to represent a random sample of size n from a population with a continuous frequency function. For ease of explanation, assume for the time being that n is an even number, say $n = 2k$, so that there will be the same number of values (k) above and below the median. Now as explained in 13.2, each of the $n!$ possible permutations of the variables x_1', x_2', $\cdots$, x_n' has the same probability of being the ordered set of values denoted by x_1, x_2, $\cdots$, x_n. From this property, it will follow that every distinct permutation of the a's and b's will have the same probability of occurring. This fact can be seen in the following manner.

Let $b\,a\,b\,b\,a\,a\,\cdots\,a$ denote any permutation of the k a's and the k b's and consider the number of the $n!$ permutations of the x''s that will yield this particular permutation of a's and b's. The first b in this permutation means that the first sample value x_1' was smaller than the median of the set of values; hence x_1' could have occupied any one of the first k order positions in the ordered set. The first a in this permutation means that the second sample value x_2' was larger than the median; hence x_2' could have occupied any one of the last k order positions in the ordered set. Thus there are k choices of order positions for the first b and also for the first a. In a similar manner, there are $k - 1$ remaining choices of order positions for the second b and the second a. Filling order positions in this manner, there are $k!\,k!$ choices of order positions for the x''s to yield the desired arrangement of a's and b's. Since this number of choices does not depend on the particular permutations of a's and b's and since all order permutations of the x''s have the same probability of occurring, it follows that all distinct permutations of the a's and b's have the same probability of occurring. The same arguments apply for the case in which n is an odd number with $n = 2k + 1$.

In view of the preceding discussion, the probability that r_a and r_b will have specified values is given by the ratio of the number of permutations of the a's and b's possible when n_a, n_b, r_a, and r_b are held fixed to the number of permutations possible when only n_a and n_b are held fixed. This assumes that only samples of size n which give rise to n_a a's and n_b b's are being considered and that the two random variables here are r_a and r_b.

The denominator of this probability ratio, which is the number of permutations when n_a and n_b are held fixed, is equal to the number of ways of permuting n things of which n_a are alike and n_b are alike. From (18), Chapter 2, the denominator is therefore

(8)
$$\frac{n!}{n_a!\, n_b!}$$

For the purpose of counting the number of permutations when n_a and n_b and also r_a and r_b are held fixed, concentrate first on the a's. As far as runs of a's are concerned, the b's in a sequence such as (7) merely serve to separate the a's into blocks. In order to simplify matters, these separations are made by means of vertical bars rather than by means of b's. Thus (7) would be designated

$$a\, |a\, a\, a|\, a\, |a\, a|\, a$$

The bar at the end was omitted because it does not separate a's and thus does not affect runs of a's. Since n_a and r_a are being held fixed, the number of a's and the number of blocks are fixed. Under these restrictions, different permutations can be obtained only by moving a's from one block to another without destroying any blocks. The number of such possible permutations can be counted in the following manner.

If the n_a a's are arranged in a line, they can be separated into r_a blocks by placing $r_a - 1$ vertical bars in distinct spaces between the a's. Since there are $n_a - 1$ spaces between the a's and $r_a - 1$ of them are to be chosen, the number of distinct permutations possible is the number of ways of choosing $r_a - 1$ things from $n_a - 1$ things, which by (17), Chapter 2, is given by

(9)
$$\binom{n_a - 1}{r_a - 1} = \frac{(n_a - 1)!}{(r_a - 1)!\,(n_a - r_a)!}$$

The same arguments apply to the b's; hence the number of permutations of the b's subject to n_b and r_b being held fixed is

(10)
$$\binom{n_b - 1}{r_b - 1} = \frac{(n_b - 1)!}{(r_b - 1)!\,(n_b - r_b)!}$$

In order to combine the a's and b's, suppose that the sequence begins with an a. Then, for each permutation of the a's, the b's can be permuted in all possible ways in their blocks to give distinct permutations of the a's and b's jointly; consequently the total number of permutations of the a's and b's together, starting with an a and subject to r_a and r_b being fixed, is the product of (9) and (10), namely

(11)
$$\binom{n_a - 1}{r_a - 1} \cdot \binom{n_b - 1}{r_b - 1}$$

This same result applies if the sequence begins with the letter b. Since blocks of a's and b's alternate, either $r_a = r_b$ or $r_a = r_b \pm 1$. If $r_a = r_b + 1$, the sequence must begin and end with an a. If $r_a = r_b - 1$, the sequence must begin and end with a b. However, if $r_a = r_b$, the sequence can begin with either letter. For the first two cases there is no choice of beginning letter; hence (11) gives the desired number of permutations. For the third case the number of permutations is twice as large because one can fit the a and b blocks together by starting either with the letter a or the letter b and any permutation beginning with the letter a must be different from one beginning the letter with b. In every case the number of desired permutations is given by

$$(12) \qquad \binom{n_a - 1}{r_a - 1}\binom{n_b - 1}{r_b - 1}c, \quad \text{where} \quad c = \begin{cases} 2 \text{ if } r_a = r_b \\ 1 \text{ if } r_a \neq r_b \end{cases}$$

The ratio of (12) and (8) gives the desired probability. The result that has just been demonstrated may be summarized in the following theorem.

THEOREM: *If r_a and r_b denote the respective number of runs above and below the median for a random sample of size n for a continuous variable x, and if n_a and n_b denote the respective number of values of x above and below the median, then the joint distribution of r_a and r_b is given by*

$$f(r_a, r_b) = \frac{c(n_a - 1)!\,(n_b - 1)!\,n_a!\,n_b!}{(r_a - 1)!\,(r_b - 1)!\,(n_a - r_a)!\,(n_b - r_b)!\,n!}$$

where $c = 2$ if $r_a = r_b$ and $c = 1$ if $r_a \neq r_b$.

It will be observed that this theorem is not concerned with the form of the frequency function of x; consequently, any test derived directly from this theorem will be a nonparametric test.

Now consider the problem discussed at the beginning of this section, namely the problem of obtaining the frequency function for the total number of runs u when n_a and n_b are held fixed. Since $u = r_a + r_b$, the probability that u will assume a fixed value is obtained by summing the probabilities $f(r_a, r_b)$, given by the theorem for all values of r_a and r_b whose sum is this fixed value. If u is even, $r_a = r_b = u/2$; consequently there is but one pair of values to be considered. If u is odd, $r_a = (u \pm 1)/2$ and $r_b = (u \mp 1)/2$; consequently there are but two pairs of values to be considered. If $f(u)$ denotes the desired frequency function, it therefore follows from the theorem that

$$f(u) = \frac{2(n_a - 1)!\,(n_b - 1)!\,n_a!\,n_b!}{\left(\dfrac{u}{2} - 1\right)!\left(\dfrac{u}{2} - 1\right)!\left(n_a - \dfrac{u}{2}\right)!\left(n_b - \dfrac{u}{2}\right)!\,n!}, \quad \text{if } u \text{ is even}$$

and

$$f(u) = \frac{(n_a - 1)!\,(n_b - 1)!\,n_a!\,n_b!}{\left(\dfrac{u-1}{2}\right)!\,\left(\dfrac{u-3}{2}\right)!\,n!}\left[\frac{1}{\left(n_a - \dfrac{u+1}{2}\right)!\left(n_b - \dfrac{u-1}{2}\right)!}\right.$$

$$\left. + \frac{1}{\left(n_a - \dfrac{u-1}{2}\right)!\left(n_b - \dfrac{u+1}{2}\right)!}\right], \quad \text{if } u \text{ is odd}$$

These probabilities have been used to construct tables of $\sum\limits_{u=2}^{u'} f(u)$ for various values of n_a, n_b, and u'. Such tables enable one to test whether a sample value of u is unusually large or small compared to what would be expected if the sequence of values constituted a random sequence. In order to illustrate the use of such tables, a few entries have been extracted from one of them and have been recorded in Table 2. In this table $u_{.05}$ and $u_{.95}$ are the largest and smallest integers, respectively, such that $P\{u \le u_{.05}\} \le .05$ and $P\{u \ge u_{.95}\} \le .05$. These values may therefore be used as 5 per cent critical values for testing randomness against the alternative of too few, or too many, runs. Because of the manner in which $u_{.05}$ and $u_{.95}$ were chosen, a sample value of u equal to either of these critical values lies in the critical region, and therefore would lead to the rejection of the hypothesis of randomness. Table 2 requires that $n_a = n_b$; however, since the median of a set of observations is being chosen for assigning letters, this requirement will be satisfied, or very nearly so.

As a numerical illustration, consider the data introduced at the beginning of this section. There $u = 10$, $n_a = 8$, and $n_b = 8$. Suppose that there is reason to believe that the diameters of parts may vary from morning to afternoon so that there may be too many runs. In order to test for randomness against this possibility, the right tail of the distribution is chosen as the critical region. Interpolating in the $u_{.95}$ row of Table 2,

TABLE 2

$n_a = n_b$	5	10	15	20	25	30	40	50	60	70	80	90	100
$u_{.05}$	3	6	11	15	19	24	33	42	51	60	70	79	88
$u_{.95}$	8	15	20	26	32	37	48	59	70	81	91	102	113
$u_{.025}$	2	6	10	14	18	22	31	40	49	58	68	77	86
$u_{.975}$	9	15	21	27	33	39	50	61	72	83	93	104	115

it will be found that the critical value of u is approximately 12.2. Thus, $u = 10$ is not large enough to refute randomness here. A considerably larger sequence might reveal a lack of randomness of the type conjectured, if such a lack exists.

As a second illustration, consider the data of problem 57, Chapter 5. There are reasons for believing that the expected percentage may be shifting here from time to time; hence consider testing the hypothesis of randomness against the possibility of too many long runs. If these percentages are assigned letters on the basis of lying above or below the median 2.5, with values equal to the median ignored, it will be found that the resulting sequence of a's and b's is

$$b\ b\ b\ b\ a\ b\ b\ b\ a\ b\ a\ a\ a\ a\ a\ a\ a\ a$$
$$a\ a\ b\ a\ b\ b\ b\ b\ b\ b\ b\ b\ a\ a\ b\ a\ a\ a$$

Here $n_a = 18$, $n_b = 18$, and $u = 12$. Interpolation in Table 2 gives $u_{.05} = 13.4$. Since $u < u_{.05}$, this result is significant at the 5 per cent level; therefore, the hypothesis of randomness is rejected. There appear to be too few runs because of too many very long runs; consequently an investigation of the long runs should be made to determine the cause of nonrandomness.

The preceding theory depends only on the assumption that all distinct permutations of the a's and b's are equally likely and does not require that the a's and b's be obtained from measurements on some continuous variable. Thus the theory can be applied, for example, to such problems as determining whether a group of men and women seated along a lunch counter is arranged in a random order.

Several other tests for randomness are based on functions of runs. One such test, for example, is based on the probability of obtaining at least one run of a length greater than a specified length. Such a test might be helpful in the problem just considered because a run of length 10 for such a short sequence seems unlikely.

The foregoing test based on the total number of runs is a poor test in many respects. It is effective only when the lack of randomness shows up in producing too many or too few runs. There are many types of nonrandomness that produce the correct number of total runs associated with a random sequence. Tests based on counting the number of runs of various lengths are less likely to be deceived.

13.4 Serial Correlation

As explained in the preceding paragraph, the test for randomness based on total runs possesses weaknesses. In particular it is not likely to discover certain types of nonrandomness of a cyclical nature unless the observations are spaced just right. There are many other types of nonrandomness that may occur but will be undetected by the runs test because the total number of runs is approximately equal to the number expected for a random sequence.

For data that possess cyclical features it is to be expected that a test based on correlation would be more effective than the runs test in discovering such features. If observations have been ordered with respect to time and time is irrelevant, no correlation would be expected to exist, for example, between successive pairs of values of the sequence. However, if there is a cyclical movement in the sequence, neighboring pairs of values will tend to be high or low together and thus produce a value of the correlation coefficient that differs significantly from zero. If the frequency function of a correlation coefficient of this type could be found, it would be possible to test the hypothesis that the population correlation is zero and in this sense test the sequence for randomness. The derivation of such frequency functions is complicated; consequently only the results of one such derivation is described here.

Let $x_1, x_2, \cdots, x_n$ denote the sequence to be tested for randomness and consider the ordinary correlation coefficient calculated for this sequence when y_i is chosen as x_{i+1} for $i = 1, 2, \cdots, n - 1$. With this choice for y, the corresponding values of x and y are those indicated in Table 3.

The correlation coefficient of the values given in Table 3 is called the *serial correlation coefficient* with lag 1. If y_i had been chosen equal to x_{i+k}, the correlation coefficient of the resulting x and y values would have been called the serial correlation coefficient with lag k.

If the sequence $x_1, x_2, \cdots, x_n$ could be treated as a random sample of size n from a normal population, one would expect to be able to apply some normal distribution theory such as the regression theory of Chapter 11 to solve the present problem. However, since the y_i no longer constitute a set of random sample values for a fixed set of x's, nor do the pairs of values (x_i, y_i) constitute a set of random sample values from a joint distribution, the ordinary regression and correlation theory is not applicable here. Furthermore, since this chapter is concerned with methods that do not require a normality or similar assumption, the methods of Chapter 11 would not be available for this reason also.

TABLE 3

x	x_1	x_2	$\cdots$	x_i	$\cdots$	x_{n-1}
y	x_2	x_3	$\cdots$	x_{i+1}	$\cdots$	x_n

A nonparametric method based on serial correlation can be devised if it is assumed that all permutations of the sequence being considered are equally probable. For each such permutation, one can calculate the value of the serial correlation coefficient. Since there are $n!$ permutations possible, there are $n!$ values of the serial correlation coefficient to be computed. The ordered set of values obtained, together with the frequencies of those values that are obtained more than once, give the distribution of the serial correlation coefficient with respect to the set of $n!$ permutations of the sequence. For most sequences one would expect the distribution to be fairly symmetrical and to be centered near the origin. If the sequence being tested yielded a large positive or negative value of the serial correlation coefficient, its randomness would be questioned. In order to obtain a critical region for testing randomness, it would be necessary to find two values of the serial correlation coefficient, one for each tail of the distribution, such that say 5 per cent of the $n!$ values of the serial correlation coefficient lay outside the interval determined by the two values.

It is obvious from the preceding discussion that the computational difficulties of the proposed test become prohibitive for n at all large; hence it is necessary to find an approximation for the distribution of the serial correlation coefficient when n is large. This problem is considered next.

For ease of discussion, let y_n be defined to be x_1. Then Table 3 will contain n pairs of values rather than $n - 1$ pairs. The resulting correlation coefficient is called the *circular form* of the serial correlation coefficient. For the extended table the serial correlation coefficient may be expressed in the form

$$r = \frac{\sum_{i=1}^{n} x_i x_{i+1} - n\bar{x}\bar{y}}{n s_x s_y}$$

Since all n values of the sequence occur in both rows of the extended Table 3 and the statistics $\bar{x}$, $\bar{y}$, s_x, and s_y are independent of the order of the sample values, it follows that $\bar{x}$, $\bar{y}$, s_x, and s_y are unchanged under permutations of the sequence. Now the only quantity in r that is affected by permutations of the sequence is the sum $\sum_{i=1}^{n} x_i x_{i+1}$; therefore it suffices to study the distribution of this sum rather than the distribution of r itself. Furthermore, as n becomes large, any differences in the distribution of r, or of this sum, for the standard definition and the circular definition of the serial correlation coefficient disappear, and it is enough to consider the statistic

$$R = \sum_{i=1}^{n} x_i x_{i+1}$$

If it is assumed that the values of the sequence being tested constitute a random sample from a population that possesses low order moments, then it can be shown that the random variable R has an approximate normal distribution for large n. In order to test the hypothesis of zero serial correlation, one must know the mean and variance of R. The necessary values are given by the formulas

$$E(R) = \frac{S_1^2 - S_2}{n - 1}$$

and

$$\sigma_R^2 = \frac{S_2^2 - S_4}{n - 1} + \frac{S_1^4 - 4S_1^2 S_2 + 4S_1 S_3 + S_2^2 - 2S_4}{(n - 1)(n - 2)} - E^2(R)$$

where

$$S_k = x_1^k + x_2^k + \cdots + x_n^k$$

Unfortunately, the computations involved in evaluating the mean and variance are somewhat lengthy if n is at all large. Since the test is not affected by adding the same constant to each member of the sequence or multiplying each member by the same constant, these computations can be simplified considerably by replacing the observed values by reduced values.

As an illustration of how the modified serial correlation test is applied, consider the first sequence used in 13.3 to illustrate the run test. If .218 is subtracted from each value and the resulting values are multiplied by 1000, the following sequence will be obtained:

$$2, -5, 3, 4, 1, -4, 4, -2, -6, 3, 5, -4, 3, -2, -1, -3$$

Computations yield the values

$$S_1 = -2, \quad S_2 = 200, \quad S_3 = -170, \quad S_4 = 3944$$

If these values are substituted in the formulas for $E(R)$ and σ_R^2, it will be found that

$$E(R) = -13.1 \quad \text{and} \quad \sigma_R = 48.7$$

It will also be found that $R = -67$, hence that

$$\tau = \frac{R - E(R)}{\sigma_R} = -1.11$$

If one wishes to test for randomness against possible variation from morning to afternoon, as was done earlier, one would test for zero correlation against possible negative correlation because alternating high and low values of x will produce negative serial correlation. Thus in this problem, assuming that the normal approximation is satisfactory, one would choose the left tail of the approximating normal curve as the critical region. Since, for a normal variable,

$$P\{\tau \leq -1.11\} = .13$$

it follows that the hypothesis of randomness would not be rejected.

It should be pointed out that the preceding theory was discussed from the point of view of the serial correlation with lag 1; however, it is applicable to other lags also. One calculates the corresponding value of R and performs the test as usual.

The preceding two sections have been concerned with two nonparametric tests for deciding whether a sequence in time is random. The problem of discovering a lack of randomness in time data and the nature of it is a very important and difficult problem in statistics. The two techniques presented here are two of the simplest available to describe and are intended only as a mild introduction to one feature of the analysis of time series.

The tests in this and the preceding section were constructed on what is known as the *randomization principle*. In the ordinary test a statistic such as t or F is chosen and then its sampling distribution in repeated sampling is found in order to determine a critical region for the test. A test based on the randomization principle is constructed in much the same manner, except that in determining the critical region one considers the distribution of the statistic under all possible permutations of the observational values that are compatible with the hypothesis. Thus one does not compare the sample value of a statistic with its possible values under repeated sampling experiments but rather with the possible values under all possible permutations of the values that were actually observed. This principle can be used to construct nonparametric versions of the standard parametric statistics such as t or F. The difficulty is to find the distribution of such statistics under randomization, even approximately, so that a critical region can be determined.

13.5   Kolmogorov-Smirnov Statistic

The preceding nonparametric methods have been concerned with testing hypotheses. In this section a technique for finding a confidence band for the distribution function of a continuous variable is presented. By modifying this technique slightly, it can also be used to test hypotheses of the type treated in 13.1 and 13.2.

As before, let $x_1', x_2', \cdots, x_n'$ denote a random sample from a population with distribution function $F(x)$ and let $x_1, x_2, \cdots, x_n$ denote the ordered sample. The problem now is to use this ordered sample to obtain a confidence band for $F(x)$. It should be noted that it is the distribution function $F(x)$ and not the frequency function $f(x)$ that is being considered here.

The desired method, which was first presented by the two Russian mathematicians whose names are attached to it, consists in using the ordered sample to construct an upper and lower step function such that $F(x)$ will be contained between them with a specified probability. Toward this end, consider the sample distribution function, which is a step function, given by the formula

$$S_n(x) = \begin{cases} 0, & x < x_1 \\ \dfrac{k}{n}, & x_k \le x < x_{k+1} \\ 1, & x \ge x_n \end{cases}$$

The graph of this function for a typical sample, together with the graph of a typical $F(x)$, is shown in Fig. 2.

Now suppose that $F(x)$ is known. Then it would be possible to calculate the value of $|F(x) - S_n(x)|$ for any desired value of x. Furthermore, it is clear from Fig. 2 that it would be possible to calculate the value of the quantity

$$\max_x |F(x) - S_n(x)|$$

which is the maximum vertical distance between the graphs of $F(x)$ and $S_n(x)$ over the range of possible x values. It can be shown that the distribution of this maximum distance does not depend on $F(x)$. As a consequence, this quantity, which is denoted by D_n, can be used as a nonparametric variable for constructing a confidence band for $F(x)$.

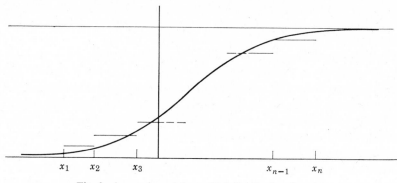

Fig. 2. A sample and theoretical distribution function.

Since $S_n(x)$ varies from sample to sample, D_n is obviously a random variable. In order to use it as a tool for finding a confidence band for $F(x)$, it is necessary to find its distribution. This distribution can be worked out numerically for any particular value of n by using combinatorial methods that are too lengthy and involved to be presented here. Certain critical values of this distribution, however, are given in Table VIII in Appendix 2. Let $D_n{}^\alpha$ denote such a critical value that satisfies the relation

(13) $$P\{D_n \le D_n{}^\alpha\} = 1 - \alpha$$

In view of the definition of D_n and (13), the following successive equalities can be written down:

$$1 - \alpha = P\{\max_x |F(x) - S_n(x)| \le D_n{}^\alpha\}$$
$$= P\{|F(x) - S_n(x)| \le D_n{}^\alpha \text{ for all } x\}$$
$$= P\{S_n(x) - D_n{}^\alpha \le F(x) \le S_n(x) + D_n{}^\alpha \text{ for all } x\}$$

This last equality shows that the two step functions, $S_n(x) + D_n{}^\alpha$ and $S_n(x) - D_n{}^\alpha$, yield a confidence band with confidence coefficient $1 - \alpha$ for the unknown distribution function $F(x)$.

To illustrate the preceding technique, the sample values for the variable x in Table 1 are employed to construct a 95 per cent confidence band for $F(x)$. The ordered values of this sample are 8.2, 10.4, 10.6, 11.5, 12.6, 12.9, 13.3, 13.3, 13.4, 13.4, 13.6, 13.8, 14.0, 14.0, 14.1, 14.2, 14.6, 14.7, 14.9, 15.0, 15.4, 15.6, 15.9, 16.0, 16.2, 16.3, 17.2, 17.4, 17.7, 18.1. From Table VIII it will be found that the value of $D_{30}^{.05}$ is .24; consequently this is the value that must be added to and subtracted from the sample distribution function $S_{30}(x)$ to yield the desired confidence band. Since the step function $S_{30}(x)$ increases by the amount $\frac{1}{30}$ at each distinct sample point, it is easily constructed. The graph of $S_{30}(x)$, together with the graphs of the step functions that determine the desired confidence band, are shown in Fig. 3. Vertical lines have been added to the confidence band step function graphs for better delineation.

The statistic D_n can also be used to test the hypothesis that a random sample came from a population with a specified distribution function. This is accomplished by calculating the maximum difference between the hypothetical distribution function, say $F_0(x)$, and the sample distribution function $S_n(x)$, and then determining whether this difference exceeds the critical value given in Table VIII. This use of the D_n statistic yields another method for solving the "goodness of fit" problem that was treated in Chapter 10 by means of the χ^2 test. The D_n statistic possesses the advantage that it is an exact method, whereas the χ^2 method is valid only for

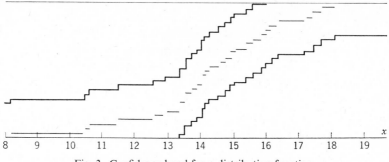

Fig. 3. Confidence band for a distribution function.

fairly large samples. There is no such restriction here as requiring all cell frequencies to exceed 5 as in the case of the χ^2 test because there is no necessity to classify the observations in carrying out the present test. The data may be classified, but then the test is no longer an exact one because the maximum difference for classified and unclassified data may not be the same; however, the discrepancy is usually slight if the classification is not too coarse.

The problem of testing "goodness of fit" is ordinarily a parametric type problem, and therefore strictly speaking it does not belong in this chapter; however, it is included here because it arises naturally in a discussion of confidence band methods. Furthermore, the test based on D_n possesses such striking advantages over the χ^2 test in certain respects that it is important to make this test available to students.

As an illustration of how D_n is used to test a hypothetical distribution, consider the problem in 10.5 in which the χ^2 distribution was used to test whether the observed and normal curve frequencies of Table 2, Chapter 5, are compatible. Since the normal distribution parameters are estimated from the data, the test based on D_n will not be an exact test here. In carrying out the test it is first necessary to accumulate the observed and expected class frequencies in Table 2 for consecutive intervals in order to obtain distribution function values. Such calculations yielded the following values, in which the theoretical frequencies have been rounded off to

Observed	6	34	122	302	549	809	942	984	995	1000
Theoretical	6	34	123	309	564	794	932	984	997	999

the nearest integer. If these values are divided by 1000, they will give the desired approximate distribution function values. An inspection of this table of values will show that the maximum difference is .015, which occurs in both the fifth and sixth sets of cells. Thus $D_n = .015$ here. From

Table VIII it will be observed that the .05 critical value of D_n is given by

$$\frac{1.36}{\sqrt{n}} = \frac{1.36}{\sqrt{1000}} = .043$$

Since $D_n = .015$ is considerably smaller than this critical value, the normal curve fit would be judged to be satisfactory. This may be a questionable conclusion because the value of D_n is likely to be somewhat smaller than normal when distribution parameters are estimated from data. Since the test based on D_n is valid only for unclassified data and hence is inappropriate here, this illustration and similar exercises should be treated as merely exercises in applying the formulas.

The preceding methods can also be adapted to testing the hypothesis $H_0 : f_1(x) = f_2(x)$; however, since they do not seem to possess any advantage over other nonparametric methods available for treating this problem, they are not considered here.

The nonparametric methods that have been presented in this chapter were constructed on an intuitive basis. The critical region for each test was chosen by analogy with the critical region selected in a similar parametric problem. A theory of "best tests" has not yet been developed for nonparametric methods; therefore it is necessary to rely heavily on intuition and attempt to show that the nonparametric test selected is superior to other available tests of this type for the problem being considered.

REFERENCES

Additional nonparametric tests may be found in the following books:
Dixon and Massey, *An Introduction to Statistical Analysis*, McGraw-Hill Book Co.
Siegel, S., *Nonparametric Statistics*, McGraw-Hill Book Co.
The theory related to the rank sum test is given in H. B. Mann and D. R. Whitney, "On a Test of Whether One of Two Random Variables is Stochastically Larger than the Other," *Annals of Mathematical Statistics*, **18**, 50–60.
The tables from which Table 2 was extracted are available in F. Swed and C. Eisenhart, "Tables for Testing Randomness of Grouping in a Sequence of Alternatives," *Annals of Mathematical Statistics*, **14**, 66–87.
The derivation of the formulas for serial correlation is based on advanced mathematics. It will be found in A. Wald and J. Wolfowitz, "An Exact Test for Randomness in the Non-Parametric Case Based on Serial Correlation," *Annals of Mathematical Statistics*, **14**, 378–388.

EXERCISES

1. Find the probability that (a) the larger of 2 observations taken from a continuous distribution will exceed the true median and (b) the smaller of 2 observations will exceed the median.

2. Using the frequency function for the smallest and largest observations in a sample of size n, derive the frequency function for the smallest observation.

3. In an elementary school 17 pairs of first grade children were formed on the basis of similarity of intelligence and background. One child of each pair was taught to read by method I and the other child by method II. After a period of training, the children were given a reading test with the following results.

Method I	65	68	70	63	64	62	73	75	72	78	64	73	79	80	67	74	82
Method II	63	68	68	60	65	60	72	75	73	70	66	70	77	78	63	74	78

Using the sign test and ignoring ties, test to see whether the methods are equally effective.

4. Use the sign test to work problem 16, Chapter 11.

5. Work problem 3 by means of the rank sum test. Why is the rank sum test not strictly applicable to a problem such as this?

6. Compare the results in problems 3 and 5 with those obtained by applying the t test to the differences of paired values.

7. Take random samples of size 10 each from the two horizontal distributions given by $f_1(x) = 1, 0 < x < 1$ and $f_2(x) = 2, 0 < x < \frac{1}{2}$ by choosing the proper sets of numbers from the table of random numbers. Test the hypothesis $H_0 : f_1(x) = f_2(x)$ by (a) pairing values and applying the sign test (b) applying the rank sum test.

8. The following 2 sets of observed values were obtained from sampling 2 populations. Using the rank sum test, test the hypothesis that the 2 populations possess the same frequency function.

I	25	30	28	34	24	25	13	32	24	30	31	35		
II	44	34	22	8	47	31	40	30	32	35	18	21	35	29	22

9. Test a set of 200 random digits for randomness by means of runs.

10. A row of snapdragon plants was inspected for rust. The sequence of healthy and infected plants was as follows: $H H H H I H I H I I I H I I I H H H H H$ $H H I I I I$. Use total runs to test for randomness of the infection.

11. Toss a coin 50 times, recording the sequence of heads and tails, and then test for randomness by means of total runs.

12. Write down a sequence of a's and b's totaling 50 letters that you feel is random. Test the randomness by total runs.

13. Given the sequence of numbers 1, 1, 3, 3, 1, 1, 3, 3, 1, 1, 3, 3, 1, 1, 3, 3, 1, 1, 3, 3, would you expect total runs to show up the lack of randomness here?

14. The following data give the number of defective bricks for samples of 100 each from day to day. Test for homogeneity of quality from day to day by using

total runs above and below the median 12.5. Read down consecutive columns to obtain consecutive counts.

11	12	8	13	16	11	8	12
12	10	14	16	21	9	8	18
10	8	14	13	9	12	14	21
9	7	13	16	13	12	16	18
19	13	13	15	11	8	9	17

15. Alternate the two sets of values obtained in problem 7 to obtain a sequence of 20 values. Test for randomness by means of (a) runs (b) serial correlation.

16. Obtain the annual rainfall records for your community for the last 50 years and apply the 2 tests for randomness to the data.

17. Name 2 lags that would be particularly effective in using serial correlation to detect the lack of randomness in the sequence given in problem 13.

18. Test the following set of measurements for a trend by means of serial correlation, applying the formulas to the measurements after they have been reduced by the subtraction of 28. The measurements are 28, 32, 37, 25, 31, 29, 33, 28, 27, 28, 23, 22, 18, 17.

19. Prove that the serial correlation test is unaffected by subtracting the same constant from each observed value.

20. Prove that the serial correlation test is unaffected by multiplying each observed value by the same constant.

21. Work problem 7, Chapter 10, by means of the Kolmogorov-Smirnov test.

22. Test the goodness of fit in problem 44, Chapter 5, by means of the Kolmogorov-Smirnov test.

23. Find an 80 per cent confidence band for the distribution function corresponding to the y values of Table 1 in 13.1.

24. Find a 95 per cent confidence band for the distribution function corresponding to the data of problem 7, Chapter 10.

CHAPTER 14

Other Methods

The hypothesis testing methods that have been presented thus far possess two restrictive characteristics. They are based on the assumption that a sample of fixed size is to be taken and that a choice is to be made in favor of one of two possible decisions.

If samples can be taken one at a time and the information from them accumulated, one would expect to be in a better position to make decisions than if no attempt were made to look at the data until a sample of fixed size had been taken. There are methods available, known as *sequential methods*, that operate on this accumulation-of-information basis and that require considerably less sampling on the average than the fixed-size sample methods.

The restriction that only two choices for decision making are possible can be bothersome in a problem in which there are several natural choices available. Thus, in the study of blood types there are four natural categories, and it would be unrealistic to reduce them to two because one's statistical techniques were designed for only two possibilities. There are methods, known as *multiple decision methods*, for treating such more general problems.

The material in this chapter is devoted principally to explaining some of the basic but elementary ideas in these two new decision-making methods.

14.1 Sequential Analysis

Sequential methods possess striking advantages for testing hypotheses; therefore they are discussed here from that point of view.

In testing a hypothesis, the sequential method gives a rule of procedure for making one of the following three decisions at each stage of the experiment: (1) accept the hypothesis, (2) reject the hypothesis, or (3) continue the experiment by taking an additional observation.

For the purpose of describing a sequential test, consider a single continuous variable x whose frequency function $f(x; \theta)$ depends on the single parameter θ. Although the sequential test about to be described may be applied to either discrete or continuous variables, the description is given for a continuous variable.

Let the hypothesis to be tested be

$$H_0: \theta = \theta_0$$

and let the alternative hypothesis be

$$H_1: \theta = \theta_1$$

Since a simple hypothesis is being tested against a simple alternative, the Neyman-Pearson lemma given in 9.1.3 would suggest using the likelihood ratio

$$\frac{\prod\limits_{i=1}^{n} f(x_i; \theta_1)}{\prod\limits_{i=1}^{n} f(x_i; \theta_0)}$$

as a basis for deciding between H_0 and H_1. For a fixed-size sample of size n, the Neyman-Pearson method chooses as critical region those sample points for which this likelihood ratio is larger than a certain constant k. The region in which this ratio is smaller than k would then constitute the region for accepting H_0. A sequential test can be constructed by extending this fixed-size sample method slightly to include a region for continuing sampling.

In discussing sequential methods, it is convenient to use the letter m in place of n to denote the size of a sample in order to distinguish it from the fixed n situation. The letter n is reserved for the size sample that is required to reach a final decision. As a consequence, n is a random variable in sequential methods. Another convenient symbol is p_{im} to denote the likelihood function when H_i is true and a sample of size m is taken. Now consider the likelihood ratio

$$(1) \qquad \frac{p_{1m}}{p_{0m}} = \frac{\prod\limits_{i=1}^{m} f(x_i; \theta_1)}{\prod\limits_{i=1}^{m} f(x_i; \theta_0)}, \quad (m = 1, 2, \cdots)$$

By analogy with the fixed-size sample test, one would choose as the region for accepting H_0 those sample points for which (1) is small and as the region for accepting H_1 those sample points for which (1) is large. The new idea in sequential testing is to use part of the sample space for a third region such that if the sample point falls in this region the decision to accept H_0 or H_1 will be postponed. From the preceding remarks, this postponement region should consist of those points for which (1) is neither small nor large. Thus in the sequential test being described two numbers c_1 and c_2 are chosen and successive observations are taken, $m = 1, 2, \cdots$ as long as

$$c_1 < \frac{p_{1m}}{p_{0m}} < c_2$$

However, whenever $p_{1m}/p_{0m} \leq c_1$, sampling ceases and the decision is made to accept H_0, and, whenever $p_{1m}/p_{0m} \geq c_2$, sampling ceases and the decision is made to accept H_1.

Now it can be shown that if c_1 and c_2 are chosen properly this sequential test will have prescribed values, α and β, for the two types of error. The exact values of c_1 and c_2 are not available; however, excellent approximations are given by choosing

(2) $$c_1 = \frac{\beta}{1 - \alpha} \quad \text{and} \quad c_2 = \frac{1 - \beta}{\alpha}$$

A justification for these approximations is given in 14.1.1. With these choices for c_1 and c_2, the test is now complete. The name given to this test and the technique for carrying it out may be expressed as follows.

(3)   SEQUENTIAL PROBABILITY RATIO TEST: *To test the hypothesis $H_0: \theta = \theta_0$ against the alternative $H_1: \theta = \theta_1$, calculate the likelihood ratio p_{1m}/p_{0m} and proceed as follows:*

   (i) if $\dfrac{p_{1m}}{p_{0m}} \leq \dfrac{\beta}{1 - \alpha}$, accept H_0

   (ii) if $\dfrac{p_{1m}}{p_{0m}} \geq \dfrac{1 - \beta}{\alpha}$, accept H_1

   (iii) if $\dfrac{\beta}{1 - \alpha} < \dfrac{p_{1m}}{p_{0m}} < \dfrac{1 - \beta}{\alpha}$, take an additional observation

One of the striking features of this test is that it is not necessary to derive the frequency function of a statistic such as t or F in order to carry out the test. Furthermore, one can decide in advance what size type I and type II errors to tolerate rather than fix the type I error and then be forced to calculate the type II error as in fixed-size sample tests. On the other hand, one never knows how large a sample will be required to arrive at a decision because n, the size sample needed, is now a random variable. A general formula exists for calculating the mean value of n, so that one can determine in advance how large n is likely to be.

As an illustration of how a sequential test is constructed, consider the problem of determining whether the mean of a normal variable with variance 1 has the mean θ_0 or the mean θ_1. Here

$$f(x; \theta) = \frac{e^{-\frac{1}{2}(x-\theta)^2}}{\sqrt{2\pi}}$$

hence (1) becomes

$$\frac{p_{1m}}{p_{0m}} = \frac{\prod_{i=1}^{m} e^{-\frac{1}{2}(x_i-\theta_1)^2}}{\prod_{i=1}^{m} e^{-\frac{1}{2}(x_i-\theta_0)^2}} = \frac{e^{-\frac{1}{2}\sum_{i=1}^{m}(x_i-\theta_1)^2}}{e^{-\frac{1}{2}\sum_{i=1}^{m}(x_i-\theta_0)^2}}$$

$$= e^{(\theta_1-\theta_0)\sum_{i=1}^{m} x_i + \frac{m}{2}(\theta_0{}^2-\theta_1{}^2)}$$

Now (iii) of (3) is equivalent to

$$\log \frac{\beta}{1-\alpha} < \log \frac{p_{1m}}{p_{0m}} < \log \frac{1-\beta}{\alpha}$$

For this problem, these inequalities become

$$\log \frac{\beta}{1-\alpha} + \frac{m}{2}(\theta_1{}^2 - \theta_0{}^2) < (\theta_1 - \theta_0)\sum_{i=1}^{m} x_i$$

$$< \log \frac{1-\beta}{\alpha} + \frac{m}{2}(\theta_1{}^2 - \theta_0{}^2)$$

If $\theta_1 > \theta_0$, this is equivalent to

(4) $$\frac{1}{\theta_1 - \theta_0}\log\frac{\beta}{1-\alpha} + \frac{m}{2}(\theta_0 + \theta_1) < \sum_{i=1}^{m} x_i$$

$$< \frac{1}{\theta_1 - \theta_0}\log\frac{1-\beta}{\alpha} + \frac{m}{2}(\theta_0 + \theta_1)$$

For $\theta_1 < \theta_0$, these inequalities would be reversed.

As a numerical illustration, suppose that $\alpha = .05$, $\beta = .10$, $\theta_0 = 9.5$, and $\theta_1 = 10$. Then (4) becomes

$$-4.50 + 9.75m < \sum_{i=1}^{m} x_i < 5.78 + 9.75m$$

Following (3), the test now proceeds as follows:

(i) if $\sum_{i=1}^{m} x_i \leq -4.50 + 9.75m$, accept $\theta = 9.5$

(ii) if $\sum_{i=1}^{m} x_i \geq 5.78 + 9.75m$, accept $\theta = 10$

(iii) if neither inequality is satisfied, take another observation

TABLE 1

$5.78 + 9.75m$	15.53	25.28	35.03	44.78	54.53	64.28	74.03	83.78	93.53	103.28	113.03	122.78
Σx_i	10.47	20.98	30.76	42.93	52.88	64.10	73.41	83.16	91.72	101.24	112.89	123.24
$-4.50 + 9.75m$	5.25	15.00	24.75	34.50	44.25	52.00	61.75	71.50	81.25	91.00	100.75	110.50

An experiment was performed by taking successive samples from a normal population with mean $\theta = 10$ and variance 1 until a decision was reached. The decision to accept H_1, which is the correct decision here, occurred at the twelfth observation. The values of Σx_i obtained in the experiment, together with the values of the decision boundaries, are displayed in Table 1.

As a second illustration, consider the problem of determining whether $p = p_0$ or $p = p_1$ for a binomial distribution. If one chooses $x = 1$ for success and $x = 0$ for failure, $f(x; \theta)$ will be given by $f(1; p) = p$ and $f(0; p) = q$. Now, suppose that the first m trials of the event produced d_m successes. Then the likelihood function $\prod_{i=1}^{m} f(x_i; \theta)$ will consist of the product of p's and q's, a p occurring as a factor whenever a success occurred and a q otherwise. The likelihood ratio (1) then becomes

$$\frac{p_{1m}}{p_{0m}} = \frac{p_1{}^{d_m} q_1{}^{m-d_m}}{p_0{}^{d_m} q_0{}^{m-d_m}}$$

If this expression is substituted in (3) and the desired numerical values are assigned to p_0, p_1, α, and β, the test procedure will be determined.

As a numerical illustration, let $p_0 = .5$, $p_1 = .7$, $\alpha = .10$, and $\beta = .20$. These values may be thought of as those that might be used to test the honesty of a coin when that coin is suspected of giving too many heads. Here $\beta/(1 - \alpha) = \frac{2}{9}$, $(1 - \beta)/\alpha = 8$, and

$$\frac{p_{1m}}{p_{0m}} = \frac{(.7)^{d_m}(.3)^{m-d_m}}{(.5)^{d_m}(.5)^{m-d_m}} = \left(\frac{3}{5}\right)^m \left(\frac{7}{3}\right)^{d_m}$$

The first inequality in (3),

$$\left(\frac{3}{5}\right)^m \left(\frac{7}{3}\right)^{d_m} \le \frac{2}{9}$$

can be written more conveniently in the form

$$d_m \le \frac{\log \frac{2}{9}}{\log \frac{7}{3}} + m \frac{\log \frac{5}{3}}{\log \frac{7}{3}}$$

In a similar manner the second inequality becomes

$$d_m \ge \frac{\log 8}{\log \frac{7}{3}} + m \frac{\log \frac{5}{3}}{\log \frac{7}{3}}$$

TABLE 2

m	1	2	3	4	5	6	7	8	9	10	11	12	13	14	15
x_m	0	0	1	1	1	0	1	1	0	1	0	0	1	0	0
d_m	0	0	1	2	3	3	4	5	5	6	6	6	7	7	7

If these logarithms are evaluated, the test will proceed as follows:

  (i) if $d_m \leq -1.78 + .603m$, accept $p = .5$

  (ii) if $d_m \geq 2.45 + .603m$, accept $p = .7$

  (iii) if neither inequality is satisfied, take another trial

Tosses of a coin gave the results shown in Table 2. For the purpose of determining when one of the inequalities is satisfied, it is convenient to represent these inequalities and the results of the successive trials graphically. If m and d_m are treated as the coordinates of a point, the straight lines $d_m = -1.78 + .603m$ and $d_m = 2.45 + .603m$ will serve to divide the m, d_m plane into three regions corresponding to the three possible decisions at each trial. The graph corresponding to this problem is given in Fig. 1. From this graph it will be observed that the experiment terminated after 15 trials because inequality (i) was then satisfied. In

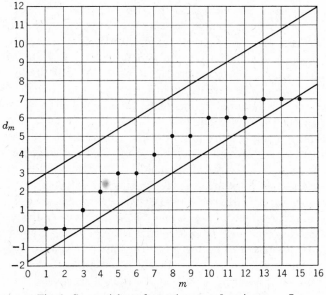

Fig. 1. Sequential test for testing $p = .5$ against $p = .7$.

accepting the hypothesis that $p = .5$, the experimenter does so in preference to accepting the hypothesis that $p = .7$.

As stated earlier, sequential methods often reduce considerably the size sample needed to arrive at a reliable decision in testing hypotheses. For example, in the preceding illustration it is not difficult to show that a fixed-size sample of approximately 26 will suffice to test $H_0:p = .5$ against $H_1:p = .7$ with $\alpha = .10$ and yield a type II error of $\beta = .20$. However, in the theory of sequential analysis it can be shown that the average size sample needed to arrive at a decision in this illustration with $\alpha = .10$ and $\beta = .20$ is approximately 13. The experimental result of 15 is in good agreement with expectation. For problems of this type it can be shown that one saves 40 to 50 per cent in sampling by using sequential methods. This follows from a formula in 14.1.1 which gives a good approximation to the value of $E[n]$.

The reason for the advantage of the sequential approach over the fixed-size-sample approach lies in the ability of the sequential method to reach an early decision for samples that are extremely favorable to either H_0 or H_1. Thus, if a good coin were tossed a number of times and gave rise to a fairly high percentage of tails, it would be clear rather early that $p = .5$ should be accepted in preference to $p = .7$. Conversely, if the coin were biased toward heads and if a high percentage of heads occurred in the early stages one would accept $p = .7$ without continuing the experiment further.

The savings that can be realized by the sequential approach may be even greater than theory would indicate because in real-life experiments the actual value of p, for example, might heavily favor either H_0 or H_1. Thus in the preceding illustration, if it were true that $p = .4$, the sequential test would quickly accept H_0 in preference to H_1. This ability to arrive at an early decision can be very useful in such fields as sampling inspection, where it is not uncommon for lots to be very bad when they are bad or very good when they are good.

The sequential probability ratio test given by (3) possesses the disadvantage that, strictly speaking, it applies only to testing a simple hypothesis $\theta = \theta_0$ against a simple alternative $\theta = \theta_1$. This disadvantage can often be circumvented by properly rephrasing the problem to be solved. For example, suppose that a consumer wishes to determine whether a producer's fraction defective is actually p_0 as claimed by the producer. He may fear that the true fraction defective is larger than p_0; consequently he would be interested in testing $p = p_0$ against $p > p_0$. But he may be willing to state a value of $p > p_0$, say $p = p_1$, such that it would begin to become a serious matter if p exceeded p_1; whereas, if p were less than p_1, even though $p > p_0$, no serious harm would result. By this device of deciding on an upper limit p_1 for p, the problem can be reduced to the ordinary sequential test of testing $H_0:p = p_0$ against $H_1:p = p_1$. Similar devices can often be used to arrive at satisfactory tests for composite hypotheses as well.

14.1.1 Approximations for c_1, c_2, and $E[n]$

For each value of $m = 1, 2, 3, \cdots$, let the sample space be divided into the three regions R_{0m}, R_{1m}, and R_{cm} corresponding to the three possible decisions of accepting H_0, accepting H_1, or continuing to sample, respectively. These regions are in the m-dimensional space determined by the variables $x_1, x_2, \cdots, x_m$. When $m = n$, the sample point must have fallen in R_{cm} for all values of $m < n$ because n denotes the sample size for which the decision to accept H_0 or H_1 is first made. In terms of this notation, consider the problem of calculating the value of $1 - \beta$. In this calculation the sample point is denoted by x, regardless of the dimension of the sample space. Thus

$$1 - \beta = P\{\text{accept } H_1 \mid H_1\} = \sum_{n=1}^{\infty} P\{x \in R_{1n} \mid H_1\}$$

$$= \sum_{n=1}^{\infty} \int_{R_{1n}} \cdots \int p_{1n} \, dx_1 \cdots dx_n$$

The symbol $P\{x \in R_{1n} \mid H_1\}$ denotes the probability that the sample point x will fall in the region R_{1n}, given that H_1 holds. But the sample point x can be in R_{1n} only if it satisfies the inequality $p_{1n}/p_{0n} \geq c_2$; consequently this inequality holds for all points in R_{1n}. As a result,

$$1 - \beta \geq \sum_{n=1}^{\infty} \int_{R_{1n}} \cdots \int c_2 p_{0n} \, dx_1 \cdots dx_n$$

$$= c_2 \sum_{n=1}^{\infty} \int_{R_{1n}} \cdots \int p_{0n} \, dx_1 \cdots dx_n$$

$$= c_2 \sum_{n=1}^{\infty} P\{x \in R_{1n} \mid H_0\}$$

$$= c_2 P\{\text{accept } H_1 \mid H_0\} = c_2 \alpha$$

This shows that the number c_2 satisfies the inequality

(5)
$$c_2 \leq \frac{1 - \beta}{\alpha}$$

The same type of calculations when applied to finding the value of β will lead to the inequality

(6)
$$c_1 \geq \frac{\beta}{1 - \alpha}$$

It is illuminating to look at these inequalities from a geometrical point of view. For this purpose the two lines in the α,β plane whose equations are

(7) $c_2\alpha = 1 - \beta$ and $c_1(1 - \alpha) = \beta$

have been graphed in Fig. 2 for a typical choice of c_1 and c_2. These are merely the relations given by the formulas in (2). The shaded area represents all pairs of α,β that satisfy the inequalities (5) and (6).

Suppose α and β are temporarily chosen equal to .10 and that c_1 and c_2 are chosen to be the corresponding values given by (2). Then

$$c_1 = \tfrac{1}{9} \quad \text{and} \quad c_2 = 9$$

The values of c_1 and $1/c_2$ shown in Fig. 2 are somewhat larger than these values; consequently the shaded region for these choices would be smaller and more nearly a square region than that shown in Fig. 2. The point of intersection of the two lines would, of course, be given by $\alpha = .10$ and $\beta = .10$. Since the shaded region is very nearly square, it follows that when c_1 and c_2 are chosen in this manner, the actual value of α (and similarly of β) can possibly exceed .10 by only a small amount. Furthermore, if one of them should exceed .10, then the shaded area shows that the other would need to be less than .10. The greater the excess over .10 for one of them, the smaller in value the other must be.

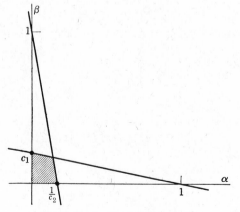

Fig. 2. Inequality region for α, β.

In view of the preceding discussion, if c_1 and c_2 are chosen to be the values given by (2), the true values of α and β will probably differ very little from those that were selected to be used in (2), particularly when c_1 and $1/c_2$ are very small. As a consequence, if a sequential test is constructed with values of c_1 and c_2 given by (2), it will for all practical purposes possess sizes of the two types of error that do not exceed the selected values of α and β. Thus one can decide in advance what protection against error is desirable and then by choosing c_1 and c_2 as in (2) be assured that at least this much protection will be realized in carrying out the test.

The derivation of the formula alluded to earlier for approximating the value of $E[n]$ is quite lengthy; consequently, only the result of the derivation is given here. In this connection, let $P(\theta)$ denote the probability of rejecting H_0 if θ is the true parameter value. Thus $P(\theta_0)$ is equal to α and $1 - P(\theta_1)$ is equal to β when testing $H_0 : \theta = \theta_0$ against $H_1 : \theta = \theta_1$. Further, let $z = \log f(x; \theta_1) - \log f(x; \theta_0)$. Then the desired formula may be expressed as follows:

$$(8) \qquad E[n] \doteq \frac{P(\theta) \log c_2 + [1 - P(\theta)] \log c_1}{E[z]}$$

In applying this formula, one uses the approximations for c_1 and c_2 given in (2).

For the purpose of illustrating how to use this formula, consider the binomial distribution problem that was discussed in the preceding section. For that problem,

$$f(x; \theta) = \begin{cases} p, & \text{if } x = 1 \\ q, & \text{if } x = 0 \end{cases}$$

Since the value of $E[n]$ depends on what value is assigned to θ, it is necessary to specify the value of p. The hypothesis H_0 was actually true here; consequently in making comparisons the value of $E_0[n]$ will be used. When H_0 is true

$$E_0[z] = E_0\left[\log \frac{f(x; \theta_1)}{f(x; \theta_0)}\right]$$

$$= q_0 \log \frac{q_1}{q_0} + p_0 \log \frac{p_1}{p_0}$$

In view of the numerical values $p_0 = .5$, $p_1 = .7$, $\alpha = .10$, and $\beta = .20$ and the fact that $P(\theta_0) = \alpha$, it follows from (8) and calculations that

$$E_0[n] \doteq \frac{.10 \log 8 + .90 \log \frac{2}{9}}{.5 \log \frac{3}{5} + .5 \log \frac{7}{5}} \doteq 13$$

This is the value that was claimed for $E[n]$ in the earlier illustration. Similar calculations will show that if H_1 is true then $E_1[n] \doteq 17$.

14.2 Multiple Classification Techniques

In all the problems of testing hypotheses that have been considered thus far it was necessary either to accept or reject some hypothesis. This is true for sequential methods also, even though a final decision may be postponed for some time. There are many problems, however, that cannot be treated in this simple manner because they involve more than just two possible decisions. For example, a botanist may wish to classify a group of plants belonging to three different varieties into their proper variety. This is a three-decision problem and it is unnatural to attempt to solve it, say, by successive two-decision-problem methods. In this section a multiple-decision technique for such classification problems is presented as an introduction to general multiple decision methods.

For simplicity of exposition the following discussion is limited to the case in which there are three possible categories of classification; however, the method presented can obviously be extended to any number of categories.

Let $x_1, x_2, \cdots, x_k$ denote k random variables corresponding to k different measurements that are to be taken on an individual of some population. Thus, for a population of flowers, the x's might represent such characteristics as petal length, petal width, and stamen length. Let the population to be sampled consist of the three subpopulations π_1, π_2, and π_3 and let these subpopulations constitute the proportions $p_1, p_2,$ and p_3 of this population.

Since an individual will be determined by his values of $x_1, x_2, \cdots, x_k$, the problem of classification is the problem of dividing the k-dimensional sample space into three parts, say, S_1, S_2, and S_3, corresponding to the three subpopulations, and agreeing to classify an individual as belonging to subpopulation π_i if his sample point lies in S_i. In this connection, it seems reasonable to choose as a criterion of optimality a division of the sample space that will maximize the probability of classifying an individual correctly.

From the theory in 9.1.3 on how best tests are constructed and from the theory of sequential analysis, one would guess that the ratios of likelihood functions will undoubtedly play a leading role in the determination of a best set of S's. For example, a sample point at which the probability density under π_1 is considerably larger than under either π_2 or π_3 should certainly be placed in the region S_1. The feature that makes this problem somewhat different from earlier problems, in addition to that of having more possibilities for decisions, is the introduction of the proportions p_1, p_2, and p_3 for the relative frequency of occurrence of samples from the various subpopulations. If p_1, for example, were close to zero, then for all practical purposes the problem would reduce to a two-decision problem and earlier methods could be used to solve it. Thus it is clear that the p's must also enter in the determination of a best set of S's. As in the theory of best tests, a theorem will be stated, and then proved, that yields the desired optimum solution. In this theorem the letter x is used to denote the vector variable $x = (x_1, x_2, \cdots, x_k)$ and $f_i(x)$ will denote the frequency function of the variables $x_1, x_2, \cdots, x_k$ in the subpopulation π_i $(i = 1, 2, 3)$.

THEOREM: *The regions R_i $(i = 1, 2, 3)$ into which a k-dimensional sample space should be divided to maximize the probability of correctly classifying an individual selected at random from the population composed of the subpopulations $\pi_i (i = 1, 2, 3)$, which constitute ·the proportions p_i $(i = 1, 2, 3)$ of that population and which possess the frequency functions $f_i(x)$ $(i = 1, 2, 3)$, are determined by the points x that satisfy the inequalities*

$$R_i: p_i f_i(x) \geq p_j f_j(x), \quad \text{for all } j \neq i$$

Proof: Let S_1, S_2, S_3 be any other division of the sample space. Now any one of these regions S_i $(i = 1, 2, 3)$ can be divided into three subregions S_{i1}, S_{i2}, and S_{i3} such that S_{ij} $(j = 1, 2, 3)$ contains only points found in R_j. Thus S_{ij} contains all the points common to the two regions S_i and R_j. This subdivision of S_i can be expressed by means of the formula

(9) $$S_i = S_{i1} + S_{i2} + S_{i3}, \quad (i = 1, 2, 3)$$

In terms of this notation, it is also true that

(10) $$R_j = S_{1j} + S_{2j} + S_{3j}, \quad (j = 1, 2, 3)$$

This formula follows from the fact that every point in R_j must belong to one of the three regions S_1, S_2, S_3.

Now the probability of correctly classifying an individual selected at random from the population when using the division of the sample space determined by the S's is given by

$$P_S = \sum_{i=1}^{3} p_i P\{x \in S_i \mid \pi_i\}$$
$$= \sum_{i=1}^{3} p_i \int_{S_i} f_i(x)\, dx$$

The preceding integrals are k-dimensional multiple integrals with the arguments $x_1, x_2, \cdots, x_k$; however, they are written symbolically as single integrals with respect to x. This is the same convenient notational device that was used in 9.1.3. Now, by means of formula (9), P_S can be written in the form

$$(11) \quad P_S = \sum_{i=1}^{3} \left[\int_{S_{i1}} p_i \, f_i(x) \, dx + \int_{S_{i2}} p_i \, f_i(x) \, dx + \int_{S_{i3}} p_i \, f_i(x) \, dx \right]$$

Since all the points lying in S_{i1} are in R_1, it follows from the definition of R_1, given in the theorem, that they must satisfy the inequality

$$(12) \quad p_1 \, f_1(x) \geq p_j \, f_j(x), \quad (j = 2, 3)$$

Similarly, all points in S_{i2} must satisfy

$$(13) \quad p_2 \, f_2(x) \geq p_j \, f_j(x), \quad (j = 1, 3)$$

and all points in S_{i3} must satisfy

$$(14) \quad p_3 \, f_3(x) \geq p_j \, f_j(x), \quad (j = 1, 2)$$

In view of (12), if $p_i \, f_i(x)$ is replaced by $p_1 \, f_1(x)$ in the first of the three integrals in (11), that integral will become at least as large as it was before, for all three values of i. For $i = 1$ there is, of course, no change; however, for $i = 2$ and $i = 3$ the value of the integral will be increased unless inequality (12) is an equality for the points of S_{i1}. Similarly, because of (13), if $p_i \, f_i(x)$ is replaced by $p_2 \, f_2(x)$ in the second of the three integrals in (11), that integral will become at least as large as before. Finally, the same conclusion will hold for the third integral if $p_i \, f_i(x)$ is replaced by $p_3 \, f_3(x)$. Thus, it follows that

$$(15) \quad P_S \leq \sum_{i=1}^{3} \left[\int_{S_{i1}} p_1 \, f_1(x) \, dx + \int_{S_{i2}} p_2 \, f_2(x) \, dx + \int_{S_{i3}} p_3 \, f_3(x) \, dx \right]$$

But from (10) it follows that $S_{11} + S_{21} + S_{31} = R_1$ and therefore that the sum with respect to i of the first integral in (15) must yield the integral of $p_1 \, f_1(x)$ over the region R_1. Similar reasoning may be applied to the other two sums of integrals to yield the result

$$(16) \quad P_S \leq \int_{R_1} p_1 \, f_1(x) \, dx + \int_{R_2} p_2 \, f_2(x) \, dx + \int_{R_3} p_3 \, f_3(x) \, dx$$

If the p's are factored out and the right side is expressed in probability language, (16) will yield the desired result, namely

$$P_S \leq \sum_{i=1}^{3} p_i P\{x \in R_i \mid \pi_i\} = P_R$$

Since the set of regions S_1, S_2, S_3 was any set other than R_1, R_2, R_3 defined in the theorem, this inequality proves that R_1, R_2, R_3 is an optimum set in the sense of maximizing the probability of a correct classification.

Points that satisfy the equality part of the inequalities defining the regions R_1, R_2, R_3 may be placed in any one of the regions for which the equality holds. In applications the boundaries of the regions are usually surfaces ($k \geq 3$) so that there is seldom any problem on this score.

The preceding method of proof can obviously be applied to the case in which there are more than three categories of classification.

The difficulty in applying the preceding theorem arises from the fact that one seldom knows the values of the p's and even the values of the parameters determining the density functions. Then it is necessary to estimate such parameters by means of a random sample from the total population and in the process be able to classify each individual into its proper subpopulation. The resulting decision regions will be estimates of the optimum decision regions given by the theorem.

As an illustration of how the theorem is applied when no estimation is required, consider the following information. A population consists of three subpopulations in the proportions $\frac{1}{4}$, $\frac{1}{4}$, and $\frac{1}{2}$. Each subpopulation is a two-variable normal population with independently distributed variables possessing unit variances and means $(-1, 0)$, $(0, 1)$, and $(1, 0)$, respectively.

In the notation of the theorem $p_1 = \frac{1}{4}$, $p_2 = \frac{1}{4}$, $p_3 = \frac{1}{2}$, and

$$f_1(x) = \frac{e^{-\frac{1}{2}[(x_1+1)^2 + x_2^2]}}{2\pi}$$

$$f_2(x) = \frac{e^{-\frac{1}{2}[x_1^2 + (x_2-1)^2]}}{2\pi}$$

$$f_3(x) = \frac{e^{-\frac{1}{2}[(x_1-1)^2 + x_2^2]}}{2\pi}$$

The region R_1 is therefore the region determined by the two inequalities

$$\frac{1}{4} \frac{e^{-\frac{1}{2}[(x_1+1)^2 + x_2^2]}}{2\pi} \geq \frac{1}{4} \frac{e^{-\frac{1}{2}[x_1^2 + (x_2-1)^2]}}{2\pi}$$

and

$$\frac{1}{4} \frac{e^{-\frac{1}{2}[(x_1+1)^2 + x_2^2]}}{2\pi} \geq \frac{1}{2} \frac{e^{-\frac{1}{2}[(x_1-1)^2 + x_2^2]}}{2\pi}$$

These inequalities are easily shown to reduce to the inequalities

$$x_1 + x_2 \leq 0$$

and

$$x_1 \leq -\tfrac{1}{2} \log_e 2$$

Similar calculations will show that R_2 is determined by the inequalities

$$x_1 + x_2 \geq 0$$

and

$$x_2 - x_1 \geq \log_e 2$$

The region R_3 is clearly the remaining part of the x_1, x_2 plane not occupied by R_1 and R_2; however, one can calculate it directly from definition and show that it is determined by the inequalities

$$x_1 \geq -\tfrac{1}{2} \log_e 2$$

and

$$x_2 - x_1 \leq \log_e 2$$

In order to determine the regions R_1, R_2, and R_3, it suffices to graph the lines whose equations are

$$l_1: x_1 + x_2 = 0$$
$$l_2: x_1 = -\tfrac{1}{2} \log_e 2$$
$$l_3: x_2 - x_1 = \log_e 2$$

The graphs of these lines are shown in Fig. 3. From the inequalities defining R_1, R_2, and R_3 it is clear that R_1 is the region below line l_1 and to the left of line l_2, that R_2 is the region above l_1 and above l_3, and that R_3 is the remaining part of the x_1, x_2 plane. These regions are shown more clearly in Fig. 4.

If the p's had all been equal, log 2 would have been replaced by log $1 = 0$ in the preceding inequalities and then the regions would have been

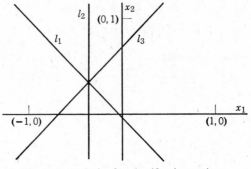

Fig. 3. Boundaries for classification regions.

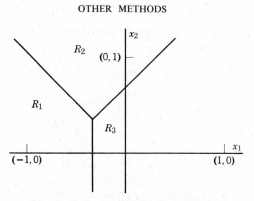

Fig. 4. Optimum classification regions.

those obtained by shifting the three-ray boundary configuration of Fig. 4 parallel to itself until the vertex was at the origin. This illustrates the effect the p's have on the classification regions.

14.3 Bayes Techniques

A somewhat different approach to decision making can be formulated in terms of economic losses or gains rather than in terms of the probability of making the correct decision. It may well be, for example, that making one of two possible incorrect decisions is not nearly so serious economically as making the other incorrect decision. In such situations it would be desirable to weight the relative importance of the various errors that can be made. Decision-making procedures based on such notions can be constructed that are capable of treating both estimation and hypothesis testing problems. One such procedure is discussed here from the estimation point of view only.

In constructing decision-making procedures of the foregoing type, it is necessary to introduce the concept of a frequency function of the parameter that is being estimated or tested. This concept essentially distinguishes Bayesian methods from the more traditional ones.

Let x be a continuous random variable with frequency function $f(x; \theta)$ and let $t = t(x_1, x_2, \cdots, x_n)$ be any estimate of θ based on a random sample of size n. Furthermore, let $W(t, \theta)$ be a weight function that measures the economic loss in claiming (estimating) that the true value of the parameter is t when it is actually θ. For example, one might choose W as the function $W(t, \theta) = c(t - \theta)^2$ if large errors of estimation are very serious or as the function $W(t, \theta) = c |t - \theta|$ if they are not quite so serious.

As a criterion for determining whether $t = t(x_1, x_2, \cdots, x_n)$ is a good estimate, one can use the expected value of the weight function. Thus one considers the quantity

$$(17) \quad r(t, \theta) = E[W(t, \theta)] = \int \cdots \int W(t, \theta) \prod_{i=1}^{n} f(x_i; \theta) \, dx_1 \cdots dx_n$$

The weight function $W(t, \theta)$ is usually called the *loss function* and the quantity $r(t, \theta)$ is called the *risk function*. An estimate that makes the risk function small in some sense would be considered a desirable estimate. The difficulty with (17) as a basis for judgment is that the result of the integration is usually a function of θ, and an estimate t seldom minimizes (17) for all possible values of θ. It is therefore necessary to introduce some further criteria before (17) can be used effectively to determine whether an estimate is a good one.

One approach to a solution is to study the behavior of the risk function and use some property of it as a basis for judgment. Since, as indicated in the preceding paragraph, it is unlikely that the graph of $r(t, \theta)$ for one estimate will lie below the graphs of all other estimates, it is customary to look only at the maximum value on the graph and then hunt for an estimate t that has the smallest such maximum value. If there exists an estimate with this property, it is called the *minimax* estimate. Figure 5 illustrates this criterion as it applies to only two possible estimates. For this situation, estimate t_2 is the minimax estimate.

A second approach to a solution is to introduce a frequency function for the parameter θ and then calculate the expected value of $r(t, \theta)$ with respect to this frequency function. Since the result will be a number rather than a function of θ, the comparison of estimates becomes a simple matter. The principal difficulty with this approach is that one seldom has any precise knowledge of what frequency function for θ is realistic or whether it is realistic to introduce such a function at all. There are problems, however, for which one can postulate a realistic distribution. For example, familiarity with manufacturing processes suggests that the assumption of a normal distribution for p, the probability of getting a

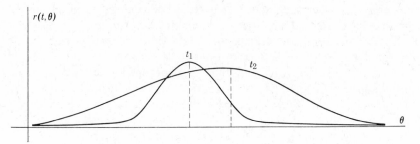

Fig. 5. Graphs of expected losses for two estimates.

head in tossing a randomly selected penny, is a reasonable one. One would probably choose the mean to be $\frac{1}{2}$ but would need to perform some experiments on pennies to obtain a variance estimate. If, however, one were interested in estimating the mean brain weight of a certain race of prehistoric people by means of skulls found in an archaeological excavation, it is unnatural to assume that this mean possesses some probability distribution.

For the purpose of developing this approach further, let $\lambda(\theta)$ denote the frequency function that has been selected for the parameter θ. Then the expected value of $r(t, \theta)$ with respect to this frequency function is given by

$$\bar{r}(t, \lambda) = \int r(t, \theta) \, \lambda(\theta) \, d\theta$$

$$= \int \cdots \int W(t, \theta) \prod_{i=1}^{n} f(x_i; \theta) \, \lambda(\theta) \, dx_1 \cdots dx_n \, d\theta$$

This expected value is usually called the *mean risk*. It depends on the estimating function $t(x_1, x_2, \cdots, x_n)$ selected and also on the frequency function $\lambda(\theta)$ chosen. For a given $\lambda(\theta)$, one tries to find an estimating function $t(x_1, x_2, \cdots, x_n)$ that minimizes the mean risk. If such a function exists, it is called the *Bayes solution* to the problem corresponding to the frequency function $\lambda(\theta)$. Different choices for $\lambda(\theta)$ may well give rise to different minimizing estimating functions; therefore one does not speak of a Bayes solution without specifying the function $\lambda(\theta)$.

Bayes methods is a name given to statistical methods that introduce distributions of parameters at some stage of their development. Although a Bayes approach to estimation has been explained here as an alternative to the minimax approach, it can be shown that the Bayes technique is often a useful one for obtaining a minimax solution; consequently, Bayes methods are useful even in situations in which it seems unrealistic to introduce a distribution for a parameter.

When the loss function in estimation is chosen as squared error, there is often a simple technique for determining a Bayes solution. For the present assume that only a single observation x is to be made. Under these assumptions the mean risk reduces to

$$\bar{r}(t, \lambda) = \iint (t - \theta)^2 f(x; \theta) \, \lambda(\theta) \, dx \, d\theta$$

When x and θ are both treated as random variables, $f(x; \theta)$ is the conditional frequency function of x with θ held fixed. Consequently, if $g(x, \theta)$ denotes the joint frequency function of x and θ, it follows that

$$g(x, \theta) = \lambda(\theta) f(x; \theta)$$

But $g(x, \theta)$ can also be written in the form

(18)
$$g(x, \theta) = h(x)\, g(\theta \mid x)$$

where $h(x)$ is the marginal frequency function of x and $g(\theta \mid x)$ is the conditional frequency function of θ with x held fixed. The equivalence of these two ways of expressing $g(x, \theta)$ enables the mean risk to be written as

$$\bar{r}(t, \lambda) = \iint (t - \theta)^2\, h(x)\, g(\theta \mid x)\, dx\, d\theta$$

or, if the order of integration is interchanged, as

$$\bar{r}(t, \lambda) = \int h(x) \left[\int (\theta - t)^2\, g(\theta \mid x)\, d\theta \right] dx$$

Now the inner integral is merely the second moment about the point t of the variable θ, for x fixed. Since the second moment of a variable is a minimum when it is taken about the mean of the variable, it follows that this integral is minimized for each value of x if t is chosen as the mean of the conditional distribution of θ for x fixed. The double integral is therefore also minimized by this choice; consequently

$$t(x) = E(\theta \mid x)$$

yields the desired solution.

The problem of finding a Bayes solution is now seen to reduce to the problem of finding the conditional expected value of the parameter θ when the variable x is held fixed. This solution is based on the assumption that only a single value of x is to be observed. It is considerably more general than this, however, because x may be chosen to be a statistic, such as a maximum likelihood estimate, from which an estimate t is to be constructed, or it may be a vector variable. Thus, in estimating the mean of a normal distribution, x might well represent $\bar{x}$ or the vector variable $x_1, x_2, \cdots, x_n$.

As an illustration of how a Bayes solution is obtained when the loss function is chosen to be the squared error, let

$$f(x; \mu) = \frac{e^{-\frac{1}{2}\left(\frac{x - \mu}{\alpha}\right)^2}}{\sqrt{2\pi}\, \alpha}$$

and

$$\lambda(\mu) = \frac{e^{-\frac{1}{2}\left(\frac{\mu - \mu_0}{\beta}\right)^2}}{\sqrt{2\pi}\, \beta}$$

Then

(19) $$g(x, \mu) = \lambda(\mu) f(x; \mu) = \frac{e^{-\frac{1}{2}\left[\left(\frac{x-\mu}{\alpha}\right)^2 + \left(\frac{\mu-\mu_0}{\beta}\right)^2\right]}}{2\pi\alpha\beta}$$

The marginal frequency function $h(x)$ is obtained by integrating the joint frequency function $g(x, \mu)$ with respect to μ; hence

$$h(x) = \frac{1}{2\pi\alpha\beta} \int_{-\infty}^{\infty} e^{-\frac{1}{2}\left[\left(\frac{\mu-x}{\alpha}\right)^2 + \left(\frac{\mu-\mu_0}{\beta}\right)^2\right]} d\mu$$

This integral can be evaluated by squaring out the two binomials, collecting terms in μ^2 and μ, completing the square in μ, and then recognizing the value of the resulting integral. The result of such manipulations is that

$$h(x) = \frac{e^{-\frac{1}{2}\frac{(x-\mu_0)^2}{\alpha^2+\beta^2}}}{\sqrt{2\pi}\sqrt{\alpha^2 + \beta^2}}$$

From (18) and (19), it then follows that

$$g(\mu \mid x) = \frac{\sqrt{\alpha^2 + \beta^2}}{\sqrt{2\pi}\alpha\beta} e^{-\frac{1}{2}\left[\left(\frac{x-\mu}{\alpha}\right)^2 + \left(\frac{\mu-\mu_0}{\beta}\right)^2 - \frac{(x-\mu_0)^2}{\alpha^2+\beta^2}\right]}$$

But the calculations that produced $h(x)$ show at once that the expression for $g(\mu \mid x)$ must reduce to

$$g(\mu \mid x) = \frac{\sqrt{\alpha^2 + \beta^2}}{\sqrt{2\pi}\alpha\beta} e^{-\frac{1}{2}\frac{\alpha^2+\beta^2}{\alpha^2\beta^2}\left(\mu - \frac{x\beta^2+\mu_0\alpha^2}{\alpha^2+\beta^2}\right)^2}$$

This result demonstrates that the conditional distribution of μ, for x fixed, is normal with the mean

$$E(\mu \mid x) = \frac{x\beta^2 + \mu_0\alpha^2}{\alpha^2 + \beta^2}$$

The Bayes solution for this estimation problem and for this particular choice of frequency function $\lambda(\mu)$ is therefore given by

$$t(x) = \frac{x\beta^2 + \mu_0\alpha^2}{\alpha^2 + \beta^2}$$

It is convenient to write this result in the form

$$t(x) = \frac{x + \mu_0\delta}{1 + \delta}$$

where $\delta = \alpha^2/\beta^2$ is the ratio of the two variances.

Suppose experience has shown that a quality characteristic, such as breaking strength of a manufactured product, is a normal variable and that if μ denotes the mean of this normal variable for a shipment of this product then μ may also be treated as a normal variable, corresponding to successive shipments. Let μ_0 denote the grand mean, that is the mean of the various shipment means, and assume that experience has yielded a grand mean of $\mu_0 = 200$ and a standard deviation of $\beta = 5$ for such shipment means. Now suppose a fresh shipment comes in and the mean μ of this shipment is to be estimated by means of a sample of 25 items selected at random from the shipment. Assume that experience has yielded a standard deviation of 50 for the random variable x that represents the quality characteristic of a single item in a shipment. If x is now chosen as $\bar{x}$ in the preceding theory, the value of α becomes $\alpha = 50/\sqrt{25} = 10$. Calculations with these values yield the estimate

$$t(\bar{x}) = \frac{\bar{x}}{5} + \frac{4}{5}\,200$$

This estimate gives four times as much weight to past experience as to the sample estimate $\bar{x}$. Additional calculations will show that the mean risk for this estimate, that is the value of $\bar{r}(t, \lambda)$, is $\alpha^2\beta^2/(\alpha^2 + \beta^2) = 20$. Similar calculations will show that the mean risk for the estimate $\bar{x}$, which is based on the sample only, is $\alpha^2 = 100$. Thus there is a very large reduction in the mean risk when past experience is incorporated into the design of the estimate.

The difficulty in applying these methods is that there is seldom experience of the kind assumed here. Furthermore, even when there is experience available, that experience often shows that successive shipments, for example, cannot be treated as random samples from a population of shipments. There is often strong correlation over time between the quality of successive shipments of a manufactured product. Thus, although the Bayes approach may yield considerably better results in the sense of mean risk, the results may not be trustworthy.

The traditional method of comparing two estimates is to base the comparison on the mean squared error. This does not require the assumption of a probability distribution for the parameter in question; therefore the comparison can always be made and there is no danger of obtaining estimates of questionable accuracy and precision.

REFERENCES

The mathematical theory behind sequential analysis may be found in A. Wald, *Sequential Analysis*, John Wiley and Sons.

The decision function approach to statistical problems can be found in H. Chernoff and L. E. Moses, *Elementary Decision Theory*, John Wiley and Sons.

EXERCISES

1. Choosing $\alpha = .2$ and $\beta = .2$, test the hypothesis $H_0:p = .5$ against $H_1:p = .4$ sequentially by tossing a coin until a decision is reached. Here p is the probability of getting a head.

2. Choosing $\alpha = .1$ and $\beta = .1$, construct a sequential test for testing $H_0:\sigma = 8$ against $H_1:\sigma = 10$ for a normal variable with 0 mean.

3. Construct a sequential test for testing $H_0:\theta = 3$ against $H_1:\theta = 2$ for the frequency function $f(x; \theta) = \theta e^{-\theta x}$, $x \geq 0$. Choose $\alpha = .1$ and $\beta = .2$.

4. Using the value of n needed to reach a decision in problem 1, calculate by means of the normal approximation to the binomial what the value of β is for $\alpha = .2$ for a nonsequential test of H_0 based on this value of n.

5. Graph the lines in the α, β plane given by formulas (2) when c_1 and c_2 are determined by $\alpha = \beta = .05$. From this graph observe to what extent α and β can exceed .05 in value.

6. Construct a sequential test for testing the hypothesis $\mu = \mu_0$ against the alternative $\mu = \mu_1 > \mu_0$ for a Poisson distribution.

7. By using random sampling numbers draw repeated samples from a Poisson population with $\mu = 2$. Use the test derived in problem 6 on these sample values to test $\mu = 2$ against $\mu = 3$ with $\alpha = .10$ and $\beta = .10$.

8. Use formula (8) and the data for the problem used to illustrate it to verify that $E_1[n] \doteq 17$ for that problem.

9. Calculate $E_1[n]$ for the problem displayed in Table 1 and compare with the value of n actually realized in that problem.

10. Calculate $E_0[n]$ for problem 3 and compare with the value of n obtained in carrying out the test.

11. For the problem related to Table 1, calculate how large a fixed-size sample you would need to use to have α and β equal to the values used in that sequential test.

12. Let 3 single-variable normal subpopulations possess unit variances and means $-1, 0, 1$, respectively. Find what the best classification regions are if the population proportions are given by (a) $p_1 = p_2 = p_3 = \frac{1}{3}$, (b) $p_1 = 2p_2 = 4p_3$.

13. Work problem 12 if the 3 subpopulations are 2-variable populations with independent variables with unit variances and means $(-1, 0)$, $(0, 0)$, $(1, 0)$, respectively. Comment on the results in these 2 problems.

14. Let 3 single-variable subpopulations possess the distributions $f(x; \theta) = \theta e^{-x\theta}$, $\theta = 1, 2$, and 3, respectively, and let $p_1 = p_2 = p_3$. Find the best classification regions.

15. Apply the best classification technique to two 2-variable normal subpopulations whose means are $(-1, 0)$ and $(1, 0)$, whose correlation coefficients are both equal to $\frac{1}{2}$, and all of whose variances are equal to 1. Assume $p_1 = p_2$.

16. Compare the method of best classification when there are 2 normal subpopulations with the method of linear discriminant functions. Assume $p_1 = p_2$ and that the sample is so large that sample estimates used in the discriminant function may be treated as population values. Assume $\rho = 0$.

17. Using $W(t, \theta) = |t - \theta|$, $f(x; \theta) = 1/\theta$, $0 \le x \le \theta$, and $\lambda(\theta) = e^{-\theta}$, $\theta > 0$, (a) calculate the risk function and the mean risk for the estimate $t = x$. (b) Compare this mean risk with that for the estimate $t = \frac{3}{2}x$.

18. Using $W(t, \theta) = (t - \theta)^2$, $f(x; \theta) = \theta e^{-x\theta}$, $x > 0$, and $\lambda(\theta) = \frac{2}{3}\theta$, $1 \le \theta \le 2$, calculate (a) the risk functions for the estimates $t_1 = x$ and $t_2 = x - 1$ and determine which is the minimax estimate with respect to these 2 estimates only. (b) Calculate the mean risk for estimate t_1. (c) Find Bayes solutions with respect to estimates t_1 and t_2.

19. Given $W(t, \theta) = (t - \theta)^2$, $f(x; \theta) = e^{-\frac{1}{2}(x - \theta)^2}/\sqrt{2\pi}$, and $\lambda(\theta) = e^{-\frac{\theta^2}{2\sigma^2}}/\sqrt{2\pi}\,\sigma$, (a) calculate the risk function for the estimate $t = \bar{x}$, (b) calculate the mean risk for this estimate.

20. Given that x is a binomial variable with parameters n and p and that p possesses the beta distribution

$$\lambda(p) = \frac{\Gamma(\alpha + \beta)}{\Gamma(\alpha)\Gamma(\beta)} p^{\alpha - 1}(1 - p)^{\beta - 1}$$

calculate the Bayes solution.

21. Given that x is a Poisson variable with parameter μ and that μ possesses the gamma distribution

$$\lambda(\mu) = \frac{1}{\Gamma(\alpha)} \mu^{\alpha - 1}e^{-\mu}$$

calculate the Bayes solution.

22. Given that x possesses the gamma distribution

$$f(x \mid \theta) = \frac{\theta^\alpha}{\Gamma(\alpha)} x^{\alpha - 1}e^{-\theta x}$$

and that θ possesses the gamma distribution

$$\lambda(\theta) = \frac{\beta^a}{\Gamma(a)} \theta^{a-1}e^{-\beta\theta}$$

calculate the Bayes solution.

APPENDIX 1

1. Properties of r

The purpose of this section is to prove that $|r| \leq 1$ and that $r = \pm 1$ if, and only if, all sample points lie on a straight line.

Let $a_i = x_i - \bar{x}$ and $b_i = y_i - \bar{y}$. Then r will assume the form

$$(1) \qquad r = \frac{\sum a_i b_i}{\sqrt{\sum a_i^2 \sum b_i^2}}$$

In order to avoid trivial cases, which can easily be treated separately, it will be assumed that the x's are not all equal and that the y's are not all equal. This assumption prevents the denominator in (1) from having the value zero.

Now consider the inequality

$$(2) \qquad \sum (za_i + b_i)^2 > 0$$

where z is any real number. Since the left side is the sum of only squared terms, this inequality will be satisfied for all values of z if, and only if, a number z_0 does not exist such that

$$(3) \qquad z_0 a_i + b_i = 0, \qquad i = 1, 2, \cdots, n$$

Assume for the present that no such number exists. Then squaring and summing in (2) will produce the inequality

$$(4) \qquad z^2 \sum a_i^2 + 2z \sum a_i b_i + \sum b_i^2 > 0$$

The left side is a quadratic function in z, which is everywhere positive; consequently the corresponding quadratic equation must have imaginary roots, which in turn implies that the discriminant of the quadratic must be negative. Thus it is necessary that

$$(2\sum a_i b_i)^2 - 4(\sum a_i^2)(\sum b_i^2) < 0$$

or that

$$(\sum a_i b_i)^2 < \sum a_i^2 \sum b_i^2$$

In view of (1), this shows that $r^2 < 1$, provided that a number z_0 satisfying (3) does not exist.

Now suppose a number z_0 does exist such that (3) holds. Then

$$\sum(z_0 a_i + b_i)^2 = 0$$

Squaring and summing will yield

$$(5) \qquad z_0^2 \sum a_i^2 + 2z_0 \sum a_i b_i + \sum b_i^2 = 0$$

This says that z_0 is a root of the corresponding quadratic equation. Since there obviously cannot be two different values of z_0 satisfying (3), z_0 must be a double root in (5). As a result, the discriminant will be equal to zero; hence

$$(\sum a_i b_i)^2 = \sum a_i^2 \sum b_i^2$$

In view of (1), this shows that if a number z_0 satisfying (3) exists, then $r^2 = 1$. Since it was shown earlier that $r^2 < 1$ unless such a number did exist, it follows that $r^2 = 1$ if, and only if, a number z_0 satisfying (3) exists. In terms of the original variables, (3) can be written in the form

$$y_i - \bar{y} = -z_0(x_i - \bar{x}), \qquad i = 1, 2, \cdots, n$$

In geometrical language, it therefore follows that $r^2 \leq 1$ and that $r^2 = 1$ if, and only if, the points (x_i, y_i) lie on some straight line.

Students who have seen the inequality of Schwartz will recognize that $r^2 \leq 1$ is merely a version of that inequality.

2. Likelihood Ratio Test for Goodness of Fit

Consider k cells with probabilities $p_1, p_2, \cdots, p_k$, where $\sum_1^k p_i = 1$. Let $n_1, n_2, \cdots, n_k$, with $\sum_1^k n_i = n$, be the observed frequencies in those cells in n trials. Then the likelihood function is

$$(1) \qquad L(p) = p_1^{n_1} p_2^{n_2} \cdots p_k^{n_k}$$

Since $\sum p_i = 1$, there are only $k - 1$ independent parameters here; consequently in maximizing $L(p)$ by calculus methods it is necessary to keep this fact in mind. In this connection, it is convenient to choose p_k as the parameter to be expressed in terms of the remaining parameters. Taking logarithms and differentiating with respect to p_i will yield

$$\log L(p) = n_1 \log p_1 + n_2 \log p_2 + \cdots + n_k \log p_k$$

$$\frac{\partial \log L(p)}{\partial p_i} = \frac{n_i}{p_i} + \frac{n_k}{p_k} \frac{\partial p_k}{\partial p_i} = \frac{n_i}{p_i} - \frac{n_k}{p_k}$$

For a maximum it is necessary that all $k - 1$ partial derivatives vanish; hence it is necessary that

(2) $$\frac{n_i}{p_i} - \frac{n_k}{p_k} = 0, \qquad i = 1, 2, \cdots, k - 1$$

If the maximum likelihood estimate of p_i is denoted by $\hat{p}_i$, it follows from (2) that

(3) $$\hat{p}_i = \frac{\hat{p}_k}{n_k} n_i, \qquad i = 1, 2, \cdots, k$$

Since these estimates must satisfy the restriction $\Sigma \hat{p}_i = 1$, summing both sides of (3) will yield

$$1 = \sum_1^k \hat{p}_i = \frac{\hat{p}_k}{n_k} \sum_1^k n_i = \frac{\hat{p}_k}{n_k} n$$

If this result is applied to (3), it will follow that

(4) $$\hat{p}_i = \frac{n_i}{n}, \qquad i = 1, 2, \cdots, k$$

Now consider the likelihood ratio test for testing the hypothesis

$$H_0 : p_i = p_{i0}, \qquad i = 1, 2, \cdots, k$$

Since there are no unspecified parameters remaining when H_0 is true, it follows from (1) and (4) that the likelihood ratio here is given by

$$\lambda = \frac{L_0(\hat{p})}{L(\hat{p})} = \frac{p_{10}{}^{n_1} p_{20}{}^{n_2} \cdots p_{k0}{}^{n_k}}{\left(\dfrac{n_1}{n}\right)^{n_1} \left(\dfrac{n_2}{n}\right)^{n_2} \cdots \left(\dfrac{n_k}{n}\right)^{n_k}}$$

$$= \left(\frac{n p_{10}}{n_1}\right)^{n_1} \left(\frac{n p_{20}}{n_2}\right)^{n_2} \cdots \left(\frac{n p_{k0}}{n_k}\right)^{n_k}$$

$$= \left(\frac{e_1}{n_1}\right)^{n_1} \left(\frac{e_2}{n_2}\right)^{n_2} \cdots \left(\frac{e_k}{n_k}\right)^{n_k}$$

where $e_i = n p_{i0}$. As a result

(5) $$-2 \log \lambda = -2 \sum_1^k n_i \log \frac{e_i}{n_i}$$

Now let $x_i = n_i - e_i$, which is the difference between the observed frequency and the expected frequency in the ith cell. Then (5) may be expressed in the following form.

$$-2 \log \lambda = -2 \sum (e_i + x_i) \log \frac{e_i}{e_i + x_i}$$

$$= 2 \sum (x_i + e_i) \log \frac{e_i + x_i}{e_i}$$

$$= 2 \sum (x_i + e_i) \log \left(1 + \frac{x_i}{e_i}\right)$$

$$= 2 \sum (x_i + e_i) \left[\frac{x_i}{e_i} - \frac{1}{2}\left(\frac{x_i}{e_i}\right)^2 + \frac{1}{3}\left(\frac{x_i}{e_i}\right)^3 - \cdots\right]$$

$$= 2 \left(\sum \frac{x_i^2}{e_i} - \frac{1}{2}\sum \frac{x_i^3}{e_i^2} + \frac{1}{3}\sum \frac{x_i^4}{e_i^3} - \cdots\right.$$

$$\left. + \sum x_i - \frac{1}{2}\sum \frac{x_i^2}{e_i} + \frac{1}{3}\sum \frac{x_i^3}{e_i^2} - \cdots\right)$$

(6) $$= \sum \frac{x_i^2}{e_i} - \frac{1}{3}\sum \frac{x_i^3}{e_i^2} + \cdots$$

The variable n_i is a binomial variable with mean $\mu_i = np_{i0} = e_i$ and variance $\sigma_i^2 = np_{i0}(1 - p_{i0}) = e_i(1 - p_{i0})$; consequently the variable x_i/e_i may be expressed in the form

(7) $$\frac{x_i}{e_i} = \frac{n_i - e_i}{e_i} = \frac{n_i - \mu_i}{\sigma_i} \sqrt{\frac{1 - p_{i0}}{np_{i0}}}$$

Now from Theorem 2, Chapter 5, the variable $(n_i - \mu_i)/\sigma_i$ has a distribution approaching that of a standard normal variable as $n \to \infty$, whereas the square root factor in (7) approaches zero at the same rate as $1/\sqrt{n}$. Thus, for large n, x_i/e_i will almost certainly be very small and of the order of $1/\sqrt{n}$; consequently the successive terms in the above expansion will be of order $1/\sqrt{n}$ times the preceding term. As a result, the large sample approximate value of $-2 \log \lambda$ is given by the first term in (6). Thus

$$-2 \log \lambda \sim \sum_{i=1}^{k} \frac{x_i^2}{e_i} = \sum_{i=1}^{k} \frac{(n_i - e_i)^2}{e_i}$$

Since from (12), Chapter 9, it is known that $-2 \log \lambda$ possesses an approximate χ^2 distribution, this derivation shows that the quantity $\Sigma(n_i - e_i)^2/e_i$ possesses an approximate χ^2 distribution. With a little more attention to details the preceding derivation can be made to yield a mathematical theorem, which essentially states in the language of limiting distributions what has been said here concerning approximate distributions.

3. Cramer-Rao Inequality

Consider the problem of how to find the best unbiased estimate of the parameter θ in the continuous frequency function $f(x; \theta)$. The solution of the problem lies in obtaining an inequality for the variance of any unbiased estimator $t = t(x_1, x_2, \cdots, x_n)$ of θ. This inequality is derived in the following manner.

Since $x_1, x_2, \cdots, x_n$ is a random sample from $f(x; \theta)$, its frequency function, which for brevity of notation is denoted by L, is given by

$$L = \prod_{i=1}^{n} f(x_i; \theta)$$

It therefore follows that

(1) $$\int \cdots \int L \, dx_1 \cdots dx_n = 1$$

Since $t = t(x_1, x_2, \cdots, x_n)$ is assumed to be an unbiased estimator of θ, it follows that

(2) $$E[t] = \int \cdots \int tL \, dx_1 \cdots dx_n = \theta$$

Formulas (1) and (2) are identities in θ; therefore they may be differentiated with respect to θ. In doing so, it will be assumed that it is permissible to differentiate under the integral sign and that the limits of integration do not depend on θ. Differentiation of (1) will give

(3) $$\int \cdots \int \frac{\partial L}{\partial \theta} dx_1 \cdots dx_n = 0$$

Differentiation of (2) yields

(4) $$\int \cdots \int t \frac{\partial L}{\partial \theta} dx_1 \cdots dx_n = 1$$

The value of $\partial L / \partial \theta$ is most easily obtained by calculating

$$\frac{\partial \log L}{\partial \theta} = \frac{1}{L} \frac{\partial L}{\partial \theta}$$

Thus

$$\frac{\partial L}{\partial \theta} = L \sum_{i=1}^{n} \frac{\partial \log f(x_i; \theta)}{\partial \theta}$$

To simplify the notation somewhat, let

(5) $$T = \sum_{i=1}^{n} \frac{\partial \log f(x_i; \theta)}{\partial \theta}$$

Equation (3) can now be expressed as follows.

(6)
$$0 = \int \cdots \int TL \, dx_1 \cdots dx_n = E[T]$$

Similarly, equation (4) will assume the form

(7)
$$1 = \int \cdots \int tTL \, dx_1 \cdots dx_n = E[tT]$$

Next, consider the value of the correlation coefficient between the two random variables t and T. From formula (13), Chapter 8, it may be written as

$$\rho_{tT} = \frac{E[tT] - E[t]E[T]}{\sigma_t \sigma_T}$$

In view of the results in (6) and (7), this will reduce to

(8)
$$\rho_{tT} = \frac{1}{\sigma_t \sigma_T}$$

Since any correlation coefficient satisfies the inequality $\rho^2 \leq 1$, it follows from (8) that σ_t and σ_T must satisfy the inequality

(9)
$$\sigma_t^2 \geq \frac{1}{\sigma_T^2}$$

In view of (5) and the independence of the terms in that sum, it follows that

(10)
$$\sigma_T^2 = \sum_{i=1}^{n} \sigma_i^2$$

where σ_i^2 is the variance of $\partial \log f(x_i; \theta)/\partial\theta$. But from (5) and (6)

$$\sum_{i=1}^{n} E \frac{\partial \log f(x_i; \theta)}{\partial\theta} = 0$$

Since the x_i possess the same distribution, the quantities $\partial \log f(x_i; \theta)/\partial\theta$, $i = 1, 2, \cdots, n$ must possess the same distribution, hence the same expected value. Since the sum of such expected values is zero, it follows that each expected value must be zero and therefore the variance σ_i^2 of $\partial \log f(x_i; \theta)/\partial\theta$ is equal to its second moment. Thus

$$\sigma_i^2 = E \left[\frac{\partial \log f(x_i; \theta)}{\partial\theta} \right]^2$$

Consequently, from (10),

$$\sigma_T^2 = nE \left[\frac{\partial \log f(x; \theta)}{\partial\theta} \right]^2$$

because each x_i has the same distribution as the basic variable x. When this result is substituted in (9), one will obtain the desired inequality, namely

$$(11) \qquad \sigma_t^2 \geq \frac{1}{nE\left[\dfrac{\partial \log f(x;\theta)}{\partial \theta}\right]^2}$$

Since a best unbiased estimate is by definition one with minimum variance, it follows that if one can find an unbiased estimate whose variance is equal to the quantity on the right of (11) he will have found a best unbiased estimate.

This formula can be used to show that $\bar{x}$ is a best unbiased estimate for the mean of a normal distribution. Toward this end, write

$$f(x;\mu) = \frac{e^{-\frac{1}{2}\left(\frac{x-\mu}{\sigma}\right)^2}}{\sqrt{2\pi}\,\sigma}$$

and assume that the value of σ is known. Then

$$\log f(x;\mu) = -\log\sqrt{2\pi}\,\sigma - \frac{1}{2}\left(\frac{x-\mu}{\sigma}\right)^2$$

and

$$\frac{\partial \log f(x;\mu)}{\partial \mu} = \frac{x-\mu}{\sigma^2}$$

Hence

$$E\left[\frac{\partial \log f(x;\mu)}{\partial \mu}\right]^2 = \frac{1}{\sigma^4}E(x-\mu)^2 = \frac{1}{\sigma^2}$$

Substituting this result in (11) will yield

$$\sigma_t^2 \geq \frac{\sigma^2}{n}$$

But it is known that $\sigma_{\bar{x}}^2 = \sigma^2/n$; therefore $\bar{x}$ must be a best unbiased estimate of μ for a normal distribution.

4. Transformations and Jacobians

Geometrically, the functions $u = u(x, y)$ and $v = v(x, y)$ represent a transformation from the coordinate system x,y to the coordinate system u,v. Now there exists a calculus formula that enables one to evaluate the integral of the function $f(x, y)$ over a region R in the x,y plane by means of the proper integral over a corresponding region R' in the u,v plane. This formula is

(1) $$\iint\limits_{R} f(x, y) \, dx \, dy = \iint\limits_{R'} f(x, y) \, |J| \, du \, dv$$

where the quantity J, called the Jacobian of the transformation, is given by the formula

(2) $$\frac{1}{J} = \begin{vmatrix} \dfrac{\partial u}{\partial x} & \dfrac{\partial u}{\partial y} \\ \dfrac{\partial v}{\partial x} & \dfrac{\partial v}{\partial y} \end{vmatrix}$$

The region of integration R' on the right is the region in the u,v plane that corresponds to the region R in the x,y plane. It is understood that the variables x and y in the right integrand of (1) are to be replaced by their values in terms of u and v by solving the relations $u = u(x, y)$ and $v = v(x, y)$ for x and y. It will be assumed that these functions are such that each point in the x,y plane corresponds to exactly one point in the u,v plane, and conversely.

The integral on the left of (1) yields the probability that the sample point x,y will lie in the region R. Because of the one-to-one correspondence between points in the two coordinate systems, this can occur if, and only if, the sample point u,v lies in the corresponding region R'; consequently the integral on the right must yield the probability that the sample point u,v will lie in the region R'. Now formula (1) holds for all possible regions R in the x,y plane, hence for all possible regions R' in the u,v plane; consequently the integrand in the integral on the right side of (1) must be the frequency function of the random variables u and v. Thus, denoting this function by $g(u, v)$, it follows that

(3) $$g(u, v) = f(x, y) \, |J|$$

where J is given by (2).

As an illustration, consider the problem solved earlier in (2), Chapter 11. Here one may choose $u = z = t(x, y)$ and $v = x$. Then (2) becomes

$$\frac{1}{J} = \begin{vmatrix} \dfrac{\partial z}{\partial x} & \dfrac{\partial z}{\partial y} \\ 1 & 0 \end{vmatrix} = -\frac{\partial z}{\partial y}$$

Application of (3) then yields

$$g(u, v) = \frac{f(x, y)}{\left| \dfrac{\partial z}{\partial y} \right|}$$

which is the result given earlier.

The method that has just been explained for finding the frequency function of two transformed variables u and v can be generalized to any number of variables. The formula that results is a direct consequence of probability considerations applied to the formula for evaluating a multiple integral by means of a new coordinate system. The following theorem, in which the functions u_i are assumed to satisfy certain regularity conditions, yields the desired general result for k variables.

THEOREM: *If the continuous variables* $x_1, x_2, \cdots, x_k$ *possess the frequency function* $f(x_1, x_2, \cdots, x_k)$ *and the transformed variables* $u_i = u_i(x_1, x_2, \cdots, x_k)$, $i = 1, 2, \cdots, k$ *yield a one-to-one transformation of the two coordinate systems, the frequency function of the u's will be given by the formula*

(4) $$g(u_1, u_2, \cdots, u_k) = f(x_1, x_2, \cdots, x_k) \, |J|$$

where

$$\frac{1}{J} = \begin{vmatrix} \dfrac{\partial u_1}{\partial x_1} \cdots \dfrac{\partial u_1}{\partial x_k} \\ \cdots \cdots \cdots \\ \dfrac{\partial u_k}{\partial x_1} \cdots \dfrac{\partial u_k}{\partial x_k} \end{vmatrix}$$

and where the x's on the right of (4) *are to be replaced by their values in terms of the u's by solving the relations* $u_i = u_i(x_1, x_2, \cdots, x_k)$ *for the x's.*

5. Independence of $\bar{x}$ and s^2 for Normal Distributions

Consider the n independent normal variables $x_1, x_2, \cdots, x_n$ with means $\mu_1, \mu_2, \cdots, \mu_n$ and the common variance σ^2. Their joint frequency function is given by

(1) $$f(x_1, x_2, \cdots, x_n) = \frac{e^{-\frac{1}{2\sigma^2} \sum\limits_{i=1}^{n} (x_i - \mu_i)^2}}{(2\pi\sigma^2)^{\frac{n}{2}}}$$

Now $\Sigma(x_i - \mu_i)^2 = c^2$ is the equation of a sphere in n dimensions with center at the point $(\mu_1, \mu_2, \cdots, \mu_n)$ and with radius c. As a consequence, the geometrical interpretation of (1) is that the probability density is constant on the surface of any sphere with center at $(\mu_1, \mu_2, \cdots, \mu_n)$ and the magnitude of the density for any point on such a sphere is given by replacing $\Sigma(x_i - \mu_i)^2$ in (1) by the square of the radius of the sphere. These two geometrical properties completely determine the distribution of

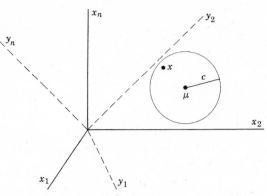

Fig. 1. Distribution of n independent normal variables.

$x_1, x_2, \cdots, x_n$. A sketch illustrating these properties is shown in Fig. 1 where x and μ denote the sample point $(x_1, x_2, \cdots, x_n)$ and the mean point $(\mu_1, \mu_2, \cdots, \mu_n)$, respectively.

Now suppose one rotates the axes of this coordinate system in any desired manner. If the new axes are denoted by $y_1, y_2, \cdots, y_n$, as indicated in Fig. 1, the equation of the sphere sketched there will become $\Sigma(y_i - \nu_i)^2 = c^2$, where $(\nu_1, \nu_2, \cdots, \nu_n)$ denotes the coordinates of the mean point μ in terms of the new coordinate system. The typical sample point $x = (x_1, x_2, \cdots, x_n)$ becomes the point $y = (y_1, y_2, \cdots, y_n)$ in the new system. The y's are random variables because they are functions of the random variables $x_1, x_2, \cdots, x_n$. Since the only effect of rotating axes is to change the coordinates of the mean of the distribution, the geometrical properties of the distribution being considered show that the distribution of the new variables $y_1, y_2, \cdots, y_n$ must be given by the frequency function

(2)
$$ g(y_1, y_2, \cdots, y_n) = \frac{e^{-\frac{1}{2\sigma^2} \sum_{i=1}^{n} (y_i - \nu_i)^2}}{(2\pi\sigma^2)^{\frac{n}{2}}} $$

The preceding discussion will now be specialized to the case in which $\mu_1 = \mu_2 = \cdots = \mu_n$ and in which one rotates the axes in such a way that the y_1 axis becomes the line that makes equal angles with the positive x axes, as shown in Fig. 2.

In the new coordinate system the mean point μ will be on the y_1 axis, and therefore its coordinates with respect to the new axes are given by $(\nu, 0, \cdots, 0)$, where ν is the distance from the origin to the point μ in the old coordinate system. It is clear from Figs. 1 and 2 that this distance is given by $\nu = \sqrt{\mu_1^2 + \mu_2^2 + \cdots + \mu_n^2} = \mu\sqrt{n}$, where μ here denotes the common numerical value of the equal-valued μ_i. As a result, formula (2) may be applied to give

(3) $$g(y_1, y_2, \cdots, y_n) = \frac{e^{-\frac{1}{2\sigma^2}[(y_1 - \mu\sqrt{n})^2 + y_2^2 + \cdots + y_n^2]}}{(2\pi\sigma^2)^{\frac{n}{2}}}$$

Thus the y's are independent normal variables with a common variance σ^2, and all have zero means except y_1, which has a mean of $\mu\sqrt{n}$.

Now consider the geometrical meaning of the equation defining the sample mean, namely

(4) $$x_1 + x_2 + \cdots + x_n = n\bar{x}$$

This is the equation of a plane in n dimensions. Since the coefficients of the variables $x_1, x_2, \cdots, x_n$ are direction numbers of a normal (perpendicular) to the plane and since all these coefficients are equal, it follows that the y_1 axis is a normal, hence perpendicular, to this plane because the y_1 axis makes equal angles with the positive x axes. Further, since the coordinates of the point $(\bar{x}, \bar{x}, \cdots, \bar{x})$ satisfy equation (4) and since this point lies on the y_1 axis, it follows that the point of intersection of this plane with the y_1 axis is the point $(\bar{x}, \bar{x}, \cdots, \bar{x})$, which has been labeled $\bar{x}$ in Fig. 2. The point x lies in this plane also.

Now $ns^2 = \Sigma(x_i - \bar{x})^2$ is the square of the distance between the points labeled x and $\bar{x}$ in Fig. 2. In the new coordinate system the square of this distance is given by $y_2^2 + y_3^2 + \cdots + y_n^2$ because the points x and $\bar{x}$ possess the coordinates $(y_1, y_2, \cdots, y_n)$ and $(y_1, 0, \cdots, 0)$, respectively, in the new coordinate system. Thus

$$ns^2 = y_2^2 + y_3^2 + \cdots + y_n^2$$

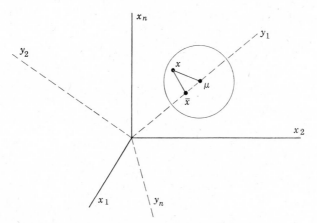

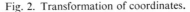

Fig. 2. Transformation of coordinates.

Furthermore, since the distance from the origin to the plane given by (4) is $\sqrt{n}\bar{x}$ and y_1, respectively, in the two coordinate systems, it follows that

$$\bar{x} = \frac{y_1}{\sqrt{n}}$$

This shows that $\bar{x}$ is a function of the variable y_1 only and that s^2 is a function of the variables $y_2, y_3, \cdots, y_n$ only. Since the y's are independent random variables, it therefore follows that $\bar{x}$ and s^2 must be independent random variables.

APPENDIX 2

Tables

Table I. Squares and Square Roots

N	N²	√N	√10N	N	N²	√N	√10N
1.00	1.0000	1.00000	3.16228	**1.50**	2.2500	1.22474	3.87298
1.01	1.0201	1.00499	3.17805	1.51	2.2801	1.22882	3.88587
1.02	1.0404	1.00995	3.19374	1.52	2.3104	1.23288	3.89872
1.03	1.0609	1.01489	3.20936	1.53	2.3409	1.23693	3.91152
1.04	1.0816	1.01980	3.22490	1.54	2.3716	1.24097	3.92428
1.05	1.1025	1.02470	3.24037	1.55	2.4025	1.24499	3.93700
1.06	1.1236	1.02956	3.25576	1.56	2.4336	1.24900	3.94968
1.07	1.1449	1.03441	3.27109	1.57	2.4649	1.25300	3.96232
1.08	1.1664	1.03923	3.28634	1.58	2.4964	1.25698	3.97492
1.09	1.1881	1.04403	3.30151	1.59	2.5281	1.26095	3.98748
1.10	1.2100	1.04881	3.31662	**1.60**	2.5600	1.26491	4.00000
1.11	1.2321	1.05357	3.33167	1.61	2.5921	1.26886	4.01248
1.12	1.2544	1.05830	3.34664	1.62	2.6244	1.27279	4.02492
1.13	1.2769	1.06301	3.36155	1.63	2.6569	1.27671	4.03733
1.14	1.2996	1.06771	3.37639	1.64	2.6896	1.28062	4.04969
1.15	1.3225	1.07238	3.39116	1.65	2.7225	1.28452	4.06202
1.16	1.3456	1.07703	3.40588	1.66	2.7556	1.28841	4.07431
1.17	1.3689	1.08167	3.42053	1.67	2.7889	1.29228	4.08656
1.18	1.3924	1.08628	3.43511	1.68	2.8224	1.29615	4.09878
1.19	1.4161	1.09087	3.44964	1.69	2.8561	1.30000	4.11096
1.20	1.4400	1.09545	3.46410	**1.70**	2.8900	1.30384	4.12311
1.21	1.4641	1.10000	3.47851	1.71	2.9241	1.30767	4.13521
1.22	1.4884	1.10454	3.49285	1.72	2.9584	1.31149	4.14729
1.23	1.5129	1.10905	3.50714	1.73	2.9929	1.31529	4.15933
1.24	1.5376	1.11355	3.52136	1.74	3.0276	1.31909	4.17133
1.25	1.5625	1.11803	3.53553	1.75	3.0625	1.32288	4.18330
1.26	1.5876	1.12250	3.54965	1.76	3.0976	1.32665	4.19524
1.27	1.6129	1.12694	3.56371	1.77	3.1329	1.33041	4.20714
1.28	1.6384	1.13137	3.57771	1.78	3.1684	1.33417	4.21900
1.29	1.6641	1.13578	3.59166	1.79	3.2041	1.33791	4.23084
1.30	1.6900	1.14018	3.60555	**1.80**	3.2400	1.34164	4.24264
1.31	1.7161	1.14455	3.61939	1.81	3.2761	1.34536	4.25441
1.32	1.7424	1.14891	3.63318	1.82	3.3124	1.34907	4.26615
1.33	1.7689	1.15326	3.64692	1.83	3.3489	1.35277	4.27785
1.34	1.7956	1.15758	3.66060	1.84	3.3856	1.35647	4.28952
1.35	1.8225	1.16190	3.67423	1.85	3.4225	1.36015	4.30116
1.36	1.8496	1.16619	3.68782	1.86	3.4596	1.36382	4.31277
1.37	1.8769	1.17047	3.70135	1.87	3.4969	1.36748	4.32435
1.38	1.9044	1.17473	3.71484	1.88	3.5344	1.37113	4.33590
1.39	1.9321	1.17898	3.72827	1.89	3.5721	1.37477	4.34741
1.40	1.9600	1.18322	3.74166	**1.90**	3.6100	1.37840	4.35890
1.41	1.9881	1.18743	3.75500	1.91	3.6481	1.38203	4.37035
1.42	2.0164	1.19164	3.76829	1.92	3.6864	1.38564	4.38178
1.43	2.0449	1.19583	3.78153	1.93	3.7249	1.38924	4.39318
1.44	2.0736	1.20000	3.79473	1.94	3.7636	1.39284	4.40454
1.45	2.1025	1.20416	3.80789	1.95	3.8025	1.39642	4.41588
1.46	2.1316	1.20830	3.82099	1.96	3.8416	1.40000	4.42719
1.47	2.1609	1.21244	3.83406	1.97	3.8809	1.40357	4.43847
1.48	2.1904	1.21655	3.84708	1.98	3.9204	1.40712	4.44972
1.49	2.2201	1.22066	3.86005	1.99	3.9601	1.41067	4.46094
1.50	2.2500	1.22474	3.87298	**2.00**	4.0000	1.41421	4.47214
N	N²	√N	√10N	N	N²	√N	√10N

Squares and Square Roots (*Continued*)

N	N²	√N	√10N	N	N²	√N	√10N
2.00	4.0000	1.41421	4.47214	**2.50**	6.2500	1.58114	5.00000
2.01	4.0401	1.41774	4.48330	2.51	6.3001	1.58430	5.00999
2.02	4.0804	1.42127	4.49444	2.52	6.3504	1.58745	5.01996
2.03	4.1209	1.42478	4.50555	2.53	6.4009	1.59060	5.02991
2.04	4.1616	1.42829	4.51664	2.54	6.4516	1.59374	5.03984
2.05	4.2025	1.43178	4.52769	2.55	6.5025	1.59687	5.04975
2.06	4.2436	1.43527	4.53872	2.56	6.5536	1.60000	5.05964
2.07	4.2849	1.43875	4.54973	2.57	6.6049	1.60312	5.06952
2.08	4.3264	1.44222	4.56070	2.58	6.6564	1.60624	5.07937
2.09	4.3681	1.44568	4.57165	2.59	6.7081	1.60935	5.08920
2.10	4.4100	1.44914	4.58258	**2.60**	6.7600	1.61245	5.09902
2.11	4.4521	1.45258	4.59347	2.61	6.8121	1.61555	5.10882
2.12	4.4944	1.45602	4.60435	2.62	6.8644	1.61864	5.11859
2.13	4.5369	1.45945	4.61519	2.63	6.9169	1.62173	5.12835
2.14	4.5796	1.46287	4.62601	2.64	6.9696	1.62481	5.13809
2.15	4.6225	1.46629	4.63681	2.65	7.0225	1.62788	5.14782
2.16	4.6656	1.46969	4.64758	2.66	7.0756	1.63095	5.15752
2.17	4.7089	1.47309	4.65833	2.67	7.1289	1.63401	5.16720
2.18	4.7524	1.47648	4.66905	2.68	7.1824	1.63707	5.17687
2.19	4.7961	1.47986	4.67974	2.69	7.2361	1.64012	5.18652
2.20	4.8400	1.48324	4.69042	**2.70**	7.2900	1.64317	5.19615
2.21	4.8841	1.48661	4.70106	2.71	7.3441	1.64621	5.20577
2.22	4.9284	1.48997	4.71169	2.72	7.3984	1.64924	5.21536
2.23	4.9729	1.49332	4.72229	2.73	7.4529	1.65227	5.22494
2.24	5.0176	1.49666	4.73286	2.74	7.5076	1.65529	5.23450
2.25	5.0625	1.50000	4.74342	2.75	7.5625	1.65831	5.24404
2.26	5.1076	1.50333	4.75395	2.76	7.6176	1.66132	5.25357
2.27	5.1529	1.50665	4.76445	2.77	7.6729	1.66433	5.26308
2.28	5.1984	1.50997	4.77493	2.78	7.7284	1.66733	5.27257
2.29	5.2441	1.51327	4.78539	2.79	7.7841	1.67033	5.28205
2.30	5.2900	1.51658	4.79583	**2.80**	7.8400	1.67332	5.29150
2.31	5.3361	1.51987	4.80625	2.81	7.8961	1.67631	5.30094
2.32	5.3824	1.52315	4.81664	2.82	7.9524	1.67929	5.31037
2.33	5.4289	1.52643	4.82701	2.83	8.0089	1.68226	5.31977
2.34	5.4756	1.52971	4.83735	2.84	8.0656	1.68523	5.32917
2.35	5.5225	1.53297	4.84768	2.85	8.1225	1.68819	5.33854
2.36	5.5696	1.53623	4.85798	2.86	8.1796	1.69115	5.34790
2.37	5.6169	1.53948	4.86826	2.87	8.2369	1.69411	5.35724
2.38	5.6644	1.54272	4.87852	2.88	8.2944	1.69706	5.36656
2.39	5.7121	1.54596	4.88876	2.89	8.3521	1.70000	5.37587
2.40	5.7600	1.54919	4.89898	**2.90**	8.4100	1.70294	5.38516
2.41	5.8081	1.55242	4.90918	2.91	8.4681	1.70587	5.39444
2.42	5.8564	1.55563	4.91935	2.92	8.5264	1.70880	5.40370
2.43	5.9049	1.55885	4.92950	2.93	8.5849	1.71172	5.41295
2.44	5.9536	1.56205	4.93964	2.94	8.6436	1.71464	5.42218
2.45	6.0025	1.56525	4.94975	2.95	8.7025	1.71756	5.43139
2.46	6.0516	1.56844	4.95984	2.96	8.7616	1.72047	5.44059
2.47	6.1009	1.57162	4.96991	2.97	8.8209	1.72337	5.44977
2.48	6.1504	1.57480	4.97996	2.98	8.8804	1.72627	5.45894
2.49	6.2001	1.57797	4.98999	2.99	8.9401	1.72916	5.46809
2.50	6.2500	1.58114	5.00000	**3.00**	9.0000	1.73205	5.47723
N	N²	√N	√10N	N	N²	√N	√10N

390

Squares and Square Roots (*Continued*)

N	N²	√N	√10N	N	N²	√N	√10N
3.00	9.0000	1.73205	5.47723	**3.50**	12.2500	1.87083	5.91608
3.01	9.0601	1.73494	5.48635	3.51	12.3201	1.87350	5.92453
3.02	9.1204	1.73781	5.49545	3.52	12.3904	1.87617	5.93296
3.03	9.1809	1.74069	5.50454	3.53	12.4609	1.87883	5.94138
3.04	9.2416	1.74356	5.51362	3.54	12.5316	1.88149	5.94979
3.05	9.3025	1.74642	5.52268	3.55	12.6025	1.88414	5.95819
3.06	9.3636	1.74929	5.53173	3.56	12.6736	1.88680	5.96657
3.07	9.4249	1.75214	5.54076	3.57	12.7449	1.88944	5.97495
3.08	9.4864	1.75499	5.54977	3.58	12.8164	1.89209	5.98331
3.09	9.5481	1.75784	5.55878	3.59	12.8881	1.89473	5.99166
3.10	9.6100	1.76068	5.56776	**3.60**	12.9600	1.89737	6.00000
3.11	9.6721	1.76352	5.57674	3.61	13.0321	1.90000	6.00833
3.12	9.7344	1.76635	5.58570	3.62	13.1044	1.90263	6.01664
3.13	9.7969	1.76918	5.59464	3.63	13.1769	1.90526	6.02495
3.14	9.8596	1.77200	5.60357	3.64	13.2496	1.90788	6.03324
3.15	9.9225	1.77482	5.61249	3.65	13.3225	1.91050	6.04152
3.16	9.9856	1.77764	5.62139	3.66	13.3956	1.91311	6.04979
3.17	10.0489	1.78045	5.63028	3.67	13.4689	1.91572	6.05805
3.18	10.1124	1.78326	5.63915	3.68	13.5424	1.91833	6.06630
3.19	10.1761	1.78606	5.64801	3.69	13.6161	1.92094	6.07454
3.20	10.2400	1.78885	5.65685	**3.70**	13.6900	1.92354	6.08276
3.21	10.3041	1.79165	5.66569	3.71	13.7641	1.92614	6.09098
3.22	10.3684	1.79444	5.67450	3.72	13.8384	1.92873	6.09918
3.23	10.4329	1.79722	5.68331	3.73	13.9129	1.93132	6.10737
3.24	10.4976	1.80000	5.69210	3.74	13.9876	1.93391	6.11555
3.25	10.5625	1.80278	5.70088	3.75	14.0625	1.93649	6.12372
3.26	10.6276	1.80555	5.70964	3.76	14.1376	1.93907	6.13188
3.27	10.6929	1.80831	5.71839	3.77	14.2129	1.94165	6.14003
3.28	10.7584	1.81108	5.72713	3.78	14.2884	1.94422	6.14817
3.29	10.8241	1.81384	5.73585	3.79	14.3641	1.94679	6.15630
3.30	10.8900	1.81659	5.74456	**3.80**	14.4400	1.94936	6.16441
3.31	10.9561	1.81934	5.75326	3.81	14.5161	1.95192	6.17252
3.32	11.0224	1.82209	5.76194	3.82	14.5924	1.95448	6.18061
3.33	11.0889	1.82483	5.77062	3.83	14.6689	1.95704	6.18870
3.34	11.1556	1.82757	5.77927	3.84	14.7456	1.95959	6.19677
3.35	11.2225	1.83030	5.78792	3.85	14.8225	1.96214	6.20484
3.36	11.2896	1.83303	5.79655	3.86	14.8996	1.96469	6.21289
3.37	11.3569	1.83576	5.80517	3.87	14.9769	1.96723	6.22093
3.38	11.4244	1.83848	5.81378	3.88	15.0544	1.96977	6.22896
3.39	11.4921	1.84120	5.82237	3.89	15.1321	1.97231	6.23699
3.40	11.5600	1.84391	5.83095	**3.90**	15.2100	1.97484	6.24500
3.41	11.6281	1.84662	5.83952	3.91	15.2881	1.97737	6.25300
3.42	11.6964	1.84932	5.84808	3.92	15.3664	1.97990	6.26099
3.43	11.7649	1.85203	5.85662	3.93	15.4449	1.98242	6.26897
3.44	11.8336	1.85472	5.86515	3.94	15.5236	1.98494	6.27694
3.45	11.9025	1.85742	5.87367	3.95	15.6025	1.98746	6.28490
3.46	11.9716	1.86011	5.88218	3.96	15.6816	1.98997	6.29285
3.47	12.0409	1.86279	5.89067	3.97	15.7609	1.99249	6.30079
3.48	12.1104	1.86548	5.89915	3.98	15.8404	1.99499	6.30872
3.49	12.1801	1.86815	5.90762	3.99	15.9201	1.99750	6.31664
3.50	12.2500	1.87083	5.91608	**4.00**	16.0000	2.00000	6.32456
N	N²	√N	√10N	N	N²	√N	√10N

N	N²	√N	√10N	N	N²	√N	√10N
4.00	16.0000	2.00000	6.32456	**4.50**	20.2500	2.12132	6.70820
4.01	16.0801	2.00250	6.33246	4.51	20.3401	2.12368	6.71565
4.02	16.1604	2.00499	6.34035	4.52	20.4304	2.12603	6.72309
4.03	16.2409	2.00749	6.34823	4.53	20.5209	2.12838	6.73053
4.04	16.3216	2.00998	6.35610	4.54	20.6116	2.13073	6.73795
4.05	16.4025	2.01246	6.36396	4.55	20.7025	2.13307	6.74537
4.06	16.4836	2.01494	6.37181	4.56	20.7936	2.13542	6.75278
4.07	16.5649	2.01742	6.37966	4.57	20.8849	2.13776	6.76018
4.08	16.6464	2.01990	6.38749	4.58	20.9764	2.14009	6.76757
4.09	16.7281	2.02237	6.39531	4.59	21.0681	2.14243	6.77495
4.10	16.8100	2.02485	6.40312	**4.60**	21.1600	2.14476	6.78233
4.11	16.8921	2.02731	6.41093	4.61	21.2521	2.14709	6.78970
4.12	16.9744	2.02978	6.41872	4.62	21.3444	2.14942	6.79706
4.13	17.0569	2.03224	6.42651	4.63	21.4369	2.15174	6.80441
4.14	17.1396	2.03470	6.43428	4.64	21.5296	2.15407	6.81175
4.15	17.2225	2.03715	6.44205	4.65	21.6225	2.15639	6.81909
4.16	17.3056	2.03961	6.44981	4.66	21.7156	2.15870	6.82642
4.17	17.3889	2.04206	6.45755	4.67	21.8089	2.16102	6.83374
4.18	17.4724	2.04450	6.46529	4.68	21.9024	2.16333	6.84105
4.19	17.5561	2.04695	6.47302	4.69	21.9961	2.16564	6.84836
4.20	17.6400	2.04939	6.48074	**4.70**	22.0900	2.16795	6.85565
4.21	17.7241	2.05183	6.48845	4.71	22.1841	2.17025	6.86294
4.22	17.8084	2.05426	6.49615	4.72	22.2784	2.17256	6.87023
4.23	17.8929	2.05670	6.50384	4.73	22.3729	2.17486	6.87750
4.24	17.9776	2.05913	6.51153	4.74	22.4676	2.17715	6.88477
4.25	18.0625	2.06155	6.51920	4.75	22.5625	2.17945	6.89202
4.26	18.1476	2.06398	6.52687	4.76	22.6576	2.18174	6.89928
4.27	18.2329	2.06640	6.53452	4.77	22.7529	2.18403	6.90652
4.28	18.3184	2.06882	6.54217	4.78	22.8484	2.18632	6.91375
4.29	18.4041	2.07123	6.54981	4.79	22.9441	2.18861	6.92098
4.30	18.4900	2.07364	6.55744	**4.80**	23.0400	2.19089	6.92820
4.31	18.5761	2.07605	6.56506	4.81	23.1361	2.19317	6.93542
4.32	18.6624	2.07846	6.57267	4.82	23.2324	2.19545	6.94262
4.33	18.7489	2.08087	6.58027	4.83	23.3289	2.19773	6.94982
4.34	18.8356	2.08327	6.58787	4.84	23.4256	2.20000	6.95701
4.35	18.9225	2.08567	6.59545	4.85	23.5225	2.20227	6.96419
4.36	19.0096	2.08806	6.60303	4.86	23.6196	2.20454	6.97137
4.37	19.0969	2.09045	6.61060	4.87	23.7169	2.20681	6.97854
4.38	19.1844	2.09284	6.61816	4.88	23.8144	2.20907	6.98570
4.39	19.2721	2.09523	6.62571	4.89	23.9121	2.21133	6.99285
4.40	19.3600	2.09762	6.63325	**4.90**	24.0100	2.21359	7.00000
4.41	19.4481	2.10000	6.64078	4.91	24.1081	2.21585	7.00714
4.42	19.5364	2.10238	6.64831	4.92	24.2064	2.21811	7.01427
4.43	19.6249	2.10476	6.65582	4.93	24.3049	2.22036	7.02140
4.44	19.7136	2.10713	6.66333	4.94	24.4036	2.22261	7.02851
4.45	19.8025	2.10950	6.67083	4.95	24.5025	2.22486	7.03562
4.46	19.8916	2.11187	6.67832	4.96	24.6016	2.22711	7.04273
4.47	19.9809	2.11424	6.68581	4.97	24.7009	2.22935	7.04982
4.48	20.0704	2.11660	6.69328	4.98	24.8004	2.23159	7.05691
4.49	20.1601	2.11896	6.70075	4.99	24.9001	2.23383	7.06399
4.50	20.2500	2.12132	6.70820	**5.00**	25.0000	2.23607	7.07107
N	N²	√N	√10N	N	N²	√N	√10N

N	N²	√N	√10N	N	N²	√N	√10N
5.00	25.0000	2.23607	7.07107	**5.50**	30.2500	2.34521	7.41620
5.01	25.1001	2.23830	7.07814	5.51	30.3601	2.34734	7.42294
5.02	25.2004	2.24054	7.08520	5.52	30.4704	2.34947	7.42967
5.03	25.3009	2.24277	7.09225	5.53	30.5809	2.35160	7.43640
5.04	25.4016	2.24499	7.09930	5.54	30.6916	2.35372	7.44312
5.05	25.5025	2.24722	7.10634	5.55	30.8025	2.35584	7.44983
5.06	25.6036	2.24944	7.11337	5.56	30.9136	2.35797	7.45654
5.07	25.7049	2.25167	7.12039	5.57	31.0249	2.36008	7.46324
5.08	25.8064	2.25389	7.12741	5.58	31.1364	2.36220	7.46994
5.09	25.9081	2.25610	7.13442	5.59	31.2481	2.36432	7.47663
5.10	26.0100	2.25832	7.14143	**5.60**	31.3600	2.36643	7.48331
5.11	26.1121	2.26053	7.14843	5.61	31.4721	2.36854	7.48999
5.12	26.2144	2.26274	7.15542	5.62	31.5844	2.37065	7.49667
5.13	26.3169	2.26495	7.16240	5.63	31.6969	2.37276	7.50333
5.14	26.4196	2.26716	7.16938	5.64	31.8096	2.37487	7.50999
5.15	26.5225	2.26936	7.17635	5.65	31.9225	2.37697	7.51665
5.16	26.6256	2.27156	7.18331	5.66	32.0356	2.37908	7.52330
5.17	26.7289	2.27376	7.19027	5.67	32.1489	2.38118	7.52994
5.18	26.8324	2.27596	7.19722	5.68	32.2624	2.38328	7.53658
5.19	26.9361	2.27816	7.20417	5.69	32.3761	2.38537	7.54321
5.20	27.0400	2.28035	7.21110	**5.70**	32.4900	2.38747	7.54983
5.21	27.1441	2.28254	7.21803	5.71	32.6041	2.38956	7.55645
5.22	27.2484	2.28473	7.22496	5.72	32.7184	2.39165	7.56307
5.23	27.3529	2.28692	7.23187	5.73	32.8329	2.39374	7.56968
5.24	27.4576	2.28910	7.23878	5.74	32.9476	2.39583	7.57628
5.25	27.5625	2.29129	7.24569	5.75	33.0625	2.39792	7.58288
5.26	27.6676	2.29347	7.25259	5.76	33.1776	2.40000	7.58947
5.27	27.7729	2.29565	7.25948	5.77	33.2929	2.40208	7.59605
5.28	27.8784	2.29783	7.26636	5.78	33.4084	2.40416	7.60263
5.29	27.9841	2.30000	7.27324	5.79	33.5241	2.40624	7.60920
5.30	28.0900	2.30217	7.28011	**5.80**	33.6400	2.40832	7.61577
5.31	28.1961	2.30434	7.28697	5.81	33.7561	2.41039	7.62234
5.32	28.3024	2.30651	7.29383	5.82	33.8724	2.41247	7.62889
5.33	28.4089	2.30868	7.30068	5.83	33.9889	2.41454	7.63544
5.34	28.5156	2.31084	7.30753	5.84	34.1056	2.41661	7.64199
5.35	28.6225	2.31301	7.31437	5.85	34.2225	2.41868	7.64853
5.36	28.7296	2.31517	7.32120	5.86	34.3396	2.42074	7.65506
5.37	28.8369	2.31733	7.32803	5.87	34.4569	2.42281	7.66159
5.38	28.9444	2.31948	7.33485	5.88	34.5744	2.42487	7.66812
5.39	29.0521	2.32164	7.34166	5.89	34.6921	2.42693	7.67463
5.40	29.1600	2.32379	7.34847	**5.90**	34.8100	2.42899	7.68115
5.41	29.2681	2.32594	7.35527	5.91	34.9281	2.43105	7.68765
5.42	29.3764	2.32809	7.36206	5.92	35.0464	2.43311	7.69415
5.43	29.4849	2.33024	7.36885	5.93	35.1649	2.43516	7.70065
5.44	29.5936	2.33238	7.37564	5.94	35.2836	2.43721	7.70714
5.45	29.7025	2.33452	7.38241	5.95	35.4025	2.43926	7.71362
5.46	29.8116	2.33666	7.38918	5.96	35.5216	2.44131	7.72010
5.47	29.9209	2.33880	7.39594	5.97	35.6409	2.44336	7.72658
5.48	30.0304	2.34094	7.40270	5.98	35.7604	2.44540	7.73305
5.49	30.1401	2.34307	7.40945	5.99	35.8801	2.44745	7.73951
5.50	30.2500	2.34521	7.41620	**6.00**	36.0000	2.44949	7.74597
N	N²	√N	√10N	N	N²	√N	√10N

Squares and Square Roots (*Continued*)

N	N²	√N	√10N	N	N²	√N	√10N
6.00	36.0000	2.44949	7.74597	**6.50**	42.2500	2.54951	8.06226
6.01	36.1201	2.45153	7.75242	6.51	42.3801	2.55147	8.06846
6.02	36.2404	2.45357	7.75887	6.52	42.5104	2.55343	8.07465
6.03	36.3609	2.45561	7.76531	6.53	42.6409	2.55539	8.08084
6.04	36.4816	2.45764	7.77174	6.54	42.7716	2.55734	8.08703
6.05	36.6025	2.45967	7.77817	6.55	42.9025	2.55930	8.09321
6.06	36.7236	2.46171	7.78460	6.56	43.0336	2.56125	8.09938
6.07	36.8449	2.46374	7.79102	6.57	43.1649	2.56320	8.10555
6.08	36.9664	2.46577	7.79744	6.58	43.2964	2.56515	8.11172
6.09	37.0881	2.46779	7.80385	6.59	43.4281	2.56710	8.11788
6.10	37.2100	2.46982	7.81025	**6.60**	43.5600	2.56905	8.12404
6.11	37.3321	2.47184	7.81665	6.61	43.6921	2.57099	8.13019
6.12	37.4544	2.47386	7.82304	6.62	43.8244	2.57294	8.13634
6.13	37.5769	2.47588	7.82943	6.63	43.9569	2.57488	8.14248
6.14	37.6996	2.47790	7.83582	6.64	44.0896	2.57682	8.14862
6.15	37.8225	2.47992	7.84219	6.65	44.2225	2.57876	8.15475
6.16	37.9456	2.48193	7.84857	6.66	44.3556	2.58070	8.16088
6.17	38.0689	2.48395	7.85493	6.67	44.4889	2.58263	8.16701
6.18	38.1924	2.48596	7.86130	6.68	44.6224	2.58457	8.17313
6.19	38.3161	2.48797	7.86766	6.69	44.7561	2.58650	8.17924
6.20	38.4400	2.48998	7.87401	**6.70**	44.8900	2.58844	8.18535
6.21	38.5641	2.49199	7.88036	6.71	45.0241	2.59037	8.19146
6.22	38.6884	2.49399	7.88670	6.72	45.1584	2.59230	8.19756
6.23	38.8129	2.49600	7.89303	6.73	45.2929	2.59422	8.20366
6.24	38.9376	2.49800	7.89937	6.74	45.4276	2.59615	8.20975
6.25	39.0625	2.50000	7.90569	6.75	45.5625	2.59808	8.21584
6.26	39.1876	2.50200	7.91202	6.76	45.6976	2.60000	8.22192
6.27	39.3129	2.50400	7.91833	6.77	45.8329	2.60192	8.22800
6.28	39.4384	2.50599	7.92465	6.78	45.9684	2.60384	8.23408
6.29	39.5641	2.50799	7.93095	6.79	46.1041	2.60576	8.24015
6.30	39.6900	2.50998	7.93725	**6.80**	46.2400	2.60768	8.24621
6.31	39.8161	2.51197	7.94355	6.81	46.3761	2.60960	8.25227
6.32	39.9424	2.51396	7.94984	6.82	46.5124	2.61151	8.25833
6.33	40.0689	2.51595	7.95613	6.83	46.6489	2.61343	8.26438
6.34	40.1956	2.51794	7.96241	6.84	46.7856	2.61534	8.27043
6.35	40.3225	2.51992	7.96869	6.85	46.9225	2.61725	8.27647
6.36	40.4496	2.52190	7.97496	6.86	47.0596	2.61916	8.28251
6.37	40.5769	2.52389	7.98123	6.87	47.1969	2.62107	8.28855
6.38	40.7044	2.52587	7.98749	6.88	47.3344	2.62298	8.29458
6.39	40.8321	2.52784	7.99375	6.89	47.4721	2.62488	8.30060
6.40	40.9600	2.52982	8.00000	**6.90**	47.6100	2.62679	8.30662
6.41	41.0881	2.53180	8.00625	6.91	47.7481	2.62869	8.31264
6.42	41.2164	2.53377	8.01249	6.92	47.8864	2.63059	8.31865
6.43	41.3449	2.53574	8.01873	6.93	48.0249	2.63249	8.32466
6.44	41.4736	2.53772	8.02496	6.94	48.1636	2.63439	8.33067
6.45	41.6025	2.53969	8.03119	6.95	48.3025	2.63629	8.33667
6.46	41.7316	2.54165	8.03741	6.96	48.4416	2.63818	8.34266
6.47	41.8609	2.54362	8.04363	6.97	48.5809	2.64008	8.34865
6.48	41.9904	2.54558	8.04984	6.98	48.7204	2.64197	8.35464
6.49	42.1201	2.54755	8.05605	6.99	48.8601	2.64386	8.36062
6.50	42.2500	2.54951	8.06226	**7.00**	49.0000	2.64575	8.36660
N	N²	√N	√10N	N	N²	√N	√10N

Squares and Square Roots (*Continued*)

N	N²	√N	√10N	N	N²	√N	√10N
7.00	49.0000	2.64575	8.36660	**7.50**	56.2500	2.73861	8.66025
7.01	49.1401	2.64764	8.37257	7.51	56.4001	2.74044	8.66603
7.02	49.2804	2.64953	8.37854	7.52	56.5504	2.74226	8.67179
7.03	49.4209	2.65141	8.38451	7.53	56.7009	2.74408	8.67756
7.04	49.5616	2.65330	8.39047	7.54	56.8516	2.74591	8.68332
7.05	49.7025	2.65518	8.39643	7.55	57.0025	2.74773	8.68907
7.06	49.8436	2.65707	8.40238	7.56	57.1536	2.74955	8.69483
7.07	49.9849	2.65895	8.40833	7.57	57.3049	2.75136	8.70057
7.08	50.1264	2.66083	8.41427	7.58	57.4564	2.75318	8.70632
7.09	50.2681	2.66271	8.42021	7.59	57.6081	2.75500	8.71206
7.10	50.4100	2.66458	8.42615	**7.60**	57.7600	2.75681	8.71780
7.11	50.5521	2.66646	8.43208	7.61	57.9121	2.75862	8.72353
7.12	50.6944	2.66833	8.43801	7.62	58.0644	2.76043	8.72926
7.13	50.8369	2.67021	8.44393	7.63	58.2169	2.76225	8.73499
7.14	50.9796	2.67208	8.44985	7.64	58.3696	2.76405	8.74071
7.15	51.1225	2.67395	8.45577	7.65	58.5225	2.76586	8.74643
7.16	51.2656	2.67582	8.46168	7.66	58.6756	2.76767	8.75214
7.17	51.4089	2.67769	8.46759	7.67	58.8289	2.76948	8.75785
7.18	51.5524	2.67955	8.47349	7.68	58.9824	2.77128	8.76356
7.19	51.6961	2.68142	8.47939	7.69	59.1361	2.77308	8.76926
7.20	51.8400	2.68328	8.48528	**7.70**	59.2900	2.77489	8.77496
7.21	51.9841	2.68514	8.49117	7.71	59.4441	2.77669	8.78066
7.22	52.1284	2.68701	8.49706	7.72	59.5984	2.77849	8.78635
7.23	52.2729	2.68887	8.50294	7.73	59.7529	2.78029	8.79204
7.24	52.4176	2.69072	8.50882	7.74	59.9076	2.78209	8.79773
7.25	52.5625	2.69258	8.51469	7.75	60.0625	2.78388	8.80341
7.26	52.7076	2.69444	8.52056	7.76	60.2176	2.78568	8.80909
7.27	52.8529	2.69629	8.52643	7.77	60.3729	2.78747	8.81476
7.28	52.9984	2.69815	8.53229	7.78	60.5284	2.78927	8.82043
7.29	53.1441	2.70000	8.53815	7.79	60.6841	2.79106	8.82610
7.30	53.2900	2.70185	8.54400	**7.80**	60.8400	2.79285	8.83176
7.31	53.4361	2.70370	8.54985	7.81	60.9961	2.79464	8.83742
7.32	53.5824	2.70555	8.55570	7.82	61.1524	2.79643	8.84308
7.33	53.7289	2.70740	8.56154	7.83	61.3089	2.79821	8.84873
7.34	53.8756	2.70924	8.56738	7.84	61.4656	2.80000	8.85438
7.35	54.0225	2.71109	8.57321	7.85	61.6225	2.80179	8.86002
7.36	54.1696	2.71293	8.57904	7.86	61.7796	2.80357	8.86566
7.37	54.3169	2.71477	8.58487	7.87	61.9369	2.80535	8.87130
7.38	54.4644	2.71662	8.59069	7.88	62.0944	2.80713	8.87694
7.39	54.6121	2.71846	8.59651	7.89	62.2521	2.80891	8.88257
7.40	54.7600	2.72029	8.60233	**7.90**	62.4100	2.81069	8.88819
7.41	54.9081	2.72213	8.60814	7.91	62.5681	2.81247	8.89382
7.42	55.0564	2.72397	8.61394	7.92	62.7264	2.81425	8.89944
7.43	55.2049	2.72580	8.61974	7.93	62.8849	2.81603	8.90505
7.44	55.3536	2.72764	8.62554	7.94	63.0436	2.81780	8.91067
7.45	55.5025	2.72947	8.63134	7.95	63.2025	2.81957	8.91628
7.46	55.6516	2.73130	8.63713	7.96	63.3616	2.82135	8.92188
7.47	55.8009	2.73313	8.64292	7.97	63.5209	2.82312	8.92749
7.48	55.9504	2.73496	8.64870	7.98	63.6804	2.82489	8.93308
7.49	56.1001	2.73679	8.65448	7.99	63.8401	2.82666	8.93868
7.50	56.2500	2.73861	8.66025	**8.00**	64.0000	2.82843	8.94427
N	N²	√N	√10N	N	N²	√N	√10N

Squares and Square Roots (*Continued*)

N	N²	√N	√10N	N	N²	√N	√10N
8.00	64.0000	2.82843	8.94427	**8.50**	72.2500	2.91548	9.21954
8.01	64.1601	2.83019	8.94986	8.51	72.4201	2.91719	9.22497
8.02	64.3204	2.83196	8.95545	8.52	72.5904	2.91890	9.23038
8.03	64.4809	2.83373	8.96103	8.53	72.7609	2.92062	9.23580
8.04	64.6416	2.83549	8.96660	8.54	72.9316	2.92233	9.24121
8.05	64.8025	2.83725	8.97218	8.55	73.1025	2.92404	9.24662
8.06	64.9636	2.83901	8.97775	8.56	73.2736	2.92575	9.25203
8.07	65 1249	2.84077	8.98332	8.57	73.4449	2.92746	9.25743
8.08	65.2864	2.84253	8.98888	8.58	73.6164	2.92916	9.26283
8.09	65.4481	2.84429	8.99444	8.59	73.7881	2.93087	9.26823
8.10	65.6100	2.84605	9.00000	**8.60**	73.9600	2.93258	9.27362
8.11	65.7721	2.84781	9.00555	8.61	74.1321	2.93428	9.27901
8.12	65.9344	2.84956	9.01110	8.62	74.3044	2.93598	9.28440
8.13	66.0969	2.85132	9.01665	8.63	74.4769	2.93769	9.28978
8.14	66.2596	2.85307	9.02219	8.64	74.6496	2.93939	9.29516
8.15	66.4225	2.85482	9.02774	8.65	74.8225	2.94109	9.30054
8.16	66.5856	2.85657	9.03327	8.66	74.9956	2.94279	9.30591
8.17	66.7489	2.85832	9.03881	8.67	75.1689	2.94449	9.31128
8.18	66.9124	2.86007	9.04434	8.68	75.3424	2.94618	9.31665
8.19	67.0761	2.86182	9.04986	8.69	75.5161	2.94788	9.32202
8.20	67.2400	2.86356	9.05539	**8.70**	75.6900	2.94958	9.32738
8.21	67.4041	2.86531	9.06091	8.71	75.8641	2.95127	9.33274
8.22	67.5684	2.86705	9.06642	8.72	76.0384	2.95296	9.33809
8.23	67.7329	2.86880	9.07193	8.73	76.2129	2.95466	9.34345
8.24	67.8976	2.87054	9.07744	8.74	76.3876	2.95635	9.34880
8.25	68.0625	2.87228	9.08295	8.75	76.5625	2.95804	9.35414
8.26	68.2276	2.87402	9.08845	8.76	76.7376	2.95973	9.35949
8.27	68.3929	2.87576	9.09395	8.77	76.9129	2.96142	9.36483
8.28	68.5584	2.87750	9.09945	8.78	77.0884	2.96311	9.37017
8.29	68.7241	2.87924	9.10494	8.79	77.2641	2.96479	9.37550
8.30	68.8900	2.88097	9.11043	**8.80**	77.4400	2.96648	9.38083
8.31	69.0561	2.88271	9.11592	8.81	77.6161	2.96816	9.38616
8.32	69.2224	2.88444	9.12140	8.82	77.7924	2.96985	9.39149
8.33	69.3889	2.88617	9.12688	8.83	77.9689	2.97153	9.39681
8.34	69.5556	2.88791	9.13236	8.84	78.1456	2.97321	9.40213
8.35	69.7225	2.88964	9.13783	8.85	78.3225	2.97489	9.40744
8.36	69.8896	2.89137	9.14330	8.86	78.4996	2.97658	9.41276
8.37	70.0569	2.89310	9.14877	8.87	78.6769	2.97825	9.41807
8.38	70.2244	2.89482	9.15423	8.88	78.8544	2.97993	9.42338
8.39	70.3921	2.89655	9.15969	8.89	79.0321	2.98161	9.42868
8.40	70.5600	2.89828	9.16515	**8.90**	79.2100	2.98329	9.43398
8.41	70.7281	2.90000	9.17061	8.91	79.3881	2.98496	9.43928
8.42	70.8964	2.90172	9.17606	8.92	79.5664	2.98664	9.44458
8.43	71.0649	2.90345	9.18150	8.93	79.7449	2.98831	9.44987
8.44	71.2336	2.90517	9.18695	8.94	79.9236	2.98998	9.45516
8.45	71.4025	2.90689	9.19239	8.95	80.1025	2.99166	9.46044
8.46	71.5716	2.90861	9.19783	8.96	80.2816	2.99333	9.46573
8.47	71.7409	2.91033	9.20326	8.97	80.4609	2.99500	9.47101
8.48	71.9104	2.91204	9.20869	8.98	80.6404	2.99666	9.47629
8.49	72.0801	2.91376	9.21412	8.99	80.8201	2.99833	9.48156
8.50	72.2500	2.91548	9.21954	**9.00**	81.0000	3.00000	9.48683
N	N²	√N	√10N	N	N²	√N	√10N

N	N²	√N	√10N	N	N²	√N	√10N
9.00	81.0000	3.00000	9.48683	**9.50**	90.2500	3.08221	9.74679
9.01	81.1801	3.00167	9.49210	9.51	90.4401	3.08383	9.75192
9.02	81.3604	3.00333	9.49737	9.52	90.6304	3.08545	9.75705
9.03	81.5409	3.00500	9.50263	9.53	90.8209	3.08707	9.76217
9.04	81.7216	3.00666	9.50789	9.54	91.0116	3.08869	9.76729
9.05	81.9025	3.00832	9.51315	9.55	91.2025	3.09031	9.77241
9.06	82.0836	3.00998	9.51840	9.56	91.3936	3.09192	9.77753
9.07	82.2649	3.01164	9.52365	9.57	91.5849	3.09354	9.78264
9.08	82.4464	3.01330	9.52890	9.58	91.7764	3.09516	9.78775
9.09	82.6281	3.01496	9.53415	9.59	91.9681	3.09677	9.79285
9.10	82.8100	3.01662	9.53939	**9.60**	92.1600	3.09839	9.79796
9.11	82.9921	3.01828	9.54463	9.61	92.3521	3.10000	9.80306
9.12	83.1744	3.01993	9.54987	9.62	92.5444	3.10161	9.80816
9.13	83.3569	3.02159	9.55510	9.63	92.7369	3.10322	9.81326
9.14	83.5396	3.02324	9.56033	9.64	92.9296	3.10483	9.81835
9.15	83.7225	3.02490	9.56556	9.65	93.1225	3.10644	9.82344
9.16	83.9056	3.02655	9.57079	9.66	93.3156	3.10805	9.82853
9.17	84.0889	3.02820	9.57601	9.67	93.5089	3.10966	9.83362
9.18	84.2724	3.02985	9.58123	9.68	93.7024	3.11127	9.83870
9.19	84.4561	3.03150	9.58645	9.69	93.8961	3.11288	9.84378
9.20	84.6400	3.03315	9.59166	**9.70**	94.0900	3.11448	9.84886
9.21	84.8241	3.03480	9.59687	9.71	94.2841	3.11609	9.85393
9.22	85.0084	3.03645	9.60208	9.72	94.4784	3.11769	9.85901
9.23	85.1929	3.03809	9.60729	9.73	94.6729	3.11929	9.86408
9.24	85.3776	3.03974	9.61249	9.74	94.8676	3.12090	9.86914
9.25	85.5625	3.04138	9.61769	9.75	95.0625	3.12250	9.87421
9.26	85.7476	3.04302	9.62289	9.76	95.2576	3.12410	9.87927
9.27	85.9329	3.04467	9.62808	9.77	95.4529	3.12570	9.88433
9.28	86.1184	3.04631	9.63328	9.78	95.6484	3.12730	9.88939
9.29	86.3041	3.04795	9.63846	9.79	95.8441	3.12890	9.89444
9.30	86.4900	3.04959	9.64365	**9.80**	96.0400	3.13050	9.89949
9.31	86.6761	3.05123	9.64883	9.81	96.2361	3.13209	9.90454
9.32	86.8624	3.05287	9.65401	9.82	96.4324	3.13369	9.90959
9.33	87.0489	3.05450	9.65919	9.83	96.6289	3.13528	9.91464
9.34	87.2356	3.05614	9.66437	9.84	96.8256	3.13688	9.91968
9.35	87.4225	3.05778	9.66954	9.85	97.0225	3.13847	9.92472
9.36	87.6096	3.05941	9.67471	9.86	97.2196	3.14006	9.92975
9.37	87.7969	3.06105	9.67988	9.87	97.4169	3.14166	9.93479
9.38	87.9844	3.06268	9.68504	9.88	97.6144	3.14325	9.93982
9.39	88.1721	3.06431	9.69020	9.89	97.8121	3.14484	9.94485
9.40	88.3600	3.06594	9.69536	**9.90**	98.0100	3.14643	9.94987
9.41	88.5481	3.06757	9.70052	9.91	98.2081	3.14802	9.95490
9.42	88.7364	3.06920	9.70567	9.92	98.4064	3.14960	9.95992
9.43	88.9249	3.07083	9.71082	9.93	98.6049	3.15119	9.96494
9.44	89.1136	3.07246	9.71597	9.94	98.8036	3.15278	9.96995
9.45	89.3025	3.07409	9.72111	9.95	99.0025	3.15436	9.97497
9.46	89.4916	3.07571	9.72625	9.96	99.2016	3.15595	9.97998
9.47	89.6809	3.07734	9.73139	9.97	99.4009	3.15753	9.98499
9.48	89.8704	3.07896	9.73653	9.98	99.6004	3.15911	9.98999
9.49	90.0601	3.08058	9.74166	9.99	99.8001	3.16070	9.99500
9.50	90.2500	3.08221	9.74679	**10.00**	100.000	3.16228	10.0000
N	N²	√N	√10N	N	N²	√N	√10N

TABLE II. Normal Areas and Ordinates*

t	$\phi(t)$	$\int_0^t \phi(t)dt$	t	$\phi(t)$	$\int_0^t \phi(t)dt$	t	$\phi(t)$	$\int_0^t \phi(t)dt$
.00	.39894	.00000	.45	.36053	.17364	.90	.26609	.31594
.01	.39892	.00399	.46	.35889	.17724	.91	.26369	.31859
.02	.39886	.00798	.47	.35723	.18082	.92	.26129	.32121
.03	.39876	.01197	.48	.35553	.18439	.93	.25888	.32381
.04	.39862	.01595	.49	.35381	.18793	.94	.25647	.32639
.05	.39844	.01994	.50	.35207	.19146	.95	.25406	.32894
.06	.39822	.02392	.51	.35029	.19497	.96	.25164	.33147
.07	.39797	.02790	.52	.34849	.19847	.97	.24923	.33398
.08	.39767	.03188	.53	.34667	.20194	.98	.24681	.33646
.09	.39733	.03586	.54	.34482	.20540	.99	.24439	.33891
.10	.39695	.03983	.55	.34294	.20884	1.00	.24197	.34134
.11	.39654	.04380	.56	.34105	.21226	1.01	.23955	.34375
.12	.39608	.04776	.57	.33912	.21566	1.02	.23713	.34614
.13	.39559	.05172	.58	.33718	.21904	1.03	.23471	.34850
.14	.39505	.05567	.59	.33521	.22240	1.04	.23230	.35083
.15	.39448	.05962	.60	.33322	.22575	1.05	.22988	.35314
.16	.39387	.06356	.61	.33121	.22907	1.06	.22747	.35543
.17	.39322	.06749	.62	.32918	.23237	1.07	.22506	.35769
.18	.39253	.07142	.63	.32713	.23565	1.08	.22265	.35993
.19	.39181	.07535	.64	.32506	.23891	1.09	.22025	.36214
.20	.39104	.07926	.65	.32297	.24215	1.10	.21785	.36433
.21	.39024	.08317	.66	.32086	.24537	1.11	.21546	.36650
.22	.38940	.08706	.67	.31874	.24857	1.12	.21307	.36864
.23	.38853	.09095	.68	.31659	.25175	1.13	.21069	.37076
.24	.38762	.09483	.69	.31443	.25490	1.14	.20831	.37286
.25	.38667	.09871	.70	.31225	.25804	1.15	.20594	.37493
.26	.38568	.10257	.71	.31006	.26115	1.16	.20357	.37698
.27	.38466	.10642	.72	.30785	.26424	1.17	.20121	.37900
.28	.38361	.11026	.73	.30563	.26730	1.18	.19886	.38100
.29	.38251	.11409	.74	.30339	.27035	1.19	.19652	.38298
.30	.38139	.11791	.75	.30114	.27337	1.20	.19419	.38493
.31	.38023	.12172	.76	.29887	.27637	1.21	.19186	.38686
.32	.37903	.12552	.77	.29659	.27935	1.22	.18954	.38877
.33	.37780	.12930	.78	.29431	.28230	1.23	.18724	.39065
.34	.37654	.13307	.79	.29200	.28524	1.24	.18494	.39251
.35	.37524	.13683	.80	.28969	.28814	1.25	.18265	.39435
.36	.37391	.14058	.81	.28737	.29103	1.26	.18037	.39617
.37	.37255	.14431	.82	.28504	.29389	1.27	.17810	.39796
.38	.37115	.14803	.83	.28269	.29673	1.28	.17585	.39973
.39	.36973	.15173	.84	.28034	.29955	1.29	.17360	.40147
.40	.36827	.15542	.85	.27798	.30234	1.30	.17137	.40320
.41	.36678	.15910	.86	.27562	.30511	1.31	.16915	.40490
.42	.36526	.16276	.87	.27324	.30785	1.32	.16694	.40658
.43	.36371	.16640	.88	.27086	.31057	1.33	.16474	.40824
.44	.36213	.17003	.89	.26848	.31327	1.34	.16256	.40988

* Reprinted, by permission, from Kenney, *Mathematics of Statistics*, Part One, pp. 225–227, D. Van Nostrand, New York.

Normal Areas and Ordinates (*Continued*)

t	$\phi(t)$	$\int_0^t \phi(t)\,dt$	t	$\phi(t)$	$\int_0^t \phi(t)\,dt$	t	$\phi(t)$	$\int_0^t \phi(t)\,dt$
1.35	.16038	.41149	1.80	.07895	.46407	2.25	.03174	.48778
1.36	.15822	.41309	1.81	.07754	.46485	2.26	.03103	.48809
1.37	.15608	.41466	1.82	.07614	.46562	2.27	.03034	.48840
1.38	.15395	.41621	1.83	.07477	.46638	2.28	.02965	.48870
1.39	.15183	.41774	1.84	.07341	.46712	2.29	.02898	.48899
1.40	.14973	.41924	1.85	.07206	.46784	2.30	.02833	.48928
1.41	.14764	.42073	1.86	.07074	.46856	2.31	.02768	.48956
1.42	.14556	.42220	1.87	.06943	.46926	2.32	.02705	.48983
1.43	.14350	.42364	1.88	.06814	.46995	2.33	.02643	.49010
1.44	.14146	.42507	1.89	.06687	.47062	2.34	.02582	.49036
1.45	.13943	.42647	1.90	.06562	.47128	2.35	.02522	.49061
1.46	.13742	.42786	1.91	.06439	.47193	2.36	.02463	.49086
1.47	.13542	.42922	1.92	.06316	.47257	2.37	.02406	.49111
1.48	.13344	.43056	1.93	.06195	.47320	2.38	.02349	.49134
1.49	.13147	.43189	1.94	.06077	.47381	2.39	.02294	.49158
1.50	.12952	.43319	1.95	.05959	.47441	2.40	.02239	.49180
1.51	.12758	.43448	1.96	.05844	.47500	2.41	.02186	.49202
1.52	.12566	.43574	1.97	.05730	.47558	2.42	.02134	.49224
1.53	.12376	.43699	1.98	.05618	.47615	2.43	.02083	.49245
1.54	.12188	.43822	1.99	.05508	.47670	2.44	.02033	.49266
1.55	.12001	.43943	2.00	.05399	.47725	2.45	.01984	.49286
1.56	.11816	.44062	2.01	.05292	.47778	2.46	.01936	.49305
1.57	.11632	.44179	2.02	.05186	.47831	2.47	.01889	.49324
1.58	.11450	.44295	2.03	.05082	.47882	2.48	.01842	.49343
1.59	.11270	.44408	2.04	.04980	.47932	2.49	.01797	.49361
1.60	.11092	.44520	2.05	.04879	.47982	2.50	.01753	.49379
1.61	.10915	.44630	2.06	.04780	.48030	2.51	.01709	.49396
1.62	.10741	.44738	2.07	.04682	.48077	2.52	.01667	.49413
1.63	.10567	.44845	2.08	.04586	.48124	2.53	.01625	.49430
1.64	.10396	.44950	2.09	.04491	.48169	2.54	.01585	.49446
1.65	.10226	.45053	2.10	.04398	.48214	2.55	.01545	.49461
1.66	.10059	.45154	2.11	.04307	.48257	2.56	.01506	.49477
1.67	.09893	.45254	2.12	.04217	.48300	2.57	.01468	.49492
1.68	.09728	.45352	2.13	.04128	.48341	2.58	.01431	.49506
1.69	.09566	.45449	2.14	.04041	.48382	2.59	.01394	.49520
1.70	.09405	.45543	2.15	.03955	.48422	2.60	.01358	.49534
1.71	.09246	.45637	2.16	.03871	.48461	2.61	.01323	.49547
1.72	.09089	.45728	2.17	.03788	.48500	2.62	.01289	.49560
1.73	.08933	.45818	2.18	.03706	.48537	2.63	.01256	.49573
1.74	.08780	.45907	2.19	.03626	.48574	2.64	.01223	.49585
1.75	.08628	.45994	2.20	.03547	.48610	2.65	.01191	.49598
1.76	.08478	.46080	2.21	.03470	.48645	2.66	.01160	.49609
1.77	.08329	.46164	2.22	.03394	.48679	2.67	.01130	.49621
1.78	.08183	.46246	2.23	.03319	.48713	2.68	.01100	.49632
1.79	.08038	.46327	2.24	.03246	.48745	2.69	.01071	.49643

Normal Areas and Ordinates (*Continued*)

t	$\phi(t)$	$\int_0^t \phi(t)dt$	t	$\phi(t)$	$\int_0^t \phi(t)dt$	t	$\phi(t)$	$\int_0^t \phi(t)dt$
2.70	.01042	.49653	3.15	.00279	.49918	3.60	.00061	.49984
2.71	.01014	.49664	3.16	.00271	.49921	3.61	.00059	.49985
2.72	.00987	.49674	3.17	.00262	.49924	3.62	.00057	.49985
2.73	.00961	.49683	3.18	.00254	.49926	3.63	.00055	.49986
2.74	.00935	.49693	3.19	.00246	.49929	3.64	.00053	.49986
2.75	.00909	.49702	3.20	.00238	.49931	3.65	.00051	.49987
2.76	.00885	.49711	3.21	.00231	.49934	3.66	.00049	.49987
2.77	.00861	.49720	3.22	.00224	.49936	3.67	.00047	.49988
2.78	.00837	.49728	3.23	.00216	.49938	3.68	.00046	.49988
2.79	.00814	.49736	3.24	.00210	.49940	3.69	.00044	.49989
2.80	.00792	.49744	3.25	.00203	.49942	3.70	.00042	.49989
2.81	.00770	.49752	3.26	.00196	.49944	3.71	.00041	.49990
2.82	.00748	.49760	3.27	.00190	.49946	3.72	.00039	.49990
2.83	.00727	.49767	3.28	.00184	.49948	3.73	.00038	.49990
2.84	.00707	.49774	3.29	.00178	.49950	3.74	.00037	.49991
2.85	.00687	.49781	3.30	.00172	.49952	3.75	.00035	.49991
2.86	.00668	.49788	3.31	.00167	.49953	3.76	.00034	.49992
2.87	.00649	.49795	3.32	.00161	.49955	3.77	.00033	.49992
2.88	.00631	.49801	3.33	.00156	.49957	3.78	.00031	.49992
2.89	.00613	.49807	3.34	.00151	.49958	3.79	.00030	.49992
2.90	.00595	.49813	3.35	.00146	.49960	3.80	.00029	.49993
2.91	.00578	.49819	3.36	.00141	.49961	3.81	.00028	.49993
2.92	.00562	.49825	3.37	.00136	.49962	3.82	.00027	.49993
2.93	.00545	.49831	3.38	.00132	.49964	3.83	.00026	.49994
2.94	.00530	.49836	3.39	.00127	.49965	3.84	.00025	.49994
2.95	.00514	.49841	3.40	.00123	.49966	3.85	.00024	.49994
2.96	.00499	.49846	3.41	.00119	.49968	3.86	.00023	.49994
2.97	.00485	.49851	3.42	.00115	.49969	3.87	.00022	.49995
2.98	.00471	.49856	3.43	.00111	.49970	3.88	.00021	.49995
2.99	.00457	.49861	3.44	.00107	.49971	3.89	.00021	.49995
3.00	.00443	.49865	3.45	.00104	.49972	3.90	.00020	.49995
3.01	.00430	.49869	3.46	.00100	.49973	3.91	.00019	.49995
3.02	.00417	.49874	3.47	.00097	.49974	3.92	.00018	.49996
3.03	.00405	.49878	3.48	.00094	.49975	3.93	.00018	.49996
3.04	.00393	.49882	3.49	.00090	.49976	3.94	.00017	.49996
3.05	.00381	.49886	3.50	.00087	.49977	3.95	.00016	.49996
3.06	.00370	.49889	3.51	.00084	.49978	3.96	.00016	.49996
3.07	.00358	.49893	3.52	.00081	.49978	3.97	.00015	.49996
3.08	.00348	.49897	3.53	.00079	.49979	3.98	.00014	.49997
3.09	.00337	.49900	3.54	.00076	.49980	3.99	.00014	.49997
3.10	.00327	.49903	3.55	.00073	.49981			
3.11	.00317	.49906	3.56	.00071	.49981			
3.12	.00307	.49910	3.57	.00068	.49982			
3.13	.00298	.49913	3.58	.00066	.49983			
3.14	.00288	.49916	3.59	.00063	.49983			

TABLE III—χ^2 Distribution

Degrees of freedom	P = 0.99	0.98	0.95	0.90	0.80	0.70	0.50	0.30	0.20	0.10	0.05	0.02	0.01
1	0.000157	0.000628	0.00393	0.0158	0.0642	0.148	0.455	1.074	1.642	2.706	3.841	5.412	6.635
2	0.0201	0.0404	0.103	0.211	0.446	0.713	1.386	2.408	3.219	4.605	5.991	7.824	9.210
3	0.115	0.185	0.352	0.584	1.005	1.424	2.366	3.665	4.642	6.251	7.815	9.837	11.341
4	0.297	0.429	0.711	1.064	1.649	2.195	3.357	4.878	5.989	7.779	9.488	11.668	13.277
5	0.554	0.752	1.145	1.610	2.343	3.000	4.351	6.064	7.289	9.236	11.070	13.388	15.086
6	0.872	1.134	1.635	2.204	3.070	3.828	5.348	7.231	8.558	10.645	12.592	15.033	16.812
7	1.239	1.564	2.167	2.833	3.822	4.671	6.346	8.383	9.803	12.017	14.067	16.622	18.475
8	1.646	2.032	2.733	3.490	4.594	5.527	7.344	9.524	11.030	13.362	15.507	18.168	20.090
9	2.088	2.532	3.325	4.168	5.380	6.393	8.343	10.656	12.242	14.684	16.919	19.679	21.666
10	2.558	3.059	3.940	4.865	6.179	7.267	9.342	11.781	13.442	15.987	18.307	21.161	23.209
11	3.053	3.609	4.575	5.578	6.989	8.148	10.341	12.899	14.631	17.275	19.675	22.618	24.725
12	3.571	4.178	5.226	6.304	7.807	9.034	11.340	14.011	15.812	18.549	21.026	24.054	26.217
13	4.107	4.765	5.892	7.042	8.634	9.926	12.340	15.119	16.985	19.812	22.362	25.472	27.688
14	4.660	5.368	6.571	7.790	9.467	10.821	13.339	16.222	18.151	21.064	23.685	26.873	29.141
15	5.229	5.985	7.261	8.547	10.307	11.721	14.339	17.322	19.311	22.307	24.996	28.259	30.578
16	5.812	6.614	7.962	9.312	11.152	12.624	15.338	18.418	20.465	23.542	26.296	29.633	32.000
17	6.408	7.255	8.672	10.085	12.002	13.531	16.338	19.511	21.615	24.769	27.587	30.995	33.409
18	7.015	7.906	9.390	10.865	12.857	14.440	17.338	20.601	22.760	25.989	28.869	32.346	34.805
19	7.633	8.567	10.117	11.651	13.716	15.352	18.338	21.689	23.900	27.204	30.144	33.687	36.191
20	8.260	9.237	10.851	12.443	14.578	16.266	19.337	22.775	25.038	28.412	31.410	35.020	37.566
21	8.897	9.915	11.591	13.240	15.445	17.182	20.337	23.858	26.171	29.615	32.671	36.343	38.932
22	9.542	10.600	12.338	14.041	16.314	18.101	21.337	24.939	27.301	30.813	33.924	37.659	40.289
23	10.196	11.293	13.091	14.848	17.187	19.021	22.337	26.018	28.429	32.007	35.172	38.968	41.638
24	10.856	11.992	13.848	15.659	18.062	19.943	23.337	27.096	29.553	33.196	36.415	40.270	42.980
25	11.524	12.697	14.611	16.473	18.940	20.867	24.337	28.172	30.675	34.382	37.652	41.566	44.314
26	12.198	13.409	15.379	17.292	19.820	21.792	25.336	29.246	31.795	35.563	38.885	42.856	45.642
27	12.879	14.125	16.151	18.114	20.703	22.719	26.336	30.319	32.912	36.741	40.113	44.140	46.963
28	13.565	14.847	16.928	18.939	21.588	23.647	27.336	31.391	34.027	37.916	41.337	45.419	48.278
29	14.256	15.574	17.708	19.768	22.475	24.577	28.336	32.461	35.139	39.087	42.557	46.693	49.588
30	14.953	16.306	18.493	20.599	23.364	25.508	29.336	33.530	36.250	40.256	43.773	47.962	50.892

For degrees of freedom greater than 30, the expression $\sqrt{2\chi^2} - \sqrt{2n' - 1}$ may be used as a normal deviate with unit variance, where n' is the number of degrees of freedom.

Reproduced from *Statistical Methods for Research Workers*, 6th ed., with the permission of the author, R. A. Fisher, and his publisher, Oliver and Boyd, Edinburgh.

TABLE IV. Student's t Distribution*

Degrees of freedom n	Probability of a deviation greater than t					
	.005	.01	025	.05	.1	.15
1	63.657	31.821	12.706	6.314	3.078	1.963
2	9.925	6.965	4.303	2.920	1.886	1.386
3	5.841	4.541	3.182	2.353	1.638	1.250
4	4.604	3.747	2.776	2.132	1.533	1.190
5	4.032	3.365	2.571	2.015	1.476	1.156
6	3.707	3.143	2.447	1.943	1.440	1.134
7	3.499	2.998	2.365	1.895	1.415	1.119
8	3.355	2.896	2.306	1.860	1.397	1.108
9	3.250	2.821	2.262	1.833	1.383	1.100
10	3.169	2.764	2.228	1.812	1.372	1.093
11	3.106	2.718	2.201	1.796	1.363	1.088
12	3.055	2.681	2.179	1.782	1.356	1.083
13	3.012	2.650	2.160	1.771	1.350	1.079
14	2.977	2.624	2.145	1.761	1.345	1.076
15	2.947	2.602	2.131	1.753	1.341	1.074
16	2.921	2.583	2.120	1.746	1.337	1.071
17	2.898	2.567	2.110	1.740	1.333	1.069
18	2.878	2.552	2.101	1.734	1.330	1.067
19	2.861	2.539	2.093	1.729	1.328	1.066
20	2.845	2.528	2.086	1.725	1.325	1.064
21	2.831	2.518	2.080	1.721	1.323	1.063
22	2.819	2.508	2.074	1.717	1.321	1.061
23	2.807	2.500	2.069	1.714	1.319	1.060
24	2.797	2.492	2.064	1.711	1.318	1.059
25	2.787	2.485	2.060	1.708	1.316	1.058
26	2.779	2.479	2.056	1.706	1.315	1.058
27	2.771	2.473	2.052	1.703	1.314	1.057
28	2.763	2.467	2.048	1.701	1.313	1.056
29	2.756	2.462	2.045	1.699	1.311	1.055
30	2.750	2.457	2.042	1.697	1.310	1.055
∞	2.576	2.326	1.960	1.645	1.282	1.036

The probability of a deviation *numerically* greater than t is twice the probability given at the head of the table.

* This table is reproduced from *Statistical Methods for Research Workers*, with the generous permission of the author, Professor R. A. Fisher, and the publishers, Messrs. Oliver and Boyd.

Student's t Distribution (*Continued*)

Degrees of freedom n	Probability of a deviation greater than t					
	.2	.25	.3	.35	.4	.45
1	1.376	1.000	.727	.510	.325	.158
2	1.061	.816	.617	.445	.289	.142
3	.978	.765	.584	.424	.277	.137
4	.941	.741	.569	.414	.271	.134
5	.920	.727	.559	.408	.267	.132
6	.906	.718	.553	.404	.265	.131
7	.896	.711	.549	.402	.263	.130
8	.889	.706	.546	.399	.262	.130
9	.883	.703	.543	.398	.261	.129
10	.879	.700	.542	.397	.260	.129
11	.876	.697	.540	.396	.260	.129
12	.873	.695	.539	.395	.259	.128
13	.870	.694	.538	.394	.259	.128
14	.868	.692	.537	.393	.258	.128
15	.866	.691	.536	.393	.258	.128
16	.865	.690	.535	.392	.258	.128
17	.863	.689	.534	.392	.257	.128
18	.862	.688	.534	.392	.257	.127
19	.861	.688	.533	.391	.257	.127
20	.860	.687	.533	.391	.257	.127
21	.859	.686	.532	.391	.257	.127
22	.858	.686	.532	.390	.256	.127
23	.858	.685	.532	.390	.256	.127
24	.857	.685	.531	.390	.256	.127
25	.856	.684	.531	.390	.256	.127
26	.856	.684	.531	.390	.256	.127
27	.855	.684	.531	.389	.256	.127
28	.855	.683	.530	.389	.256	.127
29	.854	.683	.530	.389	.256	.127
30	.854	.683	.530	.389	.256	.127
∞	.842	.674	.524	.385	.253	.126

The probability of a deviation *numerically* greater than t is twice the probability given at the head of the table.

TABLE V. F Distribution*

5% (Roman Type) and 1% (Bold-Face Type) Points for the Distribution of F

Degrees of freedom for denominator (v_2)	Degrees of freedom for numerator (v_1)																							
	1	2	3	4	5	6	7	8	9	10	11	12	14	16	20	24	30	40	50	75	100	200	500	∞
1	161 **4052**	200 **4999**	216 **5403**	225 **5625**	230 **5764**	234 **5859**	237 **5928**	239 **5981**	241 **6022**	242 **6056**	243 **6082**	244 **6106**	245 **6142**	246 **6169**	248 **6208**	249 **6234**	250 **6258**	251 **6286**	252 **6302**	253 **6323**	253 **6334**	254 **6352**	254 **6361**	254 **6366**
2	18.51 **98.49**	19.00 **99.01**	19.16 **99.17**	19.25 **99.25**	19.30 **99.30**	19.33 **99.33**	19.36 **99.34**	19.37 **99.36**	19.38 **99.38**	19.39 **99.40**	19.40 **99.41**	19.41 **99.42**	19.42 **99.43**	19.43 **99.44**	19.44 **99.45**	19.45 **99.46**	19.46 **99.47**	19.47 **99.48**	19.47 **99.48**	19.48 **99.48**	19.49 **99.49**	19.49 **99.49**	19.50 **99.50**	19.50 **99.50**
3	10.13 **34.12**	9.55 **30.81**	9.28 **29.46**	9.12 **28.71**	9.01 **28.24**	8.94 **27.91**	8.88 **27.67**	8.84 **27.49**	8.81 **27.34**	8.78 **27.23**	8.76 **27.13**	8.74 **27.05**	8.71 **26.92**	8.69 **26.83**	8.66 **26.69**	8.64 **26.60**	8.62 **26.50**	8.60 **26.41**	8.58 **26.30**	8.57 **26.27**	8.56 **26.23**	8.54 **26.18**	8.54 **26.14**	8.53 **26.12**
4	7.71 **21.20**	6.94 **18.00**	6.59 **16.69**	6.39 **15.98**	6.26 **15.52**	6.16 **15.21**	6.09 **14.98**	6.04 **14.80**	6.00 **14.66**	5.96 **14.54**	5.93 **14.45**	5.91 **14.37**	5.87 **14.24**	5.84 **14.15**	5.80 **14.02**	5.77 **13.93**	5.74 **13.83**	5.71 **13.74**	5.70 **13.69**	5.68 **13.61**	5.66 **13.57**	5.65 **13.52**	5.64 **13.48**	5.63 **13.46**
5	6.61 **16.26**	5.79 **13.27**	5.41 **12.06**	5.19 **11.39**	5.05 **10.97**	4.95 **10.67**	4.88 **10.45**	4.82 **10.27**	4.78 **10.15**	4.74 **10.05**	4.70 **9.96**	4.68 **9.89**	4.64 **9.77**	4.60 **9.68**	4.56 **9.55**	4.53 **9.47**	4.50 **9.38**	4.46 **9.29**	4.44 **9.24**	4.42 **9.17**	4.40 **9.13**	4.38 **9.07**	4.37 **9.04**	4.36 **9.02**
6	5.99 **13.74**	5.14 **10.92**	4.76 **9.78**	4.53 **9.15**	4.39 **8.75**	4.28 **8.47**	4.21 **8.26**	4.15 **8.10**	4.10 **7.98**	4.06 **7.87**	4.03 **7.79**	4.00 **7.72**	3.96 **7.60**	3.92 **7.52**	3.87 **7.39**	3.84 **7.31**	3.81 **7.23**	3.77 **7.14**	3.75 **7.09**	3.72 **7.02**	3.71 **6.99**	3.69 **6.94**	3.68 **6.90**	3.67 **6.88**
7	5.59 **12.25**	4.74 **9.55**	4.35 **8.45**	4.12 **7.85**	3.97 **7.46**	3.87 **7.19**	3.79 **7.00**	3.73 **6.84**	3.68 **6.71**	3.63 **6.62**	3.60 **6.54**	3.57 **6.47**	3.52 **6.35**	3.49 **6.27**	3.44 **6.15**	3.41 **6.07**	3.38 **5.98**	3.34 **5.90**	3.32 **5.85**	3.29 **5.78**	3.28 **5.75**	3.25 **5.70**	3.24 **5.67**	3.23 **5.65**
8	5.32 **11.26**	4.46 **8.65**	4.07 **7.59**	3.84 **7.01**	3.69 **6.63**	3.58 **6.37**	3.50 **6.19**	3.44 **6.03**	3.39 **5.91**	3.34 **5.82**	3.31 **5.74**	3.28 **5.67**	3.23 **5.56**	3.20 **5.48**	3.15 **5.36**	3.12 **5.28**	3.08 **5.20**	3.05 **5.11**	3.03 **5.06**	3.00 **5.00**	2.98 **4.96**	2.96 **4.91**	2.94 **4.88**	2.93 **4.86**
9	5.12 **10.56**	4.26 **8.02**	3.86 **6.99**	3.63 **6.42**	3.48 **6.06**	3.37 **5.80**	3.29 **5.62**	3.23 **5.47**	3.18 **5.35**	3.13 **5.26**	3.10 **5.18**	3.07 **5.11**	3.02 **5.00**	2.98 **4.92**	2.93 **4.80**	2.90 **4.73**	2.86 **4.64**	2.82 **4.56**	2.80 **4.51**	2.77 **4.45**	2.76 **4.41**	2.73 **4.36**	2.72 **4.33**	2.71 **4.31**

* Reprinted, by permission, from Snedecor, *Statistical Methods*, Collegiate Press, Iowa State College, Amer.

10	2.54 / 3.91	2.55 / 3.93	2.56 / 3.96	2.59 / 4.01	2.61 / 4.03	2.64 / 4.12	2.67 / 4.17	2.70 / 4.25	2.74 / 4.33	2.77 / 4.41	2.82 / 4.52	2.86 / 4.60	2.91 / 4.71	2.94 / 4.78	2.97 / 4.85	3.02 / 4.95	3.07 / 5.06	3.14 / 5.21	3.22 / 5.39	3.33 / 5.64	3.48 / 5.99	3.71 / 6.55	4.10 / 7.56	4.96 / 10.04
11	2.40 / 3.60	2.41 / 3.62	2.42 / 3.66	2.45 / 3.70	2.47 / 3.74	2.50 / 3.80	2.53 / 3.86	2.57 / 3.94	2.61 / 4.02	2.65 / 4.10	2.70 / 4.21	2.74 / 4.29	2.79 / 4.40	2.82 / 4.46	2.86 / 4.54	2.90 / 4.63	2.95 / 4.74	3.01 / 4.88	3.09 / 5.07	3.20 / 5.32	3.36 / 5.67	3.59 / 6.22	3.98 / 7.20	4.84 / 9.65
12	2.30 / 3.36	2.31 / 3.38	2.32 / 3.41	2.35 / 3.46	2.36 / 3.49	2.40 / 3.56	2.42 / 3.61	2.46 / 3.70	2.50 / 3.78	2.54 / 3.86	2.60 / 3.98	2.64 / 4.05	2.69 / 4.16	2.72 / 4.22	2.76 / 4.30	2.80 / 4.39	2.85 / 4.50	2.92 / 4.65	3.00 / 4.82	3.11 / 5.06	3.26 / 5.41	3.49 / 5.95	3.88 / 6.93	4.75 / 9.33
13	2.21 / 3.16	2.22 / 3.18	2.24 / 3.21	2.26 / 3.27	2.28 / 3.30	2.32 / 3.37	2.34 / 3.42	2.38 / 3.51	2.42 / 3.59	2.46 / 3.67	2.51 / 3.78	2.55 / 3.85	2.60 / 3.96	2.63 / 4.02	2.67 / 4.10	2.72 / 4.19	2.77 / 4.30	2.84 / 4.44	2.92 / 4.62	3.02 / 4.86	3.18 / 5.20	3.41 / 5.74	3.80 / 6.70	4.67 / 9.07
14	2.13 / 3.00	2.14 / 3.02	2.16 / 3.06	2.19 / 3.11	2.21 / 3.14	2.24 / 3.21	2.27 / 3.26	2.31 / 3.34	2.35 / 3.43	2.39 / 3.51	2.44 / 3.62	2.48 / 3.70	2.53 / 3.80	2.56 / 3.86	2.60 / 3.94	2.65 / 4.03	2.70 / 4.14	2.77 / 4.28	2.85 / 4.46	2.96 / 4.69	3.11 / 5.03	3.34 / 5.56	3.74 / 6.51	4.60 / 8.86
15	2.07 / 2.87	2.08 / 2.89	2.10 / 2.92	2.12 / 2.97	2.15 / 3.00	2.18 / 3.07	2.21 / 3.12	2.25 / 3.20	2.29 / 3.29	2.33 / 3.36	2.39 / 3.48	2.43 / 3.56	2.48 / 3.67	2.51 / 3.73	2.55 / 3.80	2.59 / 3.89	2.64 / 4.00	2.70 / 4.14	2.79 / 4.32	2.90 / 4.56	3.06 / 4.89	3.29 / 5.42	3.68 / 6.36	4.54 / 8.68
16	2.01 / 2.75	2.02 / 2.77	2.04 / 2.80	2.07 / 2.86	2.09 / 2.89	2.13 / 2.96	2.16 / 3.01	2.20 / 3.10	2.24 / 3.18	2.28 / 3.25	2.33 / 3.37	2.37 / 3.45	2.42 / 3.55	2.45 / 3.61	2.49 / 3.69	2.54 / 3.78	2.59 / 3.89	2.66 / 4.03	2.74 / 4.20	2.85 / 4.44	3.01 / 4.77	3.24 / 5.29	3.63 / 6.23	4.49 / 8.53
17	1.96 / 2.65	1.97 / 2.67	1.99 / 2.70	2.02 / 2.76	2.04 / 2.79	2.08 / 2.86	2.11 / 2.92	2.15 / 3.00	2.19 / 3.08	2.23 / 3.16	2.29 / 3.27	2.33 / 3.35	2.38 / 3.45	2.41 / 3.52	2.45 / 3.59	2.50 / 3.68	2.55 / 3.79	2.62 / 3.93	2.70 / 4.10	2.81 / 4.34	2.96 / 4.67	3.20 / 5.18	3.59 / 6.11	4.45 / 8.40
18	1.92 / 2.57	1.93 / 2.59	1.95 / 2.62	1.98 / 2.68	2.00 / 2.71	2.04 / 2.78	2.07 / 2.83	2.11 / 2.91	2.15 / 3.00	2.19 / 3.07	2.25 / 3.19	2.29 / 3.27	2.34 / 3.37	2.37 / 3.44	2.41 / 3.51	2.46 / 3.60	2.51 / 3.71	2.58 / 3.85	2.66 / 4.01	2.77 / 4.25	2.93 / 4.58	3.16 / 5.09	3.55 / 6.01	4.41 / 8.28
19	1.88 / 2.49	1.90 / 2.51	1.91 / 2.54	1.94 / 2.60	1.96 / 2.63	2.00 / 2.70	2.02 / 2.76	2.07 / 2.84	2.11 / 2.92	2.15 / 3.00	2.21 / 3.12	2.26 / 3.19	2.31 / 3.30	2.34 / 3.36	2.38 / 3.43	2.43 / 3.52	2.48 / 3.63	2.55 / 3.77	2.63 / 3.94	2.74 / 4.17	2.90 / 4.50	3.13 / 5.01	3.52 / 5.93	4.38 / 8.18
20	1.84 / 2.42	1.85 / 2.44	1.87 / 2.47	1.90 / 2.53	1.92 / 2.56	1.96 / 2.63	1.99 / 2.69	2.04 / 2.77	2.08 / 2.86	2.12 / 2.94	2.18 / 3.05	2.23 / 3.13	2.28 / 3.23	2.31 / 3.30	2.35 / 3.37	2.40 / 3.45	2.45 / 3.56	2.52 / 3.71	2.60 / 3.87	2.71 / 4.10	2.87 / 4.43	3.10 / 4.94	3.49 / 5.85	4.35 / 8.10
21	1.81 / 2.36	1.82 / 2.38	1.84 / 2.42	1.87 / 2.47	1.89 / 2.51	1.93 / 2.58	1.96 / 2.63	2.00 / 2.72	2.05 / 2.80	2.09 / 2.88	2.15 / 2.99	2.20 / 3.07	2.25 / 3.17	2.28 / 3.24	2.32 / 3.31	2.37 / 3.40	2.42 / 3.51	2.49 / 3.65	2.57 / 3.81	2.68 / 4.04	2.84 / 4.37	3.07 / 4.87	3.47 / 5.78	4.32 / 8.02
22	1.78 / 2.31	1.80 / 2.33	1.81 / 2.37	1.84 / 2.42	1.87 / 2.46	1.91 / 2.53	1.93 / 2.58	1.98 / 2.67	2.03 / 2.75	2.07 / 2.83	2.13 / 2.94	2.18 / 3.02	2.23 / 3.12	2.26 / 3.18	2.30 / 3.26	2.35 / 3.35	2.40 / 3.45	2.47 / 3.59	2.55 / 3.76	2.66 / 3.99	2.82 / 4.31	3.05 / 4.82	3.44 / 5.72	4.30 / 7.94
23	1.76 / 2.26	1.77 / 2.28	1.79 / 2.32	1.82 / 2.37	1.84 / 2.41	1.88 / 2.48	1.91 / 2.53	1.96 / 2.62	2.00 / 2.70	2.04 / 2.78	2.10 / 2.89	2.14 / 2.97	2.20 / 3.07	2.24 / 3.14	2.28 / 3.21	2.32 / 3.30	2.38 / 3.41	2.45 / 3.54	2.53 / 3.71	2.64 / 3.94	2.80 / 4.26	3.03 / 4.76	3.42 / 5.66	4.28 / 7.88
24	1.73 / 2.21	1.74 / 2.23	1.76 / 2.27	1.80 / 2.33	1.82 / 2.36	1.86 / 2.44	1.89 / 2.49	1.94 / 2.58	1.98 / 2.66	2.02 / 2.74	2.09 / 2.86	2.13 / 2.93	2.18 / 3.03	2.22 / 3.09	2.26 / 3.17	2.30 / 3.25	2.36 / 3.36	2.43 / 3.50	2.51 / 3.67	2.62 / 3.90	2.78 / 4.22	3.01 / 4.72	3.40 / 5.61	4.26 / 7.82
25	1.71 / 2.17	1.72 / 2.19	1.74 / 2.23	1.77 / 2.29	1.80 / 2.32	1.84 / 2.40	1.87 / 2.45	1.92 / 2.54	1.96 / 2.62	2.00 / 2.70	2.06 / 2.81	2.11 / 2.89	2.16 / 2.99	2.20 / 3.05	2.24 / 3.13	2.28 / 3.21	2.34 / 3.32	2.41 / 3.46	2.49 / 3.63	2.60 / 3.86	2.76 / 4.18	2.99 / 4.68	3.38 / 5.57	4.24 / 7.77
26	1.69 / 2.13	1.70 / 2.15	1.72 / 2.19	1.76 / 2.25	1.78 / 2.28	1.82 / 2.36	1.85 / 2.41	1.90 / 2.50	1.95 / 2.58	1.99 / 2.66	2.05 / 2.77	2.10 / 2.86	2.15 / 2.96	2.18 / 3.02	2.22 / 3.09	2.27 / 3.17	2.32 / 3.29	2.39 / 3.42	2.47 / 3.59	2.59 / 3.82	2.74 / 4.14	2.89 / 4.64	3.37 / 5.53	4.22 / 7.72

TABLE V. F Distribution (Continued)

5% (Roman Type) and 1% (Bold-Face Type) Points for the Distribution of F

Degrees of freedom for numerator (ν_1)

Degrees of freedom for denominator (ν_2)	1	2	3	4	5	6	7	8	9	10	11	12	14	16	20	24	30	40	50	75	100	200	500	∞
27	4.21 / 7.68	3.35 / 5.49	2.96 / 4.60	2.73 / 4.11	2.57 / 3.79	2.46 / 3.56	2.37 / 3.39	2.30 / 3.26	2.25 / 3.14	2.20 / 3.06	2.16 / 2.98	2.13 / 2.93	2.08 / 2.83	2.03 / 2.74	1.97 / 2.63	1.93 / 2.55	1.88 / 2.47	1.84 / 2.38	1.80 / 2.33	1.76 / 2.25	1.74 / 2.21	1.71 / 2.16	1.68 / 2.12	1.67 / 2.10
28	4.20 / 7.64	3.34 / 5.45	2.95 / 4.57	2.71 / 4.07	2.56 / 3.76	2.44 / 3.53	2.36 / 3.36	2.29 / 3.23	2.24 / 3.11	2.19 / 3.03	2.15 / 2.95	2.12 / 2.90	2.06 / 2.80	2.02 / 2.71	1.96 / 2.60	1.91 / 2.52	1.87 / 2.44	1.81 / 2.35	1.78 / 2.30	1.75 / 2.22	1.72 / 2.18	1.69 / 2.13	1.67 / 2.09	1.65 / 2.06
29	4.18 / 7.60	3.33 / 5.52	2.93 / 4.54	2.70 / 4.04	2.54 / 3.73	2.43 / 3.50	2.35 / 3.33	2.28 / 3.20	2.22 / 3.08	2.18 / 3.00	2.14 / 2.92	2.10 / 2.87	2.05 / 2.77	2.00 / 2.68	1.94 / 2.57	1.90 / 2.49	1.85 / 2.41	1.80 / 2.32	1.77 / 2.27	1.73 / 2.19	1.71 / 2.15	1.68 / 2.10	1.65 / 2.06	1.64 / 2.03
30	4.17 / 7.56	3.32 / 5.39	2.92 / 4.51	2.69 / 4.02	2.53 / 3.70	2.42 / 3.47	2.34 / 3.30	2.27 / 3.17	2.21 / 3.06	2.16 / 2.98	2.12 / 2.90	2.09 / 2.84	2.04 / 2.74	1.99 / 2.66	1.93 / 2.55	1.89 / 2.47	1.84 / 2.38	1.79 / 2.29	1.76 / 2.24	1.72 / 2.16	1.69 / 2.13	1.66 / 2.07	1.64 / 2.03	1.62 / 2.01
32	4.15 / 7.50	3.30 / 5.34	2.90 / 4.46	2.67 / 3.97	2.51 / 3.66	2.40 / 3.42	2.32 / 3.25	2.25 / 3.12	2.19 / 3.01	2.14 / 2.94	2.10 / 2.86	2.07 / 2.80	2.02 / 2.70	1.97 / 2.62	1.91 / 2.51	1.86 / 2.42	1.82 / 2.34	1.76 / 2.25	1.74 / 2.20	1.69 / 2.12	1.67 / 2.08	1.64 / 2.02	1.61 / 1.98	1.59 / 1.96
34	4.13 / 7.44	3.28 / 5.29	2.88 / 4.42	2.65 / 3.93	2.49 / 3.61	2.38 / 3.38	2.30 / 3.21	2.23 / 3.08	2.17 / 2.97	2.12 / 2.89	2.08 / 2.82	2.05 / 2.76	2.00 / 2.66	1.95 / 2.58	1.89 / 2.47	1.84 / 2.38	1.80 / 2.30	1.74 / 2.21	1.71 / 2.15	1.67 / 2.08	1.64 / 2.04	1.61 / 1.98	1.59 / 1.94	1.57 / 1.91
36	4.11 / 7.39	3.26 / 5.25	2.86 / 4.38	2.63 / 3.89	2.48 / 3.58	2.36 / 3.35	2.28 / 3.18	2.21 / 3.04	2.15 / 2.94	2.10 / 2.86	2.06 / 2.78	2.03 / 2.72	1.98 / 2.62	1.93 / 2.54	1.87 / 2.43	1.82 / 2.35	1.78 / 2.26	1.72 / 2.17	1.69 / 2.12	1.65 / 2.04	1.62 / 2.00	1.59 / 1.94	1.56 / 1.90	1.55 / 1.87
38	4.10 / 7.35	3.25 / 5.21	2.85 / 4.34	2.62 / 3.86	2.46 / 3.54	2.35 / 3.32	2.26 / 3.15	2.19 / 3.02	2.14 / 2.91	2.09 / 2.82	2.05 / 2.75	2.02 / 2.69	1.96 / 2.59	1.92 / 2.51	1.85 / 2.40	1.80 / 2.32	1.76 / 2.22	1.71 / 2.14	1.67 / 2.08	1.63 / 2.00	1.60 / 1.97	1.57 / 1.90	1.54 / 1.86	1.53 / 1.84
40	4.08 / 7.31	3.23 / 5.18	2.84 / 4.31	2.61 / 3.83	2.45 / 3.51	2.34 / 3.29	2.25 / 3.12	2.18 / 2.99	2.12 / 2.88	2.07 / 2.80	2.04 / 2.73	2.00 / 2.66	1.95 / 2.56	1.90 / 2.49	1.84 / 2.37	1.79 / 2.29	1.74 / 2.20	1.69 / 2.11	1.66 / 2.05	1.61 / 1.97	1.59 / 1.94	1.55 / 1.88	1.53 / 1.84	1.51 / 1.81
42	4.07 / 7.27	3.22 / 5.15	2.83 / 4.29	2.59 / 3.80	2.44 / 3.49	2.32 / 3.26	2.24 / 3.10	2.17 / 2.96	2.11 / 2.86	2.06 / 2.77	2.02 / 2.70	1.99 / 2.64	1.94 / 2.54	1.89 / 2.46	1.82 / 2.35	1.78 / 2.26	1.73 / 2.17	1.68 / 2.08	1.64 / 2.02	1.60 / 1.94	1.57 / 1.91	1.54 / 1.85	1.51 / 1.80	1.49 / 1.78
44	4.06 / 7.24	3.21 / 5.12	2.82 / 4.26	2.58 / 3.78	2.43 / 3.46	2.31 / 3.24	2.23 / 3.07	2.16 / 2.94	2.10 / 2.84	2.05 / 2.75	2.01 / 2.68	1.98 / 2.62	1.92 / 2.52	1.88 / 2.44	1.81 / 2.32	1.76 / 2.24	1.72 / 2.15	1.66 / 2.06	1.63 / 2.00	1.58 / 1.92	1.56 / 1.88	1.52 / 1.82	1.50 / 1.78	1.48 / 1.75
46	4.05 / 7.21	3.20 / 5.10	2.81 / 4.24	2.57 / 3.76	2.42 / 3.44	2.30 / 3.22	2.22 / 3.05	2.14 / 2.92	2.09 / 2.82	2.04 / 2.73	2.00 / 2.66	1.97 / 2.60	1.91 / 2.50	1.87 / 2.42	1.80 / 2.30	1.75 / 2.22	1.71 / 2.13	1.65 / 2.04	1.62 / 1.98	1.57 / 1.90	1.54 / 1.86	1.51 / 1.80	1.48 / 1.76	1.46 / 1.72
48	4.04 / 7.19	3.19 / 5.08	2.80 / 4.22	2.56 / 3.74	2.41 / 3.42	2.30 / 3.20	2.21 / 3.04	2.14 / 2.90	2.08 / 2.80	2.03 / 2.71	1.99 / 2.64	1.96 / 2.58	1.90 / 2.48	1.86 / 2.40	1.79 / 2.28	1.74 / 2.20	1.70 / 2.11	1.64 / 2.02	1.61 / 1.96	1.56 / 1.88	1.53 / 1.84	1.50 / 1.78	1.47 / 1.73	1.45 / 1.70

50	55	60	65	70	80	100	125	150	200	400	1000	∞
1.44 / **1.68**	1.41 / **1.64**	1.39 / **1.60**	1.37 / **1.56**	1.35 / **1.53**	1.32 / **1.49**	1.28 / **1.43**	1.25 / **1.37**	1.22 / **1.33**	1.19 / **1.28**	1.13 / **1.19**	1.08 / **1.11**	1.00 / **1.00**
1.46 / **1.71**	1.43 / **1.66**	1.41 / **1.63**	1.39 / **1.60**	1.37 / **1.56**	1.35 / **1.52**	1.30 / **1.46**	1.27 / **1.40**	1.25 / **1.37**	1.22 / **1.33**	1.16 / **1.24**	1.13 / **1.19**	1.11 / **1.15**
1.48 / **1.76**	1.46 / **1.71**	1.44 / **1.68**	1.42 / **1.64**	1.40 / **1.62**	1.38 / **1.57**	1.34 / **1.51**	1.31 / **1.46**	1.29 / **1.43**	1.26 / **1.39**	1.22 / **1.32**	1.19 / **1.28**	1.17 / **1.25**
1.52 / **1.82**	1.50 / **1.78**	1.48 / **1.74**	1.46 / **1.71**	1.45 / **1.69**	1.42 / **1.65**	1.39 / **1.59**	1.36 / **1.54**	1.34 / **1.51**	1.32 / **1.48**	1.28 / **1.42**	1.26 / **1.38**	1.24 / **1.36**
1.55 / **1.86**	1.52 / **1.82**	1.50 / **1.79**	1.49 / **1.76**	1.47 / **1.74**	1.45 / **1.70**	1.42 / **1.64**	1.39 / **1.59**	1.37 / **1.56**	1.35 / **1.53**	1.32 / **1.47**	1.30 / **1.44**	1.28 / **1.41**
1.60 / **1.94**	1.58 / **1.90**	1.56 / **1.87**	1.54 / **1.84**	1.53 / **1.82**	1.51 / **1.78**	1.48 / **1.73**	1.45 / **1.68**	1.44 / **1.66**	1.42 / **1.62**	1.38 / **1.57**	1.36 / **1.54**	1.35 / **1.52**
1.63 / **2.00**	1.61 / **1.96**	1.59 / **1.93**	1.57 / **1.90**	1.56 / **1.88**	1.54 / **1.84**	1.51 / **1.79**	1.49 / **1.75**	1.47 / **1.72**	1.45 / **1.69**	1.42 / **1.64**	1.41 / **1.61**	1.40 / **1.59**
1.69 / **2.10**	1.67 / **2.06**	1.65 / **2.03**	1.63 / **2.00**	1.62 / **1.98**	1.60 / **1.94**	1.57 / **1.89**	1.55 / **1.85**	1.54 / **1.83**	1.52 / **1.79**	1.49 / **1.74**	1.47 / **1.71**	1.46 / **1.69**
1.74 / **2.18**	1.72 / **2.15**	1.70 / **2.12**	1.68 / **2.09**	1.67 / **2.07**	1.65 / **2.03**	1.63 / **1.98**	1.60 / **1.94**	1.59 / **1.91**	1.57 / **1.88**	1.54 / **1.84**	1.53 / **1.81**	1.52 / **1.79**
1.78 / **2.26**	1.76 / **2.23**	1.75 / **2.20**	1.73 / **2.18**	1.72 / **2.15**	1.70 / **2.11**	1.68 / **2.06**	1.65 / **2.03**	1.64 / **2.00**	1.62 / **1.97**	1.60 / **1.92**	1.58 / **1.89**	1.57 / **1.87**
1.85 / **2.39**	1.83 / **2.35**	1.81 / **2.32**	1.80 / **2.30**	1.79 / **2.28**	1.77 / **2.24**	1.75 / **2.19**	1.72 / **2.15**	1.71 / **2.12**	1.69 / **2.09**	1.67 / **2.04**	1.65 / **2.01**	1.64 / **1.99**
1.90 / **2.46**	1.88 / **2.43**	1.86 / **2.40**	1.85 / **2.37**	1.84 / **2.35**	1.82 / **2.32**	1.79 / **2.26**	1.77 / **2.23**	1.76 / **2.20**	1.74 / **2.17**	1.72 / **2.12**	1.70 / **2.09**	1.69 / **2.07**
1.95 / **2.56**	1.93 / **2.53**	1.92 / **2.50**	1.90 / **2.47**	1.89 / **2.45**	1.88 / **2.41**	1.85 / **2.36**	1.83 / **2.33**	1.82 / **2.30**	1.80 / **2.28**	1.78 / **2.23**	1.76 / **2.20**	1.75 / **2.18**
1.98 / **2.62**	1.97 / **2.59**	1.95 / **2.56**	1.94 / **2.54**	1.93 / **2.51**	1.91 / **2.48**	1.88 / **2.43**	1.86 / **2.40**	1.85 / **2.37**	1.83 / **2.34**	1.81 / **2.29**	1.80 / **2.26**	1.79 / **2.24**
2.02 / **2.70**	2.00 / **2.66**	1.99 / **2.63**	1.98 / **2.61**	1.97 / **2.59**	1.95 / **2.55**	1.92 / **2.51**	1.90 / **2.47**	1.89 / **2.44**	1.87 / **2.41**	1.85 / **2.37**	1.84 / **2.34**	1.83 / **2.32**
2.07 / **2.78**	2.05 / **2.75**	2.04 / **2.72**	2.02 / **2.70**	2.01 / **2.67**	1.99 / **2.64**	1.97 / **2.59**	1.95 / **2.56**	1.94 / **2.53**	1.92 / **2.50**	1.90 / **2.46**	1.89 / **2.43**	1.88 / **2.41**
2.13 / **2.88**	2.11 / **2.85**	2.10 / **2.82**	2.08 / **2.79**	2.07 / **2.77**	2.05 / **2.74**	2.03 / **2.69**	2.01 / **2.65**	2.00 / **2.62**	1.98 / **2.60**	1.96 / **2.55**	1.95 / **2.53**	1.94 / **2.51**
2.20 / **3.02**	2.18 / **2.98**	2.17 / **2.95**	2.15 / **2.93**	2.14 / **2.91**	2.12 / **2.87**	2.10 / **2.82**	2.08 / **2.79**	2.07 / **2.76**	2.05 / **2.73**	2.03 / **2.69**	2.02 / **2.66**	2.01 / **2.64**
2.29 / **3.18**	2.27 / **3.15**	2.25 / **3.12**	2.24 / **3.09**	2.22 / **3.07**	2.21 / **3.04**	2.19 / **2.99**	2.17 / **2.95**	2.16 / **2.92**	2.14 / **2.90**	2.12 / **2.85**	2.10 / **2.82**	2.09 / **2.80**
2.40 / **3.41**	2.38 / **3.37**	2.37 / **3.34**	2.36 / **3.31**	2.35 / **3.29**	2.33 / **3.25**	2.30 / **3.20**	2.29 / **3.17**	2.27 / **3.13**	2.26 / **3.11**	2.23 / **3.06**	2.22 / **3.04**	2.21 / **3.02**
2.56 / **3.72**	2.54 / **3.68**	2.52 / **3.65**	2.51 / **3.62**	2.50 / **3.60**	2.48 / **3.56**	2.46 / **3.51**	2.44 / **3.47**	2.43 / **3.44**	2.41 / **3.41**	2.39 / **3.36**	2.38 / **3.34**	2.37 / **3.32**
2.79 / **4.20**	2.78 / **4.16**	2.76 / **4.13**	2.75 / **4.10**	2.74 / **4.08**	2.72 / **4.04**	2.70 / **3.98**	2.68 / **3.94**	2.67 / **3.91**	2.65 / **3.88**	2.62 / **3.83**	2.61 / **3.80**	2.60 / **3.78**
3.18 / **5.06**	3.17 / **5.01**	3.15 / **4.98**	3.14 / **4.95**	3.13 / **4.92**	3.11 / **4.88**	3.09 / **4.82**	3.07 / **4.78**	3.06 / **4.75**	3.04 / **4.71**	3.02 / **4.66**	3.00 / **4.62**	2.99 / **4.60**
4.03 / **7.17**	4.02 / **7.12**	4.00 / **7.08**	3.99 / **7.04**	3.98 / **7.01**	3.96 / **6.96**	3.94 / **6.90**	3.92 / **6.84**	3.91 / **6.81**	3.89 / **6.76**	3.86 / **6.70**	3.85 / **6.66**	3.84 / **6.64**

TABLE VI. Random Digits

03991	10461	93716	16894	98953	73231	39528	72484	82474	25593
38555	95554	32886	59780	09958	18065	81616	18711	53342	44276
17546	73704	92052	46215	15917	06253	07586	16120	82641	22820
32643	52861	95819	06831	19640	99413	90767	04235	13574	17200
69572	68777	39510	35905	85244	35159	40188	28193	29593	88627
24122	66591	27699	06494	03152	19121	34414	82157	86887	55087
61196	30231	92962	61773	22109	78508	63439	75363	44989	16822
30532	21704	10274	12202	94205	20380	67049	09070	93399	45547
03788	97599	75867	20717	82037	10268	79495	04146	52162	90286
48228	63379	85783	47619	87481	37220	91704	30552	04737	21031
88618	19161	41290	67312	71857	15957	48545	35247	18619	13674
71299	23853	05870	01119	92784	26340	75122	11724	74627	73707
27954	58909	82444	99005	04921	73701	92904	13141	32392	19763
80863	00514	20247	81759	45197	25332	69902	63742	78464	22501
33564	60780	48460	85558	15191	18782	94972	11598	62095	36787
90899	75754	60833	25983	01291	41349	19152	00023	12302	80783
78038	70267	43529	06318	38384	74761	36024	00867	76378	41605
55986	66485	88722	56736	66164	49431	94458	74284	05041	49807
87539	08823	94813	31900	54155	83436	54158	34243	46978	35482
16818	60311	74457	90561	72848	11834	75051	93029	47665	64382
34677	58300	74910	64345	19325	81549	60365	94653	35075	33949
45305	07521	61318	31855	14413	70951	83799	42402	56623	34442
59747	67277	76503	34513	39663	77544	32960	07405	36409	83232
16520	69676	11654	99893	02181	68161	19322	53845	57620	52606
68652	27376	92852	55866	88448	03584	11220	94747	07399	37408
79375	95220	01159	63267	10622	48391	31751	57260	68980	05339
33521	26665	55823	47641	86225	31704	88492	99382	14454	04504
59589	49067	66821	41575	49767	04037	30934	47744	07481	83828
20554	91409	96277	48257	50816	97616	22888	48893	27499	98748
59404	72059	43947	51680	43852	59693	78212	16993	35902	91386
42614	29297	01918	28316	25163	01889	70014	15021	68971	11403
34994	41374	70071	14736	65251	07629	37239	33295	18477	65622
99385	41600	11133	07586	36815	43625	18637	37509	14707	93997
66497	68646	78138	66559	64397	11692	05327	82162	83745	22567
48509	23929	27482	45476	04515	25624	95096	67946	16930	33361
15470	48355	88651	22596	83761	60873	43253	84145	20368	07126
20094	98977	74843	93413	14387	06345	80854	09279	41196	37480
73788	06533	28597	20405	51321	92246	80088	77074	66919	31678
60530	45128	74022	84617	72472	00008	80890	18002	35352	54131
44372	15486	65741	14014	05466	55306	93128	18464	79982	68416
18611	19241	66083	24653	84609	58232	41849	84547	46850	52326
58319	15997	08355	60860	29735	47762	46352	33049	69248	93460
61199	67940	55121	29281	59076	07936	11087	96294	14013	31792
18627	90872	00911	98936	76355	93779	52701	08337	56303	87315
00441	58997	14060	40619	29549	69616	57275	36898	81304	48585
32624	68691	14845	46672	61958	77100	20857	73156	70284	24326
65961	73488	41839	55382	17267	70943	15633	84924	90415	93614
20288	34060	39685	23309	10061	68829	92694	48297	39904	02115
59362	95938	74416	53166	35208	33374	77613	19019	88152	00080
99782	93478	53152	67433	35663	52972	38688	32486	45134	63545

Random Digits (*Continued*)

27767	43584	85301	88977	29490	69714	94015	64874	32444	48277
13025	14338	54066	15243	47724	66733	74108	88222	88570	74015
80217	36292	98525	24335	24432	24896	62880	87873	95160	59221
10875	62004	90391	61105	57411	06368	11748	12102	80580	41867
54127	57326	26629	19087	24472	88779	17944	05600	60478	03343
60311	42824	37301	42678	45990	43242	66067	42792	95043	52680
49739	71484	92003	98086	76668	73209	54244	91030	45547	70818
78626	51594	16453	94614	39014	97066	30945	57589	31732	57260
66692	13986	99837	00582	81232	44987	69170	37403	86995	90307
44071	28091	07362	97703	76447	42537	08345	88975	35841	85771
59820	96163	78851	16499	87064	13075	73035	41207	74699	09310
25704	91035	26313	77463	55387	72681	47431	43905	31048	56699
22304	90314	78438	66276	18396	73538	43277	58874	11466	16082
17710	59621	15292	76139	59526	52113	53856	30743	08670	84741
25852	58905	55018	56374	35824	71708	30540	27886	61732	75454
46780	56487	75211	10271	36633	68424	17374	52003	70707	70214
59849	96169	87195	46092	26787	60939	59202	11973	02902	33250
47670	07654	30342	40277	11049	72049	83012	09832	25571	77628
94304	71803	73465	09819	58869	35220.	09504	96412	90193	79568
08105	59987	21437	36786	49226	77837	98524	97831	65704	09514
64281	61826	18555	64937	64654	25843	41145	42820	14924	39650
66847	70495	32350	02985	01755	14750	48968	38603	70312	05682
72461	33230	21529	53424	72877	17334	39283	04149	90850	64618
21032	91050	13058	16218	06554	07850	73950	79552	24781	89683
95362	67011	06651	16136	57216	39618	49856	99326	40902	05069
49712	97380	10404	55452	09971	59481	37006	22186	72682	07385
58275	61764	97586	54716	61459	21647	87417	17198	21443	41808
89514	11788	68224	23417	46376	25366	94746	49580	01176	28838
15472	50669	48139	36732	26825	05511	12459	91314	80582	71944
12120	86124	51247	44302	87112	21476	14713	71181	13177	55292
95294	00556	70481	06905	21785	41101	49386	54480	23604	23554
66986	34099	74474	20740	47458	64809	06312	88940	15995	69321
80620	51790	11436	38072	40405	68032	60942	00307	11897	92674
55411	85667	77535	99892	71209	92061	92329	98932	78284	46347
95083	06783	28102	57816	85561	29671	77936	63574	31384	51924
90726	57166	98884	08583	95889	57067	38101	77756	11657	13897
68984	83620	89747	98882	92613	89719	39641	69457	91339	22502
36421	16489	18059	51061	67667	60631	84054	40455	99396	63680
92638	40333	67054	16067	24700	71594	47468	03577	57649	63266
21036	82808	77501	97427	76479	68562	43321	31370	28977	23896
13173	33365	41468	85149	49554	17994	91178	10174	29420	90438
86716	38746	94559	37559	49678	53119	98189	81851	29651	84215
92581	02262	41615	70360	64114	58660	96717	54244	10701	41393
12470	56500	50273	93113	41794	86861	39448	93136	25722	08564
01016	00857	41396	80504	90670	08289	58137	17820	22751	36518
34030	60726	25807	24260	71529	78920	47648	13885	70669	93406
50259	46345	06170	97965	88302	98041	11947	56203	19324	20504
73959	76145	60808	54444	74412	81105	69181	96845	38525	11600
46874	37088	80940	44893	10408	36222	14004	23153	69249	05747
60883	52109	19516	90120	46759	71643	62342	07589	08899	05985

TABLE VII. Rank-Sum Critical Values*

The sample sizes are shown in parentheses (n_1, n_2). The probability associated with a pair of critical values is the probability that $T \leq$ smaller value, or equally, it is the probability that $T \geq$ larger value. These probabilities are the closest ones to .025 and .05 that exist for integer values of T. The approximate .025 values should be used for a two-sided test with $\alpha = .05$, and the approximate .05 values for a one-sided test.

(2, 4)			(4, 4)			(6, 7)		
3	11	.067	11	25	.029	28	56	.026
(2, 5)			12	24	.057	30	54	.051
3	13	.047	(4, 5)			(6, 8)		
(2, 6)			12	28	.032	29	61	.021
3	15	.036	13	27	.056	32	58	.054
4	14	.071	(4, 6)			(6, 9)		
(2, 7)			12	32	.019	31	65	.025
3	17	.028	14	30	.057	33	63	.044
4	16	.056	(4, 7)			(6, 10)		
(2, 8)			13	35	.021	33	69	.028
3	19	.022	15	33	.055	35	67	.047
4	18	.044	(4, 8)			(7, 7)		
(2, 9)			14	38	.024	37	68	.027
3	21	.018	16	36	.055	39	66	.049
4	20	.036	(4, 9)			(7, 8)		
(2, 10)			15	41	.025	39	73	.027
4	22	.030	17	39	.053	41	71	.047
5	21	.061	(4, 10)			(7, 9)		
(3, 3)			16	44	.026	41	78	.027
6	15	.050	18	42	.053	43	76	.045
(3, 4)			(5, 5)			(7, 10)		
6	18	.028	18	37	.028	43	83	.028
7	17	.057	19	36	.048	46	80	.054
(3, 5)			(5, 6)			(8, 8)		
6	21	.018	19	41	.026	49	87	.025
7	20	.036	20	40	.041	52	84	.052
(3, 6)			(5, 7)			(8, 9)		
7	23	.024	20	45	.024	51	93	.023
8	22	.048	22	43	.053	54	90	.046
(3, 7)			(5, 8)			(8, 10)		
8	25	.033	21	49	.023	54	98	.027
9	24	.058	23	47	.047	57	95	.051
(3, 8)			(5, 9)			(9, 9)		
8	28	.024	22	53	.021	63	108	.025
9	27	.042	25	50	.056	66	105	.047
(3, 9)			(5, 10)			(9, 10)		
9	30	.032	24	56	.028	66	114	.027
10	29	.050	26	54	.050	69	111	.047
(3, 10)			(6, 6)			(10, 10)		
9	33	.024	26	52	.021	79	131	.026
11	31	.056	28	50	.047	83	127	.053

* This table was extracted from a more complete table (A-20) in *Introduction to Statistical Analysis*, 2nd edition, by W. J. Dixon and F. J. Massey, with permission from the publishers, the McGraw-Hill Book Company.

TABLE VIII. Critical Values for D_α in the Kolmogorov-Smirnov Test

α n	.20	.10	.05	.01
5	.45	.51	.56	.67
10	.32	.37	.41	.49
15	.27	.30	.34	.40
20	.23	.26	.29	.36
25	.21	.24	.27	.32
30	.19	.22	.24	.29
35	.18	.20	.23	.27
40	.17	.19	.21	.25
45	.16	.18	.20	.24
50	.15	.17	.19	.23
Large Values	$\dfrac{1.07}{\sqrt{n}}$	$\dfrac{1.22}{\sqrt{n}}$	$\dfrac{1.36}{\sqrt{n}}$	$\dfrac{1.63}{\sqrt{n}}$

Answers to Odd-Numbered Exercises

Numerical answers often depend upon the order of operations and the extent of rounding off; hence a student's answers may differ slightly from those given here. For many of the theoretical exercises, suggestions on how to proceed toward a solution have been included, but these should be used only as a last resort.

Chapter 2

1. $\frac{1}{9}$.

3. $\frac{1}{3}, \left(\frac{2}{3}\right)\frac{1}{3}, \left(\frac{2}{3}\right)^2\frac{1}{3}, \cdots$

5. $\frac{1}{16}$.

7. $(a)\frac{1}{12}, (b)\frac{2}{27}$.

9. $\frac{1}{6}$ as compared with $\frac{5}{36}$.

11. $(a)\frac{1}{32}, (b)\frac{1}{64}, (c)\frac{5}{16}$.

13. $\frac{5}{12}$.

15. $\frac{1}{3}$.

17. $(a)\frac{1}{5}, (b)\frac{1}{3}$.

19. .43.

21. $\frac{4}{7}, \frac{2}{7}, \frac{1}{7}$.

23. $\frac{2162}{54145}$.

25. $\binom{40}{10}\Big/\binom{50}{10}$.

27. $\frac{2}{n}$.

29. $\binom{4}{2}\binom{22}{11}\Big/\binom{26}{13}$.

31. $15(n^2 - 7n + 14)/(n^3 - 3n^2 + 2n)$.

33. $(a)\frac{1}{2}, (b)\frac{8}{11}$.

35. $(a)\frac{253}{4998}, (b)\frac{115}{843}$.

37. $(a)\frac{1}{73}, (b)\frac{1}{25}$.

39. (a) .184, (b) .736, $(c) \sum_{x=0}^{\infty} \frac{1}{x!} = e$.

413

41. (a) $\dfrac{5}{16}$, (b) $f(x) = 15/4x!\,(5-x)!$.   **43.** $F(x) = 0, x < 0, F(0) = \dfrac{1}{32}, F(1) = \dfrac{6}{32}$,

$$F(2) = \frac{16}{32}, \qquad F(3) = \frac{26}{32}, F(4) = \frac{31}{32},$$

$$F(x) = 1, x \geq 5.$$

45. $f(x) = \dbinom{3}{x}\dbinom{2}{2-x}\Big/\dbinom{5}{2}$. $F(x) = 0, x < 0,$

$F(x) = \dfrac{1}{10}, 0 \leq x < 1, F(x) = \dfrac{7}{10}, 1 \leq x < 2,$

$F(x) = 1, x \geq 2.$

47. $f(x) = \dfrac{3}{4}\left(\dfrac{1}{4}\right)^{x-1}$.   **49.** $f(x, y) = \dfrac{1}{4}$.

51. $f(x, y) = 5120/81x!\,y!\,(6-x-y)!\,4^{x+y}$,

53. (a) $f(1) = \dfrac{1}{4}$, (b) $g(0) = \dfrac{3}{4}$, (c) $f(0 \mid 1) = \dfrac{13}{17}, f(1 \mid 1) = \dfrac{4}{17}$,

(d) $g(0 \mid 0) = \dfrac{38}{51}, g(1 \mid 0) = \dfrac{13}{51}$.

55. $f(x) = \dfrac{1}{2}, f(y \mid x) = \dfrac{1}{2}$.   **57.** $f(1) = .40, g(3) = .054$.

59. (a) $f(0) = \dfrac{11}{20}, f(1) = \dfrac{8}{20}, f(2) = \dfrac{1}{20}$, (b) $f(y \mid 1) = \dbinom{4}{y}\dbinom{8}{1-y}\Big/12$.

61. The conditional distribution of y for x fixed will depend on x. Thus $f(1, 0) = 0$ and $f(1, 1) > 0$.

63. (a) $c = 1$, (b) .264, (c) .537.

65. (a) $F(x) = 0, x \leq 0, F(x) = x, 0 < x < 1, F(x) = 1, x \geq 1,$

(b) $F(x) = 0, x \leq 0, F(x) = \dfrac{x^2}{2}, 0 < x < 1, F(x) = -\dfrac{x^2}{2} + 2x - 1, 1 \leq x \leq 2,$

$F(x) = 1, x > 2$, (c) $F(x) = \dfrac{1}{\pi}\tan^{-1}x + \dfrac{1}{2}$.

67. (a) 500, (b) $1 - \dfrac{500}{x}$, (c) $\dfrac{1}{2}$.

69. .25.

71. (a) $\dfrac{7}{256}$, (b) $\dfrac{1}{16}$, (c) $\dfrac{31}{256}$, (d) if x and y were independent,

$P\{x < .5, y < .25\} = P\{x < .5\}P\{y < .25\}$. But not true here.

73. Find $f(x, y)$, then sum with respect to x from y to ∞ by letting $t = x - y$ and summing t from 0 to ∞.

75. $f(x, y) = \dfrac{1}{2}$ for $\begin{cases} -1 < x < 0 \\ -1 < y < 0 \end{cases}$ and $\begin{cases} 0 < x < 1 \\ 0 < y < 1 \end{cases}$.

Chapter 3

1. (a) $\alpha = .5$, $\beta = .25$, (b) $\alpha = 0$, $\beta = .75$.
3. Choose $x > 4.5$. Then $\beta = .25$.
5. (a) $\alpha = .25$, (b) $.125$.
7. $\alpha = \dfrac{1}{120}$, $\beta = \dfrac{17}{24}$.
9. $P(\theta) = \left(\dfrac{1}{2}\right)^{\theta+1}$.
11. $P(p) = p^3 - 3p^2 + 3p$. Poor critical region if p is small, good if p is close to 1.
13. $\hat{\theta} = \bar{x}$; hence $\hat{\theta} = 7$ here.
15. $\hat{\theta} = \sqrt{\Sigma x_i^2 / n}$.
17. $f(x; p) = \dbinom{10p}{x}\dbinom{10 - 10p}{2 - x} \Big/ \dbinom{10}{2}$. For $x = 0$, $p = 0$ maximizes; for $x = 1$,

$p = \dfrac{1}{2}$ maximizes; for $x = 2$, $p = 1$ maximizes.

Chapter 4

1. Boundaries $97.5 - 107.5$ and $217.5 - 227.5$. Class marks 102.5 and 222.5.
3. Class marks are $156, 159, 162, \cdots$.
5. $\bar{x} = 4.43$.
7. $\bar{x} = \dfrac{5}{3}$, $\sigma = \dfrac{\sqrt{10}}{3}$.
9. Approximately 71 per cent and 96 per cent. The right tail contributes more and the left tail less than expected for a normal distribution, but the sum is fairly close to expectation.
11. Guess the mean to be $5'8''$ and that 95 per cent have heights between $5'3''$ and $6'1''$. Then, under normality, $\sigma \doteq 2.5''$.
13. Nothing definite can be concluded; however, in a common empirical distribution, one would guess that the distribution has a long right tail.
15. $m_k = m_k' - \dbinom{k}{1} m_{k-1}' m_1' + \dbinom{k}{2} m_{k-2}' m_1'^2 - \cdots$.
17. Write $(n_1 + n_2)s^2 = \displaystyle\sum_{1}^{n_1} [(x_i - \bar{x}_1) + (\bar{x}_1 - \bar{x})]^2 + \sum_{n_1+1}^{n_1+n_2} [(x_i - \bar{x}_2) + (\bar{x}_2 - \bar{x})]^2$,

then expand the binomials, sum term by term, and evaluate.
19. The third moment about the mean is zero, yet the distribution is not symmetrical. This shows that one cannot rely on the third moment about the mean as a measure of symmetry.

Chapter 5

1. $\mu = \dfrac{7}{2}$, $\sigma^2 = \dfrac{35}{12}$.

3. $\mu = 7$.

5. $\dfrac{1}{3}$ and $\dfrac{2}{3}$.

7. $E(x) = 0$, $V(x) = \dfrac{3}{2}$. He averages the same, namely zero, but there are fewer extreme wins and losses.

9. 1.

11. (a) .27, (b) .74.

13. (a) $P\{x \le 2\} = .411$. (b) Successive days are not likely to behave like independent trials. Storms often last more than one day.

15. (a) $\dfrac{9}{16}$, (b) $\dfrac{27}{128}$.

17. $p = \dfrac{1}{3}$, $n = 36$.

21. .60.

23. 124, using a normal approximation.

25. .423.

27. (a) In the expression for $M_x(\theta)$, write $e^{\theta x}\mu^x = (\mu e^{\theta})^x$, factor out $e^{-\mu}$, and recognize the resulting series as the expansion of $e^{\mu e^{\theta}}$.

29. $\dfrac{2}{3}$.

31. $\dfrac{3}{4}$.

33. $a = \dfrac{1}{3}$, $b = 2$.

35. (a) $c = 2$, (b) $\dfrac{2}{k+2}$, (c) $2(\theta e^{\theta} - e^{\theta} + 1)/\theta^2$, (d) expand e^{θ} and simplify.

37. (a) $c = 1/\alpha!$, (b) $(\alpha + k)!/\alpha!$, (c) $(1 - \theta)^{-(\alpha+1)}$.

39. $M_x(\theta) = (e^{\theta} - 1)^2/\theta^2$.

41. (a) $x_0 = 3.56$, (b) $x_0 = -2.68$.

43. .43.

45. $\mu_{2k} = (2k)!\, \sigma^{2k}/2^k k!$ and $\mu_{2k+1} = 0$.

47. (a) .240, (b) .620.

49. (a) .112, (b) .112.

51. Yes, since 180–220 includes 215.

53. Not typical.

55. .006.

57. $\bar{p} = .0255$; hence limits are $.0255 \pm .0150$. Out of control on days numbered 18, 22, and 38.

59. (a) 1614, (b) 1681, since n is a maximum for $p = .5$.

61. .003.

63. (a) $P\{x \geq 20.5\} \doteq .00045$, (b) .973.

65. (a) .60, (b) .0104.

67. (a) 2.48, (b) 62.

69. Using $\bar{x}/n = .2175$ as the estimate for p, the binomial frequencies to the nearest unit are 7, 19, 24, 18, 9, 3, 1, 0, 0, 0, 0.

71. .74, .70.

73. $\dfrac{128}{729}$.

75. $\dfrac{5}{108}$.

77. .0034.

79. (a) $(y-1)e^{-\frac{1}{2}(y-1)^2}$, (b) $e^{-\frac{y}{2}}/2$, (c) $e^{2y-\frac{1}{2}e^{2y}}$.

81. (a) $e^{-\frac{1}{2}\left(\frac{y-1}{2}\right)^2}/2\sqrt{2\pi}$, (b) $(y-1)^{-\frac{1}{2}}e^{-\left(\frac{y-1}{4}\right)}/2\sqrt{\pi}$.

83. $\dfrac{1}{\sqrt{z}} - 1$.

85. $e^{-\frac{1}{2}\log^2 x}/x\sqrt{2\pi}$.

89. $\displaystyle\int_{47.5}^{\infty} \dfrac{e^{-\frac{(x-100p)^2}{200p(1-p)}}}{\sqrt{200\pi p(1-p)}}\, dx$.

91. $\displaystyle\sum_{x=0}^{49} e^{-10t}(10t)^x/x!$. Calculate the probability that less than 50 tickets will be sold in t minutes, assuming a Poisson distribution is valid for a time interval of t minutes.

Chapter 6

7. If n_1 and n_2 represent the number of trials for each binomial variable, $n = n_1 + n_2$ represents the number of trials for the combined experiment because p is the same for both.

9. The moment generating function of $x_1 - x_2$ cannot be expressed in the form $e^{c(e^\theta-1)}$, where c is some constant.

11. $E(z) = (n-1)/2$, $V(z) = (n+1)/12$. The latter follows from calculating $E\left[\displaystyle\sum_1^{n-1}\left(x_i - \frac{1}{2}\right)^2 + 2\sum_{i<j}\left(x_i - \frac{1}{2}\right)\left(x_j - \frac{1}{2}\right)\right]$ by using the fact that $E\left(x_i - \dfrac{1}{2}\right)\left(x_j - \dfrac{1}{2}\right) = 0$ unless $j = i+1$, in which case it has the value $\left(\dfrac{1}{4}\right)\left(\dfrac{2}{6}\right) + \left(-\dfrac{1}{4}\right)\left(\dfrac{4}{6}\right) = -\dfrac{1}{12}$ because $x_i = 1$ and $x_{i+1} = 1$ implies $n_i < n_{i+1} < n_{i+2}$ which occurs with probability $\frac{1}{6}$.

13. (a) 400 ± 7.5, (b) 225.

15. 64.

17. 9.

21. (a) $\sigma_{\bar{x}-\bar{y}} \doteq 1.3$; hence reject the hypothesis, (b) $\bar{x} - \bar{y}$ very likely differs from $\mu_x - \mu_y$ by less than 2.6 units, (c) $n = 656$.

23. $n = 13.3$; hence 14 will suffice.   25. 84.

27. $t = 1.66$; hence accept $p_1 = p_2$.

29. $\sigma_{p_1'-p_2'} = .09$. If testing against $p_1 \neq p_2$, not significant. If testing against $p_1 > p_2$, significant. A significant result corresponds to a discriminating question.

31. $t = 1.68$; hence reject $p_1 - p_2 = .10$ as against $p_1 - p_2 > .10$.

33. (a) $\bar{x} = 71.6, s = 31.1$; hence limits are 30–113. (b) One would hardly be justified on the basis of this small and seemingly irregular sample to assume that production was under control.

35. $M_{x+y}(\theta) = (e^\theta - 1)^2/\theta^2$. Since this is not of the form $(e^{\theta b} - e^{\theta a})/\theta(b - a)$, which is the moment generating function for a horizontal variable in the interval (a, b), the variable cannot have a horizontal distribution.

37. $M_{n\bar{x}}(\theta) = (1 - \theta)^{-n}$; hence, from problem 34, $f(n\bar{x}) = e^{-n\bar{x}}(n\bar{x})^{n-1}/(n - 1)!$.

41. $nf(z)F^{n-1}(z)$.

Chapter 7

1. .91.

3. Relationship is not likely to be linear. For large amounts of fertilizer there may be a loss; hence the range of values here for the amount of fertilizer added is probably fairly large.

5. Maximum traffic occurs around 8–9 A.M. and near 5 P.M. Maximum tides occur around 8 A.M. and 8 P.M. Thus maxima and minima occur fairly close together in time, yielding a scatter diagram that is strongly linear in character.

7. $t = -1.2$; hence accept the hypothesis.

9. $y' = 6.29x - 274$.

11. $a \sum x_i^2 \exp\left[-2b(x_i - c)^2\right] = \sum y_i x_i \exp\left[-b(x_i - c)^2\right]$

    $a \sum (x_i - c)x_i^2 \exp\left[-2b(x_i - c)^2\right] = \sum y_i(x_i - c)x_i \exp\left[-b(x_i - c)^2\right]$

    $a \sum (x_i - c)^2 x_i^2 \exp\left[-2b(x_i - c)^2\right] = \sum y_i(x_i - c)^2 x_i \exp\left[-b(x_i - c)^2\right]$.

15. $y' = .39x_1 + .25x_2$.   17. $s^2 = (n^2 - 1)/12$.

19. (a) $r = .61$ for a 6×6 classification, (b) $y' = .0116x_1 - 1.11$, (c) $y' = .0120x_1 - .007x_2 - .97$, (d) additional variable in (c) gives very little improvement.

21. $y' = .857e^{.331x}$.

23. Direct least squares, if y increases with x.

27. (a) $z = x_1 - .753x_2$. (b) Very little improvement over x_1 alone.

29. $a_i = \sum_{k=1}^{n} y_k P_i(x_k)$.   31. .11.

Chapter 8

1. (a) .15, (b) .5, (c) .5, (d) 0, (e) .5, (f) .75, (g) .5, (h) $\pi/4$.

3. (a) $f(x) = 2x, g(y) = 2(1 - y)$, (b) $f(y \mid x) = 1/x, f(x \mid y) = 1/(1 - y)$, (c) $\mu_{y|x} = x/2$.

5. (a) $f(x) = e^{-x}, g(y) = (y + 1)^{-2}$, (b) $f(y \mid x) = xe^{-xy}, f(x \mid y) = (y + 1)^2 xe^{-x(y+1)}$, (c) $\mu_{y|x} = 1/x$.

7. (a) $\mu_{pq}' = 1/(p + 1)(q + 1)$, (b) $\rho = 0$, (c) $\mu_{y|x} = \dfrac{1}{2}$.

9. (a) $c = 1$, (b) $y = -x/2$, $-1 < x < 0$, $y = x/2$, $0 < x < 1$, (c) 0.

11. Any $f(x)$ times any conditional distribution $f(y\,|\,x)$ which has the curve $y = x^2$ value as its mean value.

13. (a) $\mu_x = 1$, $\mu_y = -2$, $\sigma_x^2 = \dfrac{20}{64}$, $\sigma_y^2 = \dfrac{5}{64}$, $\rho = .6$,

    (b) $f(x) = 4e^{-\frac{8}{5}(x-1)^2}/\sqrt{10\pi}$, (c) $\mu_{y|x} = .3(x - 1) - 2$.

15. (a) multiply it by 2, (b) divide it by the integral of $f(x)$ from 0 to ∞.

17. $\mu_{y|x} = \mu_y$.

19. $E(x) = np$, $E(y) = n(n + 1)p/2$, $E(xy) = [1 + (n - 1)p]\,pn(n + 1)/2$, $\mu_{11} = n(n + 1)p(1 - p)/2$.

21. $\dfrac{7}{16}$ as compared to 1.

23. $\mu_{00}' = 1$, $\mu_{10}' = \mu_x$, $\mu_{01}' = \mu_y$, $\mu_{20} = \sigma_x^2$, $\mu_{02} = \sigma_y^2$ are verified by employing result (18) in the text and symmetry, whereas $\mu_{11} = \rho\sigma_x\sigma_y$ requires the evaluation of the integral defining μ_{11}.

25. For example, a uniform distribution in an ellipse.

31. $1/(1 + x)^2$.

Chapter 9

1. Choose as critical region the sample points below the line $x_1 + x_2 = c$, where c is the proper constant. This is given by the Neyman-Pearson lemma.

3. .69.

5. Normal approximation yields $x > 24.0$ as critical region.

    $$P(p) = \dfrac{1}{\sqrt{2\pi}} \int_{\frac{24.5 - 40p}{\sqrt{40pq}}}^{\infty} e^{-\frac{1}{2}t^2} dt. \quad P(.6) = .44.$$

7. $n = 13.6$; hence a sample of 14 is needed.

9. Critical region given by $\Sigma \log x_i \leq$ constant.

11. $\Sigma x_i \geq$ constant. Yes.

13. $\lambda = (e/n)^{\frac{1}{2}n}[\Sigma(x_i - \bar{x})^2]^{\frac{1}{2}n}e^{-\Sigma(x_i-\bar{x})^2/2}$.

15. Critical region given by $(p_0/\hat{p})^x(q_0/\hat{q})^{n-x} < \lambda_0$, where $\hat{p} = x/n$ and $\hat{q} = 1 - (x/n)$. No.

17. Critical region given by $(\pi x_i)^{\theta_0 - \hat{\theta}}/(1 + \hat{\theta})^n < \lambda_0$, where $\hat{\theta} = -(1 + n/\Sigma \log x_i)$.

19. $\chi^2 = 5.1$ with 1 degree of freedom; hence reject H_0.

21. $\Sigma a_i b_i \sigma_i^2/\sqrt{\Sigma a_i^2 \sigma_i^2 \Sigma b_i^2 \sigma_i^2}$.

23. (a) $\frac{60}{137}$, (b) $\frac{3}{5}$, (c) equal weights variance is about 37 per cent larger than for minimizing weights.

27. Calculate the probability of $x - 1$ successes in $N - 1$ trials, followed by a success.

29. $\displaystyle\sum_1^N x_i/nN$.   31. $\hat{\mu} = \bar{x}$, $\hat{\sigma} = \sqrt{\Sigma(x_i - \bar{x})^2/n}$.

33. $\hat{q} = \Sigma x_i/(\Sigma x_i + n)$.   37. $10.1 - 11.9$.

39. Treat as a binomial problem with $p = x/N$ and z successes in y trials.

41. $17.8 - 22.5$.

Chapter 10

3. $\chi^2 = 1.3$ with 1 degree of freedom; hence compatible.
5. $\chi^2 = 35$ with 3 degrees of freedom; hence not compatible with theory.
7. $\chi^2 = 4.2$ with 7 degrees of freedom (combining last 2 cells); hence fit is satisfactory.
9. $\chi^2 = 8$ with 9 degrees of freedom if first 2 cells are combined and last 3 cells are combined; hence fit is satisfactory.
11. $\chi^2 = 2.9$ with 3 degrees of freedom if frequencies for $x \geq 4$ are combined; hence fit is satisfactory.
13. $\chi^2 = 4.8$ with 1 degree of freedom; hence reject the hypothesis. It appears that the serum had a harmful effect on the patients.
15. Obviously not independent, since the contribution to χ^2 from the first cell alone is larger than the critical value of χ^2 for 12 degrees of freedom.
17. $\chi^2 = 26.6$ with 9 degrees of freedom; hence reject homogeneity.
19. $\chi^2 = 20$ with 14 degrees of freedom; hence justified.
21. Take the logarithm of the multinomial frequency function for 3 cells and differentiate with respect to $q = 1 - p$.
23. Replace $a + b + c + d$ by n, $a + c$ by n_1, $b + d$ by n_2, and let $\tilde{p} = (a + b)/n$ serve as the estimate of p. Then χ will assume the form $(p_1' - p_2')/\sqrt{\tilde{p}\tilde{q}(1/n_1 + 1/n_2)}$. For 1 degree of freedom the critical value of χ^2 is the square of the corresponding normal curve critical value for this problem.

Chapter 11

1. $M_z(\theta) = (1 - 2\theta)^{-n}$; hence z possesses a χ^2 distribution with $2n$ degrees of freedom.
3. $16 < \sigma^2 < 48$.   5. $15 < \sigma^2 < 64$.
7. $\mu = \nu$ and $\sigma^2 = 2\nu$.
9. $E(ks^2 - \sigma^2)^2 = \sigma^4\{[(n + 2)/n]k^2 - 2k + 1\}$; hence choose $k = n/(n + 2)$. This shows that $\Sigma x_i^2/(n + 2)$ is a better estimate than the unbiased estimate $\Sigma x_i^2/n$.
11. (a) $t = -2.6$ and $t_0 = 2.09$; hence reject H_0. (b) $38.7 < \mu < 45.3$.
13. $17.5 < \mu < 22.5$.
15. The integrand in the integral yielding $E(t)$ is an odd function; hence the integral must vanish.
17. (a) $t = -1.6$; hence accept H_0. (b) $-9.2 < \mu_1 - \mu_2 < 1.2$.
19. $t = 2.23$ with 38 degrees of freedom; hence reject the hypothesis. The x and y values are undoubtedly correlated here.
21. $-2.43 < \mu_1 - \mu_2 < -.52$.
23. First show that $\lambda = [\Sigma(x_i - \bar{x})^2/\Sigma(x_i - \mu_0)^2]^{\frac{1}{2}n} = [1 + t^2/(n - 1)]^{-\frac{1}{2}n}$; then show the relationship between the distributions of λ and t.
25. Critical region is $[\Sigma(x_i - \bar{x})^2 + \Sigma(y_i - \bar{y})^2]/[\Sigma(x_i - \hat{\mu})^2 + \Sigma(y_i - \hat{\mu})^2] < \lambda_0$ where $\hat{\mu} = (\bar{x} + \bar{y})/2$. This can be shown to reduce to $(\bar{x} - \bar{y})^2/(ns_x^2 + ns_y^2) > c_0$, which is equivalent to the square of a Student t variable test with $2(n - 1)$ degrees of freedom.
27. $F = 2.1$; hence accept H_0.
29. Choose F_0 such that $P\{F > F_0\} = .05$ and $P\{F > F_0/2\} = .95$. Hence $F_0 = 1.41$. Tables yield $n \doteq 93$.
31.
$$\frac{n_1 s_1^2(n_2 - 1)}{n_2 s_2^2(n_1 - 1)}\frac{1}{F_0} < \frac{\sigma_1^2}{\sigma_2^2} < \frac{n_1 s_1^2(n_2 - 1)}{n_2 s_2^2(n_1 - 1)}F_0',$$

where F_0 and F_0' are the right-tail critical values of F corresponding to $\nu_1 = n_1 - 1$, $\nu_2 = n_2 - 1$ and $\nu_1 = n_2 - 1$, $\nu_2 = n_1 - 1$, respectively.

33. The variable $2\alpha x$ is a χ^2 variable with 2 degrees of freedom; hence the ratio $2\alpha x/2\alpha y = x/y$ possesses an F distribution with $\nu_1 = 2$ and $\nu_2 = 2$. Now apply a two-sided, or one-sided, F test, depending on the alternative hypothesis.

35. $(\Sigma x_i^2)^{n_1}(\Sigma y_i^2)^{n_2}/[\Sigma x_i^2 + \Sigma y_i^2]^{n_1+n_2} < \lambda_0$ is the critical region. This is equivalent to $(\Sigma y_i^2/\Sigma x_i^2)^{n_2}/(1 + \Sigma y_i^2/\Sigma x_i^2)^{n_1+n_2} < c_0$. But $n_1\Sigma y_i^2/n_2\Sigma x_i^2$ is an F variable; hence the test is equivalent to $F^{n_2}/[n_1 + n_2 F]^{n_1+n_2} < c_1$. But this will be satisfied if, and only if, $F < c_2$ or $F > c_3$; hence the test is equivalent to a two-sided F test.

37. (a) ze^{-z}, (b) $-\log_e z$.

39. Use the formula for the frequency function of a quotient.

41. $ze^{-\frac{z^2}{2}}$.   43. $(n-1)e^{-R}(1 - e^{-R})^{n-2}$.

45. 46, which is the smallest integer exceeding the positive root of the equation $(.9)^{n-1} = .5/(n + 9)$.

47. $40 \pm .58\bar{R}$.

49. $z = 1 \bigg/ \left[1 + \dfrac{n_2}{n_1}F\right]$ where F has an F distribution with $\nu_1 = n_2$ and $\nu_2 = n_1$; hence $f(z) = c_1 F^{\frac{1}{2}(n_2-2)}/(n_1 + n_2 F)^{\frac{1}{2}(n_1+n_2-4)} = c_2 z^{\frac{1}{2}(n_1-2)}(1 - z)^{\frac{1}{2}(n_2-2)}$.

51. $t = [Y_x' - \alpha - \beta(x - \bar{x})]\sqrt{n(n - 2)}/\sqrt{[1 + (x - \bar{x})^2/s_x^2]\Sigma(y_i - y_i')^2}$ with $n - 2$ degrees of freedom.

Chapter 12

1. $F = 2.5$ and $F_0 = 3.06$; hence accept H_0.
3. $\hat{\sigma}^2 = 16$.
5. $F_r = 5.76$ and $F_0 = 5.14$; hence rations differ. $F_t = 6.22$ and $F_0 = 4.76$; hence types differ.
7. $n = 85.3$; hence 86 necessary.   9. $\hat{\sigma}_w^2 = 16$, $\hat{\sigma}_v^2 = 6$.
15. Study the ratio $P\{x \mid p\}/P\{x \mid p'\}$.
17. $V(x) = E(x^2) - E^2(x) = \Sigma(1/k)E(x_i^2) - [\Sigma(1/k)E(x_i)]^2 = (1/k)\Sigma[np_iq_i + n^2p_i^2] - (n^2/k^2)(\Sigma p_i)^2$. Writing out the sums defining $n\mu_p(1 - \mu_p) + n(n - 1)V(p)$ will yield this same result.
19. $\sigma_{\bar{x}_R}^2 = \frac{1}{20}$, $\sigma_{\bar{x}}^2 = \frac{6}{20}$; hence the variance is $\frac{1}{6}$ as large.
21. Because variances of means and proportions, for example, are proportional to sample sizes. Thus ratio of variances corresponds to ratio of sample sizes needed for the same precision of estimate.

Chapter 13

1. (a) $\dfrac{3}{4}$, (b) $\dfrac{1}{4}$.
3. Eleven successes in 14 trials is not significant for a two-sided test because $\tau = (10.5 - 7)/\sqrt{3.5} = 1.87$.
5. Alternating tied pairs, but beginning with the two-group for two-and-one ties, yields $= .71$; hence accept the hypothesis.

13. No, because the total number of runs is close to what would be expected under randomness.

17. 2 or 4.

19. By algebra, or by arguing that a test based on R cannot be affected because a test based on the complete serial correlation coefficient (circular) cannot be affected.

21. $D_{.05} = 1.36/\sqrt{500} = .06$. The maximum difference between theoretical and sample distribution functions is .016; hence fit is satisfactory.

23. Order y values according to magnitude, form the sample distribution function, then add and subtract .19 to it to obtain the desired band.

Chapter 14

1. Boundaries for d_m are $\log 4/\log \frac{2}{3} - m \log \frac{6}{5}/\log \frac{2}{3}$ and $-\log 4/\log \frac{2}{3} - m \log \frac{6}{5}/\log \frac{2}{3}$.

3. Boundaries for Σx_i are $\log \frac{2}{9} - m \log \frac{2}{3}$ and $\log 8 - m \log \frac{2}{3}$.

9. $E_1(n) \doteq 19$.   **11.** $n = 34$.

13. Same solutions as for problem 12, namely $(a) - \frac{1}{2}$ and $\frac{1}{2}$ and $(b) - \frac{1}{2} - \log_e 2$ and $\frac{1}{2} - \log_e 2$; hence y is of no help here.

15. Boundary is the line $y = 2x$.

17. (a) risk $= \theta/2$, mean risk $= \frac{1}{2}$, (b) mean risk $\frac{5}{12}$; hence second estimate is better.

19. $(a) \dfrac{1}{n}$, $(b) \dfrac{1}{n}$.

21. $E(\mu \mid x) = x + \alpha$.

Index